FLORIDA STATE
UNIVERSITY LiBRARIES

JUN 24 1992

TALLAHASSEE, FLORIDA

Essentials of Geography

Essentials of

McGRAW-HILL BOOK COMPANY, INC.

GEOGRAPHY

SECOND EDITION

OTIS W. FREEMAN

EMERITUS PROFESSOR OF GEOGRAPHY

EASTERN WASHINGTON COLLEGE OF

EDUCATION

H. F. RAUP

PROFESSOR OF GEOGRAPHY AND HEAD OF

THE DEPARTMENT OF GEOGRAPHY AND

GEOLOGY, KENT STATE UNIVERSITY, OHIO

NEW YORK TORONTO LONDON 1959

G
127
.F75
1959

910
F855e
1959

ESSENTIALS OF GEOGRAPHY

Copyright © 1959 by the McGraw-Hill Book Company,
Inc. Copyright, 1949, by the McGraw-Hill Book Company,
Inc. Printed in the United States of America. All rights
reserved. This book, or parts thereof, may not be
reproduced in any form without permission of the
publishers.

Library of Congress Catalog Card Number: 58–11980

LIBRARY
FLORIDA STATE UNIVERSITY
TALLAHASSEE, FLORIDA

*This book was set in Linotype Times
Roman, a type face designed by Stanley
Morison for The Times of London. The
bold face headings are Spartan Heavy,
and the chapter titles are Latin Wide.
Maps were drawn by Lilli Mautner.*

Preface

GEOGRAPHY is a dynamic science which deals with the physical and social aspects of the earth in order to acquire knowledge of the surroundings within which man lives. The subject provides a point of view differing from that of other sciences, however, because it is concerned largely with two main streams of related material: the comparison of geographic conditions in different places on the earth, and the manner in which those conditions are related to human activities and well-being.

Concepts of the interpretation of the field of geography have been subject to change. During the Age of Discovery, which began toward the end of the Middle Ages, geography was concerned with the collection of facts about the earth and the construction of maps. Near the close of the nineteenth century, it developed as the concept of the interrelationships between man and the earth as well as an organized comparison of the terrestrial landscapes within which human activity necessarily occurs.

The substance upon which modern geography is based is derived from the facts of climate, relief of the land, soil conditions, minerals, forest cover, the seas—in other words, the elements of the widely differing environments throughout the world. These basic data are collected, classified, and studied in detail; the information assembled may then be shown in maps or in other forms of visual presentation. No single method of handling geographic data is used exclusively; different methods are required in the satisfactory solution of geographic problems. Study in field and laboratory, familiarity with maps and graphs, and the handling and interpretation of statistics as well as the orderly compilation of information from a wide range of sources—these are a few of the methods whereby the geography student learns about the environment and upon which he bases his knowledge of the world and its peoples. From such a study he should reach sound observations and conclusions which will provide an enriched background of understanding throughout his lifetime.

Geography studied conscientiously in this fashion provides a better appreciation of foreign peoples and their special problems and increases the interest in and enjoyment of literature, history, and other subjects. Knowledge of the development of landscapes adds to the pleasures of traveling and reading. A geographer should be open-minded and curious, possessed of the scientific spirit, and more interested in the truth rather than in subscribing to widely held beliefs. He should learn the techniques of geographic investigation.

There is no single method of learning geography; sometimes one system is helpful, whereas a different presentation of the subject will succeed under other conditions and in other situations. It is hoped that the interest of the student will be aroused to such a degree that he will continue the study of geography long after leaving the classroom, because material in the field is abundant and the subject lends itself readily to individual investigation. The value of a geography course to the student depends to a considerable extent on the application of his knowledge long after he leaves college.

Essentials of Geography first surveys earth relations, the atmosphere, and the tools of geography. Then follows a description of the climates of the earth and their relation to man and other organic life. Mountains, plains, and oceans receive consideration, as do the minerals, soils, forests, and inland water resources, including the problems of their conservation. After the facts concerning the natural environments of man are discussed, the balance of the text is devoted to the geography of population, cities, agriculture, manufactures, nations, transport routes, and factors affecting human activities on the different continents.

The text devotes much space and attention to the descriptions of primitive peoples and their economies, because their relationships to different natural environments are less complex than those of people who have made great cultural advances.

Questions have been included at the end of each chapter to help emphasize certain facts and principles of geography. References were selected from many found useful by the authors; the lists, however, are not intended to serve as comprehensive bibliographies. The authors will welcome suggestions from teachers concerning problems, questions, references, and geographical material that might be added or omitted to advantage.

The authors received assistance from many sources in the preparation of the manuscript. Credit for the use of photographs is given in connection with the illustrations. Certain chapters were checked critically by authorities, notably William C. Pryor of the U.S. Soil Conservation Service and C. W. Mattison and others of the U.S. Forest Service. Assistance was given by staff members of the U.S. Geological Survey, the U.S. Bureau of Mines, and the U.S. Bureau of Reclamation. The authors are deeply appreciative of the valuable suggestions offered by many of their colleagues in the geography profession and by numerous teachers who have been using the first edition in their courses. Acknowledgment is made also to those individuals and corporations who supplied information and photographs needed for the revision.

Changes in the second edition include the addition of outlines and summaries at the close of each chapter, together with a thorough revision of the questions appended to the chapters. Many parts of the book have been rewritten and all has been thoroughly revised. Some rearrangement of chapters has improved the order of presentation. The references have been brought up to date, and much material has been added to the text. There are 300 illustrations, and most of the photographs used in the second edition are new. Maps were redrawn to provide uniformity in appearance. Bound with the book is an atlas that includes color maps of all the continents. Statistics are the latest available and much of this material is presented in graphic form.

Otis W. Freeman
H. F. Raup

Contents

1. The Scope and Techniques of Geography

INTRODUCTION

MOST students are interested in what the earth looks like away from home and curious about the way other people live. Informally they acquire knowledge of the earth from the fine colored illustrations of current magazines or from motion pictures set or even taken in distant lands. Some radio and television programs provide excellent geographical material. Unorganized information about the world becomes useful and significant as well as interesting when it is placed in a framework of understanding. By explaining the underlying causes that affect geographical conditions on the earth, this text offers students both new knowledge and a method of organizing the information they have casually acquired. In his study of geography, the student will be concerned with the widely different landscapes and the changing environments in which human activities occur and with the people who carry on those activities.

WHAT IS GEOGRAPHY?

Geography fundamentally is a description of the earth's surface or that part of the earth's crust with which man is concerned. This meaning is inherent in the word itself, for the root *ge* comes from the ancient Greek, signifying any fact having to do with the earth. The second part of the word, *graph,* also comes from a Greek root meaning "to write" or having to do with writing. A literal definition of geography, therefore, would be "a writing about, or description of, the earth, including all that appears upon it." Evidently this definition of the subject includes the study of man and his activities as well as many aspects of plant and animal life and a wide variety of other subjects related to the earth.

Geography is a very broad subject with numerous relationships to other natural and social sciences. Some of these relationships are presented in the chart (Figure 1-1), which shows some geographic phases of selected fields of knowledge and the type of geographic material associated with each subject. The field of geography serves as the hub around which these topics revolve. Thus the hub is represented at the center of the diagram, and the spokes form the connections between geography and most of its allied academic disciplines.

A brief description of some relationships between geography and other subjects suggests entertaining and instructive bypaths for geography students to investigate.

Natural sciences. Every natural science has geographic relationships for those areas in which man's activities are affected. The following selected examples could be multiplied many times. Astronomy governs surveys of the earth and the determination of one's location upon the globe. Botany includes the distribution of plants in relation to their environments. Ethnology describes the characteristics of different peoples, and is closely related to geography. Forestry is concerned with natural factors that affect tree growth, the control of fire, pests and plant diseases, and the proper cutting and utilization of wood. Engineering is needed in the building of power plants, irrigation and drainage proj-

Figure 1-1   The relation of geography to other academic disciplines.

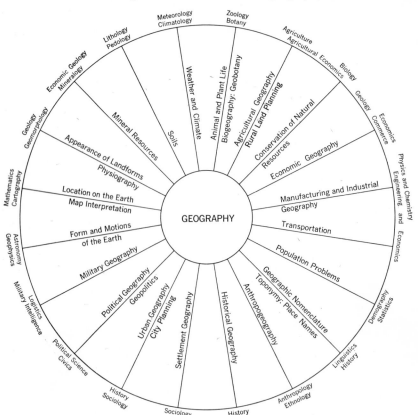

ects, flood control, and various other works.

Geology explains the origins of surface features of the earth, the occurrences of mineral deposits, and other facts that help form the foundation on which geography is built. Mineralogy deals with the many minerals found in the earth, the factors that affect their occurrence, and the varied uses made of them by man. Meteorology is the study of the atmosphere, storms, and all types of weather phenomena. Physics is a fundamental science that helps explain the weathering of rocks, movements of air and water, development of soils, and other facts important to geographers. Zoology discusses the natural factors affecting animals and their development. Studies of plant and animal life have helped man develop improved strains of plants or breeds of animals which yield more food and have greater resistance to pests and diseases.

Geography thus constantly deals with material taken from the natural sciences. Because it uses the application of various sciences to many human concerns as its own focal point, geography can help tie diverse fields together; hence it is a logical core subject. Courses of study for the public schools sometimes use geographic topics as a central theme (hub in the diagram, Figure 1-1) from which many paths lead to other fields of knowledge to form connections with both natural and social science.

Weather and climate. A satisfactory understanding of the behavior of the atmosphere is essential as background for the appreciation of human activities. It is difficult to think of any occupation that is unaffected by the weather. Members of the medical profession, for example, are aware that seasonal changes of humidity and temperature are responsible for marked increase in incidence of certain diseases, especially respiratory afflictions.

Most merchants are aware of the effects of weather on trade. Weather changes affect a wide range of commercial activities, such as the volume of gasoline sales, evaporation of stored gasoline, marketing of perishable veg-

etables, heating installations, use of insulation in houses, and sales of beverages, both hot and cold. Unwise purchases of seasonal goods may show a lack of judgment that will make a business fail. Fur wearing apparel, for example, enjoys brisk demand at certain seasons in the United States; farther north it is almost always in demand. In the tropics, however, garments made of fur are almost useless and hence cannot be sold unless the altitude is high.

Weather profoundly affects transportation, especially the operation of aircraft for both military and peaceful purposes. Fog and storms are dangerous for ocean shipping. Freezing rain, fog, snow, and storms may make highway travel difficult and dangerous.

Social sciences. The social sciences are as important as the natural sciences in studying geography, for they include the activities of man as he tries to improve his living conditions, struggling from day to day to make a more satisfying existence for himself. The economist surveys the different methods by which man earns his bread. The archeologist investigates man's activities in periods before records were written; the anthropologist studies modern preliterate peoples. The historian, too, is aware that migrations, warfare, cultural advances, and other events which concern him are closely related to their geographic backgrounds. Sociology investigates human interrelationships of many types. Specialists in agricultural research know that they must be familiar with weather differences, soils, and aspects of conservation. Those who earn their living by moving goods and people cannot ignore weather conditions, effects of land relief on construction costs, and similar problems. Political scientists studying governments know that the characteristic occupation of nations and their military capabilities may be associated with the amount and kind of raw materials available for supporting their economies and maintaining their military forces.

Historical geography. The history of a region is intimately connected with changes in the utilization of its land and resources. Near the upper Great Lakes, for example, the first European settlers sought only furs. Later they exploited timber, iron and copper ore, and fish, and made the Great Lakes their highway for transporting goods. Today the use of the region has changed. Some residents of that part of the country depend on farming, and visitors go there in large numbers for summer recreation. Waterfalls are being developed for power and manufacturing. In this way the different uses of the land, or *sequent occupance,* have changed greatly with passage of time.

Sometimes routes of exploration and settlement depend on such factors as locations of passes through highland barriers, presence of navigable rivers, type of vegetation cover, soil fertility, and even the amount of snow in winter. It took the English colonists along the Atlantic coast twice the time to work their way across the Appalachian ridges and forests to the western prairies than was required for men to go from the Mississippi River to the Pacific Ocean over country that is mainly open plains and deserts. In contrast, French settlers entering the St. Lawrence Valley used a system of waterways whose short portages led quickly to the interior of the continent. Rivers have proved valuable routes of exploration and penetration in many lands, including the Congo Basin, Siberia, and the Yukon and Columbia Basins.

Geography is a significant factor in military history. Campaigns are planned to take advantage of easy routes and favorable weather. During the Revolutionary War, England tried to separate the colonies along the Hudson–Lake Champlain Trench. When Grant captured Vicksburg in 1863, the Northern states gained full control of the Mississippi River; this divided the Confederacy and thereby hastened victory over the South.

Agricultural geography. Any successful farmer must know how to value his farm produce to the utmost without decline in fertility. The size of his fields may be governed by what the soil can yield; their shape may

be related to the relief of the land, particularly in hilly and mountainous regions. Whether the farmer sows winter wheat, spring wheat, rye, or potatoes is in itself largely governed by the weather and climate of his locality. Farm activities during the course of the year are closely tied to weather. Too much rain in harvest seasons, early autumn frosts, or late spring floods may interfere with farm routines to an extent that few but the farmer himself know; if his work is a failure, those who depend on his efforts may starve before crops can be harvested the following season.

Economic geography. Economic geography is concerned with the distribution and processing of the world's resources and their use by the world's people. Stated thus the matter sounds simple; but a thorough knowledge of the areas producing leading commodities of commerce is more complex. Some parts of the earth provide abundant goods for human consumption. In desert oases the date palm, requiring much water and freedom from frost, may produce a crop so large that the grower will have dates to sell elsewhere. On the other hand, if dates are grown far from good transport facilities or are too low in price, the grower may lose his investment of money and time. Interplay among the factors of production—cost, distribution, transport, trade, and consumption—is a principal part of economic geography. Any one of these phases may become a matter of intensive study; together they are a fascinating aspect of modern geography.

Political geography. Only fiction shows a state or nation that is not related closely to the conditions that prevail on the earth's surface. A nation represents *a part of the earth's surface* used by a particular group of people. As such, it is outlined by political boundaries and its extent may be measured. A nation may contain landscape of wide variety as in China, or its surface may be relatively uniform like that of Uruguay. It may be as large as the Soviet Union or as tiny as the principality of Monaco. Its borders may include great wealth, enabling it to attain the status of a world power, or like Andorra, a nation may exist by sufferance of more powerful neighbors. Its people may live mainly on local products, or if the nation is deficient in food or other resources, it may depend on international trade. It can maintain a strong military position, or its people and resources may be wholly inadequate to provide protection against stronger powers.

Furthermore, geographical conditions that prevail in a given locality may profoundly influence the success or failure of political effort. Chile, a desert in the north and a forest wilderness in the south, has great difficulty in providing the 2,000 miles of rail transportation that helps to maintain a degree of political control over such an extended coast. The character of the rock at Gibraltar and the narrowness of the strait—matters of local geography—combine to make the position of great military importance. Naval success elsewhere gave the United Kingdom an outpost here upon what would otherwise be regarded as Spanish soil. Such foreign outposts may cause political antagonisms which sometimes result in military hostilities.

Settlement geography. Small communities, like large urban centers, have varied geographic characteristics. A shallow stream ford or a mountain pass may provide a convenient location for a house; this in turn attracts other residents and soon a community appears differing in form and function from its neighbors. Some settlements seem to have no observable pattern; others have been rigidly planned according to surveyors' measurements. Some reflect the convergence or divergence of routes and take the form of a Y. In Western Europe settlement patterns of towns and villages often show features that originated in feudal times. Sometimes the people built houses near a castle for protection or around a market place for trade. Often the center of a city is encircled by a boulevard, located where the city wall once stood.

Human settlements may serve as centers of transport, or as market towns whose facilities for shopping are designed to attract buyers from a large tributary area. A few are educational centers, such as Oberlin, Ohio, or their activities may be mainly religious (Ste. Anne de Beaupré, Quebec). Some are military installations; others are established solely as centers of industrial activity. Though usually less complex in form and function than the larger urban centers, small settlements nevertheless display wide variations in their geographic features.

Conservation of resources. National prosperity and living standards depend largely on available resources and their utilization. If soils, forests, minerals, water, and other resources are carelessly depleted, large segments of a country may deteriorate, since raw materials and foodstuffs obtainable from the earth or the sea are not inexhaustible. Measures to conserve them for use of future generations are essential. These measures should make provision for the maximum utilization of natural resources, with minimum waste. For conservation is the wise use of resources, and not simply their preservation by nonuse. Geography, with its subject matter taken from both physical and social sciences, is well adapted to studying problems in conservation. This may involve surveys of the land, mapping of available resources, studies of alternate sources or substitute materials, and recommendations for improvement in current usage or practices.

The conservationist, for example, may concern himself with preventing waste of water in a pulp mill, or the extinction of certain types of fresh-water fish because of stream pollution from industrial plants. Both forms of destruction may be related, if fish are exterminated by chemical wastes discharged from the mill. At this point, the study of the geography of the situation may suggest a practical solution of both problems, since the subject unites physical and cultural aspects: stream flow, fall of water, amount of precipitation, and demand for paper pulp, needs of the sports enthusiast, and the use of fish for human food. Conservation requires knowledge drawn from geology, forestry, biology, engineering, and many other sciences. Because man—as farmer, businessman, sportsman, and lover of nature—is affected by the manifold phases of conservation, geography is the natural home of the subject; hence many programs in geography center about conservation. With its many applications, conservation is among the most practical subjects taught in schools.

Transportation. The best routes of land travel usually conform closely with the irregularities of the surface. Sea routes are governed largely by configuration of the coast and by ocean currents. For air travel, the presence or absence of water bodies and mountain ranges is often taken into account. Thus studying the geography of transport provides logical explanations for the selection of one route instead of another. Often, the lay of the land encourages the development of travel; surely the construction of the Erie Canal was suggested by the presence of the broad saddle of the Mohawk Valley as well as by the need to connect the Hudson River with Lake Erie. At other times, topography makes construction difficult and expensive; to bridge a strait as wide and deep as the Golden Gate required a monumental feat of engineering.

Geographical analysis of the distribution of the world's people and products indicates the trends of transportation and accounts for the presence of the leading trade routes. Familiarity with the earth's form explains a main reason for current interest in transpolar flights and the prospects of opening those remote regions by means of regularly scheduled trips. Geographers have used detailed studies of the flow and volume of automobile traffic to help select suitable locations for new shopping centers, and trained geographers have been instrumental in deciding on the best locations for newly installed landing fields for aircraft. The relations of geography and transport are increasingly significant in the complexity of modern civilization.

Geography and primitive man. Perhaps the closest relationship between human beings and their environments is exemplified by activities of primitive man. Whether he lives in polar wastes or tropical forests, he relies directly upon his own efforts to meet his needs and is in daily contact with nature. That contact provides him with food, shelter, transport, and other necessities of human existence. Natives of the Far North, for example, may be unable to obtain supplies of firearms, canned foods, or other commodities from more favored parts of the earth. They hunt the seal or walrus, or trail herds of caribou or musk ox. They also rely upon fishing in order to secure food. No day goes by in which they are free of handicaps that their environment has imposed upon them.

Geographical conditions also are unfavorable in extremely hot and very wet tropical environments where primitive man is equally handicapped in finding food and shelter. Here, too, in locations near the equator, nature has provided no great wealth of raw materials for the use of primitive people. Though food supplies may be more abundant than those of polar regions, they often are not readily obtained and usually soon deteriorate; also there may be few goods with which to carry on trade. Again, location is of the utmost significance to human activity.

Geographical conditions in high mountain and plateau areas are little better than those of the extreme tropics and polar lands. The primitive herdsman with his llama train on the Bolivian plateau may suffer from lack of food and shelter just as greatly as his brother of the polar wastes or tropical forest.

In more advanced civilizations, relationships between human activities and geographical conditions of a given locality are more difficult to observe. The modern city dweller, dependent upon efficient transportation and complex economic organization, lives in an environment which is almost entirely artificial. He is nearly unaware of weather changes, since weather is controlled in modern buildings. In many offices he will not know whether the sun shines or the day is cloudy. Most of his day-to-day needs are met in a stabilized environment, but slight dislocations of normal economic activity may disrupt this featureless existence. A temporary interruption of electrical current will disturb living and working conditions among these city dwellers.

For most of the world's people human activities lie between those of primitive man, with his intimate connection with the natural environment, and the complex conditions under which the city worker operates in his artificial environment. Most people note changes of season, periods of daylight followed by darkness, the warmth of summer days, or the falling snow of winter. Certainly no human being on the face of the earth exists without relationships to geographical conditions prevailing in his immediate neighborhood. It seems reasonable to learn as much about these geographic conditions as one can in order to understand the way in which the rest of the world lives.

THE LEADING FACTORS OF GEOGRAPHIC ENVIRONMENT

Four elements of the natural environment are particularly significant in affecting human activity. One of the important aspects of geography is the answer to a simple question: In what part of the world do you live? The surface of the earth is marked by enormous contrasts—heat and cold, barrenness and productivity, rain and drought, mountains and lowlands. Thus *location* on the earth may have significant effects upon human activity. Yet many people on the earth have succeeded in overcoming handicaps imposed upon them by unfortunate location—they have flourished not because of what nature has provided for their use, but in spite of it. Human ingenuity in overcoming obstacles that nature has placed in the path of human progress is a factor that should never be underestimated and should be taken into account in many explanations of the behavior of man in relation to his surroundings. Nevertheless, the accident of location on the earth's surface can never be wholly ignored in considering human activity.

The second factor, *climate*, is related to location. Climate affects other geographic conditions such as soils, hills and valleys of the landscape, or tree growth and grasslands. Since climatic conditions vary from place to place on the earth's surface, the location of a man's residence very largely determines the type of climate that he will experience throughout his lifetime. To be sure human choice can govern human existence to some degree; an individual who dislikes a particular climate may move to some part of the world where weather is more to his taste.

The third factor is the appearance of the landscape; that is, the irregularities or *landforms* of the earth's surface as they appear in the form of continents and islands, ocean basins, mountains, hills, or plains. The land surface of the earth is divided into a number of differing landscapes, each with its own distinctive features but nevertheless resembling selected types on other continents. The study of geography not only attempts to explain the origin and development of these, but systematically compares them. An open plain, for example, generally offers fewer interruptions to travel than rugged mountain or plateau country in which greater human effort must be expended. Certain human economies are unsuccessful in some parts of the earth; large-scale agriculture is difficult in rough country, and people who live there often herd livestock rather than farm for a living. Yet if a mountain environment will not produce enough food, men can migrate to more favorable locations, thereby improving their living conditions. Human choice may become a governing factor in the situation; if natural conditions are unfavorable, a more desirable place can be sought.

The fourth factor is the *condition of the soil* in any given location. Soils may be too light, too heavy, too infertile, or perhaps too stony to be cultivated with success. If they are so unproductive that sufficient foodstuffs cannot be grown, then it may be necessary to engage in some other occupation than farming or move to another location where the soil will produce adequate crops. Desert soils require irrigation, or may be too salty to grow crops well. Good judgment on the part of the farmer will enable him to find the soil best suited for his crops in some other location.

Coastal and interior location. Activities of many people are related to continents, coasts, or seas. Millions have never seen the sea, spending their entire lives in the interiors of continents. Their viewpoint may be limited by their experience; often they are land-bound in thinking and in knowledge of world affairs. In contrast, others spend most of their lives on the sea itself or along its shores; their food and their income often depend upon products of the sea.

Coastal locations provide a highly specialized geographic environment whose climate and land relief may be instrumental in the development of marine activities, particularly fishing. In coastal Norway, for example, little land is suitable for farming, the irregular coast is indented by many harbors, and the nearby seas swarm with fish. Under these circumstances, many Norwegians become sailors and fishermen and much of the economy of the nation is directed seaward. Similarly, most residents of the Labrador coast gain their livelihood from fishing and sealing. Nations such as the United States and France, facing on more than one ocean or sea, are in favorable positions for maintaining sea trade and foreign commerce which further development of ports and manufactures. Large islands adjacent to populous continental locations—Japan and the Asiatic continent, for example—enjoy particularly favorable sites for commercial traffic. Often residents of extensive fertile plains far from the sea are more satisfied to stay at home. This is true in places such as central China or the interior parts of the Soviet Union.

Accessibility. Any features, either land or water, that cause routes to converge make sites favorable for settlements, and a number of the world's leading cities owe their growth mainly to this factor. Of the many possible situations, we shall give only a few examples:

1. At a natural crossroads in a basin, Munich, Paris.

2. Confluence of rivers, Pittsburgh (Figure 24-10).

3. Junction of land and river routes, Kansas City; Belgrade, Yugoslavia.

4. Break from lake to land routes, Buffalo.

5. Especially favorable, a seaport where ocean shipping meets river boats and land routes entering important valleys, for example, Shanghai; Hamburg; New Orleans; Portland, Oregon; New York; Buenos Aires; Calcutta.

To be valuable for trade and to permit growth of any considerable city, a harbor must have practicable and developed routes inland to a productive hinterland. Fine harbors in Alaska, Norway, and southern Chile are sites of tiny fishing villages or remain entirely unused because they lack productive hinterlands.

Valuable resources. Raw materials upon which man depends for his needs are widely distributed over the earth. Forests are found in some places but not in others; valuable ores may be concentrated in rather small areas. The presence of these and other resources may lead to growth of large populations, particularly if cheap transportation to markets and manufacturing plants is readily available. Coal, timber, or fruit in a thinly peopled locality remote from markets and transportation are of limited use and have relatively slight value. Iron ore discovered in the interior of Labrador remained unworked until railroads, docks, and houses for workmen were built. Then the ore was mined in quantity and shipped to blast furnaces in distant locations. In contrast, low-grade iron ore beds near Birmingham, Alabama, and Newcastle, England, are worked because they occur close to coal and markets. Supplies of natural gas near Pittsburgh and Cleveland are more valuable than gas in Alberta or Alaska.

Because the modern world needs certain metals, settlement has occurred in mountains, deserts, and frozen wastes that would remain uninhabited if valuable minerals were not present. For example, the mining towns of Leadville and Cripple Creek in Colorado are nearly two miles above sea level, and the town of Cerro de Pasco in Peru is even higher. Without its rich veins of copper ore, Butte,

The maps in this atlas contain two kinds of information important in the study of geography. They picture the physical aspects of our planet—continents and islands, seas and lakes, peaks and plains—in correct relationship to each other. They present features of human culture, such as the names of countries and cities and the location of political boundaries.

One map is a general view of the earth. Another indicates by special color coding what use man makes of the land. The balance of the atlas is devoted to specific regions on a larger scale. A dramatic contrast between the areas of vegetation and the barren deserts is apparent, as is the way plant life is distributed in relation to the world's oceans, rivers, mountain chains, and plateaus.

In all the maps except the one for land use, the artist-cartographer, Hal Shelton, has shown the color differences of the surface that would be seen by an imaginary observer out in space. Summer, the chief season of growth, is represented as prevailing everywhere at the same time.

The key at the right explains the colors to be found in the maps: snow and ice, dominant types of natural vegetation, and desert. Its coloring and relief illustrate in miniature the wide variety of physical features in the maps themselves.

WORLD ATLAS

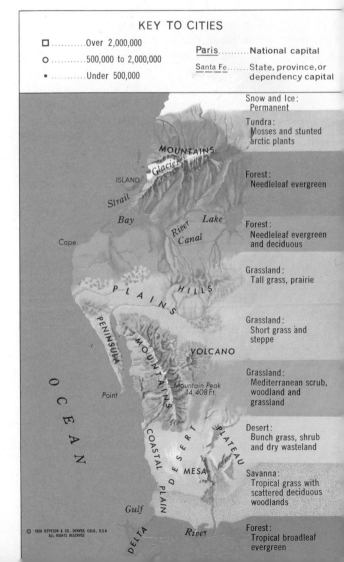

KEY TO CITIES

☐ ....Over 2,000,000
○ ....500,000 to 2,000,000
• ....Under 500,000

Paris..........National capital
Santa Fe.......State, province, or dependency capital

Snow and Ice: Permanent

Tundra: Mosses and stunted arctic plants

Forest: Needleleaf evergreen

Forest: Needleleaf evergreen and deciduous

Grassland: Tall grass, prairie

Grassland: Short grass and steppe

Grassland: Mediterranean scrub, woodland and grassland

Desert: Bunch grass, shrub and dry wasteland

Savanna: Tropical grass with scattered deciduous woodlands

Forest: Tropical broadleaf evergreen

MOUNTAINS
Glacier
ISLAND
Strait
Bay
River   Lake
Canal
Cape
PLAINS
HILLS
PENINSULA
MOUNTAINS
VOLCANO
Mountain Peak 14,408 Ft.
Point
OCEAN
COASTAL PLAIN
DESERT
PLATEAU
MESA
Gulf
DELTA
River

© 1958 JEPPESEN & CO., DENVER, COLO., U.S.A
ALL RIGHTS RESERVED

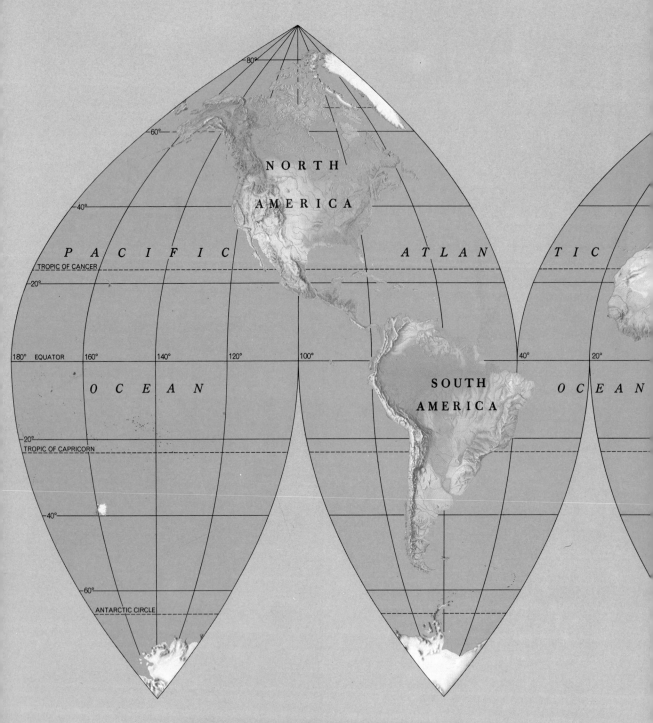

PHYSICAL MAP OF THE WORLD

Parabolic Equal-area Projection
1 square inch = 3,168,400 square miles

Linear scale 1780 miles to one inch at the Equator

| 0 | 1000 | 2000 | 3000 |

Statute miles

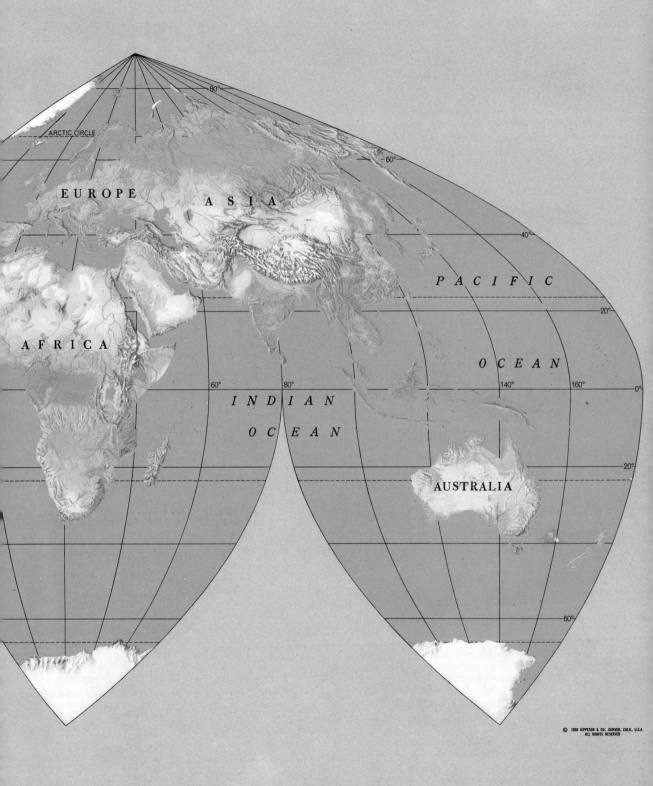

EUROPE

ASIA

AFRICA

PACIFIC

OCEAN

INDIAN

OCEAN

AUSTRALIA

ARCTIC CIRCLE

80°

60°

40°

20°

0°

20°

60°

60°

80°

60°

140°

160°

© 1958 JEPPESEN & CO., DENVER, COLO., U.S.A.
ALL RIGHTS RESERVED

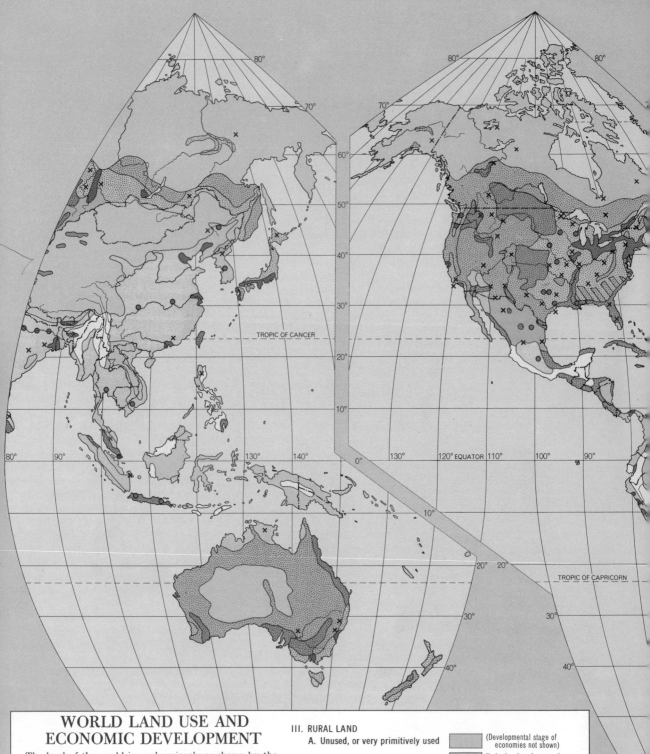

WORLD LAND USE AND ECONOMIC DEVELOPMENT

The land of the world is used variously as shown by the colors below. Superimposed on the map is the pattern of the world's economies: those that are technically advanced are indicated by a dot symbol and those that are underdeveloped are shown without this overprint. Technically advanced lands have less than 45% of their labor forces in agriculture. Considered by per capita gross national product, Chile and Japan would be removed from, and Venezuela added to, technically advanced countries. Plantations are considered technically advanced.

I. SUBMERGED LAND

 (Developmental stage not shown)
See inset map

II. URBAN AND MANUFACT-
URING LAND (Developmental stage as in country of location)

III. RURAL LAND

A. Unused, or very primitively used

B. Forest Exploitation

C. Grazing

D. Agriculture
   1. Predominantly subsis-
      tence agriculture
   2. Mixed commercial and
      subsistence agriculture,
      diversified crops and animals
   3. Predominantly commercial
      agriculture or horticulture

E. Major Mineral Extraction

(Developmental stage of
economies not shown)

Underdeveloped economies
Technically advanced economies

Underdeveloped economies
Technically advanced economies

(Entirely in underdeveloped
economies)

Underdeveloped economies
Technically advanced economies

Underdeveloped economies
Technically advanced economies

x x x (Essentially in or controlled by
technically advanced economies)

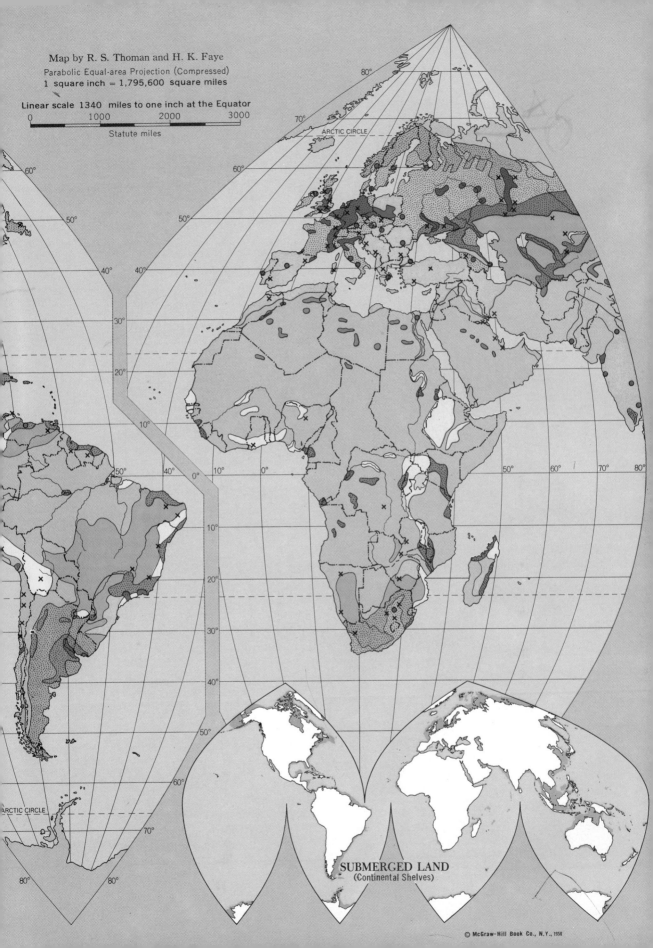

Map by R. S. Thoman and H. K. Faye
Parabolic Equal-area Projection (Compressed)
1 square inch = 1,795,600 square miles

Linear scale 1340 miles to one inch at the Equator

0   1000   2000   3000
Statute miles

SUBMERGED LAND
(Continental Shelves)

© McGraw-Hill Book Co., N.Y., 1958

THE UNITED STATES OF AMERICA
Lambert Conformal Conic Projection

National capitols underlined: Ottawa

State and province capitols underlined: Atlanta

© 1958 JEPPESEN & CO., DENVER, COLO., U.S.A.
ALL RIGHTS RESERVED

NORTH AMERICA

Parabolic Equal-area Projection
1 square inch = 360,000 square miles

Linear scale 600 miles to one inch at the Equator

0   500   1000   1500

Statute miles

© 1958 JEPPESEN & CO., DENVER, COLO., U.S.A.
ALL RIGHTS RESERVED

SOUTH AMERICA

Parabolic Equal-area Projection
1 square inch = 360,000 square miles

Linear scale 600 miles to one inch at the Equator

0   500   1000   1500

Statute miles

© 1950 JEPPESEN & CO., DENVER, COLO., U.S.A.
ALL RIGHTS RESERVED

EUROPE

Lambert Azimuthal Equal-area Projection
1 square inch = 72,900 square miles

Linear scale 270 miles to one inch

| 0 | 100 | 200 | 300 | 400 | 500 | 600 |

Statute miles

NORTH ATLANTIC OCEAN

ICELAND
Reykjavik

ARCTIC CIRCLE

NORWEGIAN SEA

FAEROES

SHETLAND IS.

LOFOTEN IS.

NORWAY

SWEDEN

Trondheim

Bergen

Oslo

Lake Vänern

Göteborg

Skagerrak

Kattegat

HEBRIDES

ORKNEY IS.

SCOTLAND
Glasgow
Dundee
Aberdeen

NORTHERN IRELAND
Belfast
Edinburgh
Newcastle

NORTH SEA

Aarhus

Copenhagen
Malmö

DENMARK

Kiel

BALTIC

Dublin
IRELAND

Manchester
Leeds

Liverpool
Sheffield

Birmingham
ENGLAND

WALES

Cardiff
London
Brighton

Cork

Lübeck

Hamburg
Bremen
Hannover

Amsterdam
NETHERLAND
The Hague
Rotterdam

Antwerp
BELGIUM
Brussels

NORTH
Dortmund
Essen
Cologne
Bonn

EAST
Berlin

Oder R.
Poznań

GERMANY

Leipzig
Dresden

SILESIA

Prague
CZECHOSL

WEST GERMANY

Karl Marx

Elbe R.

Lands End

English Channel

CHANNEL IS.

Le Havre

LUX.
SAAR
Frankfurt
Strasbourg
Stuttgart

Rhine River

Seine R.

Paris
FRANCE

Nantes
Loire
Tours

GERMANY

BAVARIA

Danube River

Brno
Vienna

Linz

AUSTRIA

Graz

Munich

Zurich
Bern
SWITZERLAND
LIECHT

Ljubljana

Zagreb

Trieste

DINARIC ALPS

YUGO

Bay of Biscay

Bordeaux

Saint Étienne
AUVERGNE MTS.

Lyons

Mont Blanc
15,78

Rhone River

Po River
Milan
Turin
Genoa

Venice
Bologna

ADRIATIC SEA

Cape Finisterre

Bilbao

Oporto

SPANISH

Ebro River

PYRENEES

ANDORRA

Saragossa

Toulouse

Marseille
Nice
MONACO
Florence

APENNINES

ITALY

Lisbon

SPAIN
Madrid

PLATEAU

Tagus River

Barcelona

PORTUGAL

Valencia

CORSICA

Rome

TYRRHENIAN SEA

Guadalquivir River

Seville

Cádiz
SA. NEVADA

Murcia

SARDINIA

Naples

Málaga

BALEARIC IS.

Cagliari

Tangier
Tetuán
Strait of Gibraltar

Oran

Algiers

MEDITERRANEA

Palermo
SICILY
Catania

Ba

Casablanca
Rabat
Fès
Meknes

MOROCCO

Bizerte
Bône

Cape Bon
Tunis

Marrakech

ATLAS MTS.

ALGERIA

Constantine

TUNISIA

Sfax

AFRICA

Parabolic Equal-area Projection
1 square inch = 490,000 square miles

Linear scale 700 miles to one inch at the Equator

0   500   1000   1500

Statute miles

© 1956 JEPPESEN & CO.,
DENVER, COLO., U.S.A.
ALL RIGHTS RESERVED

AUSTRALIA, NEW ZEALAND AND THE EAST INDIES

Parabolic Equal-area Projection

1 square inch = 490,000 square miles

Linear scale 700 miles to one inch at the Equator

| 0 | 500 | 1000 | 1500 |

Statute miles

© 1958 JEPPESEN & CO., DENVER, COLO. U.S.A. ALL RIGHTS RESERVED

NORTH POLAR REGION

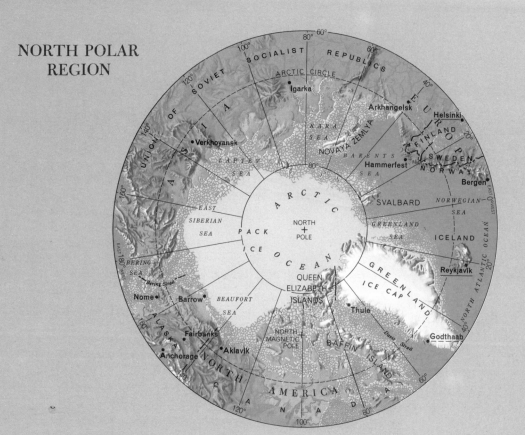

Polar Stereographic Projection
1 square inch = 1,440,000 square miles (approx.)

Linear scale 1200 miles to one inch

| 0 | 500 | 1000 | 1500 | 2000 |

Statute miles

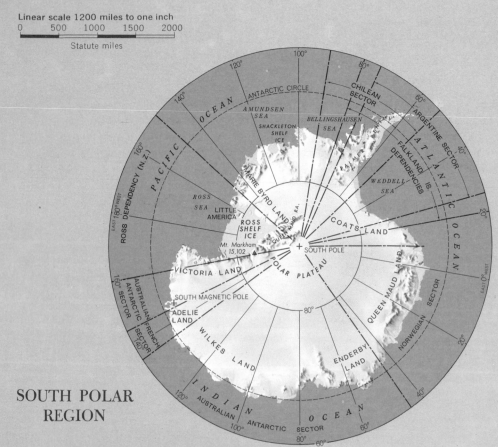

SOUTH POLAR REGION

© 1958 JEPPESEN & CO., DENVER, COLO., U.S.A.
ALL RIGHTS RESERVED

Montana, would be a hamlet supported by a few stockmen.

Neighbors.   The situation of a city or nation in relation to important nearby regions is often a leading factor affecting its development. Great Britain's location off the coast of Western Europe has been advantageous, although the development of aircraft has destroyed the military value of that country's "splendid isolation." Cities, as well as nations, are workshops that supply manufactures in exchange for foodstuffs and raw materials and grow in proportion to the development of their trade areas and the character of their near neighbors. Trade and travel, for example, are little impeded by the 2,500-mile boundary separating the United States and Canada. Newspapers, magazines, radio and television programs, and streams of visitors move freely across this line. In contrast, the multiplicity of political boundaries in Central Europe and the Balkans seriously interferes with exchange of goods, services, and ideas, partly because of mutual fears and jealousies. Suspicion of a neighbor's motives may hamper the exchange of both products and information.

GEOGRAPHIC TECHNIQUES

The trained geographer uses many devices to show the significance and relationships of a wide range of geographic facts. The best way to understand geography is to travel widely and observe different parts of the world. Some fortunate individuals can do this, but most people must gain information about distant places without benefit of travel. To a certain extent this can be done successfully by studying photographs and by some few other methods. Perhaps the most important of the methods used are visual devices like the globe and its near relative, the map.

The Globe.   The appearance of this earth should always be represented as accurately and as correctly as possible. A globe is the most satisfactory representation of the earth that has been devised; its shape is the shape of the earth, hence it shows the correct position of places on the earth in relation to each other. Facts about the earth taught pupils in primary grades can best be presented by means of the globe. Globes 8, 10, and 16 inches in diameter are more convenient in measuring distances than are 12- or 14-inch globes, because the scale of the globe is in even numbers of miles (1,000 miles to the inch for the 8-inch, 800 miles for the 10-inch) whereas the 12- and 14-inch globes have scales with odd numbers and fractions of miles.

The accurate representation of location on the globe is shown clearly in Figure 1-2, which displays the poleward swing of sailing routes, northerly in the Northern Hemisphere. Sailing routes of the Southern Hemisphere swing toward the South Pole. A taut string stretched between Los Angeles and Tokyo on a globe

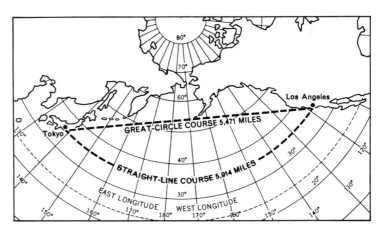

Figure 1-2 The great-circle sailing route is the shortest distance on the earth's surface between Los Angeles and Tokyo.

shows that the shortest route (the arc of a great circle) lies a short distance south of the Aleutian Islands. A string will show that the shortest distance for air travel from Chicago to Moscow or from Seattle-Tacoma to Tokyo is along a great-circle route, the first over the polar sea and the second over the North Pacific Ocean. Thus the globe presents the actual short-distance routes used in flights over hitherto remote and dangerous polar areas. As noted, these routes follow the arcs of great circles, and a great circle is defined as "any circle drawn on the globe whose plane bisects the globe."

Map Projections. Since a globe is cumbersome, not readily portable, and ill-adapted to show sufficient geographic detail, it must be supplemented by some more portable device that will also show more about the earth's sur-

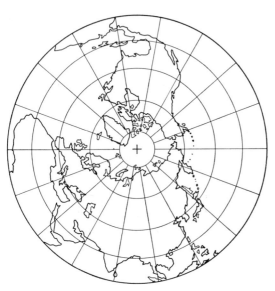

Figure 1-3 The polar equal-area map projection, or Lambert azimuthal, devised in 1772. This hemispherical map distorts shapes, particularly near its perimeter, but it provides accuracy of area throughout the whole map. This quality makes it a valuable map for the geographer. The principle employed can be expanded to include the whole earth and the resulting map will resemble the homolographic projection in Figure 2-10.

face. This can be done by the use of the map projection. Simply stated, this is an outer skin which has been removed from the curved surface of the sphere. No effort can flatten such a curved surface entirely; if much flattening occurs, then the geographic relationships shown on the surface are inevitably distorted. Indeed, too much flattening may distort the surface so greatly that one has a highly inaccurate and unreliable representation of the earth. Most map projections having any degree of accuracy consist of networks or grids of lines representing meridians of longitude and parallels of latitude. The meaning and significance of these lines will be taken up in the following chapter.

Although no flat surface, such as a map, can perfectly represent the earth's spherical surface, it is desirable to provide as high a degree of accuracy as possible. To do so, certain qualities may need to be sacrificed. Several map characteristics are of special importance, and the relative significance of these depends upon the use for which the map is intended. Since the curved surface cannot be represented on a flat surface without distortion, the map maker (cartographer) should select the projection that best suits his purposes. An ideal map should show correct shape or form of land and water bodies, correct area, and correct location; it would present northward direction at the top of the map, show the shortest distance between two points by a straight line on the map, and show all of the world on one map without interruption. Some of these good features may be had in a single projection, but only at the sacrifice of some or all of the other features. It is impossible for any map that shows a large part of the earth's surface to represent both shapes and areas correctly. One or the other and sometimes both these objectives must be sacrificed. Numerous map projections have been constructed by cartographers. Each has certain advantages and disadvantages. In their choice of a projection, cartographers keep in mind the type that will best show what they want to indicate on the map.

The following projections are among those used most frequently.

Hemispherical projections. This type of map projection represents the world as two separate circles; of all world maps such projections most resemble the appearance of a sphere. The geographer finds some of these maps particularly useful when any unit of area on any part of the map is equal to the same unit on any other part of the map. This characteristic, which is called *equivalence of area,* means that comparisons of the distribution of geographic data can be made accurately. There are some disadvantages to this projection, however, because the grid lines (meridians and parallels) are usually curved, thus making directions difficult to follow on the map. Furthermore, the two separate halves of the map make it difficult to proceed along a route from one hemisphere to the other.

There are several types of hemispheric projections. The two most commonly used are the stereographic projection (see maps of the polar regions in the Atlas section) and the Lambert polar azimuthal projection (Figure 1-3). The former is used for mapping single continents like South America, Africa, Asia, and North America; but the Lambert polar projection

Figure 1-4   The Mercator type of map projection, first drawn in 1569. This is a very useful map for navigation, but unfortunately it greatly exaggerates areas in high latitudes, and it should not be used for mapping the distribution of areal data or for measuring distances. (Note that the meridians and parallels appear as straight lines that cross each other at right angles.)

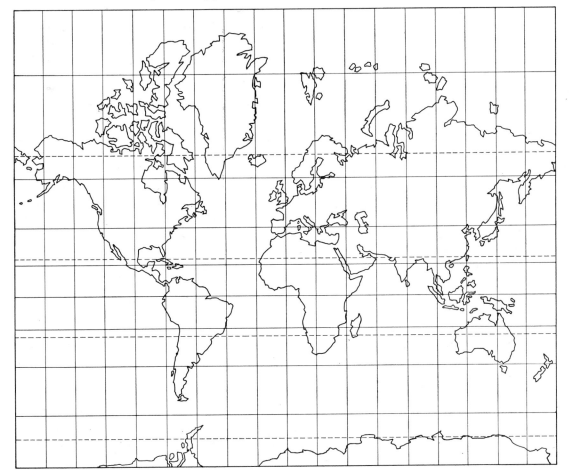

is more generally useful to the geographer. Its parallels appear as concentric circles and the meridians radiate like wheel spokes, if the pole is at the center of the hemisphere. This map is commonly used for polar hemispheres, and the projection is satisfactory for areas of continental size. The map of Europe in the Atlas section was drawn on the Lambert azimuthal equal-area projection. Careful inspection will show that both meridians and parallels are curved. Areas are delineated in their correct relationships. Distortion of the form of land or water surfaces is relatively slight, so the final map provides the student with a useful map of Europe.

Mercator projections. This familiar projection (Figure 1-4), invented by a Flemish mathematician over three hundred years ago, is constructed with its parallels and meridians at right angles. This map is particularly useful in navigation and aviation because it is comparatively easy to chart the routes of vessels or aircraft. The relative simplicity of the Mercator map led to its extensive use for purposes for which it was ill suited. The projection is drawn as though the world were a cylinder instead of a sphere, with length of the parallels at the poles the same as the equator. This is far

A   **B**

Figure 1-5   A. South America and Greenland as they appear on a Mercator projection. (South America in reality is nine times as large as Greenland.)

   B. The true areas of South America and Greenland as they appear in their correct areal relationship on the globe or on an equal-area map projection.

from the truth. To show directions clearly, distances north and south must be exaggerated in the same proportion as those east and west. Distortion of area on the Mercator map is so great that distances in Alaska are shown nearly double those that appear at the equator. As a result, Alaska is shown on the Mercator projection four times larger than it should be, and Greenland sixteen times too large. In reality Greenland is one-ninth the size of South America and much smaller than Africa, yet the Mercator map makes it look larger than South America (Figure 1-5) and as large as Africa.

The Mercator projection has two advantages: main compass directions are shown at right angles; north is at the top of the map. Furthermore, areas within short distances on either side of the equator are nearly correct. Students using the Mercator map should keep constantly in mind its great exaggeration of area near the poles. The extent of this exaggeration will be apparent when it is remembered that the circumference of the earth is about 25,000 miles at the equator and the circumference of the poles is zero *on a globe,* but the circumference of the earth at the equator and near the poles is represented *as the same distance* on a Mercator map. Thus it is possible to visualize the enormous exaggeration of areas of polar regions on a Mercator map projection. The geographical inaccuracies of area displayed on this map are so great that it has not been used for any map in the Atlas section of this book.

Mollweide or homolographic projections. The advantage of the Mollweide projection (Figure 1-6) is that the entire world is shown on one map and that areas are shown in nearly correct proportion to each other. It does not, however, show the correct shape of the globe, since it is oval in form. Shapes of land areas are greatly distorted on the outer edges of this map. The sinusoidal projection resembles the homolographic in many of its features.

Homolosine and parabolic equal-area projections. The homolosine equal-area map (Figure 1-7), a modern projection devised by

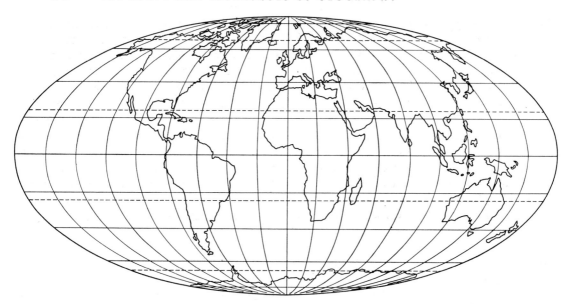

Figure 1-6   The Mollweide, or homolographic, projection, with the world drawn upon it. This type of map was devised in 1805, and its peculiar shape results from the doubling of the equatorial axis in relation to the north-south axis. Though maps drawn on this projection will appear greatly distorted in shape, their areas remain true to scale, and hence the map is particularly useful to geographers, economists, and others who map distribution of features on the earth.

the late J. Paul Goode, has the advantage of correct relative size of land and sea areas of the Mollweide map. The whole world may be shown on the homolosine projection; but the surface of the globe appears in a noninterrupted form in order to decrease curvature of meridians, thereby providing greater accuracy of shape of continents near the edges of the map. This is essentially a sinusoidal projection up to a point nearly halfway from equator to poles; in polar regions it becomes a Mollweide projection. The homolosine map may be divided over continents instead of oceans when it is necessary to map features appearing on ocean surfaces.

Six of the colored maps in the Atlas section of this book represent the parabolic equal-area projection, a type of map on which the grid is drawn to show straight lines for parallels of latitude and curved lines for meridians of longitude. It resembles the homolosine projection,

and has been used in interrupted form for the Physical Map of the World and the map of World Land Use and Economic Development. Shapes of the continents and water bodies appear on the parabolic equal-area map with relatively little distortion. The Physical Map of the World is accurate in depicting area as well as land and water surfaces in locations near the middle of the map, but the outlines of both Greenland and Antarctica are incorrect and the land masses themselves appear to have been divided. Distortion of shape (but *not* area) is even more apparent on the parabolic equal-area map of North America in the Atlas section. Here the outlines of Greenland and Alaska, both lands of the far north, appear almost deformed in shape. On the other hand, no part of South America, Africa or Australia drawn on the parabolic equal-area projection seems out of shape, because the southern portions of those continents are much

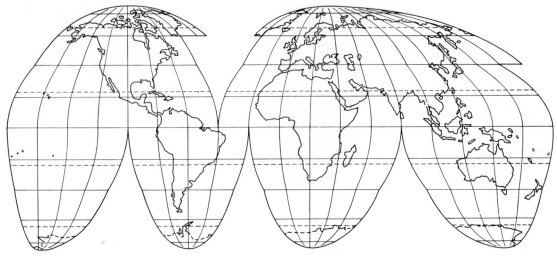

Figure 1-7   The homolosine projection, drawn by J. Paul Goode in 1923, is similar to the homolographic projection, but it retains equivalence of area, and the correctness of shape is superior to that of Figure 1-6.

nearer the equator than either Greenland or Alaska, and opportunities for distorted land shapes are correspondingly less.

Conic and polyconic projections. These projections, of which there are several types (one is shown in Figure 1-8), are in common use for maps of continents, countries, and states. They are designed as though each hemisphere of the earth was a flattened cone. Meridian lines diverge from the point or pole of the cone, crossing parallels which are represented by curved lines. Thus on the map of the United States, the student must follow the curved parallels and diverging meridians to understand compass directions correctly. If he

carelessly thinks directions are at right angles on such a map, considerable error may result. Most of the boundary between Canada and the United States appears as a curved line on conic and polyconic projections. Actually the most northern part of the United States is a little area near the Lake of the Woods in Minnesota, but on the conic map both northwestern Washington and northern Maine appear farther north because they are near the edges of the map. A study of the Atlas section map of the United States, drawn on the Lambert conformal conic projection, will clarify the point; a straight line connecting the northern tip of Maine and the city of Bellingham, Washington,

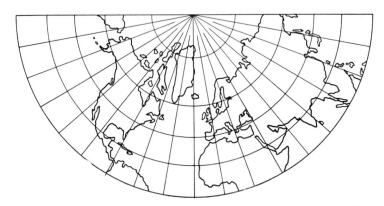

Figure 1-8   The Northern Hemisphere drawn upon a conic projection. The distortion on this map occurs near the North Pole and along the equator. The middle part of the map is least distorted. (Note the use of straight meridians and curved parallels.)

will make the Lake of the Woods *appear* to be south of either place, whereas its true position is north.

For large continental areas that are elongated north and south, the polyconic map (Figure 1-9) is useful. This projection is based upon several cones in order to reduce the curvature of parallels. It is an excellent projection for many purposes and is widely used in the United States though it does not provide complete equivalence of area nor perfection of shape.

Land Survey in the United States. Many parts of the United States, especially in the Middle and Far West, were surveyed by means of a grid of meridians and parallels; these imaginary lines were used as bases for land survey, with the result that many roads, property lines, farm and field boundaries, and even city surveys appear on the map of the United States in the form of a latticework of lines intersecting at right angles. The earliest European settlers followed no such survey pattern, but located their holdings by means of landmarks such as trees, rocks, sticks, and streams. Where rivers were navigable, frontage along the stream bank was usually desired; in tidewater Virginia, Maryland, and Quebec, old farms and plantations appear as long strips of land extending inland from the stream. This type of land survey led to plots of irregular shape and unequal size.

On the American grid system, principal meridians were run north and south as needed. The first of these to be established now serves as the state boundary between Ohio and Indiana. Others are given various names or numbers. Parallel lines called *base lines* were surveyed east and west from convenient points on the principal meridian. At intervals (usually 6 miles) lines were laid out parallel to the base line, intersecting strips of land called *ranges,* which are about 6 miles wide following the north-south courses of the principal meridians. The resulting divisions of land are termed *townships* and are numbered north or south from the base line and east or west from

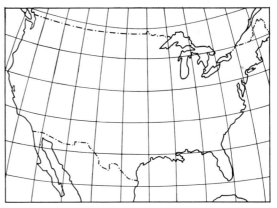

Figure 1-9 *A polyconic projection on which the map of the United States has been drawn. (Note the curvature of both meridians and parallels.) This projection does not have all the qualities desired in a map, but it so nearly attains them that it is an extremely useful grid. Most of the maps published by the U.S. Geological Survey are drawn on this projection.*

the principal meridian. Thus T. 2 N., R. 5 E. would normally be a township 6 miles square (36 square miles) on the second tier north of the base line and the fifth tier east of the principal meridian. T stands for township and R for range. Since meridians converge at the poles, thus decreasing distance between meridians from south to north, it is customary to establish correction lines every four tiers of townships, or 24 miles north or south of the base line, in order that townships will continue to be approximately 6 miles square. There a new beginning is made, and roads and fences that follow the township boundaries may have quite a jog or offset at the correction line.

Townships are divided into 36 square miles, each of which is called a *section.* Sections appear on United States surveys numbered consecutively back and forth beginning at the upper right corner and ending at the lower right corner (Figure 1-10), though there are some places where this numbering system follows a different pattern. In most states, sections 16 and 36 were designated as lands whose income was devoted to the support of public schools. Each section of 640 acres is divided

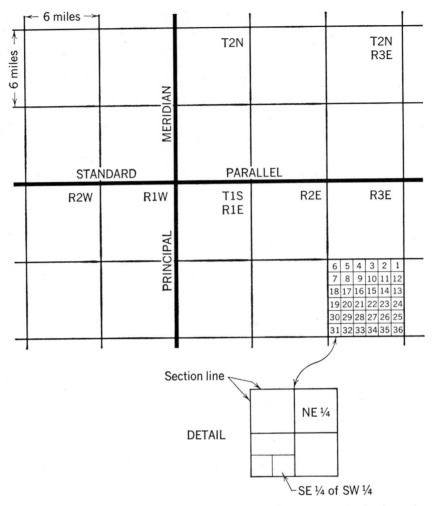

Figure 1-10 Plan of survey for most of the public lands in the central and western United States. Ranges are aligned east and west of a principal meridian; townships are measured north and south of a standard parallel. Each 6-mile-square township is divided into 36 sections of 640 acres each, and each section is subdivided into halves and quarters. (See detail of section.)

into halves, quarters, half-quarters, and quarter-quarters; for example, the SW ¼ NW ¼ sec. 10, T. 2 N., R. 5 E. would be the legal description of a certain 40 acres of land.

Map Scale. Most maps are drawn to a scale, which is the relationship of the space shown on the map to the actual distance it represents on the earth. The scale of a map is usually expressed as a ratio or fraction, with one unit on the map representing a number of the *same* units measured on the land; thus a scale of 1 inch to 1 mile means that 1 inch on the map equals 12 × 5,280, or 63,360 inches. Many maps indicate scale by a measured line (lineal scale), in addition to the ratio. A map scale of 1:62,500 is a larger scale than 1:125,000. Much of the world is mapped on the scale of 1:1,000,000, or almost ¹⁄₁₆ inch to 1 mile. It is apparent that the larger the figure in the ratio of the scale, the smaller the scale of the map.

Using the maps in the Atlas section, for example, the Physical Map of the World has been drawn to a scale expressed in two ways: area, or 1 square inch equivalent to 3,164,000 square miles; and linear, or 1 inch equivalent to 1,780 miles at the equator. In addition, a visual scale of statute miles in units of 500 and 1,000 is provided for convenience. For a much smaller area of the earth's surface, the map of the United States bears an areal scale of 1 square inch to 43,264 square miles, or a linear scale of 1 inch to 208 miles measured on the globe itself.

The scale selected by the map maker depends upon the amount of detail to be shown, the area of land to be shown, and the purpose for which the map is to be used. A map of a continent on a scale of 100 miles to 1 inch might be a satisfactory ratio, but a state map might require a scale of 10 miles to 1 inch or smaller. County maps may even be drawn on a scale of 1 mile to 1 inch. Some map projections are so designed that it is impossible to use a constant scale on all parts of the map; this is particularly true of the Mercator projection, where the scale may hold true only along the equator. In contrast, the scale of a globe remains constant on any part of the surface and in any direction.

Signs and symbols. Certain conventional signs are customarily used by the map maker. Standard symbols have been adopted for earth features such as mountains, rivers, and coast lines. If the map is of a large scale, details such as houses, roads, and railroads may be shown. The symbols selected for use on the map depend upon its purpose. Symbols for cities may be represented by circles, squares, or triangles to show proportionate populations, as they appear in the Key to Cities on the first page of the Atlas section. Dot maps, with sizes and numbers of dots arranged in proportion to concentration of population or other data, are useful in providing information quickly. Sometimes gradations of color or cross-hatching are substituted for dots. In the Atlas section, the map of World Land Use and Economic Development combines the use of color and shading (an overlay of dots in this case) to show prevailing human economies in parts of the world. In addition, those areas where mining is an important occupation are indicated by X as a symbol.

Maps in general should be drawn as simply, legibly, accurately, and attractively as possible. For classrooms, maps need only the most important places indicated in type that can be read across the schoolroom.

Methods of showing relief. Relief features are of special importance to the geographer, and various schemes have been devised for the indication of relief differences. These include black-and-white sketching (Figure 1-11), shading, hachures, and contours (Figure 1-12) (lines representing places of equal elevation

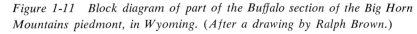
Figure 1-11   Block diagram of part of the Buffalo section of the Big Horn Mountains piedmont, in Wyoming. (After a drawing by Ralph Brown.)

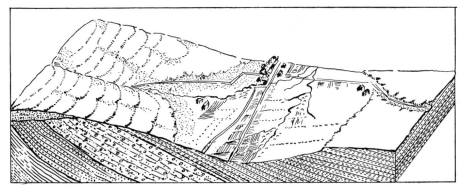

Figure 1-12   Part of a modern contour map, published by the U.S. Geological Survey, with a contour interval of 10 feet. Note the relationship of main highways to the shore of Lake Erie in this section of East Cleveland, Ohio.

above or below sea level). Another method uses different colors, usually ranging from green, representing land below 1,000 feet in elevation, through yellow and brown to red for areas higher than 10,000 feet. Sometimes shading and colors are used to show different types of land surfaces rather than actual elevations; this has been the method showing the combination of land relief (brushlike shading) and related vegetation cover (colors from yellow green through deep green, gray-green, buff, and tan to white) on the Atlas section maps as indicated on the key or legend on the first page of color.

Models may emphasize outstanding facts of relief quite clearly, but they are not easily portable. Models are generally more expensive than maps, and their use is restricted to display or class demonstration and other special purposes. Contour maps showing details of the relief features of this nation were chosen by the U.S. Geological Survey for the topographic sheets published by that bureau.

Use of maps. Maps may be used to show relationships as well as to provide needed facts of location. Many principles of geography can be shown clearly by comparing maps of population, relief, rainfall, temperature, mineral resources, natural vegetation, and economic uses of land. Two maps may show coincidence of data through accident. When coincidence is noticed, a study must be made to determine whether this is accidental or whether correlations exist. For example, very definite relationships can be shown by comparing Figure 12-1 (relief) with Figure 23-4 (world population). It will be noted that the densely populated parts of the earth in the middle latitudes are lowlands and that mountains and high plateaus are avoided as places to live. On the contrary, tropical highlands often support more people than adjacent lowlands because of more invigorating and healthful climate than that which characterizes the lowlands. A comparison of population and rainfall maps (Figure 23-4 and Figure 5-1) shows that deserts support few people unless the land has been reclaimed from its desert condition. Excessively rainy districts, unless relieved by a dry season, generally are thinly populated. Moderate rainfall without excessive heat or cold provides more favorable living conditions; large populations are generally found in these regions. Important relationships between rainfall and natural vegetation are apparent after a comparison of Figures 5-1 and 11-1.

Maps are used for many purposes. For teaching the facts of economic or commercial geography, maps are drawn to show distribution of the mineral, agricultural, pastoral, or industrial resources by such schemes as selecting colors, dots, or symbols proportionate to production. The map of World Land Use and Economic Development in the Atlas section is of this type. Routes of transportation and communication are best shown on maps that indicate locations of highways, railroads, air lines, ocean steamship routes, telephone, telegraph, and cable lines. Sometimes highway maps or the maps appearing in railway timetables are grotesquely distorted to emphasize the directions and advantages of some particular route.

Collections of maps appearing in book form are especially useful to the student. These are known as *atlases* and are important reference works when geographic facts are needed. A good atlas is indispensable, for it will provide the locations of places at a glance. It should provide much more than that; and in selecting an atlas for use in studying human geography it is well to remember that such information as economic data, precipitation, winds, relief, vegetation, trade routes, and races is more important than political boundaries, county seats, or the locations of unimportant towns.

Maps have special importance in military and naval operations, and certain types are usually devised for this purpose. Small-scale military maps are called *planning maps* or charts, and on these the movements of entire armies and navies may be charted. More detailed tactical maps are necessary in order to carry on local maneuvers; on these, details of the land relief, sources of good water supply, difficult river crossings, mountain passes, impenetrable swamps, and other hindrances to rapid movement of troops must be shown with great care. Usually these maps have "overlays" of transparent paper or plastic substances which fit over the maps and provide essential last-minute information for actual operations in the field. Special naval maps are issued, showing the condition of coast lines, the depth and character of anchorages, dangerous shoals, and other features of extreme importance to naval operations in wartime. Maps of airways, with principal natural features, high mountain ranges, beacons, and radio beams are a necessity in both war and peace. Most military and airways maps are prepared and issued by government agencies, and are frequently revised. Other maps that originate with the government include maps of soil conditions and daily weather data, maps of national forests and national parks, and a wide variety of miscellaneous maps issued for special purposes.

SUMMARY

Geography is the study of the earth as the home of men. It is a broad subject which includes material from both natural and social sciences. In general the geographic phases of related subjects are those which affect human activities.

Leading geographic factors include location, climate, landscapes or relief features, soil, relationships between lands and seas, resources, and neighbors.

The globe is the most accurate representation of the earth but is not easily portable; hence maps are particularly useful tools to geographers. Common map projections include the hemispherical, Mercator, Mollweide, homolosine, and conic. Maps are drawn to different scales. To present geographic facts graphically, signs, colors, or symbols are used. Relief is shown by contours, color, or shading and by models.

Maps are widely used in military operations, by economists, geographers, and geologists, and by many other professional people.

Outline
Geography: scope and definition
Relationship to other subjects
  Natural sciences
  Social sciences
Location related to human activities
Leading geographic factors
  Climate
  Landscape
  Soil
  Lands and seas
  Accessibility
  Resources
  Neighbors
Geographic techniques
  Globe
  Map projections
  Land survey, United States
  Map scale, signs, and symbols
  Methods of showing relief
  Use of maps

QUESTIONS

1. What map projections would you select for showing (*a*) the United States, (*b*) navigation at sea, (*c*) distribution of world's population, (*d*) the world to a first-grade pupil.

2. If the earth's axis were not inclined, how long would our daylight periods be?

3. If the representative fraction of the scale of a map is 1:63,360, how many feet will a distance of 3½ inches on the map represent? How many miles?

4. On what map projections do areas near the poles appear with the greatest distortion? On what projections do coasts near the poles appear with greatest distortion?

5. Using a convenient atlas, find the approximate location of each of the following cities in degrees of latitude and longitude (this information is often found in the back of atlases): New York, Havana, Calcutta, London, New Orleans, Melbourne, Tokyo, Moscow, Buenos Aires, Panama, Capetown.

TOPICS FOR DISCUSSION

1. Select a common school subject, such as botany or industrial arts, and mention some of its geographic relationships.

2. What geographic factors of location favor the development of your home town or city? What geographic factors seem to handicap its growth? Why?

3. What locational factors should be taken into consideration in buying or building a house?

4. What are some of the leading occupations in the area near the city or town in which your college is located?

SELECTED REFERENCES

Birch, T. W.: *Maps Topographical and Statistical,* Oxford University Press, New York, 1949.

Brunhes, Jean: *Human Geography,* George G. Harrap & Co., Ltd., London, 1952.

Colby, Charles C., and Clarence B. Odell (eds.): *Successful Teaching with Maps,* Denoyer-Geppert Company, Chicago, 1954.

Deetz, C. H., and O. S. Adams: *Elements of Map Projection,* U.S. Coast and Geodetic Survey, Washington, 1938.

Dohrs, Fred E., Lawrence M. Sommers, and Donald R. Petterson: *Outside Readings in Geography,* Thomas Y. Crowell Company, New York, 1955.

Finch, V. C., G. T. Trewartha, Arthur H. Robinson, and Edwin H. Hammond: *Elements of Geography,* 4th ed., McGraw-Hill Book Company, Inc., New York, 1957, pp. 3–17, 657–674.

Greenhood, David: *Down to Earth: Mapping for Everybody,* Holiday House, Inc., New York, 1951.

Hartshorne, Richard: *The Nature of Geography,* Association of American Geographers, Lancaster, Pa., 1939.

Huntington, Ellsworth, and Earl B. Shaw: *Principles of Human Geography,* 6th ed., rev., John Wiley & Sons, Inc., New York, 1951.

————: *Mainsprings of Civilization,* John Wiley & Sons, Inc., New York, 1945.

James, Preston E., and Clarence F. Jones (eds.): *American Geography: Inventory and Prospect,* Syracuse University Press, Syracuse, 1954.

Raisz, Erwin: *General Cartography,* McGraw-Hill Book Company, Inc., New York, 1948.

Robinson, Arthur H.: *Elements of Cartography,* John Wiley & Sons, Inc., New York, 1953.

Semple, Ellen C.: *Influences of Geographic Environment,* Henry Holt and Company, Inc., New York, 1911.

Taylor, Griffith: *Geography in the Twentieth Century,* Philosophical Library, Inc., New York, 1951.

2. The Earth and Its Setting

SINCE ancient times men have wondered about the earth. They observed and endeavored to explain the succession of day and night, the changes in position of the sun and stars, and the occurrence of the seasons; but centuries passed before they finally discovered the facts about the earth and its position in the universe.

Relation of Earth, Moon, and Sun. The earth is one of the planets of the solar system. The planets revolve around the sun, and in turn some planets have moons that revolve around them. The earth's diameter is approximately 8,000 miles; its circumference at the equator is about 25,000 miles. Our moon's diameter of over 2,000 miles makes it the largest moon in the solar system. It is the brightest object in the night sky, and its attraction is the chief cause of the tides.

The sun is one of millions of stars with temperatures so high that they are self-luminous. The sun is a glowing ball 865,000 miles in diameter, a distance nearly four times greater than the distance of our moon from the earth. Only a tiny proportion of the total radiant energy emitted by the sun reaches the earth, but this is sufficient for the growth of plants and animals and the maintenance of all activities and processes requiring heat and light.

The earth revolves around the sun once each year (365 days, 5 hours, 48 minutes, 46 seconds) at an average distance of 93 million miles in a path called the *orbit*. The moon completes one revolution around the earth in $27\frac{1}{3}$ days, but the entire series of phases from the new, crescent moon to full moon and back again requires about $29\frac{1}{2}$ days because the earth has also been moving during this time along its own orbit. The phases of the moon result from the angle at which the illuminated face of the moon is seen from the earth.

Shape of the Earth. The earth is known to be of almost spherical shape, although it is so large that to the eye any extensive plain appears flat—apparently disappearing at the horizon. Technically the earth is called an *oblate spheroid* because it is slightly flattened at the poles. One proof of the shape of the earth comes from careful calculation of the lengths of degrees of latitude, which increase slightly ($\frac{7}{10}$ mile) from the equator to the poles. This shows that the equatorial diameter of the earth is longer by 26 miles than the length of the axis from pole to pole. The earth's shadow cast on the moon during an eclipse of that body is circular, another proof of the earth's shape, since a sphere is the only geometrical solid that would produce a circular shadow at all angles. Further proofs include the facts that as ships sail away from port, their hulls disappear before their masts and that the smoke

of steamships may be seen when the boats themselves are invisible below the horizon.

The most remarkable proof of the earth's shape comes from photographs taken during rocket flights hundreds of miles up into the atmosphere. These photographs actually show the earth's surface on the horizon as a curve instead of a straight line. The often stated proof of the sphericity of the earth, that of sailing around it and returning to the starting point, is inconclusive; for if the earth were flat with the North Pole at the center, it would be possible to go around the pole and return to the place of departure. Furthermore it would be possible to sail around a world whose shape was cylindrical.

Rotation and Revolution of the Earth. Two motions of the earth exert profound geographic effects: (1) rotation of the earth on its axis once each 24 hours, causing day and night, and (2) revolution of the earth around the sun once each year. Both are factors in the change of seasons (Figure 2-1).

Figure 2-1   Earth's relationship to the sun throughout the year.

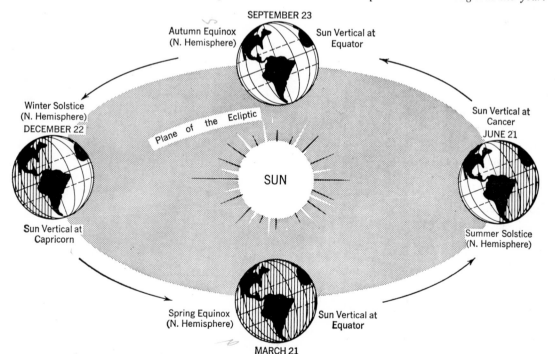

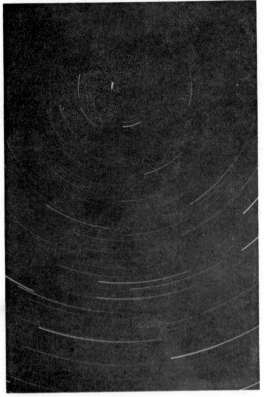

Figure 2-2   A 2-hour exposure of a film directed at the North Star, which appears in the photograph as a bright dash at the center of the vortex. The North Star is about 1 degree and 25 minutes out of line with the extension of the earth's axis into space; hence the North Star appears to have movement sufficient to register as a dash instead of a dot in the photograph.

Evidence of rotation is found in the rising and setting of sun, moon, and planets, and their daily movements across the sky. A further proof is given by the circular motion of the constellations of fixed stars completed in one 24-hour period day around the polestar, toward which the axis of the earth points (Figure 2-2). Rotation on an axis determines the location of the two poles and equator, from which measurements of latitude are made. Some deflection of winds, ocean currents, and freely moving objects is caused by the earth's rotation.

Proof of the revolution of the earth in-cludes the occurrence of seasons and the apparent changes in elevation and location of stars at different times of the year.

The distance of the earth from the sun varies some 3 million miles during the year. This affects the solar energy received by the earth slightly but not enough to bring about seasonal changes.

Inclination of the earth's axis.   The axis of the earth inclines almost 23½ degrees from a perpendicular to the plane called the *ecliptic*. This is the plane in which the earth revolves around the sun (Figure 2-3). As the revolution of the earth proceeds, this inclination produces a change in the directness of the sun's rays and in time and direction of sunrise and sunset, thereby affecting the length of time the sun shines each day. Changes in length of day and directness of the sun's rays are the chief causes of the earth's seasons. Inclination of the earth's axis is the factor that determines the location of the Tropics of Cancer and Capricorn at latitudes 23½ degrees from the equator, and the Arctic and Antarctic Circles at latitudes 23½ degrees from the poles.

Equinoxes and Solstices.   Seasonal changes in length of daylight and darkness periods result from the revolution of the earth in its orbit, inclination of its axis from the plane of that orbit, and the constant position (parallelism) of the axis. If the earth's axis were perpendicular rather than inclined to the plane of the ecliptic, daily amounts of radiant energy from the sun would approximate what we now experience at the equinoxes. Days and nights all over the world would then be of equal length, and perceptible seasonal changes would be absent.

The *vernal equinox* in the Northern Hemisphere (March 21) is the day when the point of verticality of the sun's rays crosses the equator moving north; the *autumnal equinox* (usually September 23) is the day when the sun's vertical rays cross southward over the equator (Figure 2-1). The *summer solstice* of the Northern Hemisphere (June 21) is the day when the sun's rays are inclined their greatest degree northward (maximum declination), and the *winter solstice* (usually December 22) is the day when the maximum southward inclination is attained in the Southern Hemisphere. The four dates given are customary, but one or more may vary a day in some years, primarily because of the introduction of leap year every four years. The word equinox signifies that all parts of the earth have equal periods of day and night—but in reality there may be variations of a few minutes. At a solstice the vertical rays of the sun reach their maximum distance north or south of the equator and after a momentary pause begin their return equatorward.

The height of the sun in the sky at noon during the varying seasons differs according to the distance of the observer from the equator. At the equator, however, the sun rises and sets more nearly due east or west than on any other parallel. Since the plane of the circle of illumination bisects the equator at all seasons (Figure 2-3), days and nights at the equator are of equal length throughout the year.

The more northerly from the equator the location of the observer, the farther north of east the sun rises and the farther north of west it sets during summer; in winter it rises and sets south of east and south of west respectively. Southerly from the equator the sun rises north of east and sets north of west in winter; summer sunrise will be south of east and summer sunset south of west. Of course the months of summer and winter seasons are reversed in the two hemispheres. Length of day varies greatly with change of season at great distances from the equator, and twilight and dawn periods are also much longer near the poles.

Five imaginary lines encircling the earth are important for reference. The equator placed midway between the poles is one of these. To a person on the equator, at both equinoxes, the sun is vertical—that is, in its zenith—at noon, with a maximum change to 23½ degrees from the zenith at the time of each solstice. The apparent northward movement of the sun's bundle of rays at the northern summer solstice halts at 23½° north latitude; at this

point an imaginary line is drawn around the earth, parallel to the equator. This is known as the *Tropic of Cancer*. The *Tropic of Capricorn* is placed in 23½° south latitude to mark the southward limit of the sun's advance in December. Similarly the *Arctic Circle* is located at 66½° north latitude, or 23½ degrees below the latitude of the North Pole; the *Antarctic Circle* is located at 66½° south latitude. Thus the inclination of the earth's axis at an angle of nearly 23½ degrees from the perpendicular to the plane of the ecliptic determines the positions of these imaginary lines on the earth's surface.

Changes in Length of Day. The altitude of the sun in degrees above the horizon at noon on an equinox is the complement of latitude.

Figure 2-3 The different terms used in connection with the earth. Distances are necessarily limited on the diagram; actually, the North Star is far out in space above the North Pole, and one's zenith is a point infinitely distant above the horizon plane.

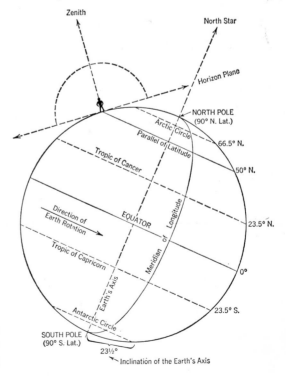

There are 90 degrees of latitude from the equator to a pole. At 10 degrees north of the equator, the sun's altitude at noon of the equinox is 80 degrees above the horizon toward the south. If the sun were seen 60 degrees above the horizon, the latitude of the observer would be 30 degrees. The same mathematical relationship holds for other latitudes.

At the North Pole the sun appears above the horizon at noon on March 21 and on successive days steadily rises to a maximum height in the sky until, on June 21, it reaches 23½ degrees above the horizon during the entire day; it then declines each day until it disappears below the horizon at noon on September 23. Because of the refraction (bending) of the rays of light by the atmosphere the dates for the appearance and the disappearance of the sun may differ by as much as a few days from those given.

The Arctic Circle (66½° north latitude) is 43 degrees from the Tropic of Cancer (23½° north latitude). On June 21 the sun's direct ray shines from a point directly over the Tropic of Cancer; since the altitude of the sun is a complement of latitude, the sun is 47 degrees above the south horizon at noon at the Arctic Circle and just reaches the northern horizon at midnight. In contrast, on December 22 there is a 24-hour period that has no direct sunlight whatever. All places between the Arctic Circle and the North Pole experience gradations from twenty-four hours to six months in length of day and night.

The altitude of the sun and the length of the day in the Southern Hemisphere during winter and summer solstices are the reverse of those described for places north of the equator.

In the United States there are marked differences in length of days and nights during the year. Along the Canadian border (49° north latitude) in June the sun is above the horizon sixteen hours per day, but in December it appears for only about eight hours. Differences in length of day are much less in the Southern states, where daylight during the summer solstice lasts about fourteen hours, and at the winter solstice only ten hours. Only half the earth's surface may receive solar energy (*insolation*) at any one time, and the imaginary line that separates the lighted from the darkened half of the globe is known as the *circle of illumination* (Figure 2-4).

The long periods of summer sunshine permit spring wheat to mature in the relatively high latitudes of northern Alberta and Saskatchewan in Canada. In most years it will ripen in central Alaska in three or four months of summer days although the same grain would require five or six months to mature in Nebraska. Garden vegetables also grow very rapidly in the long days of the high-latitude summer. In Alaska radishes can be harvested two weeks after planting, and 30-pound cabbages are not uncommon. In addition to the period of direct sunshine the long twilight of the northern summer, lasting nearly an hour after sunset, occurs because the oblique (slanting) rays of the sun follow a longer path and are diffused by the greater thickness of air which they must penetrate. In the tropics the sun's rays penetrate the earth's atmosphere directly, and the twilight period is shorter.

LOCATION

Latitude. A starting point on the earth's surface is taken for the calculation of distances, just as in many American cities streets are numbered east and west from a north-south thoroughfare, and north and south avenues from some central east-west street. The equator, an imaginary line midway between the poles, is obviously the natural starting point for measuring latitude or the distance in a north-and-south direction. The imaginary circular lines around the world used to measure latitude are named *parallels* (Figure 2-3). Since the distance from the equator to either pole is one-fourth the earth's total circum-

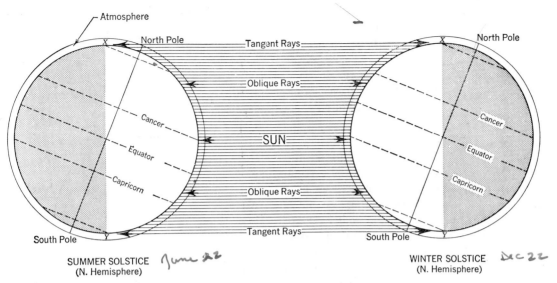

Figure 2-4 Reception of solar radiation on the earth at the time of the Northern Hemisphere solstices. XY is the circle of illumination. Note the apparent migration of the vertical rays from the Tropic of Cancer to the Tropic of Capricorn between the summer and winter solstices. Note also that the vertical rays penetrate the earth's atmosphere directly, whereas oblique and tangent rays must traverse a considerable depth of atmosphere before reaching the earth itself. The depth of the atmosphere has been exaggerated on the diagram, in relation to the size of the earth.

ference of 360 degrees, there are 90 degrees of north latitude and 90 degrees of south latitude.

Latitude may be calculated from the altitude of the sun above the horizon, and this observation is usually taken at noon. At either equinox, the sun is vertical above the equator at noon. On that day an observer located 1 degree from the equator would see the sun 1 degree below his zenith; if he were 20 degrees from the equator the sun would be 20 degrees from his zenith, and so on until at each pole he would see the sun just touching the horizon at noon. To determine latitude on an equinox, the observer merely measures how many degrees the sun appears in the sky below his zenith at noon (secured by determining the sun's altitude above the horizon in degrees and subtracting from 90) and notes whether the sun is seen toward the south or the north. Measurements of the sun's altitude

are usually made on an instrument known as a *sextant*. If the observer sees the sun toward the south horizon at noon on the date of the equinox, he is in the Northern Hemisphere; if he sees the sun toward the north, he is in the Southern Hemisphere. On any other day of the year, calculations are taken from the parallel where the sun stands vertically overhead at noon.

From March 21 the vertical noonday sun appears to an observer to move northward until it reaches the Tropic of Cancer on June 21, and it then appears to return to the equator on the autumnal equinox (September 23). From that date to the winter solstice (about December 22) the vertical noonday sun apparently moves southward until it reaches the Tropic of Capricorn on the winter solstice; it then returns to the equator to repeat the process on the vernal equinox (March 21). When calculating latitude in actual practice, a navigator usually refers to a book of tables called the *Nautical Almanac,* which will give his latitude directly for a given altitude of the sun on a certain day of the year. Northern Hemisphere latitudes may be calculated at night from the polestar, which is nearly overhead at the North Pole and just touches the horizon at the equator. The height of the star in degrees above the north horizon at any time of night on any date corresponds to the latitude of the observer. An easy proof of the rotation of the earth is a time photograph taken on a clear night with the camera pointed at the polestar. Because of the earth's rotation, the other stars appear as curving lines circling around the polestar (Figure 2-2).

Longitude.   The starting point for measurement of longitude, or distance in east and west directions, is wholly arbitrary and might begin at any selected *meridian,* which is the name chosen to designate an imaginary line from pole to pole (Figure 2-3). In practice, most nations calculate longitude from the meridian that passes through Greenwich, site of an observatory near London, England. This is known as the *prime meridian.*

Longitude is measured 180 degrees both east and west of Greenwich, at which point the longitude measured in one direction changes to the other; that is, when one travels westward and goes 1° beyond 180° west longitude, he reaches 179° east longitude, and his position is then designated in decreasing number of degrees until he returns to the prime meridian. The length of the circumference of parallel circles around the earth decreases from equator to poles, reaching zero at the poles; the length of a degree of longitude decreases accordingly, from approximately 69 miles at the equator to 50 miles in the central United States and 0 at the poles.

Since the earth rotates 360 degrees of longitude each twenty-four hours, a movement of 15 degrees on the earth's surface parallel to the equator will change the time by one hour. If a man travels eastward from Greenwich 15 degrees, his time is one hour ahead of Green-

wich (Figure 2-5). If he goes westward, it is one hour behind Greenwich. In New York, at approximately 75° west longitude (actually on the 74th meridian), the time, determined by dividing 75 degrees by 15 degrees for each hour, is five hours behind London's time. Thus when it is noon in London it is 7 A.M. in New York. By similar calculation if one goes eastward toward the rising sun, it would be 6 P.M. in Calcutta, 90° east longitude, when it is noon in London. The solar time in both Northern and Southern Hemispheres is identical at all points on any given meridian.

International Date Line.   A single rotation of the earth from west to east occurs each twenty-four hours at a speed of nearly 1,000 miles an hour at the equator. A traveler who moves eastward within that time adds the speed of his movement to that of the earth; thus he experiences less than twenty-four hours between successive noons. After circling the globe and returning to his starting point, he will find that he has seen one more sunrise and sunset than those who remained home; his date is one day too advanced. To make the date conform with that where he started his journey, he will repeat a date from the calendar at some convenient place during his trip. By custom this is done arbitrarily on or near the 180th meridian, at the *international date line,* where the date is changed at midnight. The extra day thus gained is called *meridian day.*

Moving westward, conditions are reversed, and more than twenty-four hours elapse between successive noons. Upon returning home, the traveler finds that his calendar is a day behind unless he corrected it by deleting a date as he crossed the international date line; in other words, if he crossed the date line on Sunday, the following day would be Tuesday.

The 180th meridian is half way around the earth from the prime meridian; thus they are twelve hours apart in time, and when it is noon at Greenwich it is midnight on the 180th meridian and a new day begins there. The date line and the 180th meridian are not

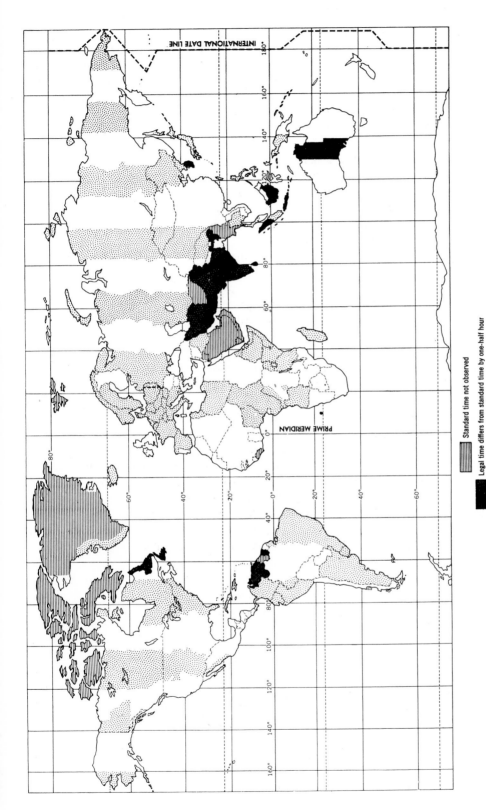

Figure 2-5 *Standard time zones of the world, shown by alternate white and stippled bands. Note that the same time of day is observed within each zone for a distance of approximately 7½ degrees of longitude on either side of the standard meridians (0, 15, 30, 45, 60, 75, etc.). Note also the four time zones in the United States.*

INTERNATIONAL DATE LINE

PRIME MERIDIAN

☐ Standard time not observed

▦ Legal time differs from standard time by one-half hour

■ Legal time differs from standard time by one-half hour

identical, however, because the former was planned so that the extreme eastern end of Siberia would observe the same date as the rest of the Soviet Union, and all of the Aleutian Islands would observe the same date as Alaska. A similar divergence occurs in the Southern Hemisphere in order that all the islands of the Fiji group and others associated with the United Kingdom may observe the same date. It is apparent that the international date line was established as a matter of convenience.

SUMMARY

The earth is a sphere, slightly flattened at the poles, rotating on an axis. The earth revolves around the sun once a year. The axis is inclined about 23½ degrees to this plane of revolution (ecliptic). This inclination, combined with rotation and revolution, causes changes during the year in the length of daily sunshine and darkness periods and directness of the sun's rays; these factors together cause the seasons.

Location on the earth's surface is determined by latitude measured in degrees north and south from the equator, and by longitude, which is measured in degrees east and west from the prime meridian. Latitude is determined by measuring the altitude of the sun and knowing the hour of the day and day of the year. Longitude is determined by comparing sun time at a given meridian with time at Greenwich.

Outline

Relations of earth, moon, and sun

Shape

Earth movements
  Rotation
  Revolution

Inclination of earth's axis
  Equinoxes and solstices
  Causes of seasons
  Changes in length of day
  Directness of sun's rays

Location
  Latitude
  Longitude
  Time zones
  International date line

QUESTIONS

1. How is your age related to the earth's revolution?

2. Of the following locations, which two have the longest period of continuous darkness in each year? 0°, 30° south latitude, 60° south latitude, 75° south latitude, 90° south latitude.

3. What is the minimum length of the daylight period at the equator?

4. When it is noon at Washington, D.C., what time is it in
  a. Chicago
  b. Denver
  c. Los Angeles

5. How many times each year can a man at your latitude see the sun in his zenith?

6. Why does radiation reaching the earth from the sun vary during the year?

7. What is the approximate speed of earth rotation at the equator?

8. At noon on December 22, in what compass direction will the residents of these cities see the sun? Mexico City, Rio de Janeiro, Buenos Aires, Marseille, Calcutta, Quito.

9. In what compass direction will you see the sun in the sky at noon in your home locality on December 22? March 21? June 21? September 23?

10. What is the total extent of latitude in degrees which may experience the vertical ray of the sun throughout the year at the different seasons?

11. How long in miles is a degree of longitude at the equator? At the North Pole?

12. Distinguish between earth rotation and earth revolution.

13. During what months will your shadow fall northward at noon at the equator?

14. Why are changes of temperature less marked at the equator than at the poles?

15. What places on the earth have the longest periods of continuous darkness each year? Why?

SELECTED REFERENCES

Finch, V. C., G. T. Trewartha, A. H. Robinson, and E. H. Hammond: *Elements of Geography,* 4th ed., McGraw-Hill Book Company, Inc., New York, 1957, chap. 1.

Harrison, Lucia C.: *Daylight, Twilight, Dark-ness, and Time,* Silver Burdett Company, Morristown, N.J., 1935.

Lobeck, A. K.: *The Earth in Space,* C. S. Hammond & Co., New York, 1929; revised 1932.

3. The

Atmosphere

AIR affects man in many ways, since people breathe, move, live, and die in this all-pervading medium. The earth's atmosphere, consisting of a mixture of gases, is as much a part of the earth as the water (hydrosphere) and solid rock (lithosphere). Physical changes in the air cause variations in weather and climate that profoundly affect human beings and are basic to an understanding of geography.

Extent of the Atmosphere. The atmosphere extends upward from the surface of the solid earth for many hundreds of miles, although its exact limits are unknown. Half of it lies below the height of 19,000 feet, so in very high altitudes the air is extremely thin. That the earth's atmosphere extends outward in a rarefied condition higher than any balloon has risen is proved by the appearance of "shooting stars" at an average height of 80 miles. These meteors, often very small objects, travel so fast they become heated to incandescence by passage through the air; they generally disappear from 30 to 60 miles above the earth's surface.

The upper air is so thin that even in the tropics no human beings live permanently more than 3 miles above sea level. In 1956, a jet plane flew to an elevation of 126,000 feet or nearly 25 miles above the earth and a helium-filled plastic balloon soared to an elevation of 142,900 feet, which was at that time a record. In 1957 a balloon carried a man in a special cubicle to a height of 96,000 feet, but at such elevations man requires oxygen tanks or air under pressure to retain consciousness and life. Also increasing our knowledge of the upper air (Figure 3-1) are instrument-equipped rockets and earth satellites which have powered thousands of miles into space, one in 1958 reaching to about 81,000 miles above the earth.

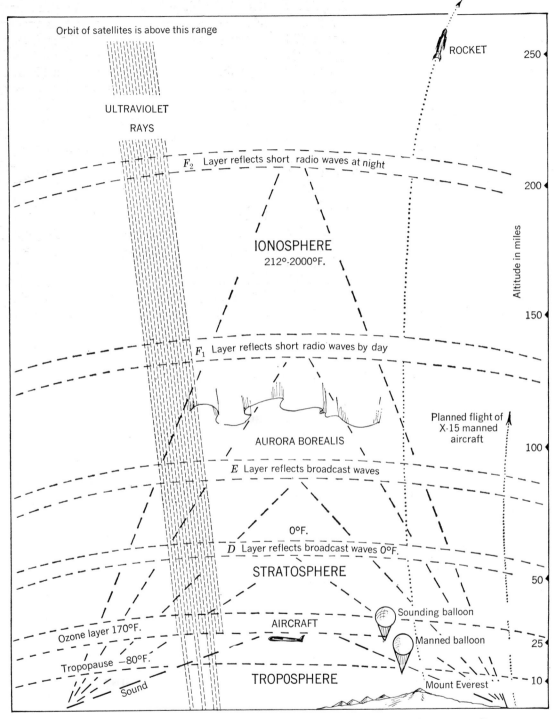

*Figure 3-1 The conditions of the earth's atmosphere, according to recent
theories.*

Air near the earth's surface consists chiefly of two gases, oxygen (21 per cent by volume or 23 per cent by weight) and nitrogen (78 per cent by volume or 76 per cent by weight). The 1 per cent remaining is divided among several gases, including argon, helium, carbon dioxide, and neon. The lower air also contains water vapor (from a trace up to 5 per cent) and dust in variable amounts. Somewhere in the upper air it is possible that the percentages of the lighter gases (hydrogen and helium, for example) increase and that those of the heavier gases decrease under the influence of gravity.

The percentage of different atmospheric gases varies slightly at different places on the earth. Above industrial cities, carbon dioxide may increase from its usual proportion of 3 or 4 parts in 10,000 to more than double that figure. Air over oceans is generally less dusty and more moist than air above land.

Uses of the Constituents of Air. The oxygen and nitrogen comprising the bulk of the lower air account for most of its pressure or weight; thus they support aircraft and provide the force exerted by the wind. Animals, including man, developed in an atmosphere containing oxygen and now cannot survive without it. Oxygen dissolved in ocean and inland waters is required to maintain fish life, and air in the soil helps the growth of plants. Combustion is merely the chemical union of oxygen and other elements. Nitrogen, inert under ordinary conditions, dilutes the oxygen and slows up the oxidation process. Certain bacteria and other organic agents remove small amounts of nitrogen from the air and fix the substance in soil where it is available for plant growth.

Condensation of water vapor forms clouds, fog, dew, and frost. When forms of condensation progress until gravity acts upon them, they fall to the earth as precipitation in the form of rain, snow, hail, and sleet.

Carbon dioxide taken from the air supports plant life and is liberated into the air by breathing of animals, burning of coal, decay of organic matter, and other forms of oxidation. Although carbon dioxide and water vapor in the atmosphere permit most radiant energy to reach the earth's surface from the sun, they have even greater effects on radiation of heat from the earth. These gases act as a thermal blanket to retain much of the radiant energy (heat) that otherwise would escape from the earth's surface. Particles of dust influence sunrise and sunset colors, produce the phenomenon of twilight, help form the thermal blanket, and serve as nuclei for the formation of raindrops.

Layers of the Atmosphere. Three layers of the atmosphere have been named *troposphere, stratosphere,* and *ionosphere.* The name *troposphere* has been applied to the lowest layer of the atmosphere, extending to a height of from 5 to 10 miles. Temperature in the troposphere decreases at the average rate of about 3.5 degrees per thousand feet of elevation. This normal vertical change in temperature with increasing altitude is called the *lapse rate* and it varies with differing conditions in the atmosphere. The troposphere was so named because of this regular change in temperature. Variations of temperature, wind direction, cloudiness, rainfall, relative humidity, and other phenomena accompany the storms that are common in the troposphere. All the changes associated with day-by-day variations in the weather of midlatitudes are limited to the troposphere. This lowest layer of air contains the clouds, almost all water vapor, and 90 per cent of the total mass of air. Most of the carbon dioxide remains in the troposphere, its relatively greater weight making its upward diffusion difficult.

The second layer of the air is called the *stratosphere* because its temperature is nearly uniform and storms seldom occur. At an elevation of about 10 miles above the equator, 7 miles above the central United States, and 5 miles above the pole, the air temperature remains steadily low. The upper limit of the troposphere and lower limit of the stratosphere is named the *tropopause* since the temperature no longer decreases regularly above that point.

Here the temperature is constantly low and the lapse rate approaches zero, probably because of a balance between absorption and radiation of heat. The stratosphere extends up to elevations of about 35 to 50 miles where atmospheric pressure is less than ½ millimeter compared with 760 millimeters of mercury at sea level. This means that less than one fifteen-hundredth of the atmosphere is higher than the stratosphere. No propeller plane or balloon can soar to such heights since the density would not furnish adequate support. Only some form of rockets, earth satellites, or jet planes propelled by reaction from explosions can navigate in the upper atmosphere.

The *ionosphere* forms the thin outermost layer of the atmosphere. This part of the air became known because of its effect on the reflection of radio waves and the occurrence of northern lights within this zone. Radio waves progressing from their source toward outer space are apparently reflected back to earth by this strongly ionized layer. The height of the reflection layers varies from about 70 miles to possibly 140 miles in elevation. Reflecting layers may vary considerably in altitude at different hours of day or night and are usually lower in the winter and at night, making for better radio reception. During periods of sunspot activity the resulting variations in transmission of solar energy affect the ionosphere and the reception of radio waves.

Atmospheric Phenomena. Many curious occurrences of interest and some of importance to mankind are apparent in the atmosphere. Reflection from different layers of atmosphere affects not only radio waves but also light rays from the sun and other stars. Rays of differing lengths may pass through, or be impeded by, certain substances. Glass transmits most visible rays of light but is nearly opaque to infrared rays. On the other hand dust and waterdrops in the air interfere with transmission of ordinary light rays and make photography and sight difficult, whereas photographs taken through haze by infrared light are sharp and clear (Figure 3-2). Fog would not hamper travel by airplane or automobile if operators could see with infrared light.

Human eyes and bodies have become adjusted to the usual solar illumination. On mountaintops skin may be sunburned in cool weather by exposure to ultraviolet rays, which readily penetrate the thin atmosphere. In the tropics the skin develops more pigment for protection against strong solar radiation. Ozone, a form of oxygen containing three

Figure 3-2 Infrared photograph looking northwest toward the lower end of Cajon Pass in southern California. The San Gabriel Mountains appear at the left; the San Bernardino Mountains at the right are at a distance of about 25 miles. Citrus groves in the foreground register white on infrared photographic film. (Photograph, courtesy of Robert Pease.)

atoms to a molecule instead of the usual two, exists in greater abundance in the stratosphere than in the lower air. This blanket of ozone reduces the intensity of ultraviolet light reaching the earth's surface (Figure 3-1). Most organisms on the earth would be destroyed if exposed for any length of time to direct ultraviolet rays, yet some of this radiation is desirable since it seems to furnish the body with vitamin D, required for proper growth. As human beings we have become adjusted to the usual amount of ultraviolet light. Much more would kill us and yet we would be harmed by a substantial decrease in this radiation.

Light-blue color of the sky results from scattering of the blue rays of light by dust and water droplets. With increasing elevation and resulting freedom from impurities the sky becomes darker blue, then a deep violet, many times darker than at the earth's surface, and finally a violet-gray or black-violet color. Toward the upper limit of the atmosphere the sky would appear black.

Various phenomena result from differences in temperature and moisture content of the air. For example, rainbows appear when the sun's rays are refracted (bent) by passing through raindrops. Mirages occur on hot clear days as the result of reflection and refraction of rays of light on layers of air at different temperatures. At sunset the sun's rays are so bent by refraction that the sun remains visible for a short time when it actually is below the horizon.

Northern lights extend from 50 to 600 miles into the atmosphere above the earth's surface. These peculiar arcs, curtains, and streamers of light in polar regions are called *aurora borealis* and *aurora australis*. They seem to be the result of electrical disturbances in the upper atmosphere which are associated with discharges of radiant energy (electrified particles) from the sun during periods of sunspot activity. It is believed that molecules of air become luminous because of bombardment by electrified particles hurled outward from the sun. The aurora colors are those

made by oxygen and nitrogen, which suggests that the upper air consists of the same gases as the lower air rather than the light gases, helium and hydrogen. Proof of their electrical character is that auroras increase in frequency toward the North and South Magnetic Poles rather than toward the geographic poles.

Insolation.   Practically all energy received by the earth comes from the sun. The earth intercepts only one two-billionth of the sun's radiation; that small part which would fall on a disk 8,000 miles in diameter, situated on a sphere of 93 million miles radius. This small fraction of the solar radiation, however, furnishes all the energy required for biological and physical activities on our globe.

The amount of insolation received at a particular place on the earth depends mainly upon length of day, directness of the sun's rays, and clearness of the atmosphere. Revolution of the earth around the sun and inclination of the earth's axis cause changes in the length of day and directness of the sun's rays as described in the preceding chapter. These are the chief causes for differences in distribution of insolation on the earth. In addition, the condition of the atmosphere, its thickness, clouds, humidity, and dust, cause changes in radiant energy received on the earth's surface (Figure 3-3).

Insolation retained or absorbed by the earth depends on conditions both in the atmosphere and on the earth. The relief, color, nature of surface, and other things determine relative amounts of absorption and reflection of light and heat from the earth's surface; and, as the condition of the atmosphere varies, so does its influence on the reception of solar radiation. Atmospheric changes also affect radiation of heat from the earth. After insolation has been absorbed it may be widely distributed by winds and ocean currents, making earth temperatures more equable.

Distribution of insolation.   Insolation is distributed by physical processes called *conduction, convection,* and *radiation.* Neither water nor solid earth is a good conductor of heat, and a few feet below the surface of either the temperature is unaffected by conduction. Thus a deep well will furnish water at a uniform temperature throughout the year. Convection results from the contraction of fluids on being cooled and their expansion on heating. Thus cooled water or air sinks and the warmer water or air is thereby forced to rise, forming a circulation or convection current. Convection is a fundamental cause of the circulation of the atmosphere and of ocean currents.

Radiation is a transfer of heat by wave motion. Radiation accounts for most of the sun's energy that reaches the solid earth. However, after absorption by the ground some of the heat it produces is again radiated into the atmosphere. These radiations have long wave lengths and do not pass through the layers of atmosphere readily. Air is heated mainly by such radiation from the earth rather than directly from the sun. Both air and water can be made to rise by application of heat. When air rises, however, it expands, the molecules that compose it are farther apart and do not strike each other so frequently and its temperature falls. In a way, since air rises when heated and its ascent causes cooling by expansion, one could almost say that air should be heated if it is to be cooled. Molecules of descending air are subjected to increased pressure, causing the molecules to come closer together and collide more frequently, thereby producing heat, which causes the temperature of the air to increase.

World Temperatures Shown by Isotherms. Temperature of the atmosphere is measured by the instrument called a *thermometer,* which is described in Chapter 4.

Distribution of temperature is shown on maps by *isotherms,* which are lines connecting places of equal temperature. In general, since insolation decreases poleward, isotherms would be expected to parallel the equator. Study of the world isothermal maps for January and July (Figures 3-4 and 3-5) shows, however, that many isotherms vary considerably from their expected east-west courses, especially in the Northern Hemisphere where land areas are large. In January, the isotherms of 40°F and lower are nearer the equator over continents than over oceans, and the coldest spots on earth are in the northern interior of continents, notably Siberia. In July, the reverse of this condition holds true, and isotherms diverge farther from the equator on passing from oceans to continents. Interiors of continents like the northern part of Africa, southern Asia, and the southwestern United States, have the highest average temperatures, whereas oceans in the same latitudes are many degrees cooler. South of the equator there is less vari-

Figure 3-3 Exchange of energy between earth's atmosphere and the ground at midday. (Based on a drawing by R. Geiger. Courtesy of John B. Leighly.)

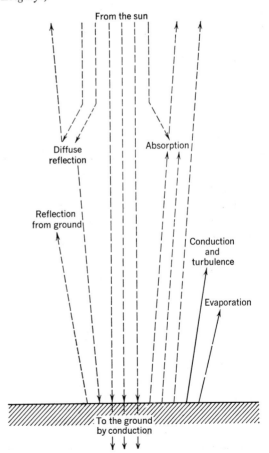

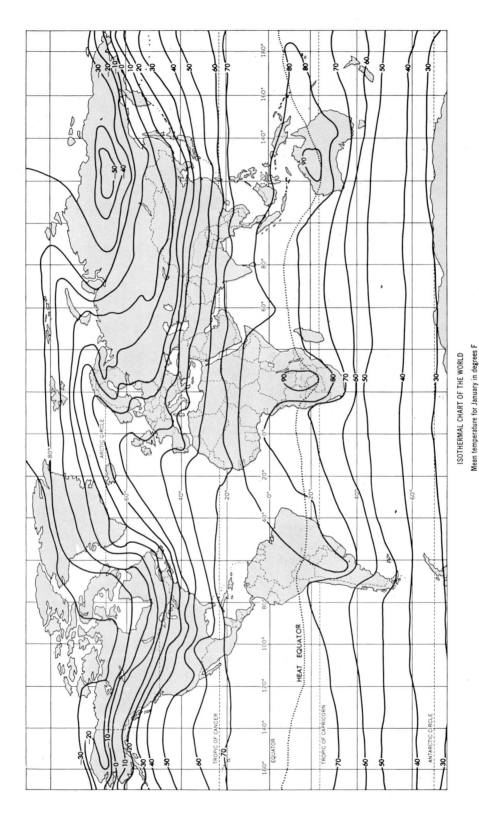

ISOTHERMAL CHART OF THE WORLD

Mean temperature for January in degrees F

Figure 3-4 Isothermal chart of the world, showing mean temperature for January reduced to sea level.

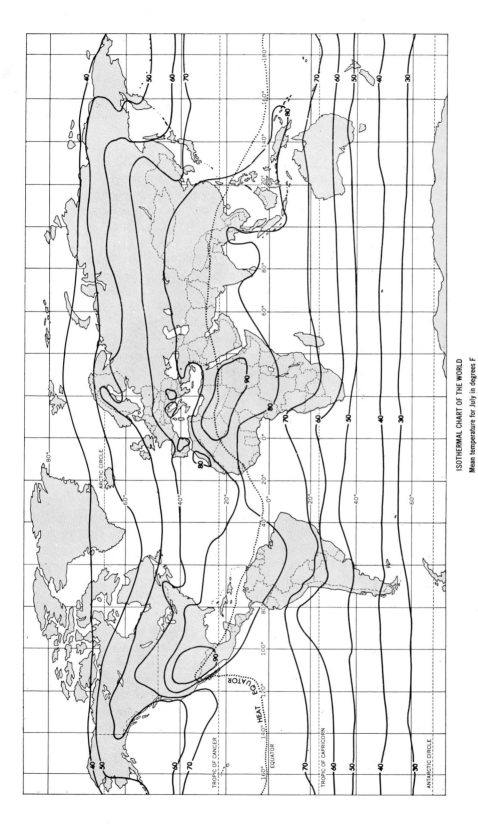

ISOTHERMAL CHART OF THE WORLD
Mean temperature for July in degrees F

Figure 3-5 Isothermal chart of the world, showing mean temperature for July reduced to sea level.

ation in the courses of the isotherms, primarily because this is the water hemisphere. It is apparent that near the equator there is little change in position of the isotherms throughout the year, although the location of the heat equator (the line connecting places of highest temperatures) shifts well north of the geographical equator in July.

In contrast to equatorial regions, the mid-latitudes and high latitudes show large annual ranges of temperature, especially in continental interiors. The seasonal temperature range in North Dakota, for example, is 60 or 70°F; in northeastern Siberia, the range is more than 100°F. Maximum and minimum temperatures of middle and high latitudes lag behind the insolation because summer temperatures continue to rise as long as receipt of solar energy exceeds loss by radiation. The hottest time of year in the Northern Hemisphere in mid-latitudes is usually July and early August. Similarly January is generally colder than December since time must pass before the earth cools after the heat of summer.

It should be noted that locations of maximum temperatures are not at the equator but from 20 to 40 degrees of latitude distant from that line, usually in desert regions where clouds seldom interfere with passage of solar energy. In these latitudes the summer sun's rays are nearly vertical at noon and the length of day is greater than at the equator.

Land heats faster than water because

1. The relative rate of heating (specific heat) of water is much higher than that of rock and soil, and the temperature of a rock can, therefore, be raised several degrees with the same heat needed to increase the temperature of an equal weight of water 1 degree.

2. Water is mobile, and heated water is distributed by convection and other currents.

3. Water reflects considerable insolation although some land surfaces, especially snow and bare sand, may reflect more rays than water.

Seasonal lag of temperature is more noticeable on windward coasts and in insular locations than in the interiors of continents be-cause large bodies of water take longer than land masses to heat and cool. This gives rise to the expression "marine influence" in referring to coastal weather conditions. Thus February is as cold as January and August is as warm as July along windward coasts in northern middle latitudes.

Weight of the Atmosphere.   Air seems light, yet it is estimated that the world's atmosphere weighs 11,850 trillion pounds. Density of air (weight per unit volume) varies widely in different parts of the atmosphere, both vertically and (in smaller amounts and often quite irregularly) horizontally. When descending a grade in an automobile one can feel the increase or decrease respectively in pressure of air on the eardrum. Swallowing will relieve this sensation because it helps equalize the pressure in the inner ear with that outside.

The *barometer* was designed to measure air pressure resulting from differences in weight of the atmosphere. The barometer is a glass tube over 30 inches long sealed at one end, filled with mercury, and inverted in a cistern of mercury (Figure 3-7). A vacuum exists above the mercury in the open cistern and balances the column of mercury in the tube. Slight variations in height of the mercury indicate changes in air pressure. When atmospheric pressure increases, the mercury is forced higher in the tube; when the air pressure decreases, the mercury column falls, thus giving a quantitative measure of that pressure. At sea level, average atmospheric pressure on the barometer is 76 centimeters of mercury, equivalent to a column of mercury about 30 inches high. Mercury is used because it is a heavy liquid and does not freeze at ordinary temperatures. Since 1940, weather maps of the United States have shown pressure in *millibars*. By definition "a millibar is a force equal to 1,000 dynes per square centimeter." (The dyne is the force that will impart a velocity of 1 centimeter per second to a mass of 1 gram in 1 second.) Sea-level pressure of 76 centimeters, equal to 29.92 inches of mercury, is equivalent to 1,013.2 millibars.

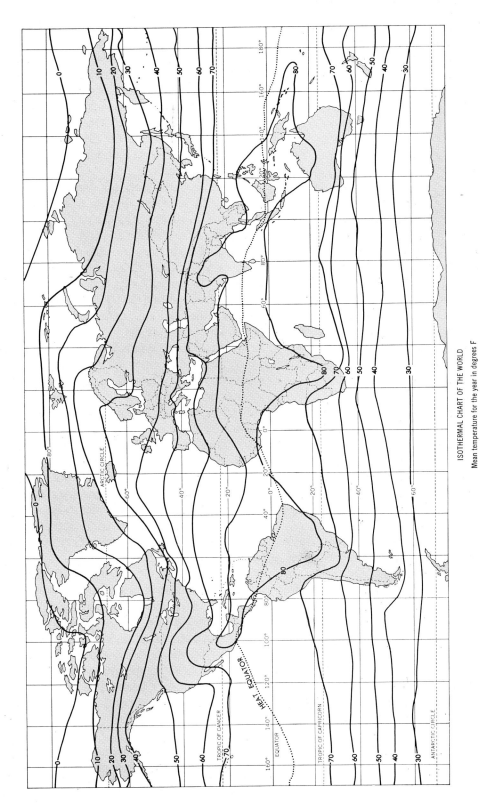

ISOTHERMAL CHART OF THE WORLD

Mean temperature for the year in degrees F

Figure 3-6 Isothermal chart of the world, showing mean temperature for the year reduced to sea level.

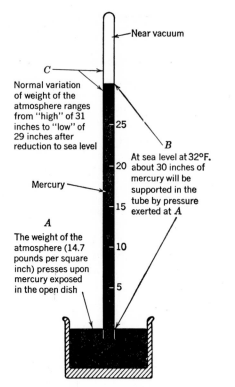

Figure 3-7 The principle of the mercurial barometer.

Pressures above that of adjacent regions are called "high," and those below, "low."

The air at higher elevations is less dense than air at sea level, and barometer readings are correspondingly lower by approximately one-thirtieth for each 900 feet of ascent. Obviously elevation can be determined with a barometer. For that purpose a portable instrument called the *aneroid barometer* (Figure 3-8) is used; its readings are made by a pointer attached to a hollow coil of assembled disks and chambers from which air has been exhausted. One end of the coil is exposed to the air, and the pointer moves with changing air pressure. The aneroid is not as accurate as the mercurial type of instrument but it is compact, light, and portable and hence is often the instrument used on airplanes to measure their elevations. When thus used it is known as an *altimeter.*

World Distribution of Pressure by Isobars. Differences in pressure on the earth's surface are the direct cause of the winds, affecting temperature, rainfall, and other weather conditions. These differences are shown by lines called *isobars,* drawn on maps and connecting places of equal pressure. On isobaric maps pressures are corrected for elevation and reduced to sea-level conditions so that they may be compared.

In the isobaric map for January (Figure 3-9) it will be noted that pressures are high over the Northern Hemisphere continents. The isothermal map for January (Figure 3-4) shows that high pressure coincides with low temperatures. Air in these continental "highs" in winter is typically dry and cold. Sunshine is common during the daytime, but snow cover on the land surface reflects much insolation and clear nights favor rapid loss of heat by radiation. Winds tend to diverge outward from the center of the "high," with moderate velocity toward surrounding oceans where air pressure is lower. Well-defined "lows," or pressure troughs, occupy the North Atlantic (Icelandic low) and North Pacific (Aleutian low). Subtropical highs, from which the northeast trade winds blow, center over the oceans near 25° north latitude. Low pressures along the heat equator are somewhat south of the geographic equator—most noticeably over the southern continents. A well-defined belt of high pressure occurs from 25° to 40° south latitude.

On the map for July (Figure 3-10), the belt of high pressure is displaced toward the equator. Less difference occurs in the Southern Hemisphere between January and July than in the Northern Hemisphere. This difference is caused by preponderance of water masses which equalizes temperatures and reduces pressure differences between land and water during seasons of winter and summer, as compared with the Northern (or land) Hemisphere.

Comparison of isothermal and isobaric maps for the same season of the year shows strong coincidence between high temperatures and high pressures. It seems certain that this distribution is a very significant factor in determining world-wide pressures and circulation of winds resulting from pressure differences (Chapter 4 and Figure 4-5). Air settles in cold regions, increasing the surface pressure and promoting outward-flowing surface winds. In warm regions air expands, and above the ground, may flow away horizontally, thus reducing surface pressure.

The July isobaric map (Figure 3-10) shows well-defined low-pressure areas in southern Asia and the middle United States; toward these blow surface winds from the higher pressures over the oceans. Two well-defined high-pressure areas in the subtropics are named the *Azores high* in the Atlantic, and the *Pacific high* in the North Pacific. When these oceanic highs spread over portions of the continents, drought may result. This happens regularly in summer in the Pacific Northwest and occasionally in the southeastern United States. Usually, however, the Azores high stands off the coast and causes moist air masses to move onshore in the southeastern United States. In consequence this region receives abundant summer rains, which often are of convectional origin. Neither the Aleutian nor the Icelandic low is much in evidence in summer (July). In the Southern Hemisphere, because water surfaces predominate, changes in pressure between July and January are small compared with those in areas north of the equator.

Water in the Air. Water vapor is the most variable gaseous constituent of the air. The quantity of water vapor in the air depends on temperature, amount of water available for evaporation, and other conditions. Generally the higher the air temperature the greater the amount of water any given volume of air can hold as vapor. Much heat is required to vaporize water; that is, to change its state from water to gas without any change in temperature. This *latent heat of vaporization,* as it is

called, is 5.4 times the heat required to raise the temperature of water from the freezing point to the boiling point. Evaporation of water is an effective way of cooling air. This is demonstrated by its use in some air-conditioning processes, by coolness following a shower, or by sprinkling that cools a house and yard. When water vapor condenses, as much heat is liberated as was absorbed by evaporation of the same moisture. In order to produce condensation it is therefore necessary to cool the air.

Relative Humidity. When a given volume of air contains the maximum quantity of moisture at a certain temperature, it is said to be *saturated.* The term *humidity* refers to the water vapor in the air. *Absolute humidity* is the total weight of water in a given volume of air. *Relative humidity,* which is always expressed as a ratio or percentage, represents the amount of water vapor actually in the air (absolute humidity) compared with the amount the same volume of air could contain if saturated at the same temperature. Thus 1 cubic foot of air contains 5.7 grains of water vapor when saturated at a temperature of

Figure 3-8   The aneroid barometer. The figure 30 indicates normal atmospheric pressure at sea level at 32°F. The illustration indicates pressure greater than 30 inches (30.4); consequently the air pressure at the time of the barometer reading was "high."

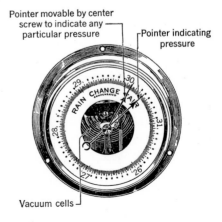

Pointer movable by center
screw to indicate any
particular pressure

Pointer indicating
pressure

Vacuum cells

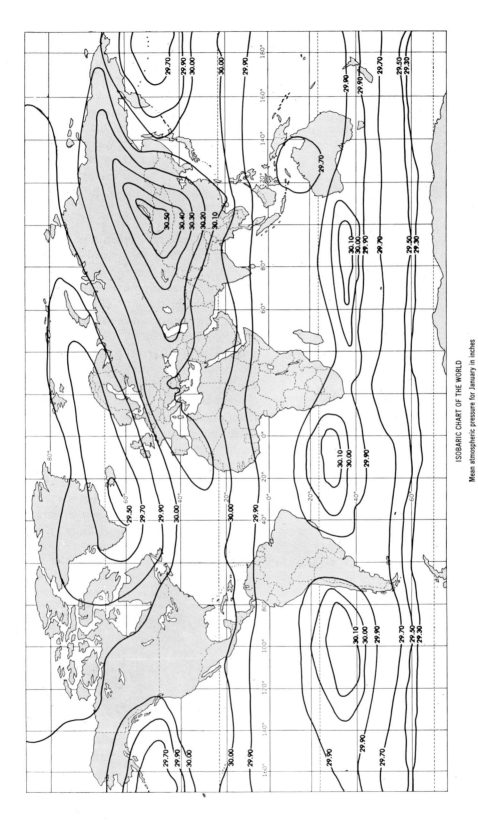

ISOBARIC CHART OF THE WORLD

Mean atmospheric pressure for January in inches

Figure 3-9 Isobaric chart of the world showing mean atmospheric pressure for January reduced to sea level.

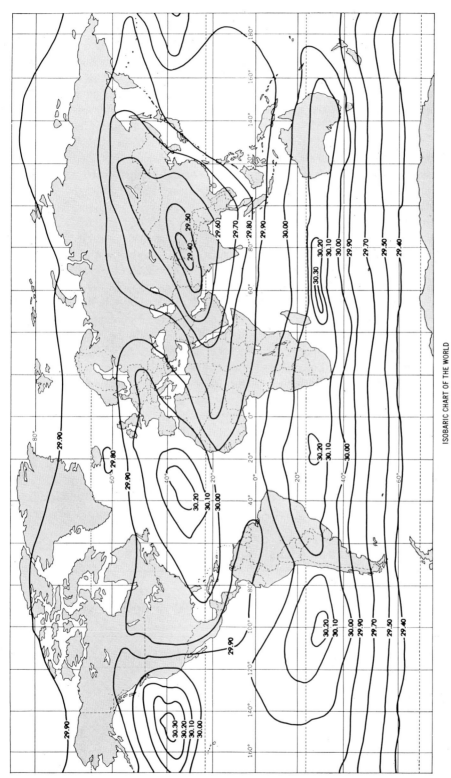

ISOBARIC CHART OF THE WORLD

Mean atmospheric pressure for July in inches

Figure 3-10 Isobaric chart of the world, showing mean atmospheric pressure for July reduced to sea level.

60°F. If experiment shows that the air actually contains 1.9 grains of water per cubic foot, the relative humidity would be one-third, or 33 per cent. Thus the term relative humidity refers to the ratio between the amount of water vapor in a certain volume of air and the maximum amount that might exist without condensation.

Another way of determining relative humidity is based on the temperatures shown in two thermometers, one of which has a dry bulb, whereas the bulb of the other is kept wet by cloth immersed in water. The wet-bulb thermometer has a lower temperature because of cooling by evaporation. Relative humidity can be calculated from Table 3-1. First the depression in degrees beween the wet- and dry-bulb thermometers is noted. If we assume the depression is 8°F, we read down that column to the temperature of the dry-bulb thermometer, which we assume is 70°F, and the relative humidity is given as 64 per cent. As another example, if the dry-bulb thermometer reads 65°F and the wet-bulb thermometer reads 55°F, the depression would be 10 degrees, and the relative humidity by the table would be 52 per cent.

If air is completely saturated and then cooled, less water can exist in the vapor form and condensation begins. Contrariwise, when the temperature increases, a given volume of air can contain more water vapor. Thus rela-

tive humidity drops with a rise in temperature, without any change in the actual quantity of vapor. A cold room seems damp, for example, because of high relative humidity, but when the room is heated it seems drier because the relative humidity falls. If air is cooled enough, even though the quantity of vapor is small, relative humidity reaches its maximum and condensation then begins. The temperature at which this occurs is called the *dew point*. In the open, clouds form when rising air currents have been cooled by expansion to the dew point. When moisture collects on the outside of a glass of ice water, it indicates that the cold surface has lowered the temperature of surrounding air below the dew point.

Relative humidity of air affects many natural phenomena as well as human activities. When relative humidity is low, air seeks moisture everywhere. For example, in the woods the duff on the forest floor dries out and creates a dangerous fire hazard. Garden plants and field crops may lose so much moisture during hot dry weather that their growth is retarded, and if these conditions last too long the plants die. Cotton fibers become brittle and fuzzy in dry air. Cotton mills formerly were located preferably in regions of damp air, but now the humidity in cotton mills can be artificially controlled, permitting the weaving of quality cloth under all weather conditions. Tobacco becomes dry and brittle

TABLE 3-1. RELATIVE HUMIDITY OF THE AIR IN PER CENT AT VARYING TEMPERATURES

Dry-bulb thermometer, °F	Depression of wet-bulb thermometer, °F								
	2	4	6	8	10	12	14	16	18
40	83	68	52	37	22	7			
50	87	74	61	49	38	27	16	5	
60	89	78	68	58	48	39	30	21	13
65	90	80	70	61	52	44	35	27	20
70	90	81	72	64	55	48	40	33	25
75	91	82	74	66	58	51	44	37	30
80	91	83	75	68	61	54	47	41	35

during days of low relative humidity. Leaf tobacco is packed for shipment during damp weather when the leaves have absorbed moisture and will not break when pressed together. Coffee roasts more quickly on dry days than during damp weather. Low relative humidity in houses permits wood and glue to dry out, causing furniture to loosen and crack. At times of low relative humidity moisture is evaporated from the body and causes the skin to become rough and cracked. Ointments or grease rubbed on the skin help to prevent such evaporation. High relative humidity nevertheless usually means discomfort. This is because air that is nearly saturated cannot rapidly evaporate perspiration from the skin which is a method of cooling the body.

To evaporate water a large amount of heat (called *latent heat of vaporization*) is required, as described previously. Condensation of vapor into liquid demands liberation of a quantity of heat equal in amount to that required for the liquid's evaporation. The absolute humidity increases rapidly with rising temperatures: a cubic foot of air when saturated at 100°F contains more than three times the quantity of water vapor that would be contained in saturated air at 60°F. Similarly the air at 60°F contains exactly three times as much weight of water vapor when saturated as it would at 30°F. When humidity is high and air is near the saturation point, a small amount of cooling will bring about condensation. Cooling of air that is saturated at a high temperature will cause much more rain than cooling of saturated air at a low temperature, since the absolute humidity is so much higher.

Condensation of Moisture. Condensation produces drops of liquid that compose the raindrops, dew, fog, and lower summer clouds. Although clouds of water droplets may exist with a temperature well below freezing, a temperature of the dew point below 32°F at the time of condensation is required for the formation of frost crystals and snowflakes. The term *adiabatic* is applied to the phenomenon of rising air cooling by expansion or

sinking air being heated by compression, without the addition or subtraction of outside sources of heat. Principal causes of the upward movement of air resulting in expansion and adiabatic cooling are (1) ascent over mountain barriers, (2) over masses of cold heavy air, or (3) in any rising air current. These air movements are commonly designated as (1) *orographic,* (2) *cyclonic,* and (3) *convectional,* respectively. Adiabatic cooling is the most common cause of rain, fogs, and clouds. Mixing of warm and cold air currents, or loss of heat by radiation and conduction may also cool air sufficiently to cause condensation of fog, dew, and frost, but seldom the formation of rain.

Dew and frost. Dew and frost do not "fall" but condense from surrounding air on cool surfaces. Some moisture for dew also comes from the ground by capillarity and from loss of water from plants. Calm, clear, cool nights favor dew formation, since surfaces lose heat by radiation in clear night air, but wind causes the dew to be reevaporated in fresh dry air. On cloudy nights radiation is at a minimum and the dew point on surfaces of objects may not be reached. Frost forms when air temperatures have fallen below the freezing point.

Vegetation may be damaged by freezing of water within the cells of a plant; this may rupture tissues and kill the plant even when wind or some other factor prevents formation of visible frost crystals. Such destruction of vegetation by freezing is sometimes called "black frost." Citrus growers who must fight frost conditions in their groves particularly fear heavy frosts, which commonly occur on nights when skies are entirely clear during the winter; at such times they try to heat the air in the groves to keep it above the freezing point. This is done by orchard heaters, or "smudge pots" (Figure 3-11). Some growers believe that smoke from the heaters helps prevent loss of heat by radiation; others contend that the protection comes from heating the air itself.

Fog. Loss of heat by radiation or other chilling of damp air may cause enough con-

Figure 3-11 Lighting a smudge pot, or orchard heater, in a citrus grove at Arlington, California. Fuel is usually crude oil, though some ranchers use coal briquettes or other substances. (Photograph, courtesy of the U.S. Department of Agriculture.)

densation to produce fog, which is essentially a cloud at the surface of the earth. When cold air, which is relatively heavy or dense, drains into lowlands from surrounding points, the chilled humid air condenses, causing radiation fog in the lowlands. Fogs resulting from radiation usually disappear during the day. When moving cold masses of air chill warmer air masses below the dew point, resulting condensation may cause thick and persistent fogs. These are called *advection* fogs to distinguish them from those resulting from radiation (Figure 3-12). Advection fogs are common on the Grand Banks of Newfoundland near the contact between air above the cold Labrador Current and that over the water of the warm Gulf Stream. They may also occur when conditions are suitable in the interior of continents. Advection fogs sometimes last several days and constitute great hazards to shipping, air travel, and automobile traffic. In a fog a temperature below freezing may cause con-

densation of moisture in the form of a film of ice on windshields and pavements, handicapping vision and making driving hazardous. Airplanes sometimes accumulate a dangerous load of ice from the condensation of cold fogs if the planes are not equipped with defrosting apparatus. Frost crystals that accumulate by condensation from cold fogs on trees and other surfaces are called *rime*. Deposits of rime add much to the beauty of winter.

Clouds. Condensation occurring well above the ground produces a cloud consisting of tiny drops of water or frost crystals suspended in the air. *Cumulus* clouds pile up above a flat base to form "cauliflower" clouds, which are common in fair weather and sometimes expand to great heights in the thunderheads that accompany local rainstorms (Figure 3-13). The flat cloud base represents the condensation level in a rising convection current. *Stratus* (layer) clouds are low-lying flat clouds which may cover the entire sky. They

Figure 3-12   Advection fog forming over the Golden Gate and moving inland over San Francisco Bay toward the right of the photograph. The Marin Peninsula appears in the distance, and part of San Francisco in the foreground. (Photograph, courtesy of the U.S. Weather Bureau.)

are most common in winter and cause the dark days and skies at that season. *Cirrus* clouds are thin fleecy forms at heights of 5 to 9 miles above the earth's surface (Figure 3-14). Because the temperature is below freezing at these elevations, cirrus clouds are always composed of icy crystals, even in summer. Halos around the moon or sun are produced by rays of light passing through light cirrus clouds. *Nimbostratus* clouds are the source of much of our rain. Combinations of various types of clouds occur, and descriptive terms are often added to the names, like altostratus ("high"), fractocumulus ("broken"), and cumulonimbus. This last type is the rain cloud of thunderstorms.

Clouds that occur at elevations of 4 or 5 miles are cirrus, cirrocumulus, and cirrostratus. Those found at heights of from 1 to 4 miles are altocumulus and altostratus. Low-lying clouds at altitudes of a few hundred feet to about a mile are stratus, nimbostratus, and stratocumulus. Special cloud types are those of lenticular shape which cap or surround a mountain top, and the crest clouds which form on leeward sides of peaks when strong winds blow.

Causes for Rainfall. The union of tiny particles of moisture in clouds produces raindrops, snow, or other forms of precipitation. Dust particles which serve as nuclei for condensation aid formation of fog and raindrops. Since molecules of gaseous water displace heavier molecules of oxygen and nitrogen, air containing water vapor is lighter than dry air. Furthermore, moist air from the oceans is often warmer and therefore lighter than colder and drier air that may be over the continents. Since humid air is lighter, it tends to rise, cool adiabatically by expansion, and produce clouds or rain. Once condensation begins, removal of water molecules from the air reduces the volume and pressure and allows air from

Figure 3-13   Cumulonimbus cloud indicating the upper limits of condensation near the top of a rising column of air. This type of cloud often develops into a thunderhead. (Photograph, courtesy of the U.S. Weather Bureau and P. A. Miller of the U.S. Department of Commerce.)

regions of higher pressure to flow in, bringing fresh supplies of warm humid air so that once rain starts, it may continue for a considerable time. Anything that cools humid air sufficiently to condense water vapor may produce precipitation. As previously stated, these are the principal causes of rain:

1. Rising of air over mountains
2. Rising of warm, humid, light air over cold heavy air
3. Cooling by expansion (adiabatic cooling) when air rises in convection currents
4. Movement of air from warm into cooler regions.

Ice storms and hail. Precipitation usually occurs in the form of rain or snow, but other types are sometimes important. Occasionally the temperature near the ground is lower than at a higher elevation. This abnormal temperature condition is known as a *temperature inversion;* if the air is calm, conditions favor the formation of fog at the contact of the cold and the warm moist air. If air near the ground is below freezing temperature when rain is falling from the warmer air aloft, rain freezes while falling and is called *sleet.* Rain may also freeze on the surface of objects cooled below freezing, even when the air is above that temperature. Under such conditions, rain freezes on the ground and other surfaces and covers everything with a glaze of ice. These ice storms are very destructive to telegraph and telephone wires and even break down trees and make highway traffic hazardous (Figure 3-15).

Hail is formed by concentric layers of ice, and is believed to result from the ascent and descent of ice pellets in air currents of freezing and warmer temperatures. Moisture condenses on the ice, and then the droplet moves again into a freezing current, which forms a layer of ice around the core. This process continues until the hailstone has grown to a size so large that it falls to the earth. Hail is an accompaniment of thunderstorms in warm seasons of the year when very strong updrafts or convection currents may carry raindrops high into air of freezing temperatures.

SUMMARY

Insolation, reaching the earth after passing through the atmosphere, becomes heat through absorption. This heat is then distributed through the air by means of radiation, conduction, and convection, and warms and lights those layers of atmosphere near the earth's surface. The outer atmosphere is less effectively warmed.

Warmth of the atmosphere is measured by the thermometer. Temperature observations for different places may be mapped; after reducing readings to sea level, those places having the same temperature at a given time are joined by a line called an isotherm. Study of isothermal maps permits comparison of temperatures throughout the world, and observation of effects of differences in latitude, nearness to bodies of water, nearness to ocean currents, and other ways in which air temperature varies from time to time and place to place.

Weight (pressure) of the atmosphere is measured by the barometer. Isobars are drawn to connect places of equal atmospheric pressure corrected for sea level.

The atmosphere may contain moisture in varying amounts. Relative humidity is the ratio of moisture in the air per given volume compared to the weight required to saturate the same volume of air at the same temperature and pressure. Condensation of moisture usually results from cooling of saturated air. In visible form, moisture in the atmosphere appears as fog, cloud, or some form of precipitation. Dew and frost may condense on ground, trees, or other cool surfaces. Precipitation forms include rain, hail, sleet, snow.

Figure 3-14 Cirrus clouds in small patches of parallel trails. These clouds usually occur at relatively high altitudes in the troposphere. (Photograph, courtesy of F. Ellerman, U.S. Weather Bureau.)

Outline

Atmosphere

Extent, constituents

Layers: troposphere, stratosphere, ionosphere

Insolation

Factors affecting: length of day, directness of rays, clouds, etc.

Distribution

Importance of radiation from earth heating the air

Convection and its relation to heat

Isotherms

Reasons land heats and cools faster than water

Isobars

Barometer

Zones of low and high pressure

Relative humidity

Condensation of water vapor

Causes for adiabatic cooling by expansion

Convectional

Orographic

Cyclonic

Dew, frost, and fog

Cloud types

Precipitation

Causes

Types: rain, snow, hail, sleet, etc.

Figure 3-15 Severe storm in New York State. Note the ice damage to wires, and broken pole caused by weight of ice. (Photograph, courtesy of the U.S. Weather Bureau.)

QUESTIONS

1. Why does one breathe more rapidly at high altitudes?

2. "Relative humidity at noon yesterday was 25 per cent." Explain the statement. Would the air seem dry, damp, or medium?

3. In your locality if the mercurial barometer reads 29.8 inches corrected for sea level, but all weather stations around you report readings higher than 29.8, are you closer to the center of a "low" or a "high"?

4. Why does a water body usually warm more slowly than a land mass?

5. If isobars on a weather map are closely spaced, what effect on air movement is probable?

6. Why does dew not form every night?

7. Referring to the isothermal chart of the world for January, Figure 3-4, in what compass direction do the isotherms generally trend? Why? How do you account for the fact that the January isotherm of 30°F is found both in New York and in Iceland? Why are the isotherms more regular in their courses in the Northern than in the Southern Hemisphere?

8. Referring to Figure 3-10, isobaric chart of the world for July, how does the atmospheric pressure over Asia compare with that shown in Figure 3-9? What causes this change?

9. Assuming that a mass of air has had access to a body of water, which will contain the greater amount of water vapor, a mass of air at 60°F or a mass at 80°F?

10. How does the weight and density of the air change with increase of altitude?

11. What, in general, is the effect of the atmosphere upon solar radiation passing through it?

12. Why is it unsafe to use an altimeter when landing planes?

13. Referring to Figure 3-5, what is the mean temperature in northwestern Australia? What pressure condition prevails south of Alaska in winter?

14. Of the following atmospheric conditions which would you prefer for active physical work? Why?

Low temperature, low relative humidity
Low temperature, high relative humidity
High temperature, low relative humidity
High temperature, high relative humidity

15. Why does air tend to flow from regions of high atmospheric pressure to those of lower atmospheric pressure?

16. What is the relationship between isotherms and isobars?

17. What is the relationship between isotherms and solar radiation?

18. Why is a man not crushed by the great weight of air (15 pounds per square inch of surface) pressing upon his body at sea level?

19. Why is relative humidity usually higher at night than in the day?

20. Indicate which are forms of condensation: rainfall, snowfall, hail, sleet, cloud, frost, fog, dew, mist, rime.

SELECTED REFERENCES

Blair, T. A.: *Weather Elements* (revised by Robert C. Fite), Prentice-Hall, Inc., Englewood Cliffs, N.J., 1957, chaps. 3, 5.

Finch, V. C., G. T. Trewartha, A. H. Robinson, and E. H. Hammond: *Elements of Geography,* 4th ed., McGraw-Hill Book Company, Inc., New York, 1957, pp. 21–87.

Humphreys, W. J.: *Physics of the Air,* McGraw-Hill Book Company, Inc., New York, 1940.

Humphreys, W. J., *Ways of the Weather,* Jaques Cattell Press, Lancaster, Pa., 1942.

Krick, Irving P.: *Sun, Sea and Sky: Weather in Our World and in Our Lives,* J. B. Lippincott Company, Philadelphia, 1954.

Miller, Denning D.: *Wind, Storm and Rain: The Story of Weather,* Coward-McCann, Inc., New York, 1952.

National Research Council: *Physics of the Earth,* vol. III, *Meteorology,* Bulletin 79, Washington, 1931.

Neuberger, H. H., and F. B. Stephens: *Weather and Man,* Prentice-Hall, Inc., Englewood Cliffs, N.J., 1948.

Shaw, Napier: *The Drama of Weather,* The Macmillan Company, New York, 1934.

Taylor, George F.: *Elementary Meteorology,* Prentice-Hall, Inc., Englewood Cliffs, N.J., 1954.

Trewartha, G. T.: *An Introduction to Weather and Climate,* McGraw-Hill Book Company, Inc., New York, 1954, chaps. 2, 3.

4. Winds and the Weather

WINDS

A HORIZONTAL movement of air is termed *wind*. Winds blow at the surface of the earth from regions of high atmospheric pressure toward those of lower air pressure. Winds are named from the direction from which they blow. Differences in air pressures on the earth appear to result chiefly from differences in temperatures following variations in the receipt and distribution of solar energy described in Chapter 3 under Insolation.

Calms are areas with no noticeable winds, although the air may be rising or descending. The velocity with which winds blow toward a low-pressure area is determined by the *pressure gradient,* which is the difference in pressure compared with the distance involved.

A difference of 1 inch in the barometer reading within a distance of a few miles would be a steep gradient and would cause winds of high velocity; spread over 1,000 miles, however, an equal difference in pressure would be a gentle gradient and would cause only a light breeze.

As the air ascends to upper levels of the troposphere, it is released from contact with the earth's surface. This freedom from land-air friction tends to increase wind velocity at high altitudes. Convection and irregularities on the earth's surface cause eddies which result in gusts and lulls in the wind. Gustiness and turbulence of the wind mix the air and carry water vapor and dust high into the atmosphere. Table 4-1 describes winds according to their velocity.

TABLE 4-1. BEAUFORT SCALE OF WIND FORCE

Beaufort number	Name	Characteristics	Velocity, miles per hour
0	Calm	Smoke rises vertically	Less than 1
1	Light air	Smoke drifts	1–3
2	Slight breeze	Leaves rustle	4–7
3	Gentle breeze	Leaves and twigs move constantly	8–12
4	Moderate breeze	Raises dust and small branches move	13–18
5	Fresh breeze	Small trees sway	19–24
6	Strong breeze	Large branches move	25–31
7	Moderate gale	Whole trees in motion	32–38
8	Fresh gale	Tree twigs are broken	39–46
9	Strong gale	Some damage occurs	47–54
10	Whole gale	Trees uprooted and limbs broken	55–63
11	Storm	Widespread damage	64–75
12	Hurricane	Great damage	Above 75

Local Winds. It has been noted that when land is intensely heated, radiation from the warmed earth in turn heats the air, which then expands and causes some of the air to move aloft. Then cooler and heavier air from surrounding regions flows in to force up the warm air, which when aloft spreads horizontally to complete the convection current. In reality, the whole operation is a continuous movement.

A common local convection current along sea and lake coasts is the *land and sea breeze* (Figure 4-1). On a sunny day the temperature of the land may be warmer than that of the adjacent ocean. In consequence air expands over the warmed land until at some height the

Figure 4-1 Daytime temperature conditions causing the sea breeze. At night, both temperatures and wind directions are reversed, causing the land breeze.

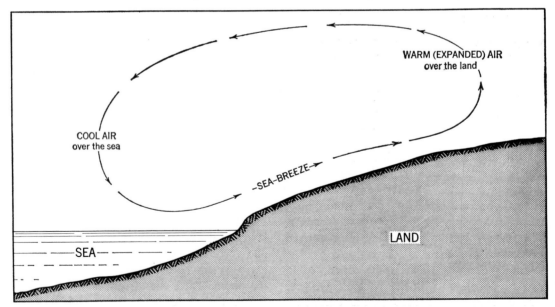

pressure exceeds that above the water, causing the air aloft to move seaward. This increases pressure over the water to more than that at the land surface, forcing a drift of air to the land from the sea and thus completing the convectional current. This results in a sea breeze during the day, usually beginning before noon and ending about sunset.

On clear nights the earth may radiate heat more rapidly than the water; in consequence during the night a land breeze blows seaward, ending about sunrise. Fishermen using sailboats may time their departure to leave with the land breeze before dawn and return with the sea breeze before sunset. The sea breeze helps make ocean beaches attractively cool to visitors in summer. It rarely extends inland more than 50 to 75 miles.

Other types of local winds blow between mountains and valleys, in opposite directions during day and night. After sunrise the earth is warmed by insolation. In turn, radiation from the earth heats the air, which rises, and cold air then flows in, forcing warm light air to move up the slopes of the mountains, forming what is often called the *valley breeze,* a daytime phenomenon. Frequently moisture in the rising cooling air condenses to form clouds over the mountain summits.

At night the air at higher elevations loses heat by radiation and becomes denser as the result of cooling. This colder and heavier air descends mountain slopes toward the valleys and plains, forming *mountain breezes.* From the lowlands the warm air is forced to rise by the colder air and flows at higher elevation toward the mountains, thereby completing a convectional current.

The temperature of air that flows thousands of feet down mountain slopes may be increased many degrees because of adiabatic warming by compression. This fact accounts for the *foehn* or *chinook* winds (Figure 4-2). Humid air rising over mountain ranges loses most of its moisture by condensation, which follows cooling by expansion. When the air sinks to leeward of mountains, it is warmed correspondingly as it descends the slopes. Unsaturated rising air is cooled $5\frac{1}{2}°F$ per 1,000 feet and sinking air is warmed at the same rate, but rising saturated air cools $3°F$ per 1,000 feet owing to addition of heat of condensation. The air descending the leeward side of mountain ranges may, therefore, have a higher temperature at the foot of the mountain than does the air beginning its ascent on the windward side (Figure 4-3). This warm dry air can melt or evaporate snow rapidly on leeward sides of mountain ranges, thereby permitting grazing of livestock most of the winter in areas that would otherwise be too cold.

Figure 4-2   Air movements illustrating the development of foehn, or chinook, winds.

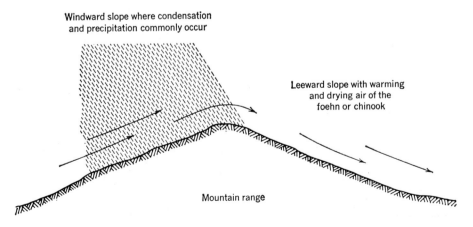

Windward slope where condensation and precipitation commonly occur

Leeward slope with warming and drying air of the foehn or chinook

Mountain range

Circulation of Winds on the Globe. Causes of the planetary circulation of winds are complicated, and the full explanation would require a mathematical treatment beyond the scope of this book. Hence the following brief explanation is necessarily incomplete, but frequent reference to Figure 4-5 will help readers understand the pattern of winds and calms.

Circulation on a nonrotating globe. Air on a nonrotating globe of uniform surface (as shown in Figure 4-4), would be warmest near the equator, where insolation is greatest. Above the ground some of the expanding air would move horizontally, thereby increasing the pressure on either side of the equatorial region and helping to cause an influx of cold air from higher latitudes. That influx would impel the warm air at the equator to rise. This condition would force a large convectional movement of air from poles to equator. There air rises and returns to the poles at a high elevation; it then descends to complete the circulation.

Effect of earth's rotation. The circulation of winds on the earth differs from the foregoing, because the rotation of the earth causes deflection of winds and changes their direc- tions. Nearly a century ago, William Ferrel showed that fluid masses moving freely over the surface of a rotating globe will be deflected to their right in the Northern Hemisphere and to their left in the Southern Hemisphere. In the Northern Hemisphere air coming from the north would be deflected toward the west, thereby becoming an easterly wind; air moving from the south would be deflected toward the east, thereby becoming a westerly wind. In the Southern Hemisphere the south wind would be deflected by the earth's rotation to the west, becoming an easterly wind, and a north wind would be deflected toward the east to become a westerly wind.

Names and Location of Wind Belts. Experience shows that, in the equatorial zone and extending a few degrees on either side, there is a belt of rising and expanding air which has rather low pressure at the earth's surface. This zone is one of light variable airs and calms and is called the *doldrums* or *belt of equatorial calms* (Figure 4-5). Here heated air is forced to rise by an inflow of colder air from either side of the equator. The rising air cools by expansion, causing almost daily

Figure 4-3 View toward the west from the San Bernardino Mountains, across Cajon Pass. A high foehn wind is carrying large amounts of dust down the pass toward the Los Angeles lowland, and the air is warming as it descends. Mountaintop coniferous forest covers the summits at this altitude. (Infrared photograph by Robert Pease.)

thunderstorms from which rainfall is often torrential.

Near 30 to 35°, both north and south latitude, the pressure is high, and masses of relatively cool air move toward the low pressure of the doldrums. These winds are called *trade winds* and are deflected by the rotation of the earth as described above. Hence they blow from the northeast in the Northern Hemisphere and from the southeast in the Southern Hemisphere. Since the trades are relatively steady winds their dependability made them very useful in the days of sailing ships. Fair weather predominates in the trades except where the winds blow from the ocean onto a mountainous coast; this situation promotes local heavy rainfall.

Intertropical front. The trade winds are not constant in physical characteristics but may vary in temperature, humidity, and density. Then, instead of the two trade winds blending together to form doldrums, the trade wind with the colder and denser mass underrides the warmer, lighter, and usually more humid mass of trade-wind air and forces it to rise, resulting in cooling and condensation. The doldrums are absent under these conditions, as for example, in the central and eastern tropical Pacific zone. The junction of the trade winds, whether the doldrums are formed or not, is called the *intertropical front.*

Poleward from the trade winds lies a zone of high atmospheric pressure called the *horse latitudes* or *subtropical calms.* Into this zone at high elevations blow winds (sometimes called *antitrades*) from the doldrums, and probably also from other sources. From aloft in the high-pressure zone the air descends, is heated adiabatically, and becomes drier. In the lower atmosphere, winds blow outward from the zone and gain in strength near its margin. The air which moves into the horse latitudes loses most of its moisture as it cools by expansion when heated in doldrums or elsewhere, and rises into higher elevations of less pressure. This movement results in the sinking air becoming dry and having a relatively high density, and causes the building

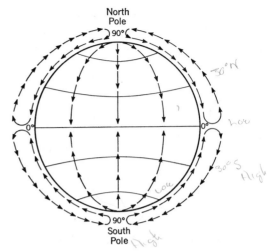

Figure 4-4 *The circulation of air on a nonrotating globe of uniform surface.*

up of a high-pressure zone which is usually elongated in an east-west direction (Figures 3-9 and 3-10). Winds of the horse latitudes are light and variable, relative humidity is low, and the sky is usually clear except near coasts where fogs may occur.

Because of the deflective force of earth rotation, winds spiral outward from the permanent anticyclone (zone of high atmospheric pressure) clockwise in the Northern Hemisphere and counterclockwise in the Southern Hemisphere. In the Northern Hemisphere, these outblowing winds become the prevailing westerlies and northeast trades. In the Southern Hemisphere, they become the prevailing westerlies and southeast trades. Not only is weather in the horse latitudes predominantly dry, but the west sides of continents in this wind zone are exceptionally dry. An example of such extreme aridity is found in the western Sahara. The subtropical high-pressure belt in the Northern Hemisphere moves north several degrees during the summer months and migrates south in winter. In the Southern Hemisphere there is a similar migration of the horse latitudes, poleward in the southern summer, and equatorward in the southern winter.

The *prevailing westerlies* are situated between 35 to 40 and 60 to 65 degrees north and south from the equator. Their boundaries

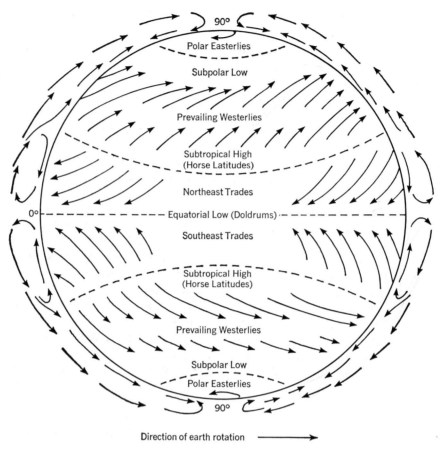

90°
Polar Easterlies
Subpolar Low
Prevailing Westerlies
Subtropical High
(Horse Latitudes)
Northeast Trades
0°   Equatorial Low (Doldrums)
Southeast Trades
Subtropical High
(Horse Latitudes)
Prevailing Westerlies
Subpolar Low
Polar Easterlies
90°

Direction of earth rotation ⟶

Figure 4-5   Surface wind and calm zones (idealized) on a rotating globe.

fluctuate, particularly along the poleward margins. Near the horse latitudes these winds come from the southwest in the Northern Hemisphere and from the northwest in the Southern Hemisphere; but the deflective effect of the earth's rotation increases poleward, causing the winds to blow predominantly from the west toward the outer limits in both hemispheres. The prevalence of cyclonic storms causing frequent changes in temperature and rainfall and other weather phenomena is an outstanding characteristic of the two zones of prevailing westerly winds.

Toward the poles, especially over ice-covered lands like Greenland and Antarctica, air that flows in at high elevations is cooled and sinks toward the earth. This cold air forms an area of high pressure (*polar high*) from which cold air moves out; and, in accordance with Ferrel's law, these winds are deflected to the west in both hemispheres to form the *polar easterlies*. The amount of deflection because of the earth's rotation in high latitudes is so great that these winds, starting south from the North Pole and north from the South Pole toward the equator, are soon deflected 90 degrees from their original courses until they blow directly from the east.

Between the polar easterlies and the prevailing westerlies lie the so-called *"subpolar lows."* Probably this zone of low pressure is caused, in part, by a withdrawal of air aloft. That withdrawal results from polar cooling and from the surface air movement away from the polar highs, but fuller discussion would not be appropriate here. Of special interest is the fact that the two subpolar lows are among the stormiest belts in the world.

Many storms that cross North America develop in the Aleutian low of the North Pacific. In the North Atlantic many storms reaching Europe come from the Icelandic low, which occupies a similar position in that ocean.

The location of the various wind belts is affected by the seasons and the resulting changes in heating of the earth. The whole system of winds shifts northward during summer months and southward during winter months of the Northern Hemisphere. The pressure (isobaric) maps of the world (Figures 3-9 and 3-10) show a belt of low pressure near the equator and a zone of high pressure in the subtropics, centering about 25 to 35 degrees from the equator, as noted previously. Trade winds blow from the belts of high pressure to those of low pressure. Then in polar regions high pressure prevails, and the winds blow equatorward toward the subpolar low-pressure belt that lies about 60 to 65 degrees from the equator. The westerlies blow between the high pressure of the subtropics and the lower pressure of the subpolar region.

The Jet Stream. Although our knowledge of air movements at high altitudes is incomplete, experiences of fliers in recent years have indicated the presence of very strong winds at heights of 30,000 to 40,000 feet above sea level, especially in the midlatitudes. Velocities in these so-called "jet streams" may range from 150 to more than 200 miles per hour. The sources or origins of such rapid air movements are unknown, nor is there much information concerning their directions or location though they seem to flow in an easterly direction with the prevailing westerlies. What part the jet stream may play in influencing weather conditions at low altitudes remains uncertain, but the presence of the streams seems to be related to contacts between polar and tropical air masses. When planes fly in the jet stream, their speed varies greatly, increasing if they go with the wind, decreasing if they fly against it. Air movement in a vertical direction at high altitudes is called a "clear air

gust" and like the jet stream, its implications are not well understood.

Monsoon Winds. The ideal pattern of wind circulation shown in Figure 4-5 is interrupted in some parts of the earth because of the different influences of large land bodies and oceans. Oceans heat more slowly than continents but retain heat longer. As a result, oceans have smaller seasonal ranges of temperature. A large continent like Asia becomes thoroughly chilled in winter and is overlain by heavy cold air, flowing as a surface wind outward to the sea. This winter monsoon is a cold dry wind. The winter monsoon brings rain only after blowing across bodies of water before striking the land, as in parts of southeastern Asia.

In summer a part of Asia, especially the Thar Desert of northwest India, becomes so hot that its air, heated by radiation from the land, expands, and part flows at high elevations out to the cooler oceans over which extensive high-pressure areas develop. From the oceanic high-pressure areas surface winds blow in from the sea, bringing summer rains to the continent, over which a large low-pressure area exists (Figure 4-6). In winter con-

Figure 4-6 Summer monsoon winds of southeastern Asia. Note the general landward movement of air in summer.

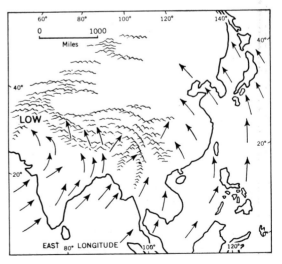

ditions essentially are reversed (Figure 4-7). Thus monsoons resemble land and sea breezes on a giant scale, because they may affect most of a continent and blow for weeks or months at a time from the sea in summer and the land in winter, completely reversing their directions with the seasons.

In India the summer monsoon originates south of the equator in the southeast trades, which are deflected toward the northeast as the wind enters the Northern Hemisphere, thus flowing directly counter to the normal direction of the northeast trades. Both summer and winter monsoons may last for several months with little respite. The summer monsoon brings rains to Southeast and East Asia as far north as Japan and northern China and is of great importance to people who live there. Some of the world's most densely populated areas are in the monsoon region. Northward from India the prevailing winds gradually change from southwest to south, then to southeast. The winter monsoon is usually dry, but rain results when it blows across a large body of water like the Bay of Bengal and then rises over a mountainous land such as Ceylon. The prevailing wind direction of the winter monsoon is the reverse of summer, and changes from northwest in northern China to

north in central China and northeast in southern China. Between monsoon seasons the normal trade winds may blow.

There are no true monsoons in the Western Hemisphere, but the southeastern United States and Rio de la Plata region of South America are among parts of the world having summer rainfall maxima from the inflow of air from nearby oceans. Both these areas and the true monsoon regions are of great importance in the production of foodstuffs for millions of the world's people.

Winds and Man. Human activities are greatly affected by the winds of the world. Winds of steady force like the trade winds, monsoons, and prevailing westerlies were an important influence in selection of the routes followed by sailing vessels. Sailing ships left Europe to arrive in the Indian Ocean in time to hasten to India with the summer monsoon wind behind them; the winter monsoon then speeded their return voyage. Today Arab sailing vessels or dhows voyage from ports in southern Arabia to the east coast of Africa and return home annually, propelled by monsoon winds in each direction.

Islands and windward coasts have a marine or oceanic climate with small range of temperature. Larger seasonal extremes of temperature occur on leeward coasts and the interiors of continents, except in the tropics. Trade winds blowing toward the equator evaporate and retain more moisture as their temperature rises; hence they may cause desert conditions unfavorable for human life except on high windward coasts where they bring much rainfall. Rainfall contrasts between southeastern and southwestern Africa (Figure 5-1) illustrate the point.

Variable weather is a feature of the prevailing westerly wind zones. Here may occur hot dry winds which cause droughts that sometimes ruin crops and deplete the water supply of cities. Torrential rainfall erodes soil and may cause severe floods. Unusually heavy snowfall blocks transportation; prolonged spells of hot, humid weather hamper human

Figure 4-7 Winter monsoon wind movements over Asia.

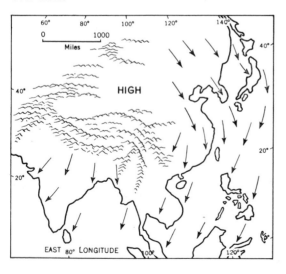

efficiency. These sudden changes in weather thus make difficult problems. In spite of extremes, the usual weather of the prevailing westerlies is pleasant, with small frequent changes of temperature, humidity, and sunshine or cloudiness. Many authorities believe that these frequent changes in winds and weather are stimulating and beneficial to man.

AIR MASSES

When the atmosphere is stationary for some time its temperature and humidity tend to become similar to that of the land or water surfaces on which it rests. In the midlatitudes, masses of warm moist air from the tropics often battle with cold air masses from the high latitudes. These conflicts cause most of the storms common in the zone of prevailing westerly winds. Although weather everywhere is largely determined by the characteristics of the large masses of air developed in various regions of the world, the midlatitudes are especially subject to storms.

An air mass is a big, stable portion (sometimes called a *cell*) of the atmosphere, in which temperature, density, and moisture content are essentially uniform for the same elevations. Air masses form over large land or sea areas called *source regions* where conditions are so nearly constant that the air in contact with the surfaces develops similar characteristics. Examples of source regions include the snow-covered plains of Siberia and northern Canada in winter, the hot dry Sahara, the arid plateau of northern Mexico in summer, the warm Gulf of Mexico, and the large expanses of warm ocean water in the horse latitudes.

From these source regions tongues of air invade adjacent areas where temperature and moisture conditions are different. Because of their great size these air masses cause profound weather changes in the regions into which they move. Such large masses of air retain their characteristics for a considerable time and do not readily mix with other air masses of different temperature and humidity. In most source regions the barometric pressure is high near the ground, and the air is slowly sinking and spreading away near the surface. The air mass or cell is built up by an influx of air aloft from other, often distant regions where air is rising and flowing elsewhere at high elevations.

The sloping edge of an air mass is called a *front,* and the sloping zone of contact between two air masses with different characteristics is called a *surface of discontinuity*. Marked weather changes normally occur along an advancing front. The density of air in a cold and dry air mass is greater than that of a warm, humid air mass. When such air masses meet, cold air slips under the warmer mass forcing the warm, moist air to rise. Adiabatic cooling of the warm air results, then condensation and precipitation of moisture. Storms are common and often violent along advancing fronts of air masses. Air masses may become stationary, or one mass may move more vigorously than another. The term *cold front* is applied where a cold mass of air moves like a wedge under warmer air and forces it to rise. The term *warm front* is used when the warm air mass invades a region of colder air and rises over it. Although a front refers to the edge of an air mass, when fronts are advancing the surface of discontinuity may cover a zone of several miles.

Origins and Characteristics of Air Masses. The primary classification of air masses is either polar (represented on weather maps by *P*) or tropical, *T*. A secondary division indicates marine *m* or continental *c* origin. Further characterization of each mass involves a description of its temperatures: warm *w* or cold *k* in comparison with the surface over which the air is moving. Air masses in which conditions favor stability at high altitudes also are labeled *s* for stability; those in which instability is present are marked *u* for unstable. Thus an air mass described by the letters *mPku* indicates that it is of oceanic origin coming from polar or subpolar regions, having temperatures cold for its latitude and season, and in a condition that would lead to instability or storminess. Air masses of this type are common over the North Atlantic Ocean in winter and over northern Siberia in summer.

In North America the principal air masses that affect the weather are

1. Polar continental (*cP*) whose source is the snow-covered northern interior of Canada and the icy Arctic Ocean. This air mass is very cold, dry, and stable. In winter it provides the "cold waves" which come from the north and sweep across central Canada and the United States, often reaching the Gulf of Mexico, and sometimes invading Florida.

2. Tropical continental (*cT*) air masses originate in northern Mexico and the plateaus of the southwestern United States. These air masses are hot and of low humidity, and sometimes cause drought and hot winds which injure crops on the Great Plains in summer. However, these *cT* masses are relatively unimportant compared to the *cP* air masses.

3. Important tropical maritime (*mT*) air masses have their sources in the Gulf of Mexico and South Atlantic Ocean. These air masses are warm, moist, and unstable. They account for most of the rainfall throughout the eastern United States as the modified weather map (Figure 4-8) illustrates.

4. The North Atlantic (*mP*) air masses are cool, moist, and stable. They have a cooling effect in summer on the coastal region north of North Carolina but supply little rainfall.

5. The tropical maritime (*mT*) air masses in the Pacific are warm and moist. Especially in winter they may supply rain to the Pacific Coast when this air is forced to rise over colder air masses. Cold air may be *cP* in origin, but some may be *mP* from the North Pacific.

6. Polar maritime Pacific (*mP*) air masses are cool, moist, and stable. In summer fair weather and clear skies predominate in such an air mass. In winter these air masses supply important amounts of precipitation.

Similarly, other continents have sources of air masses of differing temperatures and humidity. With these diverse air masses are associated rainfall and other weather elements. They are plainly the major factors affecting the weather and climate of the continents.

STORMS

Storms are among the most familiar phenomena of nature. They provide rain that falls on the earth and some of the warmth essential to life. The shifting of variable winds brings changes in temperature and many other meteorological conditions. Storms result from differences in pressure and produce the variable weather so characteristic of parts of the earth's surface especially in the midlatitudes. Some storms are local and are mere convectional thunderstorms of small extent; whereas others are so large that they may cover half the territory of the United States. A storm center has lower pressure than surrounding regions, and air tends to flow toward this center from regions of higher pressure around it. As previously described, moving air is deflected by the rotation of the earth to its right in the Northern Hemisphere and to its left in the Southern Hemisphere. Air moving in toward the storm center in the Northern Hemisphere thus tends to spiral in a counterclockwise direction; in the Southern Hemisphere it spirals in the reverse direction, or clockwise (Figure 4-9).

Cyclones. Some storms that have winds blowing in a general circular way around low-pressure centers may cover large areas. These great storms are called *cyclones*, but they should not be confused with tornadoes, the small but destructive storms to be described later. Cyclones, often called "lows" or "depressions" appear on weather maps as oval

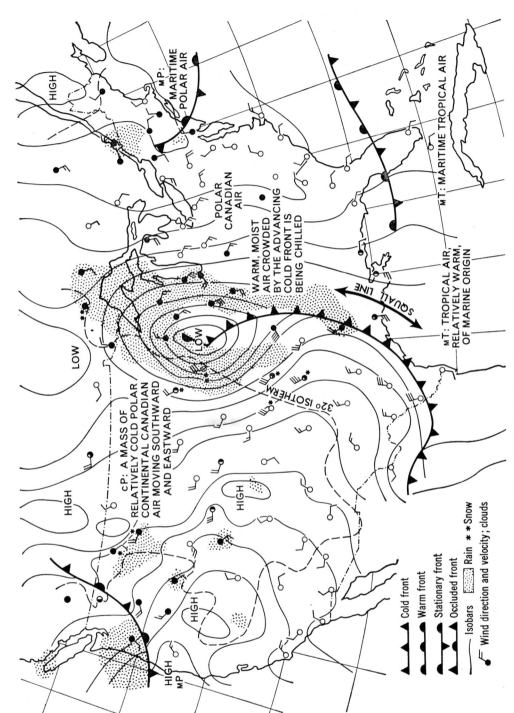

Figure 4-8 Typical weather conditions in the United States on a November day.

MP: MARITIME POLAR AIR

HIGH

POLAR CANADIAN AIR

MT: MARITIME TROPICAL AIR

WARM, MOIST AIR CROWDED BY THE ADVANCING COLD FRONT IS BEING CHILLED

SQUALL LINE

MT: TROPICAL AIR, RELATIVELY WARM, OF MARINE ORIGIN

LOW

LOW

32° ISOTHERM

cP: A MASS OF RELATIVELY COLD POLAR CONTINENTAL CANADIAN AIR MOVING SOUTHWARD AND EASTWARD

HIGH

HIGH

HIGH

HIGH

HIGH MP

Cold front
Warm front
Stationary front
Occluded front
Isobars   Rain ＊＊ Snow
Wind direction and velocity; clouds

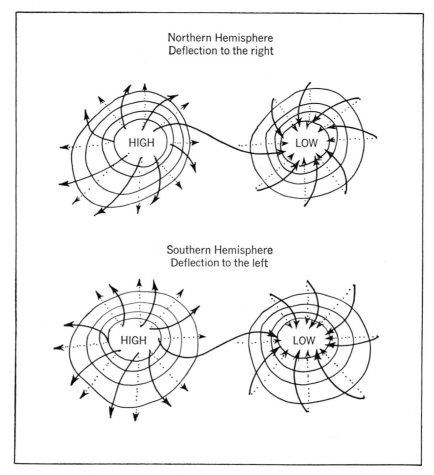

Figure 4-9 Idealized movement of air around "highs" and "lows" at ground level in the Northern and Southern Hemispheres. (Note the counterclockwise motion of air toward the center of a "low" of the Northern Hemisphere.) Dotted lines indicate the direction in which the air started to move originally; solid lines indicate the deflected movement.

or elongated areas whose air pressure is lower than that of surrounding regions. On weather maps of the United States the opposite areas of high pressure are labeled "highs" and are technically called *anticyclones*. Air descends in highs, and the wind spirals outward, clockwise in the Northern and counterclockwise in the Southern Hemisphere, as a result of the effect of the earth's rotation on the moving streams of air.

Cyclonic storms are believed to originate at the contact between cold and warm air masses. Many meteorologists state that cy-clones develop in this zone from a wave caused by friction between two air masses which are moving in opposite directions and differ in temperature, humidity, and density. At the contact zone a wedge of cold air slips under the adjacent mass of warm air thus forcing it to rise. The rising air cools by expansion and the contained moisture condenses into clouds and rain. If the underrunning cold air separates a mass of warmer air from the ground it is called an *occlusion*. Such an occlusion causes an inversion of temperature and instability of the warm, moist air. Condensation of water releases latent heat and this supply of energy makes for further expansion of the air and reduction of its pressure to form a low. Into this depression the air moves from surrounding regions in which pressure is higher, and so the storm increases in intensity. Continued condensation of water vapor brought into the storm centers, mostly by warm air masses which have originated over oceans, supplies energy for perpetuation of the cyclones. Ultimately the supply of energy is exhausted and the storm disintegrates.

At intervals of hundreds of miles, southward-moving tongues of cold air from polar regions invade the midlatitudes. Here they come into contact with northward-moving masses of warm, moist air from the tropics. Such zones of contact are especially common near the Aleutian Islands in the North Pacific Ocean, and from Greenland to Iceland in the North Atlantic. In both these areas warm air which accompanies warm ocean currents meets cold air masses; in the Pacific from the frigid Arctic Ocean, in the Atlantic from icy Greenland. After their formation cyclones usually move eastward in the prevailing westerly winds. Cyclones may originate in the tropics as well as in middle and high latitudes, but they are most frequent in the midlatitudes. Apparently tropical cyclones do not have the well-defined warm and cold fronts characteristic of those of the cooler higher latitudes, although not all meteorologists agree about this.

Cyclones resemble gigantic eddies in the lower atmosphere. They take the shape of a large flat saucer, around which winds whirl while rising toward the center of low pressure. Cyclones vary tremendously in size. Although some are only 100 miles or less across, most are very large, 500 to 1,000 miles or more; but since they are confined to the troposphere cyclones are only 5 to 8 miles in depth. In winter they are often elongated, generally in a north-south direction, and one axis may be twice as long as the other. South and southeast of the storm center where pressure is lowest is a warm, usually moist, mass

of air; west and northwest is a cold dry air mass.

The most rapid drop in temperature occurs southwest of the center where the advancing cold front underruns the warm air mass. By forcing the warm air to rise rapidly, conditions favor development of severe local thunderstorms or "line" storms which sometimes become hail storms or even destructive tornadoes. This zone is named the *squall line* or *wind-shift line*. Both rainfall and wind velocities are usually high along the squall line (Figure 4-8 and Figure 4-10).

East and northeast of an advancing cyclone, nearly stationary air of moderate temperature is generally found. The advancing warm air mass rises over this stable air and the moisture in the incoming air condenses to clouds or fog and rain. Similar weather is apt to occur around the storm center in which air is rising and cooling. Because of the earth's rotation, the winds that blow into a low are deflected, counterclockwise in the Northern Hemisphere, clockwise in the Southern Hemisphere. Usually these winds have moderate velocities; sometimes they reach 50 to 70 miles per hour or more and then cause property damage.

The storm itself usually moves eastward several hundred miles a day and may travel thousands of miles before disintegrating. A cyclone moving 500 to 600 miles a day will cross the United States in about five days, but the rate of movement varies greatly. Some storms advance less than 300 miles a day; others go over 700 miles a day. A cyclone may stagnate for a time, it can suddenly gain in speed and intensity, or it may disintegrate and cease to exist.

Certain tracks are commonly followed by cyclonic storms. For example, in winter most lows enter the United States near Puget Sound, loop across the country in a southeasterly direction to the Mississippi Valley and thence northeastward, and continue on to the Atlantic. Other storms enter the United States from the southwest and move in a northeasterly direction. In summer the paths

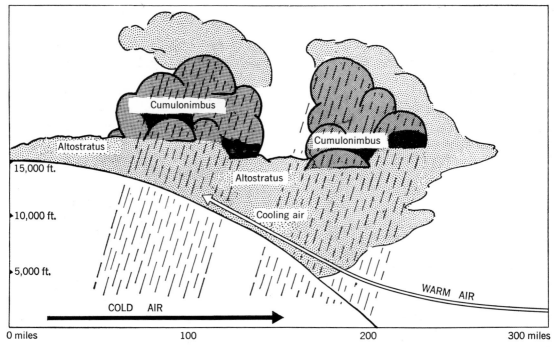

Figure 4-10 Cross section of an advancing cold front with associated weather conditions.

of the lows are generally farther north than in winter. The diagram (Figure 4-11) shows the customary paths for storms of the Northern Hemisphere.

As a low passes over an observer, a definite shift in the wind direction is usually noted. Generally, winds in front of a storm are warm and blow from the southeast, while back of the low a cold wind blows from the west, northwest, or north. A cyclone approaching from the west is usually preceded by rising temperatures and a falling barometer. High light clouds—cirrus and cirrostratus—make their appearance. Later, lower and more dense nimbostratus clouds supply rain or snow. As the storm moves eastward the temperature drops, the barometer rises, and the weather clears with arrival of the cold mass of air westward of the storm center. Thus a cyclone is preceded by warm, cloudy, and rainy weather and is followed by clear and relatively cold weather after the storm has passed. The cold air mass following the low is high in

pressure because it is cold and dry; essentially this is an anticyclone.

Along the squall line heavy dark clouds of the thunderstorm type often develop and sometimes are associated with hail. Especially in the warm season local thunderstorms may occur almost anywhere in the warm sector of a cyclone. Tornadoes are usually in advance of the squall line because the cold air comes in aloft well ahead of the surface cold air and occasionally helps to cause so much turbulence and local instability of the air that a tornado develops.

Sometimes one or both air masses in a cyclone cease to move; an anticyclone may become so well established that it lasts for days and weeks. Then weather in the stationary area may show little change for days at a time. For example, surface fogs may last many days in association with a stationary anticyclone in winter; in summer, a "heat wave" may occur in a dry high-pressure air mass in which the sun glares down for long periods from a cloudless sky. If for a considerable time, a warm and moist air mass continues to rise over stationary cold air in about the same place, the result may be very heavy rainfall and probably serious floods.

Cyclones are more numerous or more severe in some years than in others. Some evidence shows that the number of lows tends to occur in cycles. For several years storms increase to a maximum in frequency and strength and then decrease to a minimum. Some authorities recognize an 11-year cycle and another of about 35 years' duration. Others suggest there may be a swing measured in centuries rather than years. Between abundance of cyclones and frequency of sunspots there seems a fairly close correspondence, which suggests that pulsating radiation from the sun may possibly account for variations in storminess. Scientists do not agree about the cause for cyclones, however; more than one factor may be involved in the formation of these giant whirls in our atmosphere.

Thunderstorms. Thunderstorms, a common local phenomenon in hot weather, often accompany areas of moderately low pressure. The storm may originate from convectional overturning of heated humid air, or it may be associated with extensive cyclonic disturbances. Heat or convectional thunderstorms may occur almost daily at certain seasons in the calm humid equatorial regions. Scattered thunderstorms frequently come during the afternoon or evening of hot days in humid parts of midlatitudes, generally developing on sultry days. The air, heated by radiation from the earth, expands. The vapor in this air is cooled by the expansion and thus condenses to form a flat-bottomed cloud that rapidly grows into a towering thunderhead (Figure 4-12). Surface air moves in toward the low-pressure area, which develops and forces the warm air upward, and the thunderstorm begins to operate. Once begun, the thunderstorm moves with the prevailing winds until its supply of energy is exhausted and it disintegrates.

Figure 4-11   Principal storm paths of the Northern Hemisphere. (Note that the storms tend to develop over sea areas.)

Condensation of moisture and the formation and separation of raindrops develop static electricity. Some scientists believe that the larger drops carry positive electricity and smaller drops bear negative charges. Small drops are blown away or are lifted by the rising current of heated air into the cloud top, where negative electricity collects. The earth also is usually, but not always, negatively charged. When sufficient difference of electric potential has developed, possibly millions of volts, lightning passes between two oppositely charged clouds or from a cloud to the earth (Figure 4-13). Passage of the lightning requires only a small fraction of a second. The high temperature of the electric flash heats air through which it passes, causing a terrific expansion of gases, which produces the noise called *thunder*. Reflection of sound waves on clouds and other surfaces causes the reverberation of thunder. Heat lightning is only the reflection of distant lightning on clouds.

Thunderstorms may be accompanied by torrential local rains or cloudbursts. At other times the lower air may be so dry that falling rain is almost evaporated before reaching the ground. In such cases lightning sets many for-

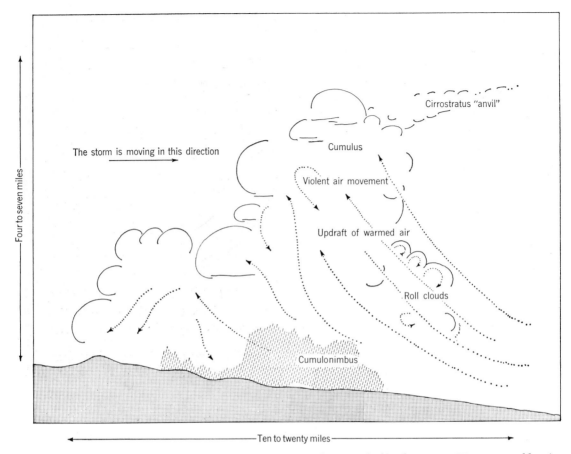

Figure 4-12 Diagram of a theoretical thunderstorm. Warm unstable air, filled with moisture, ascends while cooler, more stable air descends; between the two, squall winds, rain and hail result from extreme turbulence. The advancing "head" of the storm consists of dark cumulonimbus storm clouds, cumulus clouds at a higher level, and light-colored rounded masses of cloud in the cirrostratus "anvil."

est fires, especially in the mountains of the Pacific Northwest. A series of local lightning storms that furnished little rain has been known to set over 200 fires in one national forest in Idaho. Lightning may suddenly change a tree's sap to steam, splitting the timber and reducing it to kindling wood. Wind may blow into thunderstorms and around them with gale violence, causing damage to property. A special danger comes from the outrushing squall of cold air preceding the storm. Thunderstorms may have great turbulence because of the rapid rise and descent of

air currents. This makes the thunderstorm dangerous to aircraft.

Tornadoes and Hurricanes. Tornadoes are most common in level country like the Mississippi Valley, especially during the spring and early summer. In 1955, 870 tornadoes were recorded in the United States; 1957 saw nearly as many (Figure 4-14). A tornado in March, 1925, killed 689 persons in Illinois and Indiana, injured 1,980, and did 16 million dollars in property damage. Wind velocities in a tornado usually exceed 100 miles per hour.

Large differences of pressure within short distances account for the high velocity. Most tornadoes advance from 25 to 40 miles in an hour. These storms have a funnel shape. Near the storm center, trees, houses, and other structures may be almost completely destroyed. Fortunately such storms are small—averaging about 400 yards wide—and rarely travel more than a few score miles before disappearing. Tornadoes most often develop in advance of the wind-shift line of strongly developed cyclones, that is, near the contact of warm and cold air masses.

Hurricanes generally occur near the borders of the tropics. These storms are as extensive as cyclones; their destructive force approaches that of tornadoes. Wind velocities often exceed 100 miles per hour. Tropical cyclones, or hurricanes, most frequently develop in summer and fall. Then much warmth and moisture have accumulated in the tropics and the air in higher latitudes has cooled off with the retreating sun, giving rise to the unstable conditions that create hurricanes.

These storms are accompanied by torrential rainfall and cause damage by both wind and flood. After the first attack of the wind,

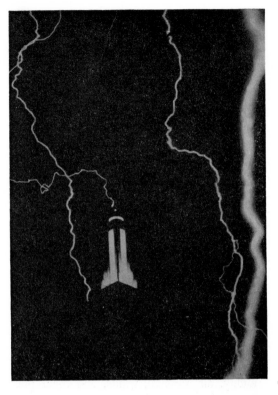

Figure 4-13   Lightning strikes the Empire State Building, New York, N.Y. (Photograph by Lt. Eldridge, courtesy of U.S. Weather Bureau.)

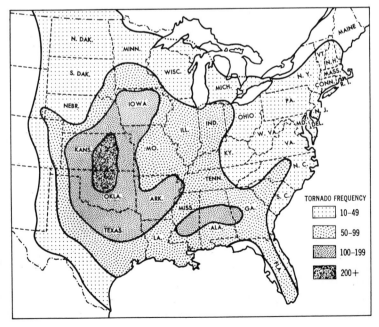

Figure 4-14   Annual tornado frequency in the eastern United States. (Adapted from Weather Bureau records and The New York Times.)

the center, or "eye" of a hurricane is calm. Then, when the storm moves on, the wind returns with renewed violence but from the opposite direction. As with cyclones, circulation of the winds of hurricanes is counterclockwise in the Northern Hemisphere and clockwise in the Southern Hemisphere.

Hurricanes off southeastern Asia are called *typhoons.* They frequently invade the Philippines, southern Japan, the South Pacific, and the Indian Ocean. Hurricanes that affect North America commonly originate east of the West Indies, move westward in the trade winds, and sometimes travel northward, striking the Gulf Coast or Florida, and occasionally the Atlantic Coast as far north as New England. On low coasts much damage results from high waves and the piling up of ocean water by the wind. Intensity of the storms decreases as they move inland, since the energy decreases with the lessened condensation of moisture. If a tropical hurricane moves northeastward up the Atlantic coast, it becomes a "nor'easter," so named because the wind blows toward the approaching storm center from that direction. In September, 1938, a destructive hurricane struck New England (Figure 4-15); in October, 1954, two hurricanes caused flood and wind damage along the Atlantic seaboard. In August, 1955, a hurricane caused the deaths of nearly 200 people and damage estimated at hundreds of millions of dollars in Pennsylvania, New York, and New England, chiefly from floods produced by rainfall of as much as 20 inches in 24 hours (Figure 4-16).

WEATHER AND WEATHER FORECASTS

The condition of the atmosphere at any one time constitutes the weather. Temperature, humidity, air pressure, winds, and other phenomena characterize it. Climate represents a composite of weather conditions over a long period of time. Weather and climate are affected by directness of the sun's rays and length of day, distribution of land and water bodies, altitude, position with respect to mountains, air pressure, storms and their fre-

Figure 4-15 Hurricane damage in New England. (Photograph by Worcester Telegram, Worcester, Massachusetts. Courtesy of U.S. Weather Bureau.)

Figure 4-16 Flood damage in 1955 at Torrington, Connecticut, factories. (Photograph, courtesy of American Brass Company.)

quency, movements of air masses, and winds and ocean currents. Climate is not only the average of all weather conditions but also takes into account the extremes or variations which may occur in departures from average conditions.

Forecasting Cyclonic Weather. The U.S. Weather Bureau forecasts are based primarily on the passage of lows and highs across the nation. When lows appear off the Pacific Coast, they usually follow recognized paths across the country. If the storm follows a usual course and moves eastward about 500 miles each day, warm and rainy weather will advance across the continent at the same rate. After the passage of a low the normal weather in the high that follows is likely to be clear and colder. Weather Bureau forecasts are made for a few days in advance; those for to-morrow's weather are correct about 90 per cent of the time. Forecasts fail when storms move faster or more slowly than the normal rate, change directions, or become nearly stationary for a day or more. Storms also occasionally disintegrate or suddenly gain in strength and destructiveness.

The weather of the country is profoundly affected by cyclones. When lows cross the southern United States in winter, usually a "norther" or cold wave moves in from the Arctic and chills the interior of the country. On the other hand if the low crosses the northern United States, warm winds from the Gulf of Mexico bring mild and usually rainy weather over most of the interior and eastern sections of the continent. Sometimes a mass of air stagnates and fails to advance as usual. Under this condition, if a warm air mass of high humidity, say from the Gulf of Mexico, continues to flow inland and precipitation results upon contact with cold polar air, the resulting rain or snow is localized over a limited area. These prolonged heavy rains may produce destructive floods, or snowfall to depths of several feet, blocking highways and railroads and disrupting traffic and human activities in general.

Use of weather forecasts. Forecasts of weather made a few hours to several days in advance serve many people both in their business enterprises and their places for recreation. Farmers need forecasts for fair weather or of rain during haying, harvesting, and fruit-picking seasons. Growers of citrus fruits, peaches, and other crops need to know whether or not frosts will occur in order to prepare for the low temperatures that may

Figure 4-17. Standard instrument shelter for co-operative weather observers. (Note that the observations are made in an open space not too closely surrounded by trees and shrubbery.) The rain gauge stands at left of the shelter. The door of the instrument shelter is open. Shelter is well ventilated by openings and by air space under the roof. (Photograph, courtesy of the U.S. Weather Bureau.)

damage their product. Shippers sending perishable foods by train should know the probable temperature extremes to protect fruit and vegetables while in transit. Snow surveys made in the mountainous regions of the western United States indicate the amount of water available for irrigation and power during the succeeding summer. River flood warnings form a part of the forecast work of the Weather Bureau. Forecasts of fire hazards are made when forests have dried out during hot, dry, windy days when forest fires might spread quickly. Stockmen need warnings of cold waves to learn whether snow, sleet, or blizzards will endanger livestock. Resort operators want to know whether particular days will be rainy or dry and hot. Commercial fishermen watch the forecasts and time their activities accordingly.

Forecasts are especially valuable to the transportation industry. Administrators responsible for highways and streets use forecasts to prepare for snow removal. Ships need hurricane warnings so that they may seek protected harbors, and inhabitants of exposed coasts need to know when to flee inland for safety before the arrival of fierce gales. Air lines seek advice about flying weather that will be encountered along courses to be flown by their planes. Cloudiness, fog, visibility, thunderstorms, dust storms, wind direction and velocity, probability of sleet, rain, and snow are among weather conditions which concern aviators.

Cooperative Observers and Weather Instruments. In collecting climatic data, the U.S. Weather Bureau has the cooperation of thousands of volunteer observers who record maximum and minimum temperatures, amount of rainfall, snowfall, condition of cloudiness, wind directions, dates of killing frosts, and other phenomena. The data thus collected supplement those secured through regular weather stations maintained by employees of the U.S. Weather Bureau.

A cooperative weather observer is furnished a rain gauge and maximum and minimum thermometers. The rain gauge is a cylinder with a funnel-shaped cover which collects rain from ten times the area of the cylinder (Figure 4-17). Depth of water in the gauge is thereby magnified ten times and $\frac{1}{10}$ inch of water collected represents $\frac{1}{100}$ inch of precipitation, the smallest amount that is recorded. Snow is melted to convert it into inches of rainfall for the records. Usually about 10 inches of newly fallen snow is equivalent to about 1 inch of rain, but snow may be lighter or denser than this.

An ordinary thermometer consists of a capillary tube attached to a bulb containing a fluid that expands and contracts in the tube in accordance with temperature increase or decrease, thus permitting reading of the temperatures. A maximum thermometer has a constriction in the tube just above the bulb which causes the column of mercury to break when the temperature falls, leaving fluid to record the highest temperature reached, Whirling the maximum thermometer forces the excess mercury to return to the bulb and resets the instrument for the next reading. A minimum thermometer has a double-headed pin in the tube which is pulled down by the surface tension of the fluid, alcohol. Alcohol is used because it has a lower freezing point than mercury (Figure 4-18B). When the alcohol is heated, it expands above the pin without moving it. The reading for the lowest temperature since the last observation is made on the right-hand head of the pin. The instrument is set by tipping, and the pin slides down the tube to the end of the column of alcohol. After the instruments are set, both the maximum and minimum thermometers are left at rest horizontally until the next observation.

Official Weather Bureau stations have automatic devices for recording rainfall, temperature, and pressure. That for temperature is called a *thermograph* and that for pressure is called a *barograph*. Wind velocity is measured by an *anemometer*.

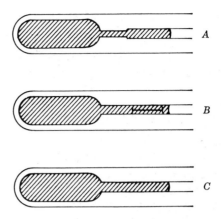

Figure 4-18   *Construction of thermometers.*

A. Lower part of maximum thermometer. (Note the constriction that holds the mercury at the maximum temperature registered until the instrument is reset by the observer.)

B. Minimum thermometer. (Note the small float that indicates the lowest temperature and remains there until the observer resets the instrument.)

C. Ordinary mercurial, or liquid, thermometer.

SUMMARY

Because of differences in insolation related to time of year and latitude there are variations in heating of the air which result in changes in atmospheric pressure. The resulting pressure gradients then cause air movements of all types, both horizontal (winds) and vertical (currents). Since warmth is unequally distributed through the atmosphere, some parts of the earth are surrounded by air that is relatively warm and light in weight; here air tends to drift upward or be forced to rise. Where air is relatively cooler and heavier, the drift tends to be downward. An example of these convection currents is the local land-and-sea breeze. Air movements of wide extent produce a pattern of air circulation—the wind zones—on the rotating globe.

The theoretical pattern of wind circulation poleward from the equator shows doldrums, trades, horse latitudes, prevailing westerlies, subpolar lows, and polar highs or easterlies. Above the surface winds may occur jet streams—winds of high velocity. Distribution of continents and oceans interferes with normal succession of wind belts, especially where monsoon winds blow toward Southeast Asia in summer and out of Asia in winter. Each wind belt forms a climatic zone, with distinctive rainfall and temperature range. The zone may be further subdivided from the effects of location with respect to mountains, oceans, and continental interiors as related to wind directions.

Cyclonic storms with centers of low pressure and spiraling wind systems are characteristic of the prevailing westerlies. They develop at contacts between cold and warm air masses. Hurricanes form above tropical oceans near the outer edge of the trade winds. Tornadoes usually develop in sultry weather on broad lowlands in the zone of prevailing westerlies. Thunderstorms are a locally important source of rainfall and are most common in humid tropics and interiors of most continents in the westerlies.

The U.S. Weather Bureau issues weather forecasts of great value to the public. These forecasts are based on movements of cyclones and cold and warm winds associated with appropriate air masses.

Weather in North America is affected chiefly by the dry and cold air mass typical of northern Canada, humid and cool air masses over the North Pacific and Atlantic Oceans, and the humid warm air mass over the Gulf of Mexico.

Outline
  Winds
    Local: land and sea, mountain and valley, chinook
    World circulation, affected by
      Pressure differences from temperature changes
      Earth's rotation
  Wind zones
    Doldrums, intertropical front
    Trades
    Horse latitudes
    Prevailing westerlies
    Subpolar lows
    Polar high
  Special winds
    Monsoons
    Jet streams
  Air masses and source regions
    Polar: continental or marine
    Tropical: continental or marine
    Stable or unstable
  Storms
    Cyclones of middle and high latitudes
    Tropical cyclones (hurricanes)
    Thunderstorms
    Tornadoes
  Weather forecasts
    Relationship to "fronts" and cyclones
    Usefulness

QUESTIONS

1. What should be included in an adequate description of the weather in your home locality?

2. Why is the weather a frequent topic of conversation?

3. Under what conditions does smoke settle in industrial areas?

4. In a cyclone
  What is the pressure condition?
  Which way is the pressure slope directed?
  Which way will the wind probably blow?
  What weather may be expected near the center?
  Will the wind direction be clockwise?

5. Which side of a mountain in the northeast trade wind zone will be the windward side? The leeward side?

6. What wind and calm zones would be encountered if one were to move from the equator in the direction of the North Pole?

7. The island of Cuba is located just south of the Tropic of Cancer.
  Which side of the island faces prevailing winds?
  Which side will probably receive heaviest rainfall?
  Which side would be most dangerous for navigation?

8. If a mass of $mTwu$ air moves into cooler latitudes and comes in contact with air of $cPks$ characteristics, what weather may be expected near the zone of contact?

9. What are the prospects for precipitation
  On a low island in the southeast trades?
  In the vicinity of nimbostratus clouds?
  Over central Greenland?
  During a pronounced temperature inversion?
  In the horse latitudes?

10. Reproduce from memory the approximate pattern of the wind and calm zones on the face of the earth.

11. What are some ways in which forecasts made by the U.S. Weather Bureau are useful in your locality?

12. Describe the changes of weather to be expected as a cyclone approaches, passes over, and recedes from a locality.

13. Name three devices intended to make living conditions more comfortable in spite of unpleasant weather.

14. Compare the usual winter storm with that of summer in the interior of the United States.

15. What conditions favor the formation of "smog"?

16. What preparations usually are made in and

around your home at about the time for the change of season from fall to winter, and from spring to summer?

17. What changes if any in the weather have af-fected your activities within the last few days?

18. Give examples of the effect of weather changes on transport by airplane, highway, and railway.

SELECTED REFERENCES

Blair, T. A.: *Weather Elements* (revised by Robert C. Fite), Prentice-Hall, Inc., Englewood Cliffs, N.J., 1957.

Finch, V. C., G. T. Trewartha, A. H. Robinson, and E. H. Hammond: *Elements of Geography,* 4th ed., McGraw-Hill Book Company, Inc., New York, 1957, chap. 5, pp. 88–122.

Humphreys, W. J.: *Physics of the Air,* 3d ed., McGraw-Hill Book Company, Inc., New York, 1940.

Petterssen, Sverre: *Weather Analysis and Forecasting,* vol. I, *Motion and Motion Systems,* 2d ed., McGraw-Hill Book Company, Inc., New York, 1956.

———: *Weather Analysis and Forecasting,* vol. II, *Weather and Weather Systems,* 2d ed., McGraw-Hill Book Company, Inc., New York, 1956.

Tannehill, I. R.: *Hurricanes, Their Nature and History,* Princeton University Press, Princeton, 1939.

Taylor, George F.: *Elementary Meteorology,* Prentice-Hall, Inc., Englewood Cliffs, N.J., 1957.

Trewartha, G. T.: *An Introduction to Weather and Climate,* McGraw-Hill Book Company, Inc., New York, 1954.

U.S. Weather Bureau: *Weather Forecasting* (revision of the publication formerly issued as Bulletin 42), Washington, 1952.

5. Climatic and

Biologic Regions

CLIMATE affects men in a multitude of ways and is probably the most important of all geographic elements. It is an important control over the distribution of plant and animal life, hence, climate exerts a large influence upon foods produced in any given area and materials available for shelter and clothing. Climate may act as a barrier to the migration of human, animal, and plant life; it markedly affects man's health and energy as well as his activities and industries.

Temperatures, rainfall, winds, and weather of the world as described in the preceding chapter, when observed over long periods of time, produce a weather complex that may conveniently be summarized in map form. The isothermal map of the world (Figure 3-6) represents the observations and means (averages) of the world's temperatures.

The Mean Annual Isothermal Map of the World. In general the isotherms as they appear on the world map of surface temperature regions tend to follow the parallels; that is, they trend east and west on the earth's surface. This is to be expected, since the earth's position in its orbit is essentially stable and its axis is constantly tilted in one position, directed toward the North Star at an angle approximately 23½ degrees away from its vertical position. This stability of the position of the axis exposes parts of the globe to the sun's rays with great regularity and (because the earth's surface is curved) controls the angle at which the sun's rays are received at any one point on the earth.

Uniformly high temperatures of the earth's surface, year in and year out, are found in regions of low latitude and low altitude near the equator. It is in this part of the world, between the Tropics of Cancer and Capricorn, that the earth receives two maxima of solar energy when the sun appears in the zenith twice each year. Furthermore, the sun's rays penetrate the atmosphere of these low latitudes directly, thereby providing greater amounts of solar energy than in higher latitudes where rays are oblique. In tropical regions, days and nights are of nearly equal length all year long, thus providing a regularity in the earth's heating which is impossible where seasonal changes of temperature are great.

Similarly, as shown on the isothermal map, those parts of the world which are near the polar regions receive smaller amounts of solar energy. There the sun is never in the zenith. Only a single period of high insolation occurs when the sun is near the Tropics of Cancer or Capricorn. Furthermore the sun's rays that reach high latitudes must penetrate a great thickness of atmosphere at low angles; consequently much of the radiation is scattered. These are among the factors which explain the reduced amount of insolation and heat that is common to polar regions compared with that of tropical regions.

The world isothermal map shows a pattern of temperature distribution in relation to winds, particularly between 40 and 60 degrees in middle latitudes of both hemispheres. Here, where winds from the west blow steadily over the oceans, they tend to moderate the temperatures of the west (windward) coasts of continents. This is noticeable in the Pacific Northwest, the British Isles, France, and the Low Countries, southern Chile, and New Zealand. In contrast, the eastern (leeward) coasts of midlatitudes usually experience higher average summer temperatures and colder winters than the west coasts. This is observable in New England, Korea and northern Japan, and Patagonia.

Slight differences in temperatures of ocean currents affect the courses of isotherms in coastal regions and over the seas. The map (Figure 15-2) indicates that the cold Peru (Humboldt) Current flows northward along the western coast of South America; this brings subnormal temperatures to the coasts of Peru and northern Chile. Similarly, the cool Benguela Current chills the southwest coast of Africa. The eastward extensions of the Japan Current and the Gulf Stream bring to southern Alaska and coastal Norway temperatures above normal for their latitudes.

The effects of altitude on temperature do not appear on the world isothermal map, because in drawing maps of this type the *observed* mountain temperatures are changed to read as though they were at sea level. This practice of "reduction to sea level" makes temperature figures comparable and eliminates the effect of altitude on temperature readings.

The Mean Annual Isohyetal Map.   The distribution of precipitation over the world throughout the year is usually shown on a map by lines that connect places having the same average annual precipitation. These lines are known as *isohyets*. A study of the precipitation distribution of the world (Figure 5-1) leads to the following conclusions:

1. Some effects of ocean currents are apparent on the precipitation map, since air above warm masses of water can contain relatively large amounts of water vapor. If this air is cooled sufficiently when it reaches comparatively cold western coasts, it provides heavy rain or snow for the land surface. This accounts for the large amounts of rain on northwestern coasts in northern latitudes— for example, on Vancouver Island and in southern Alaska, and in Eire, Scotland, and Norway. On the other hand, cold currents provide small amounts of moist air for onshore locations, as in southwestern Africa.

2. World precipitation maps show plainly the effect of mountains, for moist air of marine origin forced to rise over mountain ranges provides heavy rain and snow in western New Zealand, southern Chile, and the highlands of the Scandinavian peninsula.

3. It is apparent that the heavy rainfall in

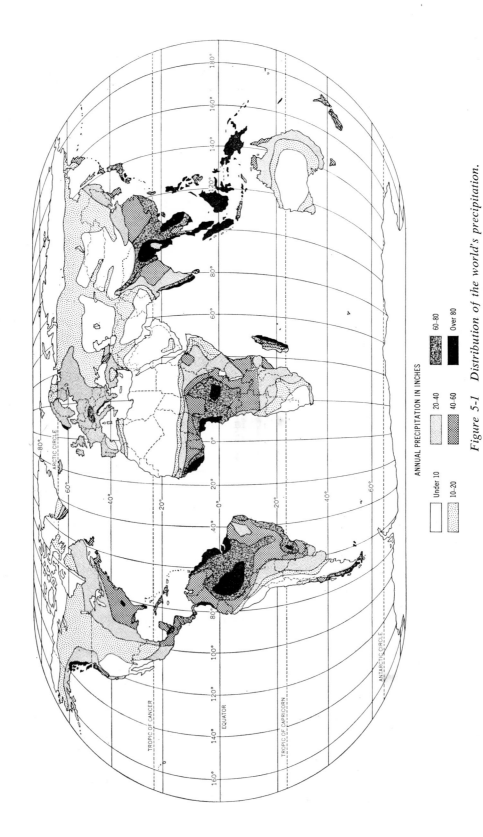

ANNUAL PRECIPITATION IN INCHES

Under 10

10-20

20-40

40-60

60-80

Over 80

Figure 5-1 Distribution of the world's precipitation.

tropical lowlands shown on the isohyetal map is related to the high annual temperatures of these regions as indicated on the isothermal map (Figure 3-6). The explanation lies in the fact that warm and moist air of the tropics expands and rises as a result of convection, or from a difference in density of two air masses in contact. It then cools adiabatically and cannot contain as much moisture at high altitudes as it can hold near sea level. This excess moisture then becomes condensed and falls as heavy rains throughout most low-latitude regions.

4. Seasonal changes of wind direction, combined with mountains and rain resulting from convection, mainly account for the pattern of rainfall in low-latitude monsoon regions. This provides sharp contrasts in windward and leeward coasts of Madagascar, New Guinea, and other islands, as well as the Malabar and Coromandel Coasts of India, and the southern and northern slopes of the Himalayas.

5. In general, those parts of the earth which lie distant from the seas—that is, interiors of continental masses outside the equatorial regions—have little access to moisture, and their annual supplies of rain and snow tend to be small. Hence, the great continents tend to become arid and semiarid in their central parts. This is particularly true of the largest land mass, Asia. Generally the interiors of continents receive maximum rainfall in summer when continental temperatures are highest and pressures lowest, a combination that causes some inflow of moist air from the oceans.

6. High latitudes usually suffer from deficiencies of rain and snow, for air of low temperature normally cannot contain large absolute amounts of moisture and hence cannot provide any large precipitation for the land.

Temperature and Rainfall; Vegetation and Climate. Plant life throughout the world is dependent upon supplies of heat and moisture. Isothermal and isohyetal maps are, therefore, especially significant in understanding the distribution of vegetation, in both type and quantity, throughout the world. Rainfall and temperature maps together provide a reasonably satisfactory basis for the correct interpretation of the vegetation map (Figure 5-2).

From consideration of these and other maps, a number of different types of climate, varying in usefulness to man, have been recognized. Even the ancient Greeks, though their travels were limited, were familiar with some of the climatic zones, and indeed our word *climate* comes indirectly from the Greek.

Human Relationship to Climate. Types of food eaten in different climates by primitive men are mostly those which can be easily grown or otherwise secured by hunting, fishing, and gathering. In any case the available food is largely determined by climatic factors. Modern transportation allows civilized man to bring food long distances from the climatic regions where it is produced. To maintain good health, man should select different foods under different climatic conditions. His food in the various climatic regions should be of a type and quantity to supply needed energy without the excess that leads to slothfulness. An Eskimo, who needs foods which furnish much heat and energy, thrives on a diet of blubber and raw meat, if he can obtain enough of these, but such a diet is wholly unsuited to a resident of the tropics, who does not need food so high in calories.

Deserts serve as an obvious climatic barrier to human activity. Absence of water, lack of food for man and beast, shifting sand dunes, stifling wind-blown dust, and hot desiccating air are trying features of deserts (Figure 5-3). In frigid regions, the eternal snow and ice, difficulties of travel, and paucity of local food and fuel may necessitate transporting most of the required foodstuffs and the means of cooking them. Severe cold taxes the resistance of the body. Man finds these conditions a great handicap to his activities on cold ice-covered land and water. Difficul-

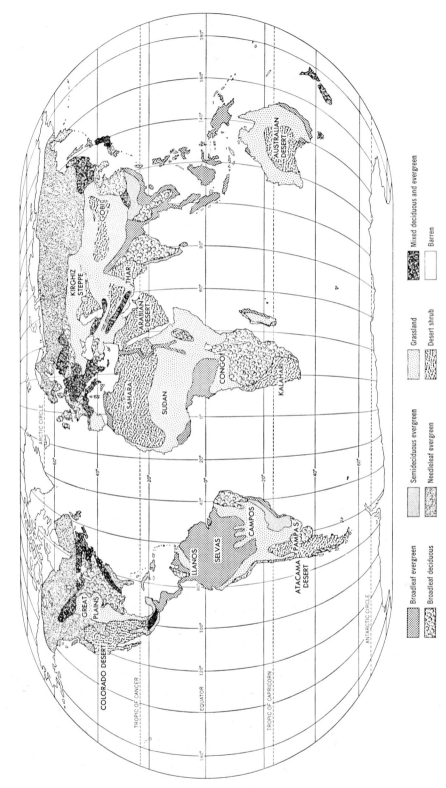

Figure 5-2 Principal natural vegetation types of the world.

Broadleaf evergreen

Broadleaf deciduous

Semideciduous evergreen

Needleleaf evergreen

Grassland

Desert shrub

Mixed deciduous and evergreen

Barren

GREAT PLAINS

COLORADO DESERT

LLANOS

SELVAS

CAMPOS

PAMPAS

ATACAMA DESERT

KIRGHIZ STEPPE

GOBI

THAR

ARABIAN DESERT

SAHARA

SUDAN

CONGO

KALAHARI

AUSTRALIAN DESERT

ARCTIC CIRCLE

TROPIC OF CANCER

EQUATOR

TROPIC OF CAPRICORN

ANTARCTIC CIRCLE

ties in crossing high mountains are to be attributed as much to cold, ice and snow, high winds, and frequent severe storms as to steep slopes and rarefied air. Dense forests, which deter travel in the Congo and Amazon Basins, are produced by the hot humid tropical climate of the equatorial zone. Damp heat is most enervating to man; diseases are prevalent, and local supplies of food are not always readily obtained.

Climate and energy. Scientific research upholds common observation in noting that weather and climate influence man's health and energy. Everyone has noticed how much better he feels on some days than on others and how much more physical or mental effort he puts forth when weather conditions are favorable. On hot muggy days human energy is low, and extreme weariness or even exhaustion may result from undue exertion. Dwellers in the humid tropics must work at slow tempo if they would retain their health, laboring in the relative coolness of early morning or late afternoon with a complete rest, or siesta, during the heat of midday. Workers in midlatitudes should follow the example of their tropical cousins when unusual heat waves sweep over the country in summer. In contrast, some natives of northern Siberia have made little advance beyond a

bare subsistence level, possibly because their energy is used to maintain body warmth and to obtain the bare essentials of existence in a cold barren environment. A very cold climate that limits the resources available for human use may handicap man just as much as a very hot and humid climate.

Small, frequent changes in weather conditions seem enlivening, whereas uniformity of weather, even if not unfavorable, may be depressing because of its monotony. Among climatically favored parts of the world are the United Kingdom, the western mainland of Europe, and much of the United States and southern Canada. These parts of the world are in the region of cyclonic storms and as a result have the variations in weather that stimulate man to reach his highest mental and physical powers (Figure 5-4).

Climatic Changes.   Weather factors, especially rainfall, vary in cycles that extend over a term of years. Where rainfall is barely sufficient for crops or grazing, a decrease in precipitation becomes serious. Crops may fail and livestock die of starvation and thirst. Then farms, ranches, and trading settlements may be abandoned and the inhabitants compelled to migrate in search of new homes.

On the Great Plains of the United States

Figure 5-3 Desert type of vegetation of the Mojave Desert, California. This represents an environment unfavorable for the support of large numbers of people. (Photograph, courtesy of Robert Pease.)

Figure 5-4 A typical small farm in the hills of the Allegheny Plateau in southeastern Ohio. Fields are planted to corn, other grains, and hay, and the farmer maintains a small dairy herd. This environment is much more favorable for human existence than the landscape appearing in Figure 5-3.

since their settlement about 1870, cycles of wet and dry years have alternated (Figure 5-5). During years of increasing rainfall, settlers pushed farther into the semiarid lands. Some established cattle ranches; others plowed up grass and planted wheat, corn, flax, and forage crops. During the dry years that followed, many grain farmers were unable to make a living and abandoned their lands. Ranchers who kept livestock had losses from drought but generally succeeded better than the farmers. Then several rainy years renewed agricultural settlement. An influx of settlers during rainy cycles and departure during dry years has occurred three or four times in parts of the Great Plains since their first settlement by white men.

In Norway, Iceland, or Eire, where the climate is quite wet and stormy, some observers state that farmers are more prosperous during dry cycles when potatoes and other root crops are less troubled with disease, grain matures better, and hay is easier to cure than in the cold wet years. Huntington believed that the Mediterranean region of Europe and parts

of Central America were once stormier; since man had been stimulated by the variable weather, civilizations then flourished in these subtropical places. Other authorities, however, disagree with Huntington's conclusions and think the climate has changed little or not at all. They would explain the rise and fall of civilization in the subtropics by other factors: soil erosion, disease, destruction by war, and poor government.

Huntington also presented evidence in the form of abandoned cities and other works of man, dried-up lakes, dry river channels, and dead forests, for cycles of rainy centuries alternating with dry centuries in central Asia. This, he believed, would account for the forced migration from such areas, bringing raids and wars for conquest into better-favored lands surrounding the critical area. Again, however, others contend that the rainfall always was deficient and that towns were abandoned because rivers changed their courses, as the Tarim did some years ago. Towns also are deserted and trees die as soil becomes impregnated by salt. Glaciers that

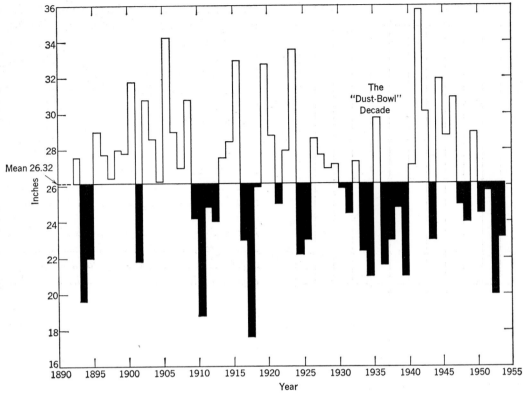

Figure 5-5 Departures from normal rainfall over a 63-year period in 12 drought-belt Great Plains states. Note the succession of years with rainfall deficiency beginning in 1929. (After Clements.)

once helped keep lakes and rivers full may have melted, forcing an exodus of the people who depended on the vanished water supply.

Rings of trees in the midlatitudes vary in thickness as conditions are favorable or unfavorable for tree growth. In the southwestern United States rainfall appears to be the chief factor affecting the annual increment of tree growth. Tree rings of the great sequoias, or "big trees," of California furnish a record of 3,000 years of climate; the yellow pines of the Colorado plateau date back several centuries. Tree-ring records from the Southwest, collected by A. E. Douglass and his coworkers, certainly show the existence of a short cycle of wet and dry years and probably a long cycle of several centuries. Douglass and his assistants have been able to date the building of certain Indian pueblos in the Southwest by cleverly correlating tree rings of

living trees with those in the timber used in some Indian dwellings.

Classification of Climate. Various schemes have been used to classify climatic types. Based on rainfall, climates may be rainy (humid), dry (arid), subhumid, and semiarid. They may have uniform rainfall, or well-defined wet and dry seasons. Near the poles the most obvious change throughout the year is that of the long day and long night; climate in those latitudes might be based on light and darkness. A better scheme uses actual temperatures or vegetation types. Sometimes temperatures and resulting plant life are combined in classifying climates. An old and very general system of classification is based on temperatures in different latitudes: tropics, subtropics, temperate, subpolar, and polar zones. According to this scheme, the tropics

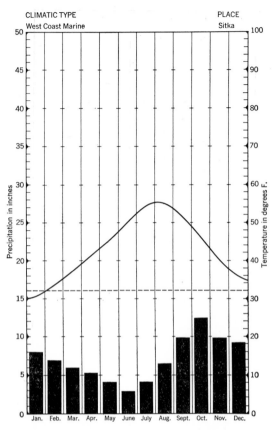

Figure 5-6   Climatic graph, Sitka, Alaska.

for this text depends primarily upon latitude, general circulation of winds, natural vegetation, and the relationship between land and sea. In general, temperatures on the earth follow parallels of latitude; yet the oceans have smaller ranges of temperature than continents, since bodies of water both heat and cool more slowly than land. Winds flowing inland from the sea, especially where a warm current may adjoin the shore, cause modifications in the type of climate on windward coasts. Thus Sitka, Alaska, has about the same mean annual temperature as Washington,

Figure 5-7   Climatic graph, Washington, D.C. Washington, 38°55′ north latitude and Sitka, 57°3′ north latitude, are separated by nearly 20 degrees of latitude, but the graphs indicate that their winter temperatures are nearly the same. Even their rainfall is similar in amount, but Washington's lower latitude shows plainly in its higher summer temperatures.

are continuously hot. The subtropics have long summers and short mild winters. The temperate zones have four seasons: hot summers, cold winters, and spring and autumn of intermediate temperature. The polar zones are nearly always cold with a very short warm season which in the coastal and higher sections is practically absent.

Interior regions in high latitudes enjoy summers long enough for growth of hardy trees like birch and conifers; these regions are called the *taiga,* and their climate may be called subpolar. Each of the four generalized climatic zones may be subdivided depending on differences in rainfall, temperature, winds, location with respect to oceans, humidity, and natural vegetation. Sometimes the subdivisions result from the location of high mountains and plateaus.

The classification of world climate adopted

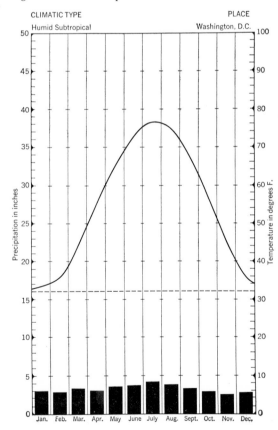

D.C. (Figures 5-6 and 5-7). Northwestern Europe has mild winters because of the Gulf Stream and winds flowing inland from the Atlantic Ocean. On the other hand, the interiors of large continents like Asia have extreme ranges of temperature. The coldest absolute temperatures recorded on the earth's surface have been observed at Verkhoyansk in northern Siberia, where the January temperature averages nearly −60°F, with the absolute minimum falling to at least −90°F (Figure 5-8).

Figure 5-8   Climatic graph. Verkhoyansk, Siberia.

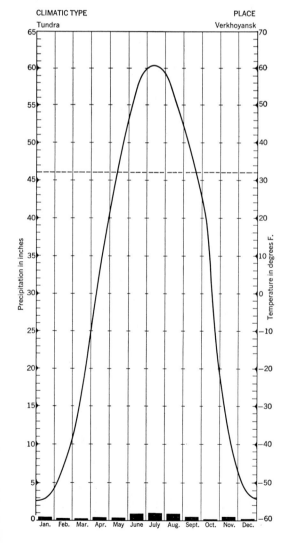

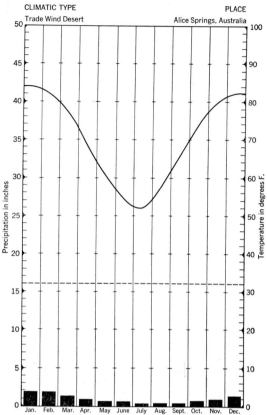

Figure 5-9   Climatic graph of trade-wind climate.

Relation between Climate and Winds. Certain types of weather are expected in each different wind zone, although local conditions may cause much variation from the usual climate. Near the equator, when an excess of sun radiation occurs, heat radiation from the earth in turn causes air to rise. On rising, the air cools by expansion and the abundant vapor contained is condensed, producing clouds and copious and frequent rains. On the other hand, the trade winds, when they blow across plains or plateaus, are drying winds (Figure 5-9). They blow toward the equator, a warmer region than their source, become heated, and absorb moisture through evaporation, thus helping to cause tropical deserts like the Sahara.

When trade winds blow across oceans and then are forced to rise over mountainous coasts, as in Madagascar, the West Indies,

Figure 5-10   Groves of coast redwoods (Sequoia sempervirens) *line the Redwood Highway in the Coast Ranges south of Humboldt Bay, California.*

and the Hawaiian Islands, they produce very heavy rainfall, since rising air expands and cools adiabatically, causing condensation of abundant moisture secured by evaporation from the sea. In the horse latitudes the air is in general descending and being warmed by the resulting compression. More water vapor can be contained without condensation, and as a result the horse latitudes have little rain.

In the prevailing westerlies, west coasts of continents have abundant rain and low range in temperature (Figure 5-10), whereas the interiors of continents have little rain and extreme ranges of temperature. This is especially marked when a mountain range on the west shuts off oceanic influences, as in the case of the Cascade Range. On east coasts the climate is usually rainy, with a considerable range of temperature though not as great as in the interior. Vegetation changes across a continent in the westerlies offer evidence of the climatic changes. Forests on the rainy west coast are replaced by grasslands (steppes) and desert plants in the interior, and these give way to hardwood and mixed forests in the eastern part.

Shifting of the wind belts causes border or transition types of climate. Thus about 8 to 15 degrees on either side of the equator are the savannas. To these grasslands mixed with open woods summer rains come with the poleward shift of equatorial calms in summer. Then drought occurs in winter when the trade winds shift toward the equator with movement of the doldrums to the other side of the "line."

The Mediterranean climate with dry summers and rainy winters occurs on west coasts about 25 to 35 degrees from the equator. Horse latitudes dominate the region in summer and with the trade winds blowing from the coast produce drought. In winter the prevailing westerlies and their associated cyclonic storms shift toward the equator and bring rain. Coastal southern California has this type of climate (Figure 5-11).

Dry conditions prevail in the center of the continents of midlatitudes. Here steppes occupy semiarid sections; continental deserts spread over the drier parts. In some places the range of temperature is extreme between winter and summer, and both rain and snowfall are light and uncertain in quantity.

On eastern sides of continents, humid conditions are found. In the same latitudes where Mediterranean climates prevail on west coasts, the humid subtropical realm is found on east coasts. Here rainfall attains a maximum in summer and is frequently associated with monsoon conditions. Range of temperature is moderate, with hot summers and mild winters. Poleward lies the humid continental realm with extreme range of temperature during the cold winters and warm summers. Rainfall and snow decrease inland, changing conditions from humid in the eastern sections to subhumid and finally to semiarid on the steppes.

Poleward from the prevailing westerlies, summers are shorter and winters lengthen. Here a coniferous forest (taiga) extends in a zone around the world in the Northern Hemisphere. Beyond the limit of tree growth lies the tundra, represented by the "barren grounds" of northern Canada, where the ground below the surface is frozen permanently and only moss and other scanty herbage grow. Higher lands in the polar zone are occupied by permanent icecaps.

In general, the position of actual climatic regions depends much on whether winds flow from the sea to the land or vice versa. In the trades the rainy regions extend farther from the equator on the windward (east) coasts than on the leeward (west) coasts. In the westerlies the west, or windward, coasts have a much broader extent of moderate climate than on the east coasts. Hence the boundary between the so-called "temperate" and subpolar zones traverses North America from the northwest in Alaska rather south of east toward the Atlantic. Locally, high altitudes may cause colder climates than their latitude warrants.

In this text, climates are classified as follows:

Low-latitude climatic realms
  1. Wet equatorial
  2. Wet-and-dry tropical
      a. Savanna type
      b. Monsoon type
  3. Dry tropical
      a. Semiarid (steppe)
      b. Desert
Mid-latitude climatic realms
  4. Mediterranean
  5. Humid subtropical
  6. West-coast marine
  7. Dry continental
      a. Semiarid grasslands (steppes)
      b. Desert
  8. Humid continental
      a. Long-summer type
      b. Short-summer type
High-latitude climatic realms (boreal)
  9. Subpolar continental (taiga)
 10. Tundra
 11. Icecaps
High elevations

Figure 5-11 View of the desert and mountains in the southeastern part of California. Different types of cacti appear in the foreground, of which the largest is the barrel cactus. (Photograph by Frashers Photos, Pomona, California.)

Geographers and climatologists have not agreed upon any single system of climatic classification, principally because of confusion concerning the locations of the boundaries of the different climates. In the main, however, they are in agreement on the locations of the great areas of tundra and desert regions. Consequently the student should consider most climatic boundaries as zones of change or transition between climates rather than as the sharp lines shown on most maps. Few climatic boundaries are sharply defined except when they coincide with the crests of high mountain ranges.

Distribution of the principal climate zones is shown on the map in the Appendix of this

Figure 5-12 The cork oak tree of Spain is typically Mediterranean. The heavy outer layers of bark are removed and sold every eight or nine years. (Photograph from Ewing Galloway, New York.)

volume. At first glance the map seems to have no discernible pattern, but as the student becomes more familiar with the climatic distinctions of the different parts of the world, he will find the principal areas fitting into their proper places in the light of the discussion in the chapters which follow.*

VEGETATION REGIONS IN RELATION TO CLIMATE

Plants closely reflect climatic environments. A good classification of climatic regions has been based on the plants that naturally grow in the different climates. Temperature and water supply are the most important climatic factors affecting plants. The banana and mahogany flourish in the rainy tropics. The drought-resistant olive is adapted to the hot dry summers and somewhat humid winters of the Mediterranean climate (Figure 5-12). The cactus is adapted to withstand desert conditions, as lichens and sphagnum moss are to those of the tundra. Thus each climatic realm has its appropriate type of vegetation.

Although the species may differ, plants that grow under similar climatic conditions, even in widely separated parts of the earth, tend to develop a similarity in appearance. For example, various species of mangrove which stand on ramifying stiltlike roots and grow only on salt tideflats in the tropics, superficially all look alike. Grass and scattered trees of the savannas in Africa, South America, and Australia resemble each other. Rain forests of the Congo and Amazon Basins look the same in photographs, even to the creeping and climbing vines. Only by the caption can the viewer tell whether the picture of the taiga he sees was taken in interior Alaska, Canada, or Siberia.

A common classification of natural vegetation regions separates them into forest trees, grasslands, and desert shrubs. Trees grow best in regions of heavy rainfall and moderate to high temperature (Figure 5-13). Trees have long roots, however, and can secure water during dry seasons from quite deep sources and some are able to store water; hence fairly good forests are found in regions of wet-and-dry climates if the period of drought only lasts a few months. Examples include the teak forests of India and live oak woodlands in California. The distribution of forests nearly coincides with the humid climatic regions of the earth. In the taiga, although total rainfall is small, the rate of evaporation is so low that available water is adequate for trees.

Grasses and associated herbage are the plants most commonly found in subhumid and semiarid climates. Grass can endure long droughts which kill most trees; so grasslands dominate in regions that experience seasonal dryness. Grass lies dormant in the dry season and springs to life with the coming of rain, especially when precipitation coincides with the warmth favorable for plant growth as in savanna and monsoon climates. The usual type of plants found in deserts consists of shrubs and bushes which are widely spaced and equipped by nature to withstand shortage of water. Extremely dry deserts are almost bare of vegetation as are also exposures of solid rock in more humid climes.

The geographic aspects of plant life will be elaborated further in following chapters. Here the purpose is to correlate climatic regions with the general types of vegetation found in each, to serve as an introduction to the chapters describing climatic realms and the biologic and human relationships therein.

SOME GEOGRAPHIC ASPECTS OF ANIMAL LIFE

Distribution of large animals as well as of small creatures like insects is a factor in the human geographic environment. Grassy plains, covered with vast herds of grazing animals, encouraged man first to hunt the beasts and then to tame and domesticate some ani-

* For comparison, some climatic classifications used by other geographers are cited in the Appendix.

mals. Asia seems to have been the original home of domestic animals such as cattle, sheep, horses, goats, camels, and pigs. In the New World only the llama in the high plateaus and the Andes Mountains of South America was tamed and taught to carry burdens, although the alpaca, a close relative, was kept in herds as a producer of wool. The dog, found nearly everywhere among the American Indians, probably accompanied the ancestors of these people in their migrations but in part may have been derived from the taming of wolves or coyotes. Several varieties of fowl have been domesticated. Although most animal life is useful to man, some forms, especially among the insects, are harmful. Even predatory mammals (coyote, fox, and mountain lion) and birds (hawks and owls) may benefit man by killing the rodents that eat his crops. Songbirds and quail consume both weed seeds and insects and therefore deserve protection.

Various types of plant life usually are associated with particular grazing or browsing animals, birds, and insects. Fauna of forests is characteristically different from that of open grasslands. During the course of their evolution, animals tend to become adapted to certain conditions; if the environment is changed, as happens when forests are cut or grasslands plowed, native animals suffer for lack of accustomed food supply.

Animals that can swim and fly possess mobility, which strictly land dwellers lack. Fish show a sort of zonation based on latitude, or perhaps better, on food supply and water temperatures. Salmon, halibut, mackerel, and herring are found mostly in cool waters of the

Figure 5-13   Live oak and cypress swamp of the humid subtropical region of the southern United States. Little Gum Swamp, Osceola National Forest, Florida. Note the dense growth of vegetation, the Spanish moss, and the hydrophytic vegetation of the swamp. (Photograph by B. W. Muir, courtesy of U.S. Forest Service.)

northern midlatitudes and subpolar areas; tuna live in the southern midlatitudes. Sailfish, swordfish, flying fish, and marlin are restricted to tropical waters. Among sea mammals the whale is found from tropical to polar seas. Walrus, sea lions, and seals live in cold northern waters, but some sea elephants and sea lions are found along tropical and subtropical coasts.

Most birds fly, and some, like the ducks and geese, migrate long distances with change in seasons. Other birds are adjusted to certain climatic zones and rarely leave their environments. The ptarmigan, auk, and penguin are restricted to cool wintry areas, the ostrich and emu to the tropics and subtropics. Some birds are adjusted to the natural vegetation. Among preferred habitats are groves of hardwood trees, conifers, brushy coverts, waterways, marshland, open grassland, and deserts.

The factor of land bridges and barriers. The original distribution of large land mammals appears to have resulted from land connections between the continents over which the creatures might travel and from natural barriers to their movement. According to the geological record, the ancestral camel and horse originated in North America and spread southward across the isthmus to South America and westward across Bering Isthmus into Asia. Later the Isth-

mus of Panama became a strait for a time, and the Bering Isthmus became another strait, which has endured to the present. Both the camel and the horse completely died out in their original home; but although the horse perished in South America, the camel persisted in the present-day llama, alpaca, vicuña, and guanaco. In Asia the camel developed into the one-humped and two-humped species, and the horse developed into several forms, one species of which became the zebra in Africa.

Similarly, the bovine species, deer, bear, dog, cat, and several other families of mammals originated in Asia and spread by land connections to other lands, where some survived and some perished. The survivals nearly always became modified by their new and different environment. Among the continents, Australia has long been separated from the rest of the world; hence it has only primitive native mammals like the marsupials, of which the kangaroo is a type. These reached that island continent before it was shut off by impassable water barriers. Birds, of course, fly freely over bodies of water; their distribution is dependent upon food supply and habitats favorable for nesting.

The following summary deals with the climatic regions and their general types of natural vegetation and animal life.

REGIONAL COMPARISONS

Climatic realms	Biologic characteristics
LOW LATITUDES	
Wet equatorial	
Constantly warm to hot temperatures with small variations through the year. Abundant rainfall the year round, with slight maxima in late spring and again in the fall, near the time of the equinoxes. East coasts in the trade winds have a broader spread of wet equatorial climate than west coasts.	Dense rain forest of broadleaf evergreens with abundance of creeping and climbing vines; epiphytes (air plants like orchids) and parasites that feed on the sap of living plants are very common. Arboreal (tree-living) animals, especially reptiles and birds, are numerous, as are insects. Large ground animals are rare except for those whose habitat is water. Wet tropical monsoon regions where the dry season is short also support a heavy rain forest.
Wet-and-dry tropical	
Seasonal rains during the period of high sun in "summer" and dry conditions	Vegetation in the savanna and moderately rainy tropical monsoon regions must withstand a dry

REGIONAL COMPARISONS (Continued)

Climatic realms	Biologic characteristics

LOW LATITUDES (Continued)

during the "winter," when the high sun is in the opposite hemisphere, characterize this climatic realm. Temperatures are warm to hot, with a range above that of the wet equatorial realm. Seasons are reversed in the Northern compared with the Southern Hemisphere. The savanna phase of this climate is found in zones from 8 to 15 degrees of latitude either side of the equator. The monsoon type is chiefly limited to Southeast Asia.

season that lasts several months. Tall grass flourishes during the rains and becomes dry and dormant in the dry season. Many shrubs and broadleaf trees shed leaves during droughts to reduce transpiration of water. Typical vegetation consists of grass, with scattered trees and clumps of bushes. Toward the rain forest and along streams, plants grow close together to form jungle; toward tropical deserts, the trees disappear and grass shortens to form steppes. Large animals of the grazing type abound, along with carnivores which prey on the herds of wild game.

Dry tropical

Deserts have negligible rainfall and large seasonal and daily ranges of temperature. Tropical deserts are most common in trade-wind and horse-latitude belts on the western side of continents, and extend 5 or 10 degrees of latitude north and south from the Tropics of Cancer and Capricorn. Tropical steppes (semiarid grasslands) surround the deserts and form transition zones which grade into more humid regions.

Vegetation of the tropical steppes is of the short-grass type and becomes scantier as the grasslands grade into desert. Shrubs and bushes, many of which have more spines than leaves, together with clumps of grass replace the sod grasses in deserts. The woody desert plants have large root systems which permit them to secure water quickly after rains. Animal life is scarce, but large mammals may enter the desert to graze after showers of rain cause short-lived plant growth.

MIDLATITUDES

Mediterranean

Regions with Mediterranean climate are usually small in size and are located on west coasts of continents poleward from trade-wind belts. The type is subhumid to semiarid in amount of rainfall, which comes principally during the winter season. Frost seldom occurs. Winters are mild and summers warm to hot.

Grass, thickets of drought-resistant shrubs, and open woodlands are customary types of vegetation. Trees and shrubs usually have leaves which are narrow, waxy, or leatherlike. Native grazing and browsing animals, once common, are now rather scarce.

Humid subtropical

This climatic type occurs normally in the eastern part of continents. It enjoys abundant rain throughout the year with maximum amount in summer. Winters are mild to cool, and summers warm to hot.

Forests originally covered most of this climatic region. Broadleaf trees include both deciduous and evergreen species. They grow on the more fertile soils. Areas of poor, sandy soils usually were occupied by conifers. Wildlife was abundant and included deer and many other forest- and swamp-living creatures.

REGIONAL COMPARISONS (Continued)

Climatic realms	Biologic characteristics

MIDLATITUDES (Continued)

West-coast marine

This is a humid realm, with maximum rainfall in winter, when temperatures are mild to cool. Summers remain cool, and there are small seasonal differences in temperature.

Very favorable for conifers, which form dense forests where trees attain maximum size. Some parts of this realm have broad-leaved as well as coniferous vegetation. Wildlife includes deer and many fur bearers.

Dry continental

This climate, found in the interior of continents or to leeward of mountains, is deficient in rainfall, with cold winters and hot summers. Daily and seasonal ranges of temperature are large, and part of the winter precipitation may be snow. The steppe or grassland type is semiarid; the desert type receives too little rainfall for crops unless irrigation is practiced.

Forests are absent and trees are found only along rivers and near springs or other supplies of ground water. Steppe vegetation consists of short grass with some sagebrush or other shrubs. In the deserts shrubs, bunchgrass, and herbage are widely separated and seldom grow in dense thickets. In order to obtain a small supply of water, the roots of desert plants spread over a larger area than stems and leaves. Originally the steppes supported great numbers of grazing animals, large and small, and much other life. These thinned out when desert conditions prevailed.

Humid continental

This type is found from eastern interiors to the eastern coasts of continents, mainly in the Northern Hemisphere. Rainfall is ample and evenly distributed throughout the year. Winters are cold and snowy; summers are warm to hot with many thunderstorms. This realm is divided in two parts, based on the relative length of summers and growing season. That on the poleward side has longer, colder winters and shorter summers. The presence of the ocean causes certain changes of temperatures along the east coast, making it a little warmer in winter and a little cooler in summer.

Forests once covered most of this region although much land is now cleared for farming. A mixed deciduous forest of many species of broadleaf trees is dominant in areas with long summers and fertile soil. Prairies may occur in subhumid places. In cooler regions poleward, or in mountains and on poor, sandy soil, conifers predominate. Mixtures of coniferous and broad-leaved trees are common. Wildlife was originally abundant and included squirrel, deer, bear, and many fur bearers.

HIGH LATITUDES

Subpolar continental

The taiga climatic regions, mainly in the Northern Hemisphere, receive moderate amounts of rain and snow. Although summers are short, the period of daily sunshine is long in these high latitudes, so the summer growing season is sufficient to support forests and allow hardy crops to mature.

Hardier conifers are the dominant forest type of the taiga, but birch, aspen, and willow are also common. Trees decrease in size poleward to the limit of trees at the tundra border. Moose are the largest of the animals. Beaver and many other fur-bearing animals are abundant.

REGIONAL COMPARISONS (Continued)

Climatic realms	Biologic characteristics

HIGH LATITUDES (Continued)

Polar tundra

These high-latitude regions, mainly in the Northern Hemisphere, have summers too short, cool, and frosty for trees or crops to grow. Winters are very long and cold, with snow cover lasting nearly eight months. The ground is usually permanently frozen (permafrost) to considerable depths.

Trees are absent. Vegetation consists of dwarf bushes, herbs, grasses, mosses, and lichens. Sphagnum moss grows in treacherous swamps called *muskegs*. Caribou or reindeer, musk ox, polar bear, wolves, and arctic fox are among the wildlife. Waterfowl nest in the summer.

Icecaps

Extensive areas of permanent ice in Greenland and Antarctica have average temperatures below the freezing point of water in every month.

Because of severe and almost constant cold there is no significant plant life except on the tundra next to the ice border. Animal life is mostly marine.

High altitudes

A variety of climates occurs in mountain regions, but these areas of high-altitude climate are too small to have great significance except on a few large high plateaus like Tibet and in the tropics.

Forests, grassland or meadows, and tundra occupy zones along the contour of the mountains, depending on elevation and resulting temperature and growing season (Figure 5-14).

Figure 5-14 Timber-line trees, principally the bristlecone pine. These trees find it difficult to live in the face of heavy winter snows, high wind, and other inhibiting features of their environment. (Photographed in Colorado by Dr. E. C. McCarty and used by permission of the U.S. Forest Service.)

SUMMARY

Chief factors used to classify climatic regions of the world are latitude, winds, temperature ranges, including length of growing season and freezing temperature, location of regions in respect to oceans and continents, highlands, and natural vegetation.

Biologic regions of the world depend primarily on types of climate. Altitude causes local variations. Animal life depends on food supply and species of animals that were introduced.

Outline
Isothermal map
Isohyetal map of world

Climatic relationships
   Human
   Natural vegetation
Climatic changes
Classification of climate
   Latitude and temperature ranges
   Winds, rainfall, storms, and seasons
   Natural vegetation
   Marine and continental contrasts
Vegetation regions in relation to climate
Geographic aspects of animal life

QUESTIONS

1. What is the difference between climate and weather in a given region?

2. High mountain ranges are interposed at right angles to the prevailing wind direction in each of the following locations:

   a. In the zone of northeast trade winds. Which side of the mountains will probably receive heavy precipitation?

   b. In the prevailing westerly winds zone of the Southern Hemisphere. Which side of the mountains will be unlikely to need irrigation?

   c. In the monsoon zones of southeastern Asia. Which will be the leeward side?

3. What would be the effect on the climate of North America of (*a*) removal of Coast Ranges, the Sierra Nevada, and the Cascade Range, (*b*) location of a high mountain system north of the Gulf of Mexico?

4. Explain the distribution of rainfall on the island of Madagascar (Figure 5-1) in terms of the material presented in Chapters 1 through 4.

5. The map of the world's precipitation (Figure 5-1) indicates that the central Sahara and central Greenland both receive less than 10 inches of precipitation yearly. How do you explain the presence of a large mass of ice in the latter area?

6. Heavy rainfall in tropical lowland regions near the equator is related to the time when the sun's rays are most nearly vertical, but the vertical ray of the sun migrates from the Tropic of Cancer to the Tropic of Capricorn and back each twelve months. What then happens to the zone of heavy rainfall associated with the vertical sun?

7. The distance from Alaska to Newfoundland represents the broadest part of North America. What significant effect does this exert upon the occupation of the continent by human beings?

8. The widest part of South America occupies a low-latitude realm. How does this affect the activities of man on that continent?

9. Name the climatic factors that affect the characteristics of plants.

10. Give examples of the way in which plants are affected by weather and climate in your locality.

11. In what parts of the United States would you seek xerophytes, mesophytes, hydrophytes, halophytes?

12. What environmental factors tend to preclude the growth of extensive forests?

13. Which of the following terms describe the native vegetation of your home locality? Drought-resistant, hydrophytic, exotic, wind-shorn, woody, grassy, deciduous, mixed forest, coniferous, evergreen, needle-leaved, broad-leaved, prairie, halophytic, bog, xerophytic, mesophytic, parasitic, hardwood.

SELECTED REFERENCES

Beaufort, L.: *Zoogeography of the Land and Inland Waters,* The Macmillan Company, New York, 1951.

Blair, T. A.: *Climatology,* Prentice-Hall, Inc., Englewood Cliffs, N.J., 1942.

Brooks, C. E. P.: *Climate in Everyday Life,* Philosophical Library, Inc., New York, 1951.

Buxton, P. A.: *Animal Life in Deserts,* Edward Arnold & Co., London, 1955.

Cain, Stanley A.: *Foundations of Plant Geography,* Harper & Brothers, New York, 1944.

Dansereau, Pierre: *Biogeography: An Ecological Perspective,* The Ronald Press Company, New York, 1957.

Finch, V. C., G. T. Trewartha, A. H. Robinson, and E. H. Hammond: *Elements of Geography,* 4th ed., McGraw-Hill Book Company, Inc., New York, 1957, pp. 123–127, 409–434.

Hardy, M. E.: *An Introduction to Plant Geography,* Oxford University Press, New York, 1913.

Hesse, R., W. C. Allee, and K. Schmidt: *Ecological Animal Geography,* John Wiley & Sons, Inc., New York, 1951.

Hill, Albert F.: *Economic Botany,* McGraw-Hill Book Company, Inc., New York, 1952.

Huntington, Ellsworth, and Earl B. Shaw: *Principles of Human Geography,* 6th ed., John Wiley & Sons, New York, 1951, chap. 14, chap. 23.

Kendrew, Wilfred G.: *Climates of the Continents,* McGraw-Hill Book Company, Inc., New York, 1955.

Kimble, George H. T.: *Our American Weather,* McGraw-Hill Book Company, Inc., New York, 1955.

Köppen, W.: *Grundriss der Klimakunde,* Walter De Gruyter & Co., Berlin, 1931.

Miller, Arthur Austin: *Climatology,* 3d ed., E. P. Dutton & Co., Inc., New York, 1953.

Newbigin, Marion I.: *Plant and Animal Geography,* E. P. Dutton & Co., Inc., New York, 1950.

Shantz, H. L., and Raphael Zon: *Atlas of American Agriculture,* Section E: *Natural Vegetation,* U.S. Department of Agriculture, Washington, 1924.

Thornthwaite, C. W.: "The Climates of the Earth," *Geographical Review,* 23:433–440, 1933.

U.S. Department of Agriculture: *Atlas of American Agriculture,* Part 2, *Climate,* Washington, 1936.

U.S. Department of Agriculture: Yearbook, *Climate and Man,* Washington, 1936.

U.S. Department of Agriculture: Yearbook, *Insects,* Washington, 1952.

U.S. Department of Agriculture: Yearbook, *Plant Diseases,* Washington, 1953.

U.S. Weather Bureau: *Summary of the Climatological Data of the United States by Sections,* Bulletin W, Washington, 1933–1934.

6. Humid and Subhumid Tropics

WET EQUATORIAL CLIMATE

WITH heat and humidity like those of a hot-house, the wet equatorial climate is better suited to plants than to human beings. Hence the rainy tropics are more notable for the riotous tangle of their luxuriant vegetation than for progressive cities, cultivated farms, or well-developed plantations. Palm-thatched huts and villages of primitive natives, rather than elaborate modern houses and industrial cities, are the rule.

The rainy equatorial climate (Figure 6-1) covers that part of the earth's surface within a few degrees of the equator, save for a few exceptions to be noted later. The location of the equatorial calms determines this type of climate. In the doldrum belt, rains of the thunderstorm type are a common occurrence throughout the year. Maximum rainfall comes near

the times of the equinoxes. Minimum rainfall occurs near the solstice period, but no time of the year is distinctly dry.

In the northern summer months, the equatorial calms and their associated rains shift northward about 10 degrees, and in the southern summer (northern winter months) the belt of calms and rains shifts southward. This results in slightly less rainfall during these two times of the year near the equator. There is little variation in annual temperature, and at some stations such as Singapore, the average monthly temperature changes from only slightly below to slightly above 80°F (Figure 6-2). The differences in temperature between day and night are generally greater than those between the hottest and coldest months. Frosts are unknown in this belt except on the highest mountains.

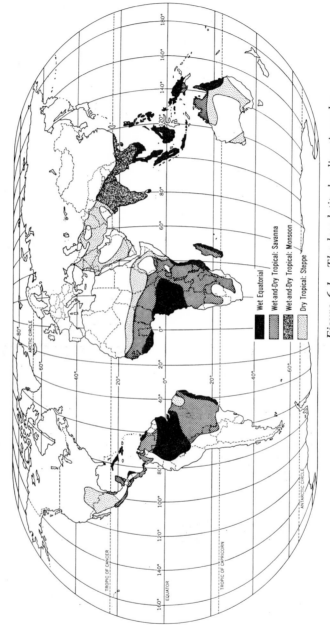

Figure 6-1 The low-latitude climatic realm.

In general, equatorial regions have high relative humidity, but extremely high temperatures are not a characteristic. The fact that the sun shines regularly about twelve hours per day at all times of the year helps prevent the excessively high temperatures that sometimes occur in higher latitudes. In addition the prevalent cloudiness and high vapor content of the air are significant factors in keeping daytime temperatures down and nighttime temperatures up. Absolute maximum temperatures are much higher in trade-wind deserts and in the so-called "temperate" latitudes in summer than during the day in rainy tropical regions. Yet when combined with the very high relative humidity of the rainy tropics, temperatures near 90°F make conditions seem as unpleasant as temperatures of 110 to 120°F with a low relative humidity. Fortunately, temperatures seldom reach 100°F, since the very high relative humidity would make conditions almost insufferable for human beings. The term *sensible temperature* is used to distinguish between the temperature recorded by the thermometer and the way people respond to the combination of heat and humidity.

General atmospheric conditions in the rainy tropics resemble those of the "muggiest" days in midlatitudes. The air seems steamy. Activity keeps the body wet with perspiration, since moisture does not readily evaporate in the damp air. High relative humidity and heat are very oppressive to the unacclimated person. Weather is cloudy much of the time, especially in the afternoon when most of the rains fall. These are of the convectional shower type, usually accompanied by torrents of rain and brilliant flashes of lightning. After the storm, which may last from a few minutes to less than an hour, the air usually clears, the temperature falls slightly, and living seems more endurable.

Modern inventions make white residents more comfortable in the rainy tropics. With transportation by air, cooling by mechanical refrigeration and other devices, these regions are habitable for larger numbers of Europeans than was the case a generation ago.

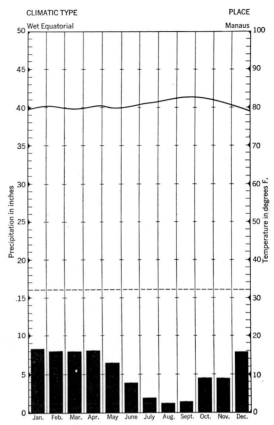

Figure 6-2   Climatic graph for Manaus, Brazil. A typical graph representing a wet equatorial climatic location. Note the following characteristics: a uniformly high mean monthly temperature, varying slightly above or below 80°F through most of the year, heavy rainfall occurring in each month of the year. Seasonal variations are noticeably lacking.

Tropical Sickness. Tropical environments may affect individuals physiologically. Exposure to the direct rays of the sun during the heat of day is generally inadvisable, especially for persons with light complexions, and may lead to heat stroke. There seems to be an actual decrease of red corpuscles in the blood of immigrants from cooler climates, and a tendency for white people, especially women, to become anemic. Frequent vacations in cooler midlatitudes or in mountain regions in the tropics help to keep light-skinned people in better health.

ESSENTIALS OF GEOGRAPHY

Much disease in the tropics results from carelessness and not from natural conditions. Surface water is commonly polluted and should not be used except when sterilized by boiling or chemicals, yet some people often dip their supply from the nearest stream and may contract dysentery or typhoid. In the course of time those die who are most susceptible to intestinal diseases from polluted water. Survivors possess a certain immunity, but these diseases remain very deadly to the newcomer. Modern insecticides, vaccines, antibiotics, and sanitation practices can work wonders in maintaining good health in the tropics.

Other diseases, especially those affecting the blood, may be carried by insects. Thus malaria and yellow fever (Figure 6-3) are transmitted by different varieties of mosquitoes. The best control for these diseases lies in vigilant supervision: isolating the victims, screening houses and cisterns, and draining swamps and stagnant water where the insects may breed. Such

practices have practically eliminated yellow fever as a deadly disease and greatly reduced mortality from malaria. Nevertheless travelers in the tropics often find it advisable to take quinine regularly to allay the severity of malaria attacks. The name itself—from *mala aria,* or "bad air"—suggests the swamp conditions in which mosquitoes breed. In the 1940s a severe epidemic of malaria killed many people in Ceylon.

Elephantiasis, a disfiguring disease caused by a worm (*Filaria*) is also transmitted by a mosquito. Other common internal parasites that affect humanity are hookworm and Bilharzia, the latter transmitted to human beings by a water snail as the intermediate host. Bilharzia is especially common in warm irrigated lands like Egypt.

In Africa the tsetse fly is a dangerous disease carrier. In man it transmits a deadly disease called *sleeping sickness* (Figure 6-3) and in livestock a different tsetse fly transmits a

Figure 6-3   Tropical disease in central Africa.

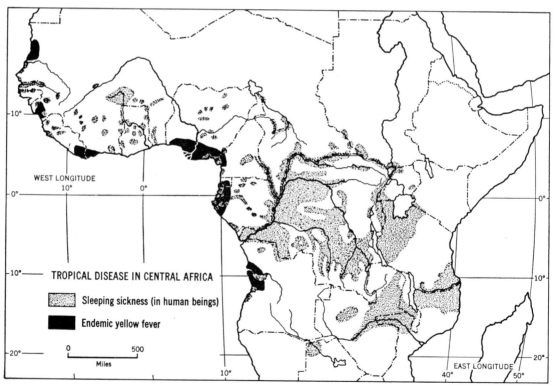

very contagious disease, nagana, of horses and cattle. The fly breeds in damp dark swamps and the borders of streams. General control measures consist of clearing lands, or in forced removal of villages to higher, drier, or windier areas not infested by the fly. For human beings a synthetic coal-tar product has been made which when injected into the blood will cure many victims of sleeping sickness. Other tropical insect pests include voracious ants, termites, and roaches. Ticks may carry diseases of both cattle and man. Parasitic worms also afflict the people of the humid tropics.

Vegetation and Animals of the Equatorial Forest.

The heat and humidity in the rainy tropics are so favorable for plants that vegetation grows remarkably and forms a dense forest (Figure 6-4). This equatorial rain forest is best developed in parts of the Congo and Amazon Basins. Brazilians call the tropical rain forest of the Amazon Valley the selva. The trees are broad-leaved evergreens and commonly form a canopy so dense that only a small amount of light filters through, making photography nearly impossible and even hindering the growth of ground plants. Many of the plants are parasites feeding upon other plants. Others are rootless epiphytes (air plants) like orchids, securing their nutriment from the air.

Along the streams a dense wall of greenery exists, but back under the shade of the leafy canopy large areas of the forest have little undergrowth. Hundreds of species of trees, vines, and smaller plants may be found in a given area, but the forests are notable for the absence of species of trees in the solid stands which characterize the coniferous forests of higher latitudes. Between the trees climbing vines, called *lianas,* form a hanging network through which an explorer must often literally hew his way. Most of the trees without branches in a straight trunk mount for 80 or 100 feet, and then their plume of foliage joins the forest canopy. Whenever a giant tree falls, dozens—even hundreds—of seeds germinate, and the plants compete for a place in the sun. The

Figure 6-4 Hauling mahogany logs to streams has always been one of the most difficult operations in this type of lumbering. For three centuries in tropical America, cattle have provided transportation over crude trails for a maximum hauling distance of about 7 miles. (Photograph used by permission of the Mahogany Association, Inc.).

weaker perish, and only a few survive to reach the leafy canopy of the forest with their trunks.

In the treetops specialized types of arboreal life exist, rarely descending to the earth. Sloths, monkeys, climbing carnivores, various rodents, lizards, snakes, and toads, great numbers of birds, and myriads of insects live in the trees. On the ground other types of life flourish. The few large animals often are of the browsing type that nibbles the brush, since grass cannot grow well in the shade.

Hunters of the Rain Forest.

Some people imagine that life in a tropical environment is simple and that food can be plucked without much difficulty from the forest. The reverse is true. Large game animals are not as common as in the open grass country. Domestic animals are seldom kept; this may be explained by the prevalence of disease, the lack of proper feed, and the customs of the inhabitants. Some primitive people, like the Pygmies in the Ituri Forest of the Congo Basin, are purely hunters and gatherers of wild fruits and other edible products. These forest hunters are few in numbers, but they require a large territory to support a small population in their roving manner of life. Their huts are temporary and little more than partial shelters against the rains.

Farmers of the Rain Forest.   Other natives practice a simple type of forest agriculture. During the least rainy season of the year, the smaller trees are slashed down and the larger trunks are girdled. Under the hot tropical sun the vegetation dries out rapidly and can be burned before the heavy rains begin. The rootstocks of bananas and certain starchy roots like cassava, yams, taro, and arrowroot, as well as seeds of corn, vegetables, or other food plants are planted in the ashes. The ground is not plowed but rather stirred with crude hoes, spades, and sharpened sticks. With the rains the gardens grow rapidly. Plants are not set out in regular rows or any definite order as in more civilized communities but are mixed together almost at random. Sometimes plantings are in "stories," with the tall banana having medium-tall and low-growing plants beneath it. Little attempt is made to cultivate the ground except to slash down the largest weeds

to give food plants an opportunity to grow.

Where gardens are located on sloping land, torrential rains erode the soil. In any case, since tropical soils are often poor because the copious rains leach soluble plant food from any well-drained ground, the life of a garden rarely exceeds three years. By that time, erosion, leaching of soil, and rapid encroachment of grass, weeds, and undergrowth cause cultivated plots to be abandoned, and new gardens to be started elsewhere (Figure 6-5). After some years all land suitable for cultivation near a village has been used. Then the village may be abandoned and moved to another spot in the virgin forest. Many trees in populated regions of the rainy tropics are second-growth as a result of this destructive type of farming operation.

Some mountain Malay tribes, like the Ifugao and Igorot of Luzon in the northern Philippines, offer interesting examples of the development of primitive agriculture in tropical highlands. Although these people hunt and gather wild products rice is the real source of their livelihood. Because very little land in the mountains is level enough to irrigate for rice, fields must be formed artificially. During the centuries that these mountain Malays have lived in their present homes, they have laboriously extended the terraces on which they grow rice by some of man's most remarkable

Figure 6-5   Shifting cultivation in a wet equatorial region.

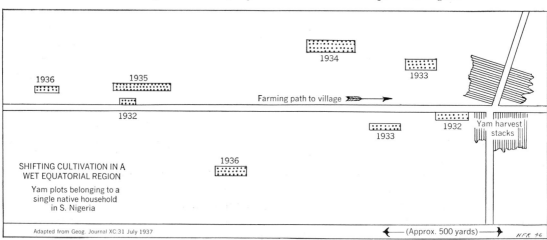

1934
1933
1936   1935
Farming path to village
1932
1933   1932   Yam harvest stacks

SHIFTING CULTIVATION IN A
WET EQUATORIAL REGION

Yam plots belonging to a
single native household
in S. Nigeria

1936

Adapted from Geog. Journal XC:31 July 1937   ←— (Approx. 500 yards) —→   *H.F.R. 46* engineering feats. Terraces a few feet wide rise one above another for between 1,000 and 3,000 feet up the sides of mountains. Streams of water conducted to upper terraces run through bamboo pipes from one terrace to the next lower level. To guard sources of water, the forests are well protected; no villager is allowed to cut timber without permission of the elders. All this engineering, including the building of stone walls set without cement often to a height of 30 feet, was done by illiterate tribesmen.

Water buffalo and oxen are kept for domestic animals and sometimes eaten. Pigs and poultry also supply food, along with some secured by hunting and fishing. These supplies supplement rice and other crops that are their chief foods. Houses are thatched, with steep roofs to shed rain. They are erected on posts above the ground to provide air circulation beneath the floor, and are well adapted to the hot and rainy climate (Figure 6-6). The tribesmen weave some cloth, make pottery and baskets, and even fabricate iron implements by working bars of iron over charcoal fires.

Rainy Coasts in the Trade Winds.   The rainy tropics extend farther from the equator on east coasts than in the interior of continents or along west coasts. The explanation is found in the fact that trade winds blow from oceans that lie east of the continents, causing increased precipitation along the windward shores. Thus East Africa from Zanzibar to Natal has rain most of the year from the trades. The east coast of the large island of Madagascar enjoys heavy rainfall from the same cause, although its west coast, which lies leeward of mountains and plateau, has a semidesert climate. Northern and eastern coasts in the West Indies, the eastern side of Middle America, part of the east coast of Australia, and other places in the world within the trade-wind zones have similar rainy coasts whose vegetation closely resembles that of equatorial rain forests. The heaviest rainfall under the United States flag, 450 inches per year, is near the summit of the mountainous island of Kauai, one of the Ha-

Figure 6-6   A dwelling among the primitive Igorot peoples of the interior of the island of Luzon in the Philippines. Houses of this type are common in tropical latitudes. The heavy thatch roof sheds rain; the supports beneath the structure keep it well above the dampness of the ground and permit circulation of air beneath the building.

waiian group that lies athwart the northeast trade winds.

Tropical Plantations.   It has been said that the Amazon Valley could raise enough food to supply the entire population of the world. This might possibly be true if the whole region were under cultivation; but only a tiny fraction is now farmed; the occasional clearings are negligible compared with the size of the area. Actually, the entire Amazon Valley is an undeveloped forest wilderness. Nearly the same situation prevails in the warmer and more humid portions of the Congo Basin. Many tropical places actually import food from midlatitudes to a greater extent than they export food products.

Production of raw materials and foodstuffs on a commercial scale has succeeded in the tropics only on plantations where natives work under supervision of managers (Figure 6-7). Capital, energy, experience, and salesmanship are provided by these outsiders. To succeed, plantations must be located along coasts or within easy reaching distance of seaports. The market for the products is in the industrial

Figure 6-7 Modern machine harvesting of sugar cane on a Hawaiian plantation. This machine takes the place of many laborers who formerly cut the cane by hand. (Photograph, courtesy of the Hawaii Visitors Bureau.)

centers of middle latitudes, and it seldom pays to transport goods from a distant interior to the coast.

The most economically successful tropical plantations produce things that cannot be grown in middle latitudes. Bananas, cacao, coconuts, and cane sugar are food products grown on rainy tropic lowlands. Palm oil, coconut oil, and copra (dried coconut meat) come from the tropics and are used both as food and raw materials for manufacture. Both coconuts and oil palms, however, grow wild and are raised only partly by plantation methods. Quinine is made from the cinchona, a native tree of the forests in eastern Peru. Today most of the world's supply comes from plantations in the island of Java, where plenty of skilled labor is available, and the product can be raised more cheaply than it can be gathered from scattered wild trees in the forest.

Many distinctive products of the rainy tropics are costly to raise on plantations and too perishable to ship easily. Only recently, therefore, have they been available to mid-latitude people, generally as luxuries. Yet, since the late nineteenth century an increasingly long list of tropical commodities—bananas, chocolate, Brazil nuts, pineapples, avocados, cashews, and mangos—has been produced commercially for mid-latitude markets. Soon, we may become equally well acquainted with papayas, cherimoyas, and babassú nuts. To a degree, success in commercial production of such commodities depends on more rapid transport and on increased use of refrigeration.

Because of accessibility to ocean transportation, tropical islands are often chosen for plantations. Trinidad, Cuba, Puerto Rico, and Jamaica in the West Indies, Mauritius and Réunion in the Indian Ocean, Java and Sumatra in the East Indies, Hawaii and Fiji in the Pacific, and São Thomé in the Gulf of Guinea are examples of tropical islands where plantation agriculture has succeeded. Coffee and tea are grown in the tropics in highland areas from one to several thousand feet above sea level. These crops thrive better in regions with a greater range of daily temperatures than the humid lowlands, which have high uniform temperatures.

Rubber. Hundreds of different trees, vines, shrubs, and herbs produce a milky latex from which rubber can be made. Several dozen plants have actually supplied rubber to the world, but only one, *Hevea brasiliensis,* a native of Brazil, has proved adaptable to plantation methods of production. Seeds secretly taken from Brazil were germinated in flower pots at the Kew Botanical Gardens near London and carried to Ceylon for planting. Today the many millions of rubber trees growing in Ceylon, Burma, the Malay Peninsula, and Indonesia have descended from these few seeds smuggled out of Brazil.

Wild rubber trees are widely scattered in the forests, and workmen must travel long distances to gather latex. Careless tapping methods were encouraged by the fact that the trees belonged to no one; as they were destroyed, rubber gatherers had to penetrate the forest more deeply along the rivers and trails to gather a supply. This of course increased the cost of gathering wild rubber. Plantation methods can produce cheaper rubber than that gathered from forests; hence, since about 1910 plantation rubber has largely replaced the wild.

WET-AND-DRY TROPICAL CLIMATE

Transition from Rainy to Dry Tropics. The climates of the tropics include the wet-and-dry tropical and the tropical desert as well as that of the rainy tropics. Tropical climates with a distinctly rainy and a dry season occur in both tropical savanna and monsoon regions. Savannas (Figure 6-1) are the result of the shift of the equatorial calms during the year. This zone begins about 5 degrees from the equator, where a well-defined rainy season occurs during the period of greatest heat, followed by a dry season during the cooler months. There is little variation in temperature throughout the year, however (Figure 6-8). Variation in seasonal rainfall is more apparent than variation in temperature; hence the terms summer and winter refer only to the time of year and not to the season in the savannas. In this belt, characterized by wet and dry seasons, the zone nearest the equator has a long rainy and short dry season. Farther away, seasons are of approximately equal length; at the edge of the trade-wind deserts there is a short rainy and a long dry season.

Savannas. Natural vegetation reflects differences in rainfall within parts of the wet-and-dry tropical climate. The forest is dense but of less height than in the equatorial rain forests. It is sometimes called a jungle rather than a forest. Where rainfall is still adequate (from 30 to 50 inches during the season) but several months of drought must nevertheless be endured, trees form an open stand with tall grass, brush, and other drought-resistant forms of vegetation. These open woods, mixed with grassland, are called *savannas* (Figure 6-9).

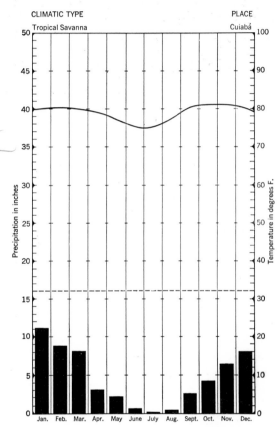

Figure 6-8 Climatic graph for Cuiabá, Brazil. A low-latitude savanna condition, differing from Figure 6-2 principally in the total annual rainfall. Note, as in Figure 6-2, that the temperature is high generally throughout the year and that the greatest amount of rainfall occurs during the months of December, January, and February. In this location, the period of lowest temperature occurs from May through September, and thus the period of heavy rainfall from October through April coincides with the period of greatest warmth.

Large parts of the Llanos of the Orinoco Valley in Colombia and Venezuela, the Campos of southern Brazil, and most of the Sudan region of Africa are examples of tropical savannas. As the length of the dry season increases, trees become stunted and widely scattered and give way to more drought-resistant forms like the acacia.

Tropical climatic belts gradually merge into each other, and natural vegetation reflects differences in amount of rainfall and relative length of wet and dry seasons. The rain forest becomes a jungle, next comes the savanna, followed by the steppes, which grade into barren desert.

Environment of the savannas is reflected in the occupance of these regions. Savannas are the habitat of many grazing animals. In Africa scores of species of antelope, elephants, zebras, giraffes, the rhinoceros, and many other grazing animals and associated carnivores that prey upon them formerly roamed in vast numbers over the country. Although the introduction of high-powered rifles has decimated the herds in some places, large numbers of big game still exist in the more remote regions. Many more big animals are found on the savannas than in the tropical rain forests of Africa (Figure 6-10).

Native Life in the Sudan.   Indigenous peoples utilize the savannas for hunting, grazing, and agriculture. In Nigeria most natives live on crops that they raise by a primitive method called *brush fallowing*. First they chop down brush and trees on 2 or 3 acres of jungle or savanna and plant crops in the crudely prepared soil. Once the crop of grain, starchy roots, and vegetables is harvested, the land is abandoned and another spot is cleared. After a piece of ground has been allowed to grow up to brush for perhaps six or eight years, it is again cleared and crops are planted. A family may control 20 acres of land and cultivate each portion only once in eight years. Vegetation that grows during the several years the land lies fallow furnishes needed humus to the soil for future cultivation.

The grasslands attract owners of domestic animals, and African tribes like the Masai of East Africa make most of their living from flocks and herds. When large tribes depend upon grazing animals, they cannot keep a sufficient number for a strictly meat diet but instead consume the milk of the animals, eating meat only on important occasions. Generally natives of Africa who are herders are bolder fighting men than the settled agriculturalists. To survive, they must be brave and capable

Figure 6-9   An African savanna landscape, showing the parklike character of the grasslands with their occasional clumps of trees. There are wide stretches of this type of landscape in parts of Africa, supporting relatively few people compared to other parts of the world. (Photograph, courtesy of the American Museum of Natural History, New York.)

of handling weapons in order to defend their herds against beasts of prey and roving robbers. These herdsmen also cooperate in handling the animals. They maintain a centralized tribal government which is more efficient than that of their agricultural neighbors. Cattle-keeping tribes usually dominate the farming people and force them to furnish tribute of grain or other supplies. If the farmers refused, their settlements would be raided by the fiercer though less numerous herdsmen.

Tropical Monsoons.   Monsoon areas, best developed in India, the Malay Peninsula, and South China, represent an extreme phase of the wet-and-dry tropical climate (Figure 6-1).

The climatic year in India is divisible into three seasons, a hot dry spring, a hot humid summer, and a moderately cool dry "winter" without frost (Figure 6-11). By the time of the spring equinox, the sun blazes down from a cloudless sky. The heat culminates in April and May, when vegetation has become dry, many plants have lost their leaves, and the land is so parched and dusty that human activities are reduced to a minimum. By June the monsoon breaks and strong winds bring in warm air masses filled with moisture from the Indian Ocean. Rains begin in the south first and may not reach northwestern India until July. The summer is hot and humid and is the period of rapid growth of crops and natural vegetation. The summer monsoon declines earliest in the north—perhaps in September in the northwest, October in Calcutta, and November in the south. Dry and relatively cool winter monsoon winds generally blow from October or November to the end of February. This is the pleasant cool season in India, though temperatures do not reach freezing, and this is the preferred time for foreigners to visit the country.

Natural vegetation in monsoon lands generally consists of jungle except in the less rainy sections, where it may be of a savanna, steppe, or even desert character, as in northern Pakistan. In the jungles man can use fire to help him clear land for cultivation. Forests in the

Figure 6-10 Savanna landscape showing typical grasslands of central Africa, and some types of wildlife: gazelles, the eland, and the hartebeest. (Photograph, courtesy of the American Museum of Natural History, New York.)

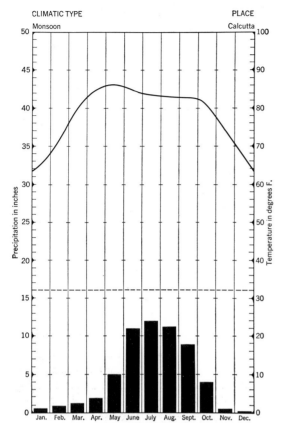

Figure 6-11 Climatic graph for Calcutta, India. Rainfall and temperature conditions in a typical monsoon location. The tropical latitude is indicated by (1) a uniformly high temperature condition throughout the year and (2) a marked lack of seasonal temperature variation. Note also (3) that the total amount of rain each year is very heavy, but (4) that it occurs in an uneven distribution, with drought in December, January, and February, and heavy rains in June, July, August, and September. Note the differences in climatic condition from those of the wet equatorial climate shown in Figure 6-2.

rainy tropics are so constantly damp that they are very difficult to clear by fire unless vegetation is cut and allowed to dry in the hot sun, but in monsoon climates, much of the jungle becomes dry enough to burn at the end of the dry season. Since land is easier to clear than in the rainy tropics and natives are better workers than those living in the hot rain forest, some rainier monsoon countries devote much land to plantation crops and raise cane sugar, tea, coffee, and other commodities for export to industrial regions in middle latitudes.

Monsoon Farming.   The most important native food in the monsoon climates is rice. This grain requires very fertile soil, an adequate amount of water, and a long growing season, usually about five months. It must be planted in artificial swamps (Figure 6-12), and much labor is needed to raise rice by the methods used in monsoon regions. Plants are started in hotbeds and transplanted spear by spear to prepared fields, where the rice grows in mud and shallow water under the hot sun. Rice is hardy and resists fungus and other diseases that would ruin wheat and similar grains. Furthermore, rice can be stored in spite of heat and humidity, whereas corn and wheat would ferment and spoil.

With a dry season and less heat during part of the year, monsoon climates are a more favorable human habitat than the rainy tropics. India, Pakistan, Indonesia, Thailand, Ceylon, Burma, and the Philippines are among countries situated mainly in the tropical monsoon climate. Half the population on earth is found in India, China, and other countries in southeastern Asia where rice is grown under tropical and "temperate" monsoon conditions. (The humid subtropical parts of China will be discussed in Chapter 8.)

Since rice requires fertile level land, areas suitable for its cultivation are intensively used. In the Ganges Delta, coastal plains of China, and floodplains of Japan, over 1,000 people per square mile are supported wholly by agriculture. In more tropical locations two crops of rice can be grown each year, and the yield per acre may be double that of wheat. Other areas may raise one crop of rice and another crop of vegetables, beans, or winter grain. Highlands and mountains in monsoon lands have less population, since the people prefer to crowd onto the limited areas of more level ground. Where monsoons furnish only scattered rainfall as in central India and the Punjab, irrigation is usually practiced although some crops may be grown without irrigation. On unirrigated dry land yields are smaller and the population far less than on rainy coastal plains. Such areas are afflicted by famine when the rains fail.

Houses. Houses built by native peoples in the tropics are generally of simple construction. A roof to keep off the downpours is the important thing. Walls are loosely made and sometimes consist of movable mats so that air may circulate. Generally the house is little more than a hut thatched with banana and palm leaves and with a floor that often is only beaten earth, but sometimes is wood and raised on posts for greater comfort. The hut is used mainly for sleeping accommodations. Cooking may be done outdoors or in the shelter of a lean-to. Only a small fire is needed, since heat is desired for cooking alone. A ditch may be dug about the hut to drain away falling rain. Sometimes the house is placed above ground on posts to keep things dry, especially the sleeping quarters. The floor of the elevated hut is often of split bamboo. Underneath, pigs and chickens find refuge and pick up scraps that fall through the open spaces.

Weather of Monsoon Climates. In India a short mild winter is followed in March, April, and May by heat and drought. Vegetation dries up and the country is covered with dust; but, with the arrival of the rains in June, everything again becomes green and the temperature drops slightly because of cloudiness and the cooling effect from evaporation of moisture. During the rainy season, Europeans find the heat and high humidity of monsoon climates very disagreeable. The rains bring a sudden growth of vegetation. Indoors, everything is affected by dampness. The leaves of books stick together and become covered with mildew, and bindings are quickly loosened.

Figure 6-12 Cultivation of paddy rice in tropical southern Japan. Note the intensive use of every bit of land that is suitable for growing the crop. (U.S. Department of Agriculture photograph.)

Wet boots uncared for over a single night will be covered with fungous growth by morning. Unoiled knives and guns may be ruined by rust. Yet summer rains make the monsoon regions a favorable place for raising crops, rice especially being easily stored for consumption during the dry season. The dry season also provides leisure during which native peoples may devote part of their time to recreation and cultural activities.

SUMMARY

Wet equatorial climate has high, steady temperature throughout the year. Rainfall is heavy annually and reaches maxima twice a year when the sun is nearest its zenith. These conditions favor the growth of dense, evergreen rain forest. Despite abundant rainfall, warmth, and freedom from frost, this climatic realm is not well adapted to farming because leached poor soils prevail. Impure water, thick vegetation cover, and disease impose further handicaps on human activity. As a result only scant population is found in the Amazon and Congo Basins. There people live in small villages and grow subsistence crops by primitive methods in little forest clearings. In some fertile areas near seaports, outsiders have developed commercial plantations to provide residents of midlatitudes with tropical products such as sugar, bananas, and rubber.

At greater distances from the equator, two zones of wet-and-dry tropical climate border the wet equatorial lands. Here the period of high sun lasts a shorter time than nearer the equator. When the sun is highest overhead in the warmer season, rains become heavy. In contrast, the cooler season with lower sun is relatively dry. These conditions lead to growth of coarse grasses and scattered trees—the savannas—where cattle grazing is carried on and subsistence crops are raised. Commercial agriculture is limited to accessible regions near seaports.

In southeastern Asia, the wet-and-dry tropical climate becomes most fully developed in the monsoon lands of India, Malaya, and southern China. Here soil and water conditions favor production of rice, which yields well and can be stored without deterioration under warm humid conditions that would spoil other grains. It is the staple food for inhabitants of the monsoon realm, and the large production of rice helps account for one-third of the world's population living in Southeast Asia.

Outline

Wet equatorial and rainy trade-wind coasts
   Characteristics of climate
   Plants and animals
   Sickness and health
   Hunters and farmers
   Plantations
Wet-and-dry tropical realms
   Transition from rainy to dry tropics
   Savannas: vegetation, native life, occupance
Monsoons of Southeast Asia
   Seasonal weather and vegetation
   Rice and other crops
   Home life

QUESTIONS

1. What industrial advances have enabled the tropical humid regions to become sources of some of the leading commodities of world trade, whereas their commercial products were formerly limited to luxury goods?

2. How have the above conditions affected world trade routes?

3. Which of the following items are related to the wet equatorial climatic realm? Convectional rainfall, low relative humidity, heavy snows, doldrums, dry season, equatorial calms, frost, steady wind, high sensible temperatures, winter rainfall.

4. What striking change in living conditions is apparent in Figure 5-3 as compared with Figure 7-6?

5. Which of the following low-latitude crops have become familiar to us because they are being produced on commercial plantations? Bananas, rubber, cane sugar, chocolate, Brazil nuts, coconuts, cinchona, pineapples, mangos, kapok, papayas, avocados, mahogany, ebony, balsa.

6. What vegetation changes mark the transition from wet equatorial to savanna lands?

7. Why has mid-latitude trade with tropical lands tended to increase during the last century?

8. Why is commercial production of bananas limited largely to the Caribbean area?

9. Why does precipitation normally occur in summer in the low-latitude wet-and-dry realm?

10. Which is better suited for occupation by the white man, tropical savanna or tropical lowland of the wet equatorial type?

11. The deltas of the Indus and the Ganges are approximately in the latitude of the Tropic of Cancer. Point out their geographical differences, and provide an explanation for your observations.

12. Why are soils of the tropical rain forests often poor?

13. What are the leading handicaps to the commercial development of interior Brazil?

14. India raises much sugar cane and more cattle than any other country. Why is India not noted for its exports of sugar and beef?

15. Though India has an area receiving the heaviest recorded rainfall in the world, it also has the most extensive irrigation projects of any nation. Explain this apparent contradiction.

16. How is India's climate related to the changes of season?

17. Diagram the usual air movements in the vicinity of southeastern Asia in summer and in winter.

18. Account for the leadership of Java in the output of tropical products, and list the principal products grown there.

SELECTED REFERENCES

Barnett, Lincoln: "The Rain Forest," *Life,* 37:76–102, Sept. 20, 1954.

Bates, Marston: *Where Winter Never Comes: A Study of Man and Nature in the Tropics,* Charles Scribner's Sons, New York, 1952.

Cressey, George B.: *Asia's Lands and Peoples,* McGraw-Hill Book Company, Inc., New York, 1951, chaps. 7, 28–39.

Gourou, Pierre: *Tropical World: Its Social and Economic Conditions and Its Future Status,* Longmans, Green & Co., Inc., New York, 1953.

James, Preston E.: *Latin America,* The Odyssey Press, Inc., New York, 1950, chaps. 2–4, 9, 12–30.

Jones, C. F., and G. G. Darkenwald, *Economic Geography,* The Macmillan Company, New York, 1954, pp. 145–236.

Kimble, George H. T.: "Resources of the Tropics: I: Africa," *Focus,* 3(4):1–6, December, 1952.

Lee, Douglas H. K.: *Climate and Economic Development in the Tropics,* Harper & Brothers, New York, 1957.

Mallory, Walter H.: *China: Land of Famine,* The American Geographical Society Special Publication 6, New York, 1928.

Masefield, Geoffrey: *Handbook of Tropical Agriculture,* Oxford University Press, New York, 1949.

Pelzer, Karl J.: *Pioneer Settlement in the Asiatic Tropics,* The American Geographical Society Special Publication 29, New York, 1945.

Price, A. Grenfell: *White Settlers in the Tropics,* The American Geographical Society Special Publication 23, New York, 1939.

Richards, Paul W.: *Tropical Rain Forest: An Ecological Study,* Cambridge University Press, New York, 1952.

Riehl, Herbert: *Tropical Meteorology,* McGraw-Hill Book Company, Inc., New York, 1954.

Spencer, Joseph E.: *Asia, East by South,* John Wiley & Sons, Inc., New York, 1954.

Stamp, L. Dudley: *Africa: A Study in Tropical Development,* John Wiley & Sons, Inc., New York, 1953.

Wilson, Charles M.: *The Tropics: World of Tomorrow,* Harper & Brothers, New York, 1951.

7. The

Dry Tropics

DRY tropical regions are located poleward of the subhumid savannas. They include tropical deserts and steppes which occupy the interior and western sides of continents in the zone where trade winds blow for at least part of the year (Figure 7-1).

Deserts are of much geographic interest because their harsh environmental conditions so affect human activities that the relationships involved are generally simpler and clearer than in lands more favored by nature. Important, too, is observation of man's success in overcoming the handicaps of a desert climate by irrigation and in finding other ways to make a living in spite of natural limitations.

THE HOT DESERTS

A desert consists of wasteland which is nearly or quite barren of vegetation. Plants may be absent because of cold, as for example, in Antarctica, or because of rainfall, as in Death Valley in southeast California. Many geographers contend that few true deserts are located in the United States because most of the dry areas have at least a little vegetation. Usually those so-called "deserts" provide some grazing and browse for livestock. The rate of evaporation in deserts always greatly exceeds precipitation, hence deserts are always too dry for raising crops unless the land is irrigated. Irrigation is frequently practiced in steppe lands, but crops also are raised without irrigation in these places.

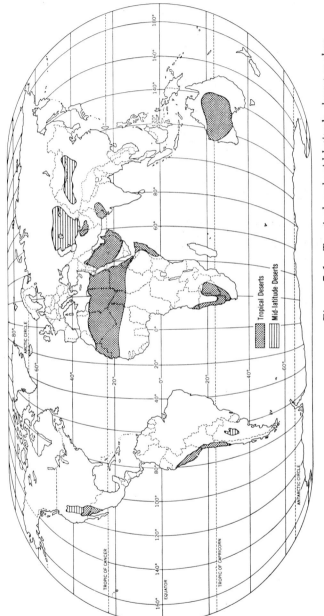

Figure 7-1 *Tropical and mid-latitude desert realms.*

Location and Causes of Tropical Deserts. Although a shortage of rainfall is the primary cause of deserts, the rate of evaporation helps to determine their actual boundaries fully as much as the amount of rainfall itself. Thus in Australia the desert plants begin to be dominant in the south in the vicinity of the 10-inch annual rainfall line; but in the north, scanty drought-resistant spiny vegetation of the desert type extends nearly to the 20-inch isohyet. The rainfall in northern Australia is of less benefit to vegetation, since it occurs during the warmest time of year when evaporation is highest and is followed by nearly eight months of drought. Deficient precipitation in deserts may be caused by a combination of several factors rather than one single reason, as shown in the following examples:

1. Air moving from colder into warmer latitudes in the trade winds becomes warmer. Such air readily absorbs any available moisture from the land beneath it, thus contributing to the formation of a desert. In the horse latitudes, when air descends vertically, it comes under compression and warms adiabatically. This results in lowering the relative humidity; precipitation under these conditions becomes almost impossible.

The largest tropical deserts are in the zones of the trade winds and horse latitudes and are best developed on the western side of continents. Here are located the Saharan, Arabian, Sonoran, Kalahari (Southwest Africa), Australian, and the Atacaman (northern Chile–western Peru) deserts. The largest desert on earth, familiarly called "the Old World Desert," includes the Sahara of Africa and the Arabian in Asia—the combination forming a broad band from the Atlantic Ocean across Africa and well into Asia. Steppes are transition zones between the tropical deserts and the subhumid to humid regions located in both poleward and equatorward directions, and also toward the east if a rainy climate occurs on that side. Savanna lands are in the equatorward direction and the rainy season on the steppes adjacent thereto occurs during the period of high sun. Lands with a Mediterranean type of climate are situated on the poleward side, and the adjoining steppes receive rains during the period of low sun. On the east are sometimes regions of humid subtropical or monsoon climate that have their maximum rainfall during the warm season (Figure 8-1). Eastern coasts in the same latitudes as the tropical deserts usually have abundant rainfall because of the prevailing onshore winds.

From the belt of the tropical trades on the Africa-Asia land mass, winds blow toward the equator and outward toward the oceans. Such air is warming and drying, and the thirsty air causes a thirsty land. The interior of Australia, from the west slopes of the highlands which border the eastern part of that continent as far as the western coast along the Indian Ocean, consists of steppes and desert, the latter occupying nearly half the continent. Lower California and the Kalahari are also in the latitudes of the trades, although as a matter of fact the trade winds rarely blow across these areas. Tropical deserts are festooned around the world on the Tropics of Cancer and Capricorn, but as indicated on the climatic map are limited to the west side of continents except in the case of North Africa.

Poleward from the trade winds is the zone of the horse latitudes. Descending air in these high-pressure belts becomes warmed by compression; the resulting low relative humidity and absence of warm-season rainfall help to extend tropical deserts into latitudes beyond the realm of the trade winds. The desert of southeast California, southwest Arizona, and Sonora in northwest Mexico, largely results from this cause.

2. Mountains are important factors in producing deserts, especially when moist prevailing winds from the ocean blow inland at right angles to the trend of high mountains. The windward sides of such ranges then receive heavy rainfall. After passing the summits the dehydrated air descends to leeward. This results in compression, adiabatic heating, and a low relative humidity for such air. Deserts often occur on the leeward side of highlands. This condition seems in part the cause for the

deserts of central Australia and South Africa. Another example is the Andes of South America which enjoy abundant rains on their sheltered western slopes along the Pacific Ocean, partly because this area lies in the rain shadow of the cordillera. Farther south in the zone of the westerlies, the rainy side of the Andes is in southern Chile, and the dry leeward side is on the east in Argentina.

Another factor contributing to the desert condition along the coasts of northern Chile and Peru stems from the cold Humboldt (Peru) Current, which parallels the shores of the Pacific, as shown on the map of ocean currents (Figure 15-1). Cool winds from the sea, which normally would bring rain to the coast, are warmed rapidly over the land by radiation from the hot desert; this counteracts the adiabatic cooling as the sea air expands when forced up the western slopes of the Andes. The net outcome produces fog and clouds rather than rain.

3. Some desert regions are deficient in precipitation because the land surface is too low to force air to rise and thus lower the temperature to a point at which condensation and precipitation will occur. Hence a desert condition will prevail though the air itself may have high relative humidity. Examples of this condition include low-lying islands in the West Indies, and the Yucatan Peninsula, where semidesert conditions prevail. The low western half of Molokai Island in Hawaii and small coral islands in the South Pacific have similar dry climates.

4. Prevailing wind directions sometimes run parallel to nearby coasts; under these circumstances the coastal belt may not receive rain in worthwhile amounts even if mountains rise a short distance inland. The Somali Desert of East Africa is an example. Here both the summer monsoon wind toward India and the winter monsoon wind away from India blow parallel to the African coast. Another dry zone is along part of the Caribbean coast in Venezuela, Colombia, and the islands of Aruba and Curaçao, where the winds are usually parallel to the coast line of South America.

5. Air moving from a continental interior toward the sea, if the distance is great, may never have had access to large amounts of moisture and cannot be expected to produce rain in any quantity. Furthermore, if air in the source region is cold when seas surrounding the land mass are warmer, the moving air will be warming as it flows outward; it will tend to secure moisture by evaporation from the land surfaces and induce drying conditions that help form a desert. This condition occurs in Australia and South Africa and probably is in part responsible for the deserts there.

6. Air moving from the sea to the interior of a large land mass may provide plenty of rainfall near the margins of the continent but will be so drained of its moisture that steppes or deserts develop toward the end of its travels. The Thar Desert in West Pakistan and northwest India is a good example. Here, damp monsoon air coming from the Bay of Bengal gives abundant rain in summer to the lower Ganges Basin, but the rainfall decreases westward until desert conditions prevail in the lower Indus River basin at the end of the roundabout route.

Surfaces of Deserts. All types of surfaces are found in deserts: sand, clay, gravel, and bare rock. The relief may be a featureless plain or a rolling surface, or considerable ranges of mountains may rise above the plainlike islands from a sea of sand. If the mountains are high, local convectional thunderstorms provide some rain, with the result that more springs, better grazing, or even forests occur at high elevations under the best conditions. In the Sahara special names are applied to different surfaces: sand heaped into dunes by the wind is called an *erg* (Figure 7-2), and gravel plains are termed *reg*. Outcrops of bare rock form the *hamada*. Wind is an effective agent in deserts for both erosion and deposition. Heaped-up sand dunes of various shapes move in the direction of prevailing winds. A crescent-shaped dune, known to the Arabs as a *barchan,* is a common landform (Figure 7-2). Elsewhere long parallel hills of sand are heaped like giant windrows in the direction of the prevailing winds, as in the Libyan Desert and parts of interior Australia. The scarcity of water in Arab lands does not require the many names for watercourses that are used in humid regions; instead the Arabs use the term *wadi* for all valleys whether they are dry or contain running water. Arabs use numerous words, however, for sand dunes of different shapes, whereas in English we use only one.

The Weather of Deserts. Characteristically the climate of deserts is one of extremes. Extreme daily ranges of temperature characterize the weather of deserts (Figure 7-3). In the Sahara the temperature has been known to change from well below the freezing point of water at night to well above 100°F in the daytime. In part this great range of temperature results from low humidity and absence of clouds. Both water vapor and clouds in the air help to keep out solar energy and also to retain heat radiation near the earth. Trade-wind deserts are in the tropics, yet freezing tempera-

tures have been recorded over a large part of the Sahara.

The low humidity of the mountains in the middle Sahara permits 10 or 15 frosty nights per year. Wide variation in temperatures of deserts results in unstable air conditions that cause frequent sudden violent windstorms. The highest temperatures ever recorded on earth have been in low-latitude deserts. At Azizia, a short distance from Tripoli near the northern coast of Africa, an absolute maximum temperature of 136.4°F has been recorded, the highest known to have been measured by accurate instruments in the shade. One station in Death Valley, California, approaches the maximum, with an observed temperature of 134°F.

Although rainfall in deserts is always very scanty, it is very variable in amount and occurrence. In fact the most reliable thing about desert rainfall is its unreliability. Over a term of years, a station may show an average of 5 inches of rainfall per year, but some years may experience no measurable rainfall; others may have double or triple the annual average

Figure 7-2 Windrow pattern of migratory sand dunes in the Grand Erg Occidental of the northwestern Sahara. (Note the crescentic barchan left of center at the lower edge of the photograph.) Life in this type of natural landscape is almost nonexistent except for an occasional animal or motor caravan. (Air Force photograph.)

precipitation. Much rainfall in tropical deserts comes from local convectional thunderstorms, which may soak a considerable portion of country heavily yet leave surfaces only a few miles distant untouched. Shifting of the wind zones and belts of calms north and south during the year causes showers to occur in summer in the southern part of the Sahara and mostly during winter in the northern part. Similar conditions of the rainfall regimen between the northern and southern sections of the Australian desert are also typical on that continent.

Plant and Animal Adaptation to Deserts.
Special types of drought-resistant plants have adapted themselves to desert conditions. In general, perennial desert shrubs, herbs, or trees have large root systems compared with the part of the plant that appears aboveground. This suffices to gather water quickly when a local shower affords the opportunity. Furthermore plants are widely spaced so that each secures the available water supply of a considerable area. Many plants, like the barrel cactus (Figure 7-4), are especially equipped to store water in their tissues to provide for needs during prolonged drought. Most desert plants possess devices that prevent rapid loss of precious moisture through evaporation. The leaves of desert plants are very small; sometimes they turn their edges to the sun, sometimes they curl up to expose little surface to the sunshine, often they consist of little more than spines. The stomata, or breathing organs, through which moisture escapes to the outer air also have hairs and guard cells to prevent excessive evaporation.

Annual plants like grasses and flowers germinate quickly after a rain. Many mature in a few weeks on the moisture from a single shower, producing seeds that lie dormant in the soil until another shower awakens them.

Desert animals must have certain attributes to survive. Some animals, like the pronghorn antelope, the gazelle, and the prairie dog and certain other rodents, seem to make the water they need from eating cellulose, which contains hydrogen and oxygen, of

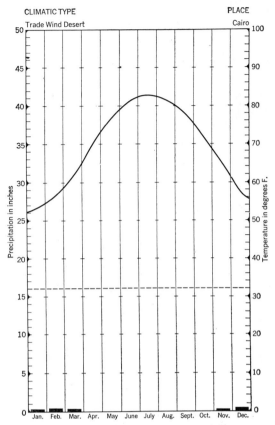

Figure 7-3 Climatic graph for Cairo, Egypt. *Conditions in the tropical deserts are readily distinguished by (1) high temperatures at all seasons though with some variation; and (2) noticeably deficient rainfall at all seasons.*

which water is composed. Others remain dormant (estivate) during a hot dry season. The Columbian ground squirrel of the intermountain basin between the Cascades and the Rockies uses this protective device. Other desert creatures live curled up in the mud left by evaporation of water after the temporary rainy season. The lungfish, one variety of which lives in the Sudan and another on a single drainage basin in Queensland, Australia, return to activity when rains soften the mud and water is again provided for them in which to swim.

The "ship" of the desert. Camels are peculiarly well adapted for desert life (Figure 7-5). Tough lips and tongues enable them to nibble harsh desert vegetation. Long legs carry

Figure 7-4 Desert vegetation in southeastern California. Most of these plants are varieties of cacti having drought-resistant spines in place of leaves. These plants are equipped to gather moisture quickly after a desert rain and to retain the water during long drought periods. A barrel cactus appears in the center foreground. (Photograph by Frashers Photos, Pomona, California.)

them easily along the trails; tough pads protect the soles of their feet from hot sands and sharp rocks. Numerous corrugations on the stomach walls permit camels to drink enough at a single watering to support the animals for a week or two. The Arabian camel is thus fitted for life in hot deserts. Usually, camels are used for bearing burdens and horses are reserved for long desert journeys where speed is essential. Although dromedary camels used for riding have made 75 miles or more per day, ordinary baggage camels seldom average more than 15 to 20 miles per day. The two-humped Bactrian camel of central Asia is adapted to deserts where winters are cold.

OCCUPANCE OF DESERTS

Contrasting uses of desert lands consist of (1) intensive farming on small areas or oases, by irrigation with the available water supply; or (2) extensive use of the scanty grazing by nomadic herding of domestic animals. In the Old World Desert the inhabitants keep camels, goats, sheep, and comparatively few horses, which are treated almost like household pets. Goats and sheep are generally preferred over cattle by desert nomads because they can survive on meager forage.

Desert Nomads. Desert nomads must travel whenever and wherever conditions require, to secure grass and water for their livestock. Since their homes and furnishings must be easily portable they live in tents and use rugs, blankets, and shawls for bedding, floor coverings, and decorations inside the tent. Clothing must protect against heat of day and cold of night (Figure 7-6). Among the Arabs the burnoose, a flowing robe, answers the requirements and is the accepted garment for the nomad in the hot desert.

Leather or skin bags are used to carry water and other liquids. Cooking may be done with a fire made of camel dung because wood is rarely obtainable. Cooking utensils are few and must be made of metal; china and pottery would break easily under conditions of desert travel. Because of lack of fodder, large numbers of animals cannot be kept for each family. Meat is eaten but is not available throughout the year; thus for long periods nomads may live largely on milk from their goats, camels, or other animals, supplemented in the Sahara and Arabia with dried dates from the oasis palms and a little barley meal or other grain procured by trading. Occasionally wild game will be hunted to vary the monotonous diet.

In their own environment nomads develop characteristics suited to their life. Leanness and muscular development, combined with bravery, hardiness, and ability to live cheerfully on a scanty monotonous diet, are characteristics of these people. Although often suspicious of strangers, since wanderers may try to rob or destroy part of the herds, once a visitor has earned their confidence, nomads are generally very hospitable. Since towns and hotels for accommodation of visitors do not exist, travelers must be received by tribesmen. Occasional visitors provide welcome information about feed and water or news from the outside world. Desert nomads are notable hunters and warriors. They must protect their herds from predatory animals, and the same weapons and ability which subdue wild beasts may be used against human enemies.

The Desert Oases.   Oases are located in deserts where water is available. The water may come from rivers that originate in rainy regions and have sufficient volume to maintain a flow across the desert. The Nile area is a striking example of this type of oasis. More often the water supply comes from underground sources, possibly hundreds of miles away. For example, much of western Queensland is underlain by a vast artesian basin where "bores," as Australians call artesian wells, supply water to cattle and sheep. In much of the Great Artesian Basin water is slightly salty and therefore unsuited for irrigation. Few cultivated crops have been supplied from this source. Elsewhere in the world wells of reasonable depth can reach supplies of ground water for irrigating dates, grain, and other crops.

Figure 7-5   A camel caravan in central Asia. (Photograph, courtesy of the American Museum of Natural History, New York.)

Figure 7-6 Bedouins of the Old World Desert regions. Note the heavy garments that protect the body against sandstorms and shelter it from the effects of low-latitude temperatures. (Photograph, courtesy of the American Museum of Natural History, New York.)

Sandy beds of the valleys that stretch from a mountain range into the desert have surface flow only at long intervals, but shallow wells can draw upon their regular subsurface supply. Numerous oases in southern Morocco and Algeria have developed from the supply of irrigation water in the sandy floors of the valleys, or wadis. Springs at the bases of mountains or toward the center of desert basins are other sources of water supply used for development of oases. Soil of deserts is often very fertile because its soluble nutrients have not been dissolved and removed by water. Hence, when irrigated, desert land may be very productive. In any desert, however, the land that can be irrigated is small in comparison with the extent of the desert itself.

Oases generally support a great density of population per unit of land area, for water is life in the desert. Thus Egypt has over 22 million people living on only 13,500 square miles of tilled land, with the number of actual farmers in excess of 1,000 persons per square mile. The remainder of Egypt covers 370,000 square miles but contains no more than 40,000 nomads eking out a precarious nonagricultural existence. The real land of Egypt is the narrow valley of the Nile River and the delta of that stream, for without the river the great ancient civilization of this country could never have existed. Iraq shows similar concentration of population on irrigated lands of the Tigris and Euphrates Valleys, with comparatively few nomads and some stockmen who live in villages thinly scattered over vast territories.

The date palm. The date palm is ideally adapted to tropical desert cultivation (Figure 7-7). To thrive, it is said that the palm should have its roots in perennial springs and its crown in the blazing sun. In actual practice, dates can be successfully raised with a thorough soaking of the ground only once or twice a year. Many varieties of dates are grown, only a few of which are dried for export trade. The date palm furnishes food for both man and beast. The seeds are ground and fed to camels. The fiber makes rope, and leaves are used for baskets and matting. Large stems and roots serve for fuel. The trunk of the tree is the only available lumber for houses and furniture. A good date palm will produce 5 or 10 bunches of dates per year weighing perhaps 100 pounds each. In the entire Sahara, which is much larger than the United States, it has been estimated that 12 million date palms are growing. Including Egyptian irrigated land, however, the entire area of the oases in the Sahara is less than the size of the state of Oregon.

The Inhabitants of Oases. The life of an oasis dweller offers sharp contrast to that of a desert nomad. Oasis inhabitants live in houses of stone, brick, or mud. Sometimes a wall surrounds the village for protection, and the houses may be built several stories high, with several families living in a single house. Towns containing buildings 8 or 10 stories high are common in the Hadramaut of southern Arabia.

A shaded oasis village appears delightful to the eye from a distance, but it is not the earthly paradise for permanent residence that is oftentimes imagined. Water is too precious for luxuries like lawns and flowers; all must be used to irrigate date palms, grains, and vegetables. Streets are dusty. Flies and myriads of other insects thrive.

Generally inhabitants of oases are less bold and vigorous than desert nomads. They are tillers of soil rather than herders, hunters, or warriors, and in Egypt they are known as the *fellahin* (peasants). Often oasis dwellers pay tribute to the nomads; in return the latter protect the village from other raiders. A few trades and crafts, such as weaving and metalworking, are carried on in oases. The community is generally self-sufficient and can get along without much intercourse with the world outside.

Religion. Perhaps because of the great hardships desert dwellers endure, they feel that a pleasant "hereafter" must exist to compensate for the difficulties of this life; hence desert nomads are often imbued with very strong religious feeling. Mohammedanism, Judaism, and Christianity all originated in deserts or near deserts; and their literature is replete with parables, stories, and attitudes that show the conditions under which nomadic herdsmen live. In Arabia and northern Africa, the tapering tower of the mosque dominates the sky line of a desert town; whatever a man's inner character may be, there everyone obeys

Figure 7-7 Date picking in the Coachella Valley, California. The dates do not ripen at the same time on any single bunch, and picking, therefore, is highly selective. Each bunch is protected from moisture and dirt by a paper cover. (Photograph by Frashers Photos, Pomona, California.)

at least the outward forms of his Moslem religion.

Stock ranches in deserts. Grazing livestock is one of the primary industries that can survive in the harsh environment of desert lands. Sometimes men keep sheep and cattle on enormous stock ranches, as large as an American county, of hundreds of square miles or scores of thousands of acres. Such ranches exist in the southwestern United States, Argentina, and central Australia. Frequently the grass deteriorates from overgrazing, and only those ranches survive which have enough irrigated land to raise hay to carry animals through drought periods. Grazing areas that lack hay land may be abandoned entirely, or the economy may deteriorate because the people must be contented with a low standard of existence.

Indian Nomads of the American Southwest.

Nomadic Indians of the Southwest hunted game: antelope on the plains, deer, mountain sheep, and bear in the mountains. They gathered cactus fruits, used mesquite beans, and collected piñon nuts from the mountains along with other fruits and roots. In addition, some desert Indians like the Papagos planted small patches of corn hoping that rain would mature a crop with flood irrigation. The nomads spent the summer in the mountains and the winter in lower desert plains and valleys. They lived in desert tents or shelters of brush or earth called *wickiups* and *hogans*. Even today on their reservations, Indians like the Papagos live little differently from the way they did before the arrival of white men, since the latter have not cared to occupy the desert except at mines and irrigation sites.

The Navahos were originally nomadic, but incoming white men brought them domestic animals: cattle, sheep, and goats. They also taught the Indians the arts of metalworking and weaving (Figure 7-8). Now the Navahos weave blankets on homemade looms and make silver ornaments for their own use and for sale to tourists. Many Navahos still lead a seminomadic existence with herds of sheep and other animals.

The southwestern Indian has shown remarkable ability in using the few plants available in his environment. Among the desert plants is the mesquite, which can send its roots 30 to 40 feet into the ground to tap underground water supplies. In spring the mesquite is covered with sweet blossoms, a favorite pasture for bees. In autumn the tree provides a crop of nutritious "beans," food for both man and animals. Fruit of the saguaro, prickly pear, and other cacti is eaten raw, dried, and cooked. A drink is prepared from the juice of some cactus plants. Numerous small plants supply greens for cooking. Yuccas and agaves furnish fruit that is occasionally eaten, but they are more important for long tough leaf fibers, woven by the Indians into textiles for clothing, sandals, cords and rope, head nets for carrying burdens, and lariats. Roots of the yuccas supply a natural soap to the Indians. Originally all necessities of the Indians in the arid Southwest came from the comparatively scanty resources of the desert.

Present-day Desert Life.

Examples of desert life previously described represent conditions among primitive peoples in most deserts of the tropical and subtropical regions. In a few places, however, modern inventions and techniques have made possible the occupation of oases by large numbers of people. Much of life in Cairo, for example, depends upon modern transportation facilities and newly devised systems of water storage and distribution. Construction of large dams at Aswan and Sennar provides irrigation for thousands of acres of Egyptian land that would otherwise be unproductive. Railroads and air lines make accessible to the outside world remote interior parts of the Sahara that have never before been used by man. The present generation has witnessed the exploration and mapping of hitherto unknown parts of the Sahara, Arabia, and central Australia. In these changes, the motorcar has played an important part in one form or other; caterpillar tractors, powerful engines, and large soft tires are used for traversing sandy stretches. Railroad lines have penetrated for some distance into the western

Sahara, and above all, the airplane has shortened the time of crossing deserts, thereby removing former threats to the safety of travelers.

Other inventions have made living in the desert more comfortable. Mechanical refrigeration in its various applications makes possible preservation of food, palatability of water, and cooling of houses. Electricity used for operating electric fans and other cooling devices has eliminated unnecessary and unpleasant heat. The radio has brought communication to lonely desert wastes, removing the solitude and isolation.

The introduction of water by dams and aqueducts has made possible the commercial development of agriculture in some parts of the New World deserts. Water from the Colorado River gives life to date plantations that provide sharp contrast to those of the Old World, for the dates are planted and grown scientifically. They must be fertilized by hand in the old way, but American dates are provided with just enough water for their needs. They are carefully protected against dampness and dirt while they ripen and are picked by hand and attractively packed under sanitary conditions. Other desert-grown products, such as grapefruit, melons, tomatoes, papayas, peppers, and carrots regularly find their way to American markets by truck or in refrigerator cars, shipped by rapid transport so they will reach the consumer in prime condition and bring high out-of-season prices. There is little indeed about life in parts of the American deserts that resembles the harsh living conditions of the Old World deserts.

If mineral deposits are discovered in desert locations and can be worked profitably, settlements are established in spite of inadequate

Figure 7-8   A Navaho woman at work before her loom, weaving a rug from wool obtained from the sheep which graze the Colorado Plateau region. This industry developed after the arrival of Europeans. (Photograph by Frashers Photos, Pomona, California.)

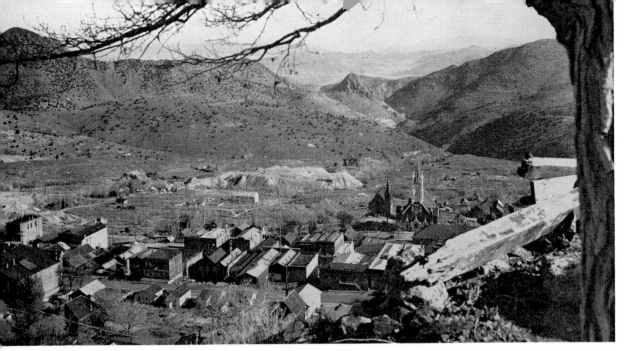

Figure 7-9 Virginia City, Nevada, had a population of 40,000 when it was the center for the Comstock gold and silver mines. It now has 600 inhabitants. (Photograph, courtesy of Sierra Press Bureau.)

water supplies and other unpleasant conditions. When the ore bodies are exhausted, the people leave and the settlement becomes a "ghost town" (Figure 7-9). If ore deposits are large and the mines continue to be profitable, a large town or small city will develop if water can be brought from a distance, as in the case of Chuquicamata, a copper-mining center in northern Chile, Kalgoorlie, a gold-mining city in western Australia, or Morenci and Ajo in Arizona, both long-lived copper centers. Mining towns also develop in desert locations where nitrates, borax, potash, and other salts resulting from evaporation are found.

Modern desert transport. Although the popular conception of desert life usually considers the camel as the basic means of trans-portation, mechanical transport under trying weather conditions has been so much improved since World War II that vehicles resembling the wartime half-track now are used for long desert trips. Because of high speeds, extreme mobility, and general toughness, these vehicles are especially adapted to deep desert sands and rock-strewn surfaces of the wastelands. The use of such mechanical "camels" permits man to penetrate what would otherwise be inaccessible corners of the African and Arabian deserts. These devices, plus advantages of air travel over the desert routes, have helped increase our knowledge of the dry lands of the low latitudes and their possible resources.

TROPICAL STEPPES

The tropical steppes which usually surround the deserts provide much better grazing than the desert lands. Hence these grasslands support more livestock and people than equal areas of unirrigated desert. Some wheat, barley, kaffir corn and other drought-tolerant crops can be raised without irrigation in most years. The results are uncertain however; if expected rains fail, farmers will have no crop to harvest. Even livestock may suffer for lack of grass and water. In contrast, ample rains bring excellent crop yields, and animals are well fed and people are prosperous.

Sometimes the steppes which have more

grass and water than deserts serve as the longer but preferred route between two populous regions separated by desert. North of the Syrian Desert is the Fertile Crescent which has both adequate supplies of grass and water for transport animals and supplies needed by human travelers. In journeying between the cities of Syria and ports along the Mediterranean, travelers and traders bound for ancient Babylon, or later, Baghdad in Mesopotamia (now Iraq) followed the Fertile Crescent even though the distance was twice that across the desert.

Nomads occupy much of the tropical steppes in North Africa, but some inhabitants are supported by a combination of herding and farming. These part-time farmers are only seminomadic; in the best-watered parts, some live in villages that are usually permanent. Large cattle ranches are located in tropical steppes in Argentina, South Africa, and the southwestern United States. The home ranches are built at springs or wells, cattle graze on surrounding grasslands, and usually some alfalfa is raised for emergency feed during the dry season. Among the most serious problems are occasional droughts which sometimes last several years. Only when steppes are irrigated can concentrations of farming population be found or trading centers grow to even a few thousand people.

Mountains and plateaus which rise above the surface of hot deserts receive more rainfall as the result of higher elevations. There grass is more luxuriant and springs and running water provide conditions favorable for livestock. Even trees may grow at the higher levels. Temperatures are cooler than in the desert below. Altogether these highland oases are favored places for desert dwellers. Yemen, sometimes called Arabia Felix (happy Arabia) in the southwest of the Arabian Peninsula, is such a place. Another is the Ahaggar in the central Sahara where the vigorous and warlike Tuareg tribes live. The Macdonnell Ranges near Alice Springs in central Australia also constitute such an oasis.

Some highland plateaus and mountain ranges in the low latitudes average 10 to 20°F cooler than lowlands because of their elevation. In many cases so much rain has fallen on windward slopes that plateau interiors and basins between the mountains are semiarid. Vegetation in such regions is that of the steppes. Much of northern Mexico, the Andean highlands in Peru and Bolivia in South America, and the East African plateaus in Kenya and Tanganyika are examples. Cattle herding and farming, sometimes by irrigation, are chief occupations.

Wildlife was originally quite abundant on tropical steppes, but now where occupied for either commercial or subsistence herding, the numbers of game animals have been much reduced.

SUMMARY

Low-latitude deserts and steppes, which experience great heat and drought, are located approximately 15 to 35 degrees north and south of the equator, mainly on western sides of continents. The deserts, in about 20 to 30° north and south latitude, are in horse latitudes and trade winds; they have precipitation so meager that much of the land is almost bare of vegetation. Strong winds move freely over the vast sand and rock surfaces.

Living conditions in low-latitude deserts are so difficult that this climatic realm supports but a small part of the world's population. Agriculture is possible in oases where dependable local water supplies can be obtained; elsewhere herds of nomadic shepherds and cattle raisers must rely on uncertain pasture afforded by torrential but unpredictable storms of convectional origin. Native plants and animals frequently develop special characteristics in order to survive with little rainfall and to conserve all available moisture under the desert conditions.

In general, desert lands do not produce commodities in amounts large enough for profitable, widespread development of commerce, although modern engineering practices have aided the expansion of irrigated tracts and made desert lands more useful to man. This is especially true in mid-latitude deserts of the Northern Hemisphere in interior North America and Asia.

Tropical steppes are situated in a zone about 5 degrees in width both poleward and equatorward of the deserts. Because of more rainfall and better grazing, the population of steppes is larger than that of deserts.

Outline

Hot deserts

Location

Causes

Surfaces

Weather

Plant and animal adaptations: the camel

Desert nomads: Arabs, Indians of Southwest

Oases: date palm, inhabitants

Present occupance

Transport: past and present

Tropical steppes

Location

Cause

Occupance

QUESTIONS

1. What is the relationship between the zones of extratropical or subtropical calms (horse latitudes) and the presence of tropical desert regions?

2. Why are soils of tropical deserts usually very fertile and productive, provided that enough water is available from sources outside the desert?

3. Study with care the type of vegetation shown in Figure 7-4. Then turn back to Figure 5-13 and summarize in a paragraph the principal differences between this and that found in humid regions.

4. Make a careful study of the photographs in Figures 7-5, 7-6, and 7-8. What conclusion do you reach concerning the mode of human life in these regions?

5. Summarize the principal physical differences between the hydrophytic plants of the wet equatorial realms and the xerophytic plants of the deserts.

6. Why have our highest observed absolute temperatures been measured in low-latitude desert realms instead of in wet equatorial realms?

7. Name and locate the five large low-latitude desert regions of the world. Which is of greatest extent? In what manner do they resemble each other? How do they differ, both in appearance of the landscape and in the mode of human life?

8. The Nile Delta and the delta of the Colorado River are located near 30° north latitude. Their conditions of climate, vegetation, and soil are not essentially different, but from the standpoint of their usefulness to human beings they vary widely. Why?

9. Investigate the commercial production of dates in the world's low-latitude deserts.

10. What desert features are found in the Atacama region of South America that are not commonly found in other low-latitude deserts?

SELECTED REFERENCES

Barnett, Lincoln: "The Land of the Sun," *Life,* 36:74–93, Apr. 5, 1954.

Bowman, Isaiah: *Desert Trails of Atacama,* The American Geographical Society Special Publication 5, New York, 1924.

Cable, Mildred: *The Gobi Desert,* The Macmillan Company, New York, 1944.

Cressey, George B.: "Water in the Desert," *Annals of the Association of American Geographers,* 47:105–124, July, 1957.

Dickson, B. T.: "The Challenge of Arid Lands," *Scientific Monthly,* 82:67–74, February, 1956.

Gautier, E. F.: *Sahara: The Great Desert,* Columbia University Press, New York, 1935.

Hoover, J. W.: "Southwestern Desert Vegetation: Its Adaptations and Utilization," *Journal of Geography,* 31:148–156, April, 1935.

McBride, George M.: *Chile: Land and Society,* The American Geographical Society Research Series 19, New York, 1936, chap. 15.

Meigs, Peveril: "Outlook for Arid North Africa: The Sahara," *Focus,* 5(4): pp. 1–6, December, 1954.

————: "Salvaging the Desert," *The Nation,* 180:577–579, June 25, 1955.

Pickwell, Gayle: *Deserts,* McGraw-Hill Book Company, Inc., New York, 1939.

Sykes, Godfrey: *The Colorado Delta,* The American Geographical Society, New York, 1937.

Taylor, Griffith: "A Comparison of American and Australian Deserts," *Economic Geography,* 13:260–268, July, 1937.

Thomas, Benjamin E.: "Motoring in the Sahara: The French Raids of 1953," *Economic Geography,* 29:327–339, October, 1953.

White, Gilbert F. (ed.): *The Future of Arid Lands,* American Association for the Advancement of Science Publication No. 43, 1956.

Wood, Gordon L.: *Australia: Its Resources and Development,* The Macmillan Company, New York, 1947.

8. The Subtropical Latitudes

A ZONE of subtropical climate separates the dry tropics of the low latitudes (described in the preceding chapter) and the more severe climates of the poleward regions of the middle latitudes. Summer weather in these subtropical locations is affected by tropical heat when direct rays of the sun approach the zenith at the time of a summer solstice in that hemisphere. Winter temperatures are mild to moderate. Weather then is influenced by the shifting of the zone of prevailing westerly winds equatorward with changes of season.

Although summers are hot in subtropical midlatitudes, winters are sufficiently cool and stormy to provide changes in weather which are more stimulating to man than a steady monotony of mild temperatures.

Precipitation ranges from moderate to heavy, and is generally associated with cyclonic storms characteristic of the westerlies.

These storms follow paths in lower latitudes during the winter months; even the subtropical Mediterranean region then receives moderate rainfall associated with cyclonic disturbances.

In addition to cyclonic storms important climatic factors are these:

1. The location of semipermanent areas of high and low pressure, especially where these pressure areas control air movements from land to sea or from sea to land.

2. Distance of continental interior regions from the ocean, which largely determines ranges of temperature.

3. High mountains and plateaus, especially where these lie broadside to prevailing winds. The Sierra Nevada–Cascade and southern Andes Mountain barriers, for example, cause heavy rainfall to windward and deserts or semiaridity to leeward of the mountains.

Middle-latitude climates are characterized

by four seasons and relatively large ranges of temperature compared with the tropics; they may be divided into the subtropics equatorward and a colder zone poleward. The subtropics include the Mediterranean dry-summer climate of west coasts and the humid subtropical climate in the southeast section of the midlatitudes. Usually semiarid steppes or deserts occupy the interior between these two diverse types. The mid-latitude climates of the prevailing westerlies are situated poleward from the subtropical latitudes.

In general the subtropical climates are favorable for human activities, especially agriculture and grazing.

THE MEDITERRANEAN CLIMATIC REGIONS

Characteristics and Causes of the Climate. Following the general nomenclature of climates based on rainfall and temperature, the transition area on western coasts of continents between trade winds and prevailing westerlies might be described as a semiarid subtropical region with dry summers and rainy winters. Since climate of this nature is characteristic of most of the shores of the Mediterranean Sea, it is usually called the Mediterranean climate (Figure 8-1). It occurs in southwestern California and between the Sierras and the Pacific Ocean, in central Chile, southern and southwestern Australia, and in the extreme southern tip of Africa near Capetown. Typically this climate has hot dry summers with most of the rain falling in winter, decreasing equatorward toward the trade-wind desert and increasing poleward as the climate grades into that of the rainy west coasts of midlatitudes. The rainy season in the Southern Hemisphere usually lasts from June to August, that is, in winter, because of the reversal of seasons in the two hemispheres.

Rainfall conditions in regions having a Mediterranean type of climate somewhat resemble those in the wet-and-dry tropical savannas. The tropical savannas, however, have a rainy season in summer, whereas regions of Mediterranean climate have their rainy season in winter.

In both cases seasonal distribution of rainfall depends on the shifting of the wind belts. In summer of the Northern Hemisphere the wind and calm zones move north from equatorial regions; on the west coasts of continents bordering the trade winds, summer weather is clear, hot, and calm, with blue skies. This is because of the northward extension of the high-pressure belts, or horse latitudes, in which the air has low relative humidity, resulting from the natural heating as the air descends from aloft.

In winter the wind zones shift toward the equator, and the subtropic west coasts are dominated by prevailing westerly winds and the cyclonic storms associated with them, giving a rainy but mild winter with frequent variations in cloudiness and temperature (Figure 8-2). Coasts of California, Portugal, and Chile have heavy fogs during the summer because of cold currents adjoining the shores of those regions. Air moving landward over these currents is chilled by contact with colder air, and condensation then produces advection fogs. Inland, radiation fog is common in winter. Frost may occur in winter in Mediterranean regions, but it is not a common phenomenon.

Mediterranean Vegetation. Natural vegetation in the Mediterranean regions must be capable of withstanding several months of drought. Trees are all drought-resistant (xerophytic) species, generally with small leathery leaves and other modifications enabling them to survive long droughts. Often the trees are of evergreen habit, shedding leaves at no regular season. Orange and lemon trees, avocado trees, the olive and the cork oak, as well as the eucalyptus tree, are all evergreens. The eucalyptus—a native of Australia—the live oak in California, the cork oak, chestnut, and olive in Spain represent trees that grow well

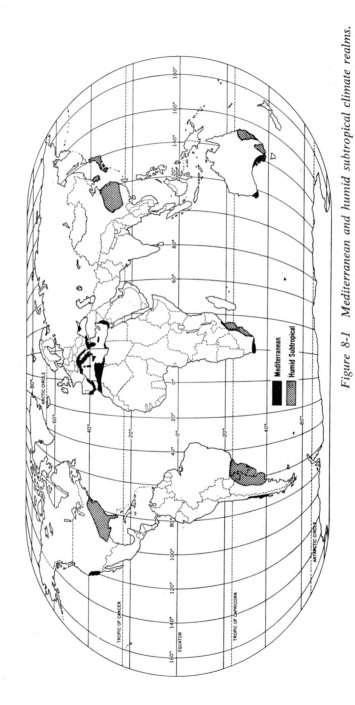

Figure 8-1 Mediterranean and humid subtropical climate realms.

in the Mediterranean climate. Originally these trees grew in open woods interspersed with grass and bushes.

Grass grows luxuriantly during the rainy season along with wild flowers and shrubs, making the hills a deep green with spots of brilliant color from the blossoming plants. In the dry season the vegetation becomes brown and dead and the hills and plains have a dusty brown and gray appearance. At this time of year danger of grass and forest fires becomes great.

A characteristic type of vegetation in Mediterranean regions consists of thickets of brush. Different plant species form the brush in different parts of the world having Mediterranean climate, but the general appearance of the hilly landscapes is similar no matter what the plant species may be. In California the brush is called *chaparral* (Figure 8-3) or *chamisal,* and its prominent species include the toyon, sage, manzanita, and yucca. On Mediterranean shores the brushland is known as *maqui* or *macchie;* in central Chile it is called *matorral.* In Australia, scrub types of eucalyptus are called the *mallee.*

Mediterranean Livestock.   In spite of summer drought, abundant grass during the winter and other pasturage available in Mediterranean regions make these areas attractive for grazing. The merino breed of sheep, producing the highest grade of wool in the world, was developed in Mediterranean Spain. Although good foragers like sheep and goats are more common, numerous cattle graze on the lush feed of subirrigated valleys and on hills where more browse than grass is available. In localities where brush predominates, the goat which utilizes such feed better than cattle serves as the poor man's cow. Since donkeys and mules require less grain, good grass, or hay than horses, they are generally preferred along with the ox for draft purposes. Pigs feed on acorns and other mast of the forest, although they are less numerous than other animals. Livestock may suffer from lack of fodder if the winter rains do not come when expected;

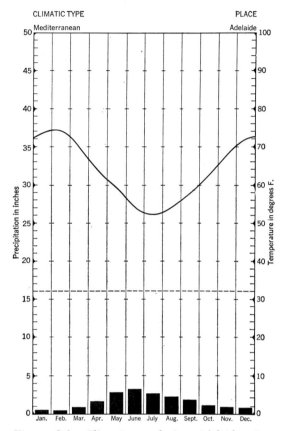

Figure 8-2   Climatic graph for Adelaide, Australia. A dry subtropical location in the Southern Hemisphere. Temperatures are fairly high throughout the year, with an average near 60°F. Note that warm and cold seasons differ little from each other in temperature and that the greatest seasonal contrasts occur in the rainfall distribution. Furthermore, precipitation, although slight, is marked during the winter season and is distinctly deficient during the summer.

regions of Mediterranean climate in which droughts frequently occur can support little agriculture, livestock, or population.

Mediterranean Agriculture.   Absence of frost and the resulting long growing season help agriculture in Mediterranean regions but summer drought and available irrigation water limit its development. Grains are planted when the rains begin in November or December in the Northern Hemisphere and mature

Figure 8-3 Chaparral on southward-facing mountains in Angeles National Forest, southern California. The thicket of chaparral in the lower left corner indicates the dense growth of chaparral plants. Bull pine tops the distant mountain ridge, and the line separating the chaparral cover and the forest cover is clearly marked. (Photograph, courtesy of the U.S. Forest Service.)

in late spring before the hot summer weather can burn the grain and shrink the kernels. Winter wheat, barley, and millet are common grains. Various vegetables and small fruits can also be raised as winter crops. During summer some hardy fruits like the chestnut, walnut, and olive can mature without irrigation (Figure 8-4). These tree crops are often planted on hilly ground with the trees widely spaced, and they grow on the normal rainfall around the Mediterranean Sea. In regions where the rainfall is about 20 inches annually, even grapes can be raised without irrigation.

Most fruits suitable for the Mediterranean climate produce best with irrigation. These include oranges, lemons, grapefruit, and other citrus fruits, the grape, fig, peach, apricot, and various other soft-fleshed deciduous fruits, and the olive. Fine-quality fruits can be produced because of the abundant sunshine and irrigation water together with the natural fertility of the soils. Some fruit is canned, dried, or preserved in other ways. Sunny weather in the harvesting season favors the drying of raisins, currants, prunes, peaches, apricots, and figs, although much fruit is dried artificially. Modern refrigeration makes it possible to ship some fruit fresh to distant markets. Typical exports of Mediterranean regions are wine, olive oil, and fresh or preserved fruits. Very dense populations can be supported on irrigated land, as many as several hundred people per square mile earning a living from farming alone. Without irrigation the farms must be larger, and in some grazing sections the ranches may be very large indeed.

Erosion in the Mediterranean region. For centuries erosion has been a problem in the Mediterranean region because of the relief features and climate as well as the human factor involved. The Mediterranean Sea is nearly surrounded by hills and mountains. Areas of level land are limited, and in many areas terraces are built to retain soil for cultivation and to make irrigation possible. In many mountains, careless cutting of the forests and overgrazing have so damaged the cover of trees, brush, and grass that erosion has long seriously affected productivity. The absence of frost, which binds the soils of colder climes, and occasional torrential downpours of rain add to the erosion problem. Some scholars go so far as to contend that deforestation, overgrazing, careless use of land, soil exhaustion, and excessive soil erosion were largely responsible for the decline of civilization in some parts of the Mediterranean world.

Life in the Mediterranean climate. As a rule, only the irrigated parts of Mediterranean regions support as great a density of farm population as that found in the rainier sections of similar latitudes, where the people eat rice as their staple food. This grain yields more food per acre than wheat or barley, the common grains of Mediterranean regions.

The small variation in temperature is reflected in the types of houses characteristic of Mediterranean lands. Lack of timber encourages the use of stone or brick in building; roofs and floors are often tiled. Roofs tend to be flat or gently sloping in part because snow is almost unknown in these latitudes.

Regions having Mediterranean climate attract the residents of colder stormier lands, and California, as well as the countries adjoining the Mediterranean Sea, has capitalized on this fact to attract tourists. Although these visitors like to come in the winter season to enjoy the sunshine, mild days, and verdure of the subtropics, actually more tourists visit California and Italy during the bright but moderately hot summer. One of the reasons why the motion-picture industry originally moved to southern California from New York and Chicago was because outdoor scenes could be photographed practically every day in the year. After its early growth near Los Angeles, this industry tends to remain concentrated there, even though indoor photography is now common and many television programs originate elsewhere.

After a region has attained a maturity of occupance, it may degenerate and lose importance in world affairs and its standing in civilization and culture. Parts of the eastern Mediterranean have had this experience. Formerly the region supported dense populations and large cities. Libya, Syria, and Crete, for example, are of minor significance in the modern world, although in ancient times they were centers of civilization.

Figure 8-4 Grove of olive trees in the San Fernando Valley, California. These trees must be irrigated to obtain a satisfactory crop. Electric transmission lines cross the groves, bringing hydroelectric power to the houses and factories of Los Angeles and other southern California cities. (Photograph, courtesy of the Los Angeles County Chamber of Commerce.)

Villages. Locations of settlements around the Mediterranean depend on both natural and human factors. Many of the enclosing mountains near the Mediterranean Sea are largely composed of limestone. This is a soluble rock in which caves often develop, and in such areas much drainage is underground. During the dry summer, many streams dry up completely on the surface. Large springs emerge in places from the cavernous limestone rock, and local inhabitants may depend on these sources for their water supply. The distribution of population naturally is quite uneven in the hilly limestone regions. Customarily, instead of living on individual land holdings, people gather in villages from which they go to till their fields and herd their stock. Some villages originally were located on hilltops for mutual defense and protection during turmoil and danger of wars and raids (Figure 8-5). These communities continue to occupy the sites because it has become the custom for people to live in towns. These must have a dependable water supply, and many urban centers have been built near perennial springs.

At mouths of rivers little deltas often furnish tillable soil to support a city; this is true also of the floodplains of the large rivers and other areas of fertile land. Rich soil seldom covers any large part of the country, but where it occurs the population becomes very dense and land is intensively cultivated, often by hand methods, so that the maximum number of people can find sustenance.

Successive occupance of California. Man's use of a region varies widely according to his

Figure 8-5 A compact mountain village in the Alpine regions of southeastern France. Ancient towns of this type were sometimes fortified. Compare this settlement with the sprawling borders of most American towns. The general use of stone for building and of tile for roofs is typical of most European settlements in the Mediterranean areas. (Photograph, courtesy of the French Embassy Press and Information Division.)

culture and experience. Often different industries or leading occupations follow each other in regular succession. Parts of California serve as a good example. There the Indians, never present in large numbers, gathered acorns, shellfish, roots, and berries to supplement the rather scant supply of game animals. The Spaniards and Mexicans introduced livestock, vast herds of cattle cropped the natural fodder, and only a little farming was carried on. Americans were attracted first by the wealth of furs and placer gold but soon turned attention to agriculture. After a period of "bonanza" wheat farming, irrigation (Figure 8-6) was begun, and the large ranches and estates were divided into small holdings intensively farmed for production of grapes, soft fruits, alfalfa, sugar beets, and vegetables. Alongside with intensive agriculture and irrigated farming, man has now built large cities and developed mines, oil deposits, forests, water power, and other resources. Thus in California at present more men are engaged in commerce, manufacturing, catering to tourists, and the professions, than are supported by agriculture, intensive though that may be.

THE DRY SOUTHERN INTERIOR

In the interior of continents situated in latitudes between regions of Mediterranean climate and those which have the humid subtropical type are dry regions of steppes or deserts (Figure 8-7). These areas are deficient in precipitation either because they are far from the ocean, or because highlands rob the winds of most of the moisture, or both. In general the summer weather is hot, but winters are fairly cold with occasional snow.

Western Texas and eastern New Mexico are situated in such subtropical steppes. Here cattle, sheep, and goats are the principal animals kept by the ranchers. Wheat, corn, grain sorghum, and cotton are grown in the Texas "Panhandle," mostly by dry-land methods, although irrigation is also practiced. Alfalfa is a leading irrigated crop. In the lower Rio Grande Valley of Texas, where killing frost is rare, the output of grapefruit, tomatoes, and other winter-grown vegetables has become of high value. To the westward are the dry regions discussed in the preceding chapter. First come the Colorado and Mexican plateaus and mountains which have moderate temperatures because of high elevation. Then

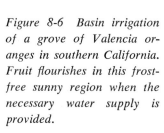

Figure 8-6 Basin irrigation of a grove of Valencia oranges in southern California. Fruit flourishes in this frost-free sunny region when the necessary water supply is provided.

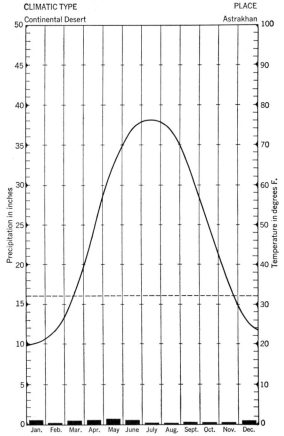

Figure 8-7 Climatic graph for Astrakhan, U.S.S.R. The interior regions of the Northern Hemisphere continents normally fail to receive large amounts of rainfall from marine origins, particularly if intervening mountain ranges interfere with rainfall distribution. This location represents a climatic type in which there are sharp seasonal contrasts in temperature and relatively slight but evenly distributed precipitation. Winter temperatures are severe. (Note the number of months each year that the mean monthly temperature falls below freezing.) The precipitation deficiency indicates a mid-latitude desert or steppe location.

beyond the highlands the land descends to the hot tropical Sonora Desert, located east and north of the Gulf of California.

South from the savanna climate and vegetation of the Gran Chaco in northern Argentina, that region grades into the semidesert and steppes of western Argentina. The Gran Chaco supports a stunted forest of quebracho, very hard wood from which tannin is extracted for use in tanning leather. On the steppes the ranchers keep horses, cattle, and goats. Several oases have been developed by irrigation. Mendoza, at the foot of the Andes, is famous for vineyards and wine. Tucumán and Salta to the north raise cotton, sugar cane, and rice as money crops.

In Asia, interior deserts and steppes of Iran and the U.S.S.R. east of the Caspian Sea are located in southern midlatitudes (Figure 8-8). Where water is available crops of cotton, alfalfa, melons, grains, fruits, and vegetables are grown under irrigation. Mountains rim and cross Iran, dividing the country into basins which are desert because the mountains have received most of the rain. In summer nomadic tribes accompany their herds of animals up to the high pastures, but in autumn they leave the mountains and return to the lowlands for the winter. This annual migration is called *transhumance,* a practice man has followed for thousands of years. Much desert land in Iran and the adjacent Caspian lowlands in the U.S.S.R. has been reclaimed by irrigation, without which the land is useful for scanty grazing only. It is too dry for unirrigated crops.

The Oriental rug. The so-called "Oriental" or Persian rug originally was a good example of the relation of steppe peoples to their environment. The nomads had a surplus of wool beyond their needs for their own clothing and the tents in which they needed permanent yet portable covering. They also had plenty of leisure for other occupations, since most of the time the herds could be watched and tended by only a few members of the tribe. With experience, these primitive herders learned to weave rugs and other articles and attained great skill in their manufacture. Sheep furnished the required raw material, and the wool was dyed from native plant sources that furnished colors of great beauty, said to last better than artificial dyes. The beauty of design and construction of the woven articles made by the nomads has rarely been equaled. Many of their rugs are genuine works of art rather than floor coverings and were used for interior decoration. Outsiders who admired the rugs gladly traded products needed by the nomads for them. Rugs were also valuable enough to afford the slow, expensive caravan transportation to market. Thus the rugs originally made by nomads to supply their need for portable floor coverings in a cold windy winter climate later became a valued article of commerce. Today many rugs are made in the cities of the Orient, and dyes are generally the cheaper imported aniline dyes instead of the lasting vegetable colors, but some of the finest rugs still come from the deserts and steppes of central Asia (Figure 8-9).

THE HUMID SUBTROPICS

Location and Characteristics. The principal humid subtropical climate areas are found in approximately the same latitudes as those of the Mediterranean regions, but on the eastern sides of the continents (Figure 8-1). The greatest extent of this type of climate is found in the southeastern United States, southeastern Asia, including locations as far north as the southern tip of Korea and Japan, east central Argentina, Uruguay, southern Paraguay, and small areas in southeastern Australia and southeastern Africa. These regions have moderate to abundant rainfall in all months of the year, with greatest concentration occurring in the summer season. Thus they resemble the monsoon climate in distribution of precipitation but lack the winter drought period (Figure 8-10). Causes of heavy summer rains in the humid subtropical regions are in large part similar to those producing monsoon conditions—marked differences in pressure and winds, built up between summer and winter seasons over the interiors of continental land masses.

Vegetation. Like the monsoon areas, the humid subtropical climate is characterized by long hot summers which produce rapid growth of vegetation. Palms, citrus fruits, cotton, tobacco, and rice, as well as many other typical subtropical crops, may be grown commercially in these parts of the world. Native vegetation may consist of coniferous and deciduous trees. Most of the conifers and many broad-leaved trees, such as the orange and live oak, are evergreen. Typical conifers include the yellow pine of our Southeastern states and the Paraná pine of southeastern Brazil. Farther inland in South America are forests of the bushy yerba maté from whose leaves an aromatic tea is brewed. Approaching the equator, the broad-leaved vegetation may be evergreen, as in southern Florida; the palmetto grows as far north as the Carolina coast. The Chinese utilize several varieties of bamboo that thrive in this climate. Grasslands are characteristic of certain regions, notably in Uruguay and Argentina. The coastal prairies of Louisiana and Texas are other examples, along with tall-grass areas in the interior parts of Texas and Alabama.

Climatic Effects. The humid subtropical growing season is long, with usually a frostless sea-

Figure 8-8 Mongols of the cold deserts of central Asia. They need heavy woolen clothing and portable substantial dwellings to protect them from winter cold. (Photograph, courtesy of the American Museum of Natural History.)

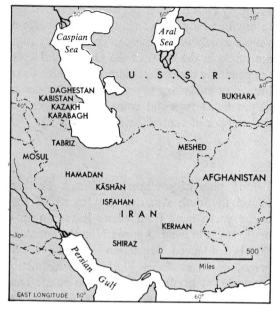

Figure 8-9 Some of the important centers of rug manufacture and markets in southwestern Asia.

son of more than 200 days per year, decreasing to 180 days or less near its border on the poleward side. This long growing season, combined with high summer temperatures and abundant rain, makes these parts of the world highly desirable for human activity, since supplies of food may be procured without too much difficulty and the rate of productivity is moderately high. Short and relatively mild winters are not serious handicaps to such activities as dairying, fishing, or lumbering.

Cold waves descend to the latitudes of humid subtropical regions as the wind zones of the earth are pulled equatorward with the approach of winter in the Northern Hemisphere, bringing cyclonic storms of low temperature to subtropical locations. Cold waves occasionally carry light snowfall to the poleward margins of subtropical regions and to interior continental locations in these latitudes. Occasional frost periods may menace commercial crops like oranges and tomatoes. Sometimes orchards are protected by heating devices similar to those used in Mediterranean regions. Modern methods of weather forecasting often provide sufficient warning so that crops may

be protected from frost damage, but in many seasons an entire winter may pass without serious threat of freezing temperatures.

Rainfall is heavy in this climatic realm, about 40 inches per year on the average and rising to 80 inches in some years. This amount is sufficient, in combination with high temperatures, to account for extensive leaching of undisturbed soils. When this occurs, the depleted soil must be restored by the addition of large quantities of fertilizer. Indeed, farmers of the southeastern United States make heavy purchases of mineral fertilizers in order to maintain the necessary level of agricultural productivity. On the other hand, soils that have been transported from their places of origin by means of the heavy stream flow in this humid climate make exceptionally fertile farm land. Floodplains of the Mississippi, Sikiang, and La Plata systems, for example, are very productive and highly desirable for agriculture, if unfavorable drainage and flood threats can be corrected.

Residents of humid subtropical regions experience long hot summers, particularly on the equatorward margins where high temperatures and high humidity generally are detrimental to human health. Furthermore insect life often makes the summer season unpleasant, and it is difficult to maintain good health conditions. Malaria is prevalent in many sections, especially in Southeast Asia; hookworm and other parasitic diseases add to the health problem. Winters are brief and relatively mild, though high humidity makes the air seem raw and damp except in coastal locations, as along the coasts of Florida where marine temperatures prevail in winter. Visitors find the winter season more pleasant than summer.

Humid subtropical regions of the Northern Hemisphere are subject to erratic storms called hurricanes (see Chapter 4). These storms may bring great damage to crops, farm structures, cities, and shipping. Hurricanes are usually most destructive along coasts, because these storms tend to subside in the interiors of land masses. Although whole seasons may pass without hurricanes, several may strike in a single year. Advances in forecasting the formation and movement of hurricanes have reduced losses of life and property to a considerable extent.

Subsistence Farming. In this region agriculture presents two strongly contrasted aspects: subsistence farming, using rather primitive methods to provide a man and his family with most of their daily food requirements, and commercial farming, based on large landholdings and designed to provide surplus supplies of food or raw materials for cash sale. Farming at the subsistence level in the southeastern United States involves production of sweet potatoes, corn, hogs, dairy cows, and small amounts of wheat, fruit, and other foodstuffs.

In China and Japan, subsistence items include peanuts, rice, fish, and root crops as well as poultry, swine, and corn in China, where quantities of fish are produced in farm ponds. With a growing season from seven to eleven months long, two or three food crops can be raised on the same ground each year. Hence a family may require only 1 or 2 acres of ground, which is worked intensively. This land must be well fertilized if it is to continue at a high level of production, and the waste of cities, "green manure" crops, and sometimes commercial fertilizers are used for this purpose.

Farmers sometimes raise two crops of rice annually, or perhaps some winter-sown grain alternates with summer-sown rice, together with a crop of vegetables between each of the grain crops. This is made possible by the practice of transplanting rice by hand from seedbeds in which the crop is started (Figure 8-11). All three major humid subtropical areas grow rice, but it is a large-scale commercial crop grown with the aid of mechanical devices in the southeastern United States and Argentina. It is, however, not so generally important or productive in humid subtropical regions as in monsoon areas like South China.

Plantation Agriculture. Among other factors, large-scale agricultural production generally

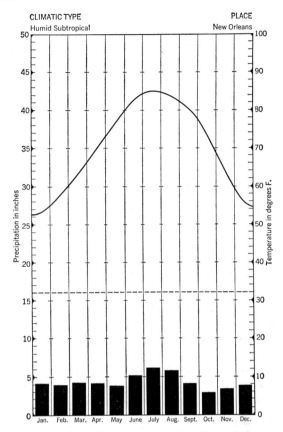

Figure 8-10 Climatic graph for New Orleans, Louisiana. The humid subtropical regions occupying the southeastern coasts of continents in the Northern Hemisphere normally experience heavy rainfall throughout the year with a slight tendency toward summer concentration of rain. Temperatures in summer are tropical, and those of winter are moderate. No month in the year has a mean temperature lower than freezing, although there are occasional winter frosts.

requires accessible markets, unusually large landholdings, mechanical equipment, excellent transportation facilities, and a large supply of cheap labor. In parts of southeastern United States, in Uruguay, and in the La Plata region, large estates or plantations serve as producing units, but this is not the case in Japan and China.

Tea. Subtropical crops, grown commercially, include tea in China and Japan, where cheap labor and long experience favor its production although not on a plantation basis. Hilly land, not generally useful for other crops, is used for small individual tea plantings, since the large populations in those countries require most of the fertile lowlands for growing rice and other food crops. Tea is also raised on tropical plantations in Java, India, and Ceylon but only in highland sections where cooler nights produce a better quality of leaf than on hot lowlands. Picking tea is not difficult but requires some experience. Because tea cannot be picked well with machinery, great numbers of poorly paid people are employed at this hand labor. Labor costs in the United States or in Argentina are too high to permit profitable production unless the industry can be mechanized.

Cotton. This fiber plant grows in subtropical regions, both humid and dry, but one of the important producing areas is in the southeastern part of the United States. There the plantation system with its supply of cheap labor was established at an early date. For many years cotton was the leading crop, ideally suited to climate and soil conditions. However, the breakup of large plantations after the Civil War, erosion or exhaustion of soils, and the steady spread of the cotton boll weevil

(Figure 18-13) brought some crop diversification. Among other crops introduced were tung oil nuts, peanuts, deciduous fruits, and market vegetables, together with poultry and livestock. Today much cotton is grown by irrigation in western Texas, Arizona, and California. Southern Brazil, Paraguay, and northern Argentina are now growing cotton on an extensive commercial scale. Cotton is grown to some extent in China, where there is plenty of labor, but there it must compete for land with the greatly needed foodstuffs.

Other crops. In general, humid subtropical regions lack the high temperatures and long growing season necessary for the successful growth of cane sugar, though other geographic factors seem favorable for its production. Relatively small amounts are produced in China, Argentina, South Africa, Australia, and Louisiana.

Tobacco is of greater importance. This was a native Western Hemisphere plant and is grown for the most part on farms south of the Ohio River, although much first-class cigar-wrapper tobacco is raised in the Connecticut Valley (Figure 8-12) and elsewhere in Northern states well outside the humid subtropical climatic region. Both cotton and tobacco re-

Figure 8-11 Japanese farmers planting rice by hand in flooded rice paddies. This type of "stoop labor" is exceedingly tiring and health is usually affected, since the farm laborer is forced to work long hours with his feet and hands immersed. In terms of human effort and time, this is an expensive form of agriculture. (Photograph, courtesy of the American Museum of Natural History, New York.)

quire soils of high fertility, plenty of moisture, a long growing season, and cheap field labor for profitable production. These factors make our Southern states the world's most important tobacco-growing area, especially in Kentucky, Virginia, and North Carolina. As yet, Argentina and southern Brazil lack the labor for cultivating tobacco, and China and Japan lack arable land for this nonedible crop.

Peanuts, grown especially for their oil content, are an important commercial crop in the humid subtropical zone of the United States where labor and machinery are available for its cultivation and harvesting. Peanuts are grown in China but are relatively unimportant as a commercial crop in Argentina or Brazil.

Other important crops in humid subtropical regions include wheat, corn, and citrus fruits. This climatic type normally is too warm and damp for the best wheat, but nevertheless some is grown in Argentina and in China. In the United States wheat is associated with more severe climates. Corn is especially well suited to the humid subtropical realm in the southern United States, as a crop grown for human consumption and livestock feed. In Argentina corn is important for export to Europe where it is fed to poultry and livestock. In Brazil corn is a sustenance crop whose actual value exceeds that of coffee. People in China and southeast Europe grow and consume much corn, but not in southern Japan where suitable land is limited.

The long frost-free growing season of our Southern states makes it possible to produce vegetables, strawberries, and other commodities for Northern markets before their locally grown product is available in springtime. Orange, grapefruit, and tangerine groves are important in parts of Florida, and many citrus fruits are produced in the lower Rio Grande Valley of Texas.

Silk. This fiber, which is regarded as a luxury commodity in most parts of the earth, is particularly associated with the humid subtropics of China and Japan, where it has been produced for centuries as a household industry. Mulberry leaves are used for feeding silk-

Figure 8-12 Stringing "hands" of tobacco on racks preparatory to hauling them to the drying shed. Polish farm laborers have taken over much of the commercialized farming of the Connecticut River valley which is farther north than most other tobacco-growing sections of the United States.

Figure 8-13 The carabao, or water buffalo, is readily domesticated and is used extensively throughout the Asiatic tropics. (Photograph, courtesy of the Hawaii Visitors Bureau.)

worms, and skilled labor is needed for tending them and preparing the fine fibers for market. Silk is not produced to any extent in the United States or Argentina because of high cost for labor although it would be entirely feasible from the climatic standpoint. Invention of synthetic fibers like rayon and nylon has affected silk production adversely.

Tree crops. Tree growth in humid subtropical parts of the United States and China is of much commercial importance. In our South, softwood forests supply lumber, paper pulp, tar, and turpentine (these industries will be described in Chapter 11). Tree crops include the native pecan, tung oil from China, camphor from Formosa, and citrus fruits which are successfully and extensively grown in Florida, southern China, Japan, and Brazil.

Farm animals. Where dense populations prevail, concentrated grains are needed as food for people and cannot be spared for horses which need grain to keep in good condition when doing hard farm work. Hence oxen or the water buffalo (carabao) are used to cultivate the land and draw carts (Figure

8-13), since these animals do well on a grass diet without grain. Furthermore animals with cloven hoofs can plow muddy rice fields better than horses. In our Southern states the hardy mule is preferred by many farmers as a work animal. By crossing cattle developed in cool climates with the brahma cattle of India, new beef breeds like the Santa Gertrudis have been produced. These are better adapted to hot weather, and their raising will improve production of beef in the humid subtropical lands.

The pig can live on wastes and is a good forager even in the woods. For the amount it eats, the pig puts on more weight than other animals, and it is thus well suited for raising in densely populated countries like China. In the United States it is particularly related to corn production, and that is its principal food. In the Southern Hemisphere pig raising has not yet developed on a large scale, partly because of the smaller population density and consuming market, and partly because of the traditional preference for beef cattle in that part of the world.

Chickens, ducks, and other poultry are usual adjuncts of farms in the humid subtropics, especially in China and the United States. Dairying has possibilities, but some breeds of dairy cows developed in our Northern states are poorly adapted to conditions in the South. The development of special breeds of dairy cows has been successful in the southern United States, where cattle raising is an increasingly important part of the agricultural economy. It is also a leading industry in humid subtropical Argentina, Uruguay, Paraguay, and southern Brazil. In China the pressure of the dense population in relation to the amount of cropland leaves little pasturage for cattle although some animals are kept for draught purposes.

SUMMARY

Between tropics and midlatitudes, in subtropical position, lie two transitional climatic realms: the semiarid subtropical or Mediterranean realm and

the humid subtropical realm. Both experience moderate temperatures in winter, and the former is deficient in summer precipitation. Summers in both realms are warm to hot except in localities cooled by nearness to the sea.

Marine influences upon temperature are especially noticeable in Mediterranean lands, which are found principally on western coasts in subtropical latitudes. Here rainfall is adequate for growth of short grass, although agricultural production may be increased by irrigation. Where this is not feasible, grazing is the usual economy.

The humid subtropical realm, located in corresponding latitudes on eastern coasts, receives sufficient moisture throughout the year to encourage the growth of trees and grass. Agriculture is usually profitable although excessive soil leaching, erosion, and poor drainage must sometimes be corrected before the land reaches its greatest productivity.

Subtropical steppes and deserts usually occur between the Mediterranean and humid subtropical regions.

Outline
Climate characteristics
Mediterranean climate
  Causes
  Vegetation
  Agriculture and erosion
  Life and villages
  Successive occupance in California
Dry southern interior steppes
  Environment
  Occupance
Humid subtropics
  Location
  Climate
  Agriculture: subsistence rice, commercial, animals

QUESTIONS

1. If farmers in Florida tried to raise wheat, what conditions of the environment would they find favorable? What would be unfavorable?

2. Florida and the southeast coast of Spain differ climatically, but both areas produce commercial supplies of citrus fruits. How do you explain this?

3. Why do southern California's rains occur in the winter season?

4. Compare the material presented in the text on desert vegetation and Mediterranean vegetation. Then summarize the principal differences and similarities of the vegetation cover in these two climatic realms.

5. What elements in the natural environment of the humid subtropical regions favor the development of commercial plantation farming?

6. What has been the sequence of occupance in California?

7. Why do so many visitors go to the desert of southeast California and southwest Arizona? What season do they choose for a visit? Why?

8. What likenesses in the climates of California and Florida attract tourists?

9. Explain why it is necessary to protect orchards against frost in Mediterranean regions although the mean monthly temperature never falls below freezing.

10. What common problem must farmers face in both Mediterranean and desert regions?

11. What weather characteristics would be experienced by anyone living in:
  a. Capetown
  b. Buenos Aires
  c. Canton
  d. Adelaide
  e. Naples

12. Why in the photograph in Figure 8-3 is there a chaparral cover on the southern slope of the mountain, and a forest cover on the northern slope?

13. In what parts of the subtropical latitudes is grazing important?

14. Why are sheep and goats commonly kept in the subtropical steppes? In Mediterranean climates? Why are the humid subtropics favorable for raising pigs? Why are comparatively few pigs raised in Mediterranean climates?

SELECTED REFERENCES

Cressey, George B.: *Asia's Lands and Peoples,* McGraw-Hill Book Company, Inc., New York, 1951.

Gottmann, Jean: *Virginia at Mid-century,* Henry Holt and Company, Inc., New York, 1955.

Hubbard, George B.: *The Geography of Europe,* Appleton-Century-Crofts, Inc., New York, 1952.

Odum, H. W.: *Southern Regions of the United States,* University of North Carolina Press, Chapel Hill, 1936.

Parkins, Almon E.: *The South,* John Wiley & Sons, Inc., New York, 1938.

Pounds, Norman J. G.: *Europe and the Mediterranean,* McGraw-Hill Book Company, Inc., New York, 1953.

Taylor, Griffith: *Australia,* E. P. Dutton & Co., Inc., New York, 1943.

Zierer, Clifford M. (ed.): *California and the Southwest,* John Wiley & Sons, Inc., New York, 1956.

9. Midlatitudes of the Prevailing Westerlies

CLIMATES of the world in latitudes of the northern half of the United States and adjacent parts of Canada are characterized by four separate seasons of approximately similar length. Winters are generally long, cold, and snowy compared to the subtropics described in Chapter 8. In contrast to the large temperature difference in the winter between the northern and southern parts of the United States, the summer shows small differences in temperature between these regions in the interior and eastern parts of the country. Except in the Pacific Northwest, summers are generally hot, but with a growing season considerably longer near the subtropics than toward the poleward side. The length and severity of winter increases toward the poleward margin of the zone, along with decreased length of summer in the same direction. The region is situated in the zone of prevailing westerly winds, in which cyclonic storms cause frequent changes in temperature, rainfall, windiness, and other weather phenomena. This results in highly variable weather in this generally cooler part of the midlatitudes which lie in the zone of prevailing westerlies for the entire year.

Middle latitudes, including both the subtropical and cooler parts, support more than half the world population. The most powerful countries of the world today are situated in middle latitudes, including most of Western Europe, the United States, southern Canada, northern China and Japan, and parts of the Soviet Union. In the Southern Hemisphere, Argentina, Chile, Uruguay, New Zealand, and southern Australia are in these latitudes. In the poleward half of the midlatitudes where weather is dominated by strong cyclones in the westerly winds, rapid variations in weather are usual throughout the entire year.

In the tropics parallel zones of climate and natural vegetation generally extend in an east-west direction, and the broad belts of different climates are largely classified by decreasing rainfall from the doldrums to the trade winds. The middle-latitude climatic zones in general extend in north-south belts across the continents and are especially marked by rainfall differences and natural vegetation. From the equator to the midlatitudes, isotherms roughly follow the parallels. However, in the realm of the prevailing westerlies the annual isotherms on west coasts are farther away from the equator than in interiors and on east coasts of continents—the result of oceanic as compared with continental influences. Even greater contrasts occur between summer and winter isotherms on west coasts compared with those of the continental interiors.

The cooler or temperate mid-latitude climates experience decreased rainfall from the west coast inland, accompanied by increased range in temperature between winter and summer. Toward the east coasts, rainfall increases again; but the temperature range remains continentally great since westerly winds from the interior predominate. Winds do not blow inland from the eastern oceans frequently enough or far enough to moderate the temperature greatly.

WEST-COAST MARINE CLIMATE

On west coasts of continents, abundant rains occur throughout the year in middle latitudes, with maximum precipitation in winter. This results from the prevailing westerlies and associated cyclonic storms moving from the oceans toward the western shores of the continents. Cyclonic storms are especially well developed in the fall, winter, and spring. The temperature shows a small range between winter and summer, providing generally mild winters and cool summers (Figure 9-1). Transition periods in spring and autumn provide four distinct seasons during the year.

In North and South America high mountains parallel the Pacific near the coast, and areas of heavy rainfall and mild marine temperature variations are limited to the narrow littoral. To leeward of the mountains, continental conditions prevail, with great extremes of temperature and limited rainfall. Abundant rainfall of a west-coast climate supports dense forests of both hardwoods and conifers. The latter include the Douglas fir, cedar, spruce, and western hemlock in northwestern North America. In Europe until cleared for agriculture the "summer" woods of deciduous trees covered much of that continent between the Mediterranean region and the northern coniferous forests of Scandinavia and Russia.

The higher hills and mountains and areas of poor sandy soil also support conifers in the midlatitudes of Europe.

South Island of New Zealand has high mountains along its west coast where dense forests grow, whereas on the eastward side grasslands are extensive. Dense forests also flourish in southern Chile; east of the Andes in Argentina, with less rainfall, grass is the dominant vegetation.

Northwestern Europe. Western Europe includes the most highly developed portions of the Continent and supports 250 million people in an area not as large as the United States east of the Mississippi. Deposits of coal, iron, and other minerals support manufacturing; the irregular coast line and navigable rivers favor the expansion of ocean shipping (in both of which endeavors Western Europe leads the world). Other important factors in the development of the region include extensive plains and fertile soils. Here the combination of geologic and geographic factors has led to growth of great states, industrial cities, and dense populations. The western part of Germany, most of France, all of Belgium and the Netherlands, the British Isles, Denmark, coastal Norway and southern Sweden, experience this climatic type (Figure 9-2). Summers are relatively cool and moist, with plenty of rain for growth of trees and grasses. Though Eurpoe was originally well-wooded, its virgin forests have long been utilized by man. However, second growth and forest plantings are carefully managed and supply considerable amounts of wood products.

The growing season is long and winters are mild, especially in relation to the latitude. With plenty of excellent forage dairying flourishes, and in fact the concentration of dairying in the Netherlands and Denmark almost provides those nations with what might be regarded as a national economy. Dutch cheeses from Alkmaar and Edam, and Danish supplies of butter and bacon, are favorably known. Sheep are important in the farm economy of this part of the world. As a dual-purpose animal supplying both meat and animal fiber, they are kept widely though seldom in large flocks. Fishing is an important occupation in all marine west-coast regions of Europe.

Other important agricultural activities in northwestern Europe include production of some grains, especially wheat in the less humid sections, and rye, oats, and barley. Northwestern Europe, however, is not prime grain country compared with other parts of the world. It grows some mid-latitude fruits, including grapes and apples; the latter are famous in northwestern France. Beet sugar is commonly grown along with potatoes, vegetables, hops, and some flax. The farms of Western Europe provide most of the foodstuffs for its large urban and industrial population. Nonagricultural activities include the exploitation and use of a wealth of raw materials and potential energy, especially coal, iron ore, and hydroelectric power. These, with skilled labor, combine to provide Europeans with necessary supplies of steel, chemicals, and other manufactures characteristic of advanced industrial states.

The Pacific Northwest. Except in Europe mid-latitude marine regions are comparatively undeveloped. The climatic type in North

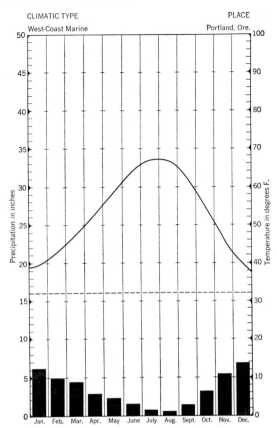

Figure 9-1   Climatic graph for Portland, Oregon. A West-coast marine location in the midlatitudes of the Northern Hemisphere. Note particularly the moderate seasonal temperature variation, with no month in the year having a mean temperature lower than freezing and the moderately heavy rainfall, occurring in all months of the year but with a tendency toward a maximum in the winter season. These conditions are related to nearness to the sea.

America is limited in extent because the Cascades and Coast Ranges of the Pacific lie so near the sea that only small areas of land are suitable for agriculture. These include the Willamette Valley and the Puget Sound lowland of western Oregon and Washington. Here cattle and sheep raising, dairying, growing tree fruits and small fruits, poultry raising, and a little grain production are principal human activities in rural sections.

Away from the lowlands, in the mountain-

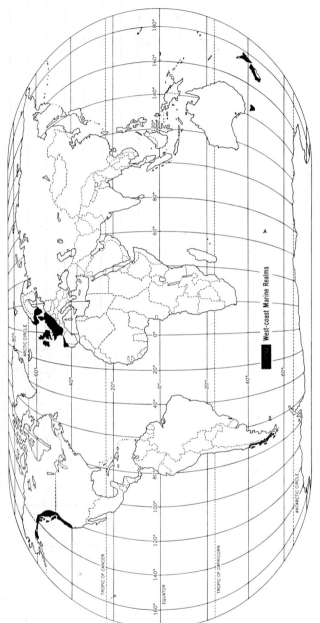

Figure 9-2   West-coast marine realms of the midlatitudes.

ous regions, remarkable stands of timber in the Pacific Northwest permit Oregon and Washington to lead other states of the nation in lumber production (Figure 9-3). Nearly half of all local wage earners are employed in forests and woodworking plants. Cities like Seattle and Tacoma started as lumber-mill towns, and the industry is still important. Puget Sound has many sawmill centers; others are found on the Columbia River. Although some inland towns such as Eugene and Bend, Oregon (Figure 9-4), are sawmill centers, most sawmills and paper mills are located on tidewater for convenience of receiving and shiping raw materials and finished goods. Large supplies of hydroelectric power are another advantage in this region.

Canning of salmon and the processing, storage, and shipment of halibut and other fish are also important on the Pacific Coast, from the Columbia River to Alaska.

Indians of the Pacific Northwest Coast. Native peoples are repelled by the dense dark forests of these regions. On the west coasts of middle latitudes hunters find few large wild animals in the forests to provide food; furthermore, because of dampness in the forests and large size of the trees, primitive farmers find it very difficult to clear land either by fire or by stone axes. As a result, the greater number of the natives originally lived along the coast and looked to the sea for their livelihood.

From the mouth of the Columbia River to the southern coast of Alaska, American Indians practiced no agriculture; they lived on fish and other sea food, supplemented to a small degree with game and berries secured from the land. Salmon that ascended streams in almost incredible numbers were caught and cured for winter use and furnished a depend-

Figure 9-3 Virgin stand of Douglas fir in the Pacific Northwest. This forest is exceptionally free from undergrowth and undesirable timber. (Photograph, courtesy of the U.S. Forest Service.)

Figure 9-4 Lumber mill at Bend, Oregon, in the Pacific Northwest, showing a large log pond and storage yard for sawed lumber. Refuse is burned in the large incinerators, but in many mills the wood wastes are sold for the manufacture of paper pulp. This mill has its own water supply and fire protection system, as the overhead tanks indicate. (Photograph used by permission of Brubaker Aerial Surveys.)

able food supply. Hence Indians built their villages near some stream up which the salmon migrated or at other locations convenient to fishing grounds. The Indians lived in houses built of hand-split cedar boards, and they used fire and crude tools to carve large seaworthy canoes from big cedar logs.

The Indians of the Queen Charlotte Islands and other places along the northwest coast traded extensively with each other and made voyages of many hundreds of miles, especially within the protected waters of the Inside Passage from Alaska to Puget Sound. The Indians cared little for penetrating the interior. Shore forests furnished material for houses, boats, fuel, and other needs. Fur-bearing animals like the otter, fur seal, bear, and beaver were common in the shore waters or forests and furnished clothing and furs for trade.

Southern Chile. Southern Chile has limited areas for agriculture because of the Andes, which, like the Cascades of the Northern Hemisphere, prevent stormy westerly winds from penetrating far inland. It is relatively unpopulated and unproductive, though possessing large amounts of potential water power and dense forests. Southern Chile has been a comparatively recent frontier of settlement. Its agriculture and industry have been retarded, partly because of a remote location from world centers of trade and population, and partly because of the presence of very hostile Indian tribes. It is a land of small villages, out of contact with the populous part of Chile, and experiencing a climate and soils that are highly unfavorable for intensive agriculture.

New Zealand and Australia.   The islands of New Zealand and a limited area in southeastern Australia lie within the path of the Southern Hemisphere westerly winds and receive the full effect of marine conditions. They, like southern Chile, are remote from centers of population, but the presence of volcanic mountains provides a limited quantity of excellent agricultural soils. Many of their people graze sheep or raise dairy cattle. Both operations are on a rather large scale. Output of meat, butter, cheese, wool, and other products beyond local needs finds ready markets in the populous cities of northwestern Europe, where demand outruns local supplies of food. New Zealand's markets for animal products, it should be noted, are linked with improved refrigeration and rapid transport by sea. Without these developments, New Zealand could scarcely compete with more favorably located areas such as Denmark. New Zealand also has excellent supplies of water power, but like southern Chile, it remains mostly undeveloped.

ARID AND SEMIARID CONTINENTAL INTERIORS

Climate and Location.   Interior parts of continents in the middle latitudes customarily experience great temperature ranges, because marine conditions cannot penetrate the centers of large land masses (Figures 9-2 and 9-5). In parts of central Asia, for example, the average temperature for January may be 80°F lower than that for July. Rainfall is generally scanty and highly variable from year to year, for moist sea air seldom reaches these regions. Most rainfall occurs in summer as the result of local convectional thunderstorms, but it is seldom sufficient to provide for more than the growth of meager supplies of grass. Occasionally in summer, rain may come from an inflowing damp air mass from the cool ocean during the period of greatest heating, but rainfall usually decreases inland from the sea as the "supply" of moisture is precipitated from the air masses. This condition is characteristic of interior Asia, where the deserts include the Gobi, Takla Makan, and Turkestan. In part the low rainfall of western Argentina and of the Wyoming Basin region in the western United States illustrates the effect of remoteness from sources of water.

Locally, mountain ranges of moderate or great height may account for some increase in the amount of rainfall. Where interiors of continents lie to the leeward of mountains trending athwart prevailing winds from the sea, "rain shadow" deserts and semiarid steppes are found. The steppes may be transitional between deserts and forests or well-watered prairies. Other grasslands or steppes lie in localities which have deficient rainfall but are not so dry that desert conditions prevail (Figure 9-5).

North American interior dry lands occupy broad basins and plateaus from the Columbia Basin in Washington and Snake River Plains in Idaho southward through the Great Basin of Nevada and Utah. The continuation across New Mexico into Mexico has been discussed in the previous chapter. East of the Rockies the rolling steppes called the *Great Plains* extend from Alberta and Saskatchewan across the whole width of the United States into north-central Mexico. Somewhat similar dry grasslands are found in southern and western Argentina. Interior deserts and steppes extend from interior China into southern U.S.S.R. In all these areas, sparse rainfall is a dominant environmental factor. Over extensive parts of interior Asia, temperature ranges are extreme and winters long, adding to the difficulties of the inhabitants.

Landscapes.   The surface appearance of deserts differs little whether their location is in

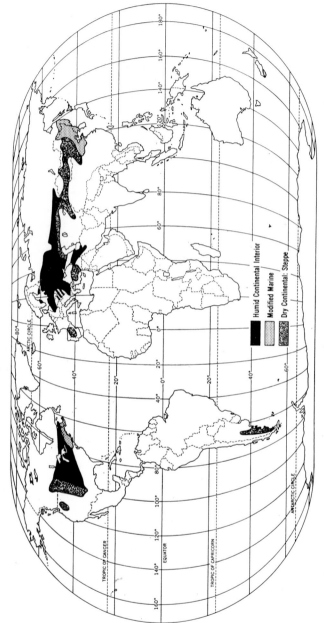

Figure 9-5 Continental climates of the midlatitudes.

the tropics or midlatitudes. In general the same statement is true of steppes or grasslands in different latitudes, although wintry scenes seasonally characterize landscapes of the interior parts of continents in the midlatitudes.

The hills and valleys tend to have steeper slopes under arid and semiarid conditions than under humid conditions. The angularity of the relief features of dry lands contrasts with the more subdued and rounded contours of surfaces formed in rainy climates. Landscapes of these interior regions are usually barren of tree growth except in locations where streams or sufficient subsurface flow provide water for small groves—a condition corresponding to the oases of deserts.

Wood for fuel and building purposes is difficult to obtain, since grasslands occupy most of the semiarid continental interiors. If rainfall is sufficient, a tall grass may prevail, forming a heavy sod, or prairie. Light and irregular rainfall produces the short grass and scattered bunch grass that characterize the steppes.

Seldom do mid-latitude steppes receive enough precipitation to provide many surface streams. These are usually small in flow, few in number, and set within low steep-sided banks. Tributary streams are not numerous. Stream channels of this type frequently have a greater flow of water underground than on the surface, and their beds may be tapped with relative ease with excavations, pipes, or other means for the use of stock or for small irrigation projects. It is difficult, however, to use these stream channels to impound water for irrigation, because their banks are too low and basins too broad and shallow to provide satisfactory sites for reservoirs. Melting snows on nearby mountain ranges may provide some water for irrigation purposes on dry-land areas.

Occupance of Steppes.   Originally great numbers of wild animals lived on the steppes of middle latitudes where they fed upon the characteristic short grass and roamed without hindrance in their search for water holes and forage. Attracted by the abundant meat supply, peoples of the steppes are typically hunters. Thus in Patagonia on grassy plains east of the Andes in southern Argentina there once roamed herds of guanaco, related to the camel and llama. Here certain Indians subsisted on its flesh and used its skin for clothing and shelter. In North America and parts of Asia similar conditions prevailed, and hunting was the principal occupation of many tribesmen on the steppes. Now, often enough, these grasslands serve for grazing domestic livestock and cultivating drought-resistant grains on an extensive scale. When man uses the steppes more intensively than he does when living by hunting, he changes the type of animal, replaces much of the original plant life, builds fences and shelters, and in other ways modifies the environment, as indicated in Figure 9-6.

The Plains Indians.   The Indians of North America who originally lived on our central prairies and Great Plains relied upon millions of buffalo or bison (Figure 9-7) and great herds of antelope, elk, and other game. The whole life of the Plains Indians was wrapped up in the buffalo as thoroughly as that of the Arab in his camel. All the men of a village joined in cooperative buffalo hunts. Great numbers of animals might be secured both by the use of weapons and by other schemes, such as driving herds of buffalo over cliffs where they might be killed by the fall or injured so that they could be dispatched easily.

No part of the buffalo was wasted by the Indian. Its meat was dried and smoked for winter use. Many of the internal organs furnished needed vitamins in the diet of the Indian. From buffalo skins, the Indians made warm robes and excellent durable hides suitable for portable tepees, wearing apparel, and other uses. Sinews from the animals served for thread, splinters of bone for needles.

The same weapons that were used in hunting the buffalo could be used for fighting human beings. Plains Indians were accustomed to teamwork in buffalo hunts; when threatened by white aggression, different tribes and villages joined together for war and offered a better defense against the encroachment of

Figure 9-6 Large flock of sheep moving from summer mountain pastures to lowland pastures in Montana, where ample forage will be provided by the native grasses through the winter season or supplies of hay or irrigated pastures will be available. (Photograph, courtesy of the U.S. Department of Agriculture.)

white men than did most Indian tribes. The introduction of the horse by the Spaniards improved the situation of the Plains Indians. The tribes, when supplied with horses, could travel farther on hunting expeditions, and men could move their families and camp equipment more quickly and easily.

White Penetration into the Great Plains. When people of European descent entered the Great Plains, they had to adapt their activities to the new environment before settlement became permanent. The Spaniards made little progress against the Plains Indians, who were fierce fighters and possessed too great mobility to be overcome with ease. Not until Americans exterminated the buffalo could these nomads be restricted to reservations.

Within a single lifetime, the white man's plow, introduction of domestic cattle, and fencing the grasslands changed the Great Plains from wild Indian and buffalo country, through brief years of open cattle range, to a land of homesteads and permanent farming.

American colonists surging westward from the Atlantic Coast crossed the Appalachian ridges, carved out homes for themselves from the hardwood forests, and finally reached the prairies. There, large plows pulled by many head of oxen or horses broke up the prairie sod. This soil proved well adapted to corn, wheat, and other crops. New home seekers kept on beyond the Mississippi through Iowa and Missouri to eastern Kansas and Nebraska and finally to the western parts of these states.

After the Civil War, cattle had been driven

north from Texas for shipment east to packing centers and for stocking the virgin-grass empire of the central and northern Great Plains. During the late 1870s and early 1880s, in years of somewhat plentiful rainfall, the first influx of farmers came to compete with the stockmen. A series of dry years, hot winds, plagues of grasshoppers, and hordes of locusts then afflicted the settlers, and many farmers failed and left the country.

Later the survivors, along with other immigrants, learned how to raise crops on the semiarid grasslands by using dry-farming methods to conserve moisture, planting varieties which could withstand droughts and severe winters. For example, wheats raised in the humid eastern United States were found unsatisfactory for planting on the Great Plains, and wheat raising became successful only when sturdy winter and spring varieties were introduced from Russia (Figure 9-8). Alfalfa provided a substitute for the red clover of the East. Grain sorghum and certain drought-resistant varieties of Indian corn helped overcome the difficulties of the farmers by furnishing grain and fodder. Unfortunately so much of the short-grass lands were plowed up that sometimes, in cycles of dry weather, the sod which formerly had held the soil in place was gone. High prevailing winds then caused much damage by drifting and blowing the soil away. Occasionally, dust storms cover such vast areas that topsoil from entire farms or sections of land is blown off and carried to leeward (Figure 9-9). In the 1930s dust even reached the cities along the Atlantic seaboard. Such experiences caused some cultivated areas on the Great Plains to be abandoned by farmers or the land to be returned to a grazing economy.

For permanent occupancy, a natural cover of grass, herbs, and other vegetation must be replanted on soil most subject to blowing. Land that is least adapted to cultivation should be used for grazing. Flocks and herds should be carefully controlled so that their grazing will not injure the natural grass cover. By carefully farming the best land, by reseeding natural grazing lands, and by irrigating where possible, the "dust bowl" and other Great Plains areas that have been damaged by overgrazing and careless working of the soil can be reclaimed.

In the dry western parts of the United States, even if all the rainfall could be used for irrigation, only a small fraction of the land could ever be farmed. The same condition holds true for Iran, Turkestan, and other

Figure 9-7 Young bison bulls on the Nebraska plains. (Photograph by G. A. Amundson, used by permission of the U.S. Fish and Wildlife Service.)

Figure 9-8   Two diesel-powered tractors pulling combines in the Palouse district of eastern Washington. One combine can cut and thresh more than 2,000 acres of wheat in a season. (Photograph, courtesy of the Caterpillar Tractor Company.)

Asiatic deserts. It is obvious that all the available supply of water in deserts can never be enough to irrigate them, since much water runs off in sudden floods following the cloudbursts characteristic of desert rainfall, and rain water also evaporates or sinks away where man cannot find it.

Occupance of Asiatic Interior Regions.   Outside the developed oases in the deserts of central Asia, part of the native peoples are nomadic and some dwell in semipermanent villages. Village houses generally are poor affairs, built of brick or clay or sometimes of stone because of scarcity of timber and poverty of the people. Nomads, who need portable dwellings, generally use the hemispherically shaped yurt because the low winter temperatures of central Asia demand a warmer house than is needed in lower-latitude deserts. The yurt is built of slabs of padded wool laid over a framework of poles (Figure 8-8); a roof opening allows the escape of smoke from the fire of wood or dried animal dung. The diet of roasted or boiled meat is supplemented with milk, often used in sour or fermented form, and grain secured by trading with farmers at the oases. Some wild game is also available. To resist the winter's cold and the sharp

drop of temperature at night, even in summer, people wear woolen and padded garments that keep out the penetrating winds (Figure 8-8). Heavy woolen rugs, sometimes woven and sometimes made of felt, are commonly used to make the interior of the yurt comfortable.

The animals are those suited to a severe climate. The Bactrian species of camel (Figure 7-5) has long woolly hair and can withstand not only drought but also the cold of winters in the interior. Horses, cattle, sheep, and goats are all of hardy breeds. In high arid and cold plateaus like Tibet, the yak with its matted hair can survive in spite of harsh conditions and so is used as a riding and draught animal.

Some governments, particularly in the Soviet Union, are attempting to induce nomads to abandon their wandering mode of life and settle in permanent villages. Irrigated areas are being extended; a few railroads have been built to reach the edge of these interior desert regions. Trucks are beginning to penetrate still farther and have begun to replace the Bactrian camel and other animals used for caravans. Yet the heart of Asia's interior desert area is still relatively unaffected by modern civilization.

In the lives of these people, religion is important and many of their activities are carried on in connection with religious beliefs and customs. The cities of Ulan Bator (Urga) in Mongolia and Lhasa in Tibet are centers of religious rites; here are the sacred residences of grand lamas, who claim both spiritual and temporal power.

In Eurasia, the Soviet Union after World War II greatly increased the planting of wheat, partly through the device of the collective farm, and partly by means of the introduction of modern mechanized methods of cultivation. New railways and highways have been built to facilitate shipments of wheat to other parts of the nation, especially in the plains lying east and northeast of the Caspian Sea. Farther west, along the lower Volga and into the Ukraine, the steppes have been Russia's principal source of wheat for many years, but methods of production were relatively backward. As in the United States and Patagonia, the Eurasian steppes produced large numbers of cattle and sheep and, in addition, goats for Russia's needs.

Steppes of South America. The steppe regions of Patagonia (southern Argentina) are not large producers of wheat, because much of the land is rough and rocky and also because the area is a relatively unsettled frontier whose agricultural capabilities have not yet been exploited. On its range, however, Patagonia does support large numbers of sheep and some cattle.

HUMID CONTINENTAL CLIMATE

The Climate. This climatic type is generally limited to the eastern side and continental interiors of the poleward section of middle latitudes in the Northern Hemisphere, since no large continental masses in the Southern Hemisphere extend into midlatitudes (Figure 9-5). The name *humid continental climate* indicates dominance of temperatures whose wide range shows pronounced lack of marine influence, in other words, continental conditions. Air masses and winds, prevailingly from the west but governed by cyclonic circulation, swing into the centers of the continents. The resulting sudden weather changes occur especially in the winter season, when masses of cold polar air migrate into these latitudes from time to time. Rainfall usually is moderate in amount and regularly distributed through all months in the year.

In winter precipitation often takes the form

Figure 9-9 Dust storm in Clayton, New Mexico. On the day of the storm the weather was calm with light winds from the southwest. The dust rolled in on a light wind, followed by a severe hurricane lasting about three hours. This heavy dust cloud was suspended in the air about half an hour. (Photograph courtesy of the U.S. Soil Conservation Service.)

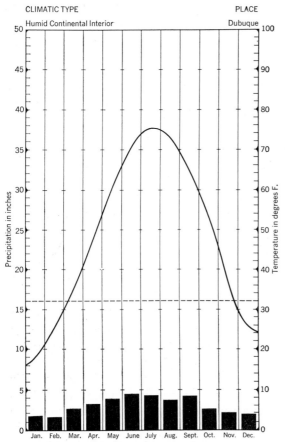

CLIMATIC TYPE   PLACE

Humid Continental Interior   Dubuque

Figure 9-10 Climatic graph for Dubuque, Iowa. This location is continental, and the climate is humid. Some places in the interior of continents in the Northern Hemisphere receive moderate well-distributed rainfall and snowfall throughout the year. Here rain or snow occurs each month, the total amount of precipitation is moderate, and the seasonal temperature range is marked, with at least one month in the year experiencing a mean temperature below freezing.

of heavy snows, but in summer masses of air move inland from the sea and supply much rainfall, frequently in connection with convectional thunderstorms (Figure 9-10). Winter rain and snow are mainly of cyclonic origin; and as the lows approach and move eastward toward the coast, masses of moisture-filled air are drawn inland, furnishing rain or snow to the interiors of continents.

Temperatures, as already noted, tend to vary widely with change of season, and in this climatic type, extreme ranges of 100 degrees or more may occur between absolute summer and winter maxima and minima. In general, the more southerly parts of the humid continental interior realms have longer and warmer summers; the northern boundaries experience very short growing seasons and long severe winters. Some modification of temperatures occurs on the eastern borders of the region, where winters and summers are slightly less severe because of nearness to the sea, as in New England.

Location. The humid continental interior climatic condition occurs in central North America east to the ocean, central Eurasia, northern China, including Manchuria, most of Korea, southeastern Siberia, and the northern part of the Japanese archipelago, especially the island of Hokkaido. In North America this climatic condition is divided into the mild phase, with long summers and shorter winters where the humid continental interior borders the northern edge of the humid subtropical regions in the Ohio and lower Missouri Valleys, and the severe phase, with shorter cooler summers and longer colder winters, experienced in the Northern states of upper Michigan, Minnesota, and the Dakotas. Slight marine effects on temperatures are noticeable in the humid continental climate of New England and the coastal parts of the Middle Atlantic states. This marine effect causes the winters to be less rigorous and the summers cooler on the east coasts than inland a hundred miles or more. There is also some temperature modification in the vicinity of the Great Lakes. Similar conditions exist near the coast in southeastern Siberia.

Farms and Forests. The humid continental interior with long summers and relatively mild winters in the United States is a highly productive region. Its soils, partly laid down by glacial action, are generally of good quality for mixed farming. Winter wheat is a specialty crop; the growing season is sufficiently long and warm for the production of large quantities of corn. Oats, sugar beets (chiefly in the more subhumid parts), potatoes, apples, and other typical mid-latitude crops are important, and dairying is a common occupation. Forests were extensive, and they still provide some timber from both hardwood (broadleaved) and softwood (needle-leaved) trees. Since soil developed under broad-leaved trees is usually of good fertility, much of the hardwood forest has been cleared and the land devoted to farm crops. Open glades, originally covered with the tall grass of the prairies, have been plowed to provide some of the richest granary lands in the nation. Mixed farming, a combination of crops and livestock, is a principal human activity, and the great wealth of resources has caused a marked development of industry and city life.

Humid continental regions experiencing short, relatively cool summers and long severe winters extend in North America from the upper Mississippi Valley eastward into New England. These sections originally were well forested, but unlike the milder phase of this climate, the trees consisted largely of conifers growing in soils of only moderate productivity. Manufacturing in this region today is based partly upon forest resources, as at Grand Rapids, Michigan, traditionally a center of furniture making.

Life in the forests.   Among the original native inhabitants in eastern America, the Iroquois Confederacy had the strongest tribal organization. These Indians occupied a very strategic pass route in the Mohawk and Genesee Valleys between the Hudson River and the Great Lakes, within the area covered by the severe phase of the humid continental interior climate. Their villages, composed of houses constructed with logs and bark, might contain as many as two or three thousand persons, and were protected by strong stockades. Near the village were fields of several hundred acres devoted to cornfields and fruit trees, each family having its own plot of land to cultivate.

The Winnebago and other tribes of Wisconsin and Minnesota depended largely upon wild rice that grew in shallow water rather than upon cultivation of maize.

Elsewhere in the eastern area the Indians supported themselves by a combination of farming and hunting. Although land trails connected the villages, journeys were more commonly made by canoe, utilizing the splendid system of glacial lakes and rivers. The light graceful birchbark canoe, perfectly adapted to the rapids, portages, and waterways, was a product of its environment.

Present occupants.   Today, mixed farming occupies the farmers of the Northern states; their activities are based upon hardier grains than those which do well in Kansas, Illinois, or Indiana. These grains include spring wheat, grown on the more fertile areas, and rye, oats, and barley on the less fertile soils. Some wrapper tobacco of high quality is produced as a specialty crop. Many fruits, tomatoes, and other vegetables are grown for processing. Cattle, sheep, and hogs are the staple farm animals, although cattle must be stall-fed in winter and losses of sheep may be serious during the most severe seasons. Farmhouses and barns must be substantial structures to give adequate shelter from the cold (Figure 9-11). Originally fur trapping was important in northern Michigan, Minnesota, Wisconsin, and parts of the Canadian provinces of Ontario and Manitoba, but this resource is relatively exhausted.

In the extreme northeastern parts of the region, along the New England coast, human activities are less concerned with farming. Soils are thin and poor, and the climate is too cold and the growing season too short for most grains. Here many people engage in dairying and forestry, with fishing important along the coast. Some deciduous fruits, such as apples, are grown. The Annapolis Valley in Nova Scotia is famous for its apples, a type of agriculture made possible by locally good soil and climatic modification afforded by the Bay of Fundy. The staple food is often the potato; Aroostook County, Maine, has achieved eco-

Figure 9-11 A typical American farm in an excellent agricultural area in Hunterdon County, New Jersey. The principal income from this farm is obtained from the sale of milk from its herd of 40 Holstein cows; poultry and hogs provide additional income for the owner. Note the use of the silo for the storage of winter feed and the detached shed for handling milk and milk cans. (Photograph, courtesy of U.S. Department of Agriculture.)

nomic success by specializing in potato production. Furs, including those produced on fur farms for fox and mink, are important as a special source of income, but in general nature's resources cannot support many people, so New Englanders turned to industry and manufactures. At first they utilized many waterfalls found along the stream valleys, but today the mills and factories normally use coal or other sources of energy. Raw materials for processing are often imported from other states and countries, and the coastal ports of New England are important centers of manufacture. The "back country" remains essentially undeveloped and rural, with dairying and general farming providing the principal livelihood.

Seasonal Changes in North America. In humid continental regions much precipitation oc-

curs when temperatures are below freezing, so it usually takes the form of snow in winter. Hence winter snows often interfere with transportation, and the expression "snowbound" has great significance for residents of these latitudes. Snow remains on the ground for long periods in winter, forcing rural people to store sufficient quantities of forage for livestock and of fuel to meet their own needs during the long winter season. During that part of the year when the ground is snow-covered and frozen, erosion of soil cannot occur—a condition not found in warmer climates. In spring, with the approach of warm weather, the snow melts, swelling the flow of streams, and providing water for power and transportation for pulpwood drives that are an annual occurrence on some streams.

Human activities are governed largely by marked seasonal changes. Upon the disappearance of the snow in spring, the soil thaws. Cultivation begins as soon as the ground is free from frost, and planting follows with arrival of the first warm days. Fences must be straightened and repaired. Stones are removed from the fields if necessary; the spring sowing begins. People remove and store "storm windows" and set about spring cleaning and painting. Winter stoves are dismantled and stored, and heavy winter clothing is placed in mothproof containers. As spring moves into midsummer and fields and woods change from brown to green, the time of greatest outdoor activity approaches. Daylight hours are longer, and farmers are busy with cultivation and planting. Cattle are pastured in the open, and with summer comes the haying season. Most farms carry on some slaughtering. Household activities include processing fruit for the coming winter season.

Upon the approach of autumn, the harvest season involves the cutting of cornstalks for fodder, storage of hay for winter feeding, and the mowing, threshing, cleaning ("winnowing"), and sacking of grain. Food in quantities sufficient to meet family needs—potatoes and other root crops—must be stored in cool but frost-free cellars. House and barn are made secure against winter storms, and fuel must be provided for the long winter to follow. When snow makes long trips difficult and isolates the farm unit, the family becomes relatively immobile for long periods, especially during snowstorms. Winter days are spent tending stock, keeping buildings properly heated, and doing household tasks best performed at this season.

Interior Regions of Eurasia. Temperature contrasts occurring with change of season are more pronounced in the interior of Asia than in the central part of North America. In spite of extremely low winter temperatures, the growing season is long enough for spring wheat to reach maturity and for raising rye, oats, and barley. Root crops, as in North America, are staple foods, and the sugar beet is commonly grown to meet local needs. The production of fibers, especially flax and hemp, is greater than in the humid continental interior of the Western Hemisphere. Forests provide sources of building material and fuel. Mid-latitude fruits, particularly apples, are grown. Farm animals are similar to those of our own North Central states—sheep, hogs, and cattle—and income from furs is generally more important than in this country.

Despite the general similarity of economic products, there is little else in common between the humid interiors of North America and Eurasia. Our farming is advanced, with much reliance upon mechanical equipment. Farms of the United States and Canada are individually owned and operated; for the most part they are profitable and productive. Except in certain areas, like some mechanized communal farms in the U.S.S.R., Eurasian farm output is lessened by inadequate equipment, poorly selected animal strains, and disease-ridden plants. Absentee farm ownership (formerly common), illiteracy, inadequate transportation facilities in Siberia, and other handicaps have prevented these lands from reaching full productivity. When completely developed, Eurasia should become an agricultural and industrial center of great importance.

Winter temperatures fall so low in east central Siberia that the air can contain only small amounts of water vapor. For this reason winters have scant precipitation. Although snow covers the ground the entire season, in terms of water it amounts to only a light rainfall. To the eastward, however, temperatures on the island of Hokkaido and the northern part of Honshu in Japan reflect the marine locations of those areas and provide that otherwise subtropical country with a small extent of "continental" climate. Here farmers grow rye, oats, and barley as staple grains. A hardy quick-growing variety of rice has been developed, but in general agriculture is backward and the extent of farmland is limited. Hokkaido, like New England, is a forested region, supplying Japan with some needed lumber, particularly softwoods. A little coal mining and much fishing are other human activities on these remote northern islands. Many fishing boats, canneries, and other aspects of marine dependence are apparent along the coasts.

In Manchuria and other humid sections of North China the summers are too short for rice; it is replaced by wheat, barley, kaoliang (a grain sorghum), and millet as the principal native grains, though some corn introduced from America is also grown. Soybeans are important both for food and as a money crop. Domestic animals are kept in moderate numbers, compared with those produced on American farmlands of equal area. Dependence on a vegetable diet allows more Chinese and Koreans to live on the land than would be possible if dairying or stock raising prevailed.

SUMMARY

In midlatitudes on western coasts, north and south of the Mediterranean regions in the respective hemispheres, the west-coast marine climatic realm receives very heavy rainfall all year, in quantities sufficient for the growth of dense forests. Once cleared, the land is often productive, especially for hay and root crops.

Farther inland, especially leeward of mountains in the prevailing westerlies, precipitation decreases and the climate becomes semiarid or arid, with continental extremes of temperature between hot summers and cold winters. The semiarid regions are steppes or grasslands; the arid have only scant desert vegetation. On better parts of the steppes, wheat can be raised by special dry-land methods, but irrigation is essential for growing crops on arid lands. Often the economy is limited to mining or grazing.

Humid continental climate extends from about the central interior to the east coasts of the larger continents of the Northern Hemisphere. There is abundant precipitation in summer and the growing season of 150 to 200 days is suitable for agriculture, especially production of corn and other grains. Winters are severe, with considerable snow. Dairying is profitable in the more northern phase of this climate, with its shorter summers. Regions that lie within the humid continental climatic realm are capable of supporting large numbers of people in spite of long winters. These conditions are more typical of the Northern than the Southern Hemisphere because of the greater extent of continental land masses in the former.

Outline
General characteristics
West-coast marine climate
    Characteristics
    Location: type of regions
    Human activities
Arid and semiarid continental interiors
    Climate
    Location
    Sequent occupance Great Plains: Indians to dry farming
    Asiatic interior
Humid continental climate
    Climate
    Forests and Indian life
    Present occupance
    Seasonal changes in North America
    Eurasian types

QUESTIONS

1. What are examples of the effect of rainfall and snowfall upon the activities of farmers in your home locality?

2. Why are the forests of humid continental interior regions of greater commercial value than those of the wet equatorial realm?

3. San Francisco and St. Louis are located equally far north of the equator, but the January mean for the former is 50°F and for the latter, 31°F. Account for this marked difference in temperature. What are its implications for residents of St. Louis?

4. If farmers in Kansas tried to raise cotton what conditions of the environment would they find favorable? What would be unfavorable?

5. Account for the large development of hydro-electric power in the New England states.

6. Explain in detail the principal reasons for the

marked unreliability of the weather usually found in humid continental realms of the middle latitudes.

7. Account for the preponderance of summer over winter rainfall in the wheat belt of the middle United States.

8. Why does the Pacific Northwest receive its maximum rainfall in the winter season?

9. In what manner is snow superior to rain as a form of precipitation?

10. Account for the heavy forest growth in the west-coast marine climate. What kind of crops or farming are suitable for this climate?

11. What elements in the natural environment of the humid continental regions encourage the development of farming? What factors operate as handicaps?

12. Northwestern Europe is not the best type of land for growing high-quality grain, compared with other parts of the world. Why?

13. With reference to the west-coast marine regions, what climate zone normally lies equatorward? What climate would be expected to the east? Why is the west-coast marine realm not found in South Africa?

14. Following the 50th parallel of north latitude, from Land's End in England to the tip of Kamchatka, outline as fully as you can the different climatic zones, vegetation zones, and other geographical features that you would encounter in making such a traverse or trip. You will need to refer to many maps and much material in other chapters of this text.

15. The Corn Belt in the United States represents one of our best agricultural regions. What limits its extent toward the north? What is the limiting factor to the west? In which phase of the humid continental interior climate is the Corn Belt located? In what other climatic realms will corn grow successfully? What combination of weather conditions will produce a "bumper" crop of corn?

16. After you study the farm shown in Figure 9-11, list the features that represent conditions you believe to be typical of a mid-latitude continental climate of the humid classification.

17. What weather characteristics would be experienced by anyone living in:
   a. Seattle
   b. Montreal
   c. Christchurch
   d. Warsaw
   e. Detroit
   f. Tokyo

TOPICS FOR DISCUSSION

1. Agriculture in the humid continental interior regions of North America is greatly advanced in output, techniques, and wealth, compared with agriculture in humid continental interior regions of Eurasia. Provide a sound explanation for the extreme contrasts in development between the two.

2. Under what geographical conditions will farmers tend to specialize in the production of dairy cattle? Beef cattle? Sheep? Pigs? Wheat? Potatoes?

SELECTED REFERENCES

Atlas of Climatic Types in the United States, 1900–1939, U.S. Department of Agriculture Miscellaneous Publication 421, Washington, 1941.

Bowman, Isaiah: *The Pioneer Fringe,* The American Geographical Society Special Publication 13, New York, 1931.

Cressey, George B.: *Asia's Lands and Peoples,* McGraw-Hill Book Company, Inc., New York, 1951, chaps. 9–27.

Freeman, O. W., and H. H. Martin: *The Pacific Northwest,* John Wiley & Sons, Inc., New York, 1954.

Garland, John H.: *The North American Midwest,* John Wiley & Sons, Inc., New York, 1955.

Hoffman, George W.: *A Geography of Europe,* The Ronald Press Company, New York, 1953.

Kimble, George H. T.: *Our American Weather,* McGraw-Hill Book Company, Inc., New York, 1955.

Miller, George J., Almon E. Parkins, and Bert

Hudgins: *Geography of North America,* John Wiley & Sons, Inc., New York, 1954.

Smith, J. R., and M. O. Phillips: *North America,* Harcourt, Brace and Company, Inc., New York, 1942.

Trewartha, Glenn T.: *Japan: A Physical, Cultural and Regional Geography,* University of Wisconsin Press, Madison, 1945.

Wissler, Clark: *Indians of the Plains,* American Museum of Natural History, New York, 1931.

———: *The American Indian,* rev. ed., Oxford University Press, New York, 1938.

Wright, Alfred J.: *United States and Canada: An Economic Geography,* Appleton-Century-Crofts, Inc., New York, 1956.

10. The High Latitudes

THE SUBPOLAR CONTINENTAL CLIMATES

NORTH of middle latitudes in the subpolar zone in the Northern Hemisphere a forested belt, predominantly of conifers, extends entirely around the world on the continents of North America, Europe, and Asia (Figure 10-1). The northern coniferous forest, called *taiga* by the Russians, is a response to its climate of short cool summers and long, extremely cold winters (Figure 10-2). Along west coasts in subpolar latitudes, winters are less severe and the growing season somewhat longer than farther inland, though summers are even cooler because of marine influence. Precipitation is heavier, with either an even distribution or a distinct winter maximum. This climate lies along or near the coasts of the Scandinavian peninsula, southern Chile, and southern Alaska.

In much of the humid midlatitudes, soil and moisture conditions favor the broad-leaved species of trees. Conditions in the interior are too dry for anything but grass. In the taiga, however, the conifers survive tremendous ranges of temperature and a short growing season that would kill most hardwood trees. In general, these forests are made up of needle-leaved evergreens. The trees grow slowly since they have a growing period only one to three months long. Mixed with the conifers are some hardy broad-leaved trees, notably birch, aspen, alder, and willow. Other hardwoods, such as beech and maple, may also occur mixed with conifers along the southern edge of the taiga (Figure 10-3). Coniferous trees of the taiga include only a few species of pines, firs, spruce, cedar, hemlock, and larch

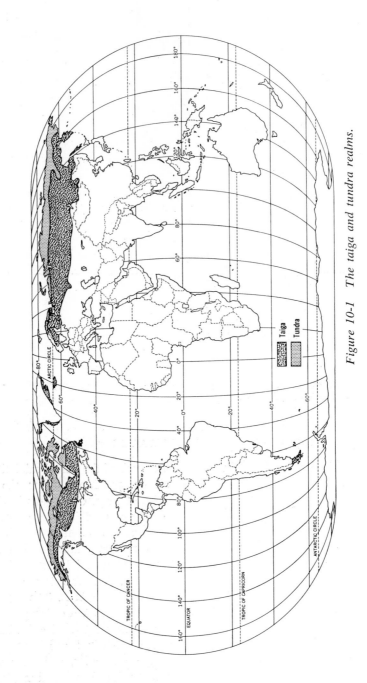

Figure 10-1 The taiga and tundra realms.

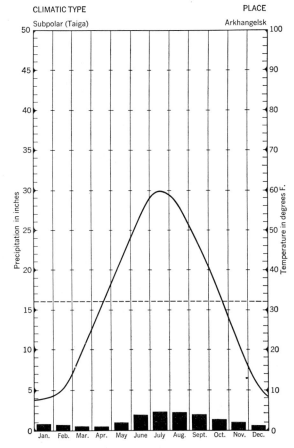

CLIMATIC TYPE — Subpolar (Taiga)

PLACE — Arkhangelsk

Figure 10-2 Climatic graph for Arkhangelsk, U.S.S.R. The taiga lands in the Northern Hemisphere experience just enough warmth during the summer season to permit the growth of coniferous forests of large extent. Seasonal temperature ranges are great, but precipitation of rain and snow is relatively small. There is no marked dry season.

(tamarack), a tree which sheds its leaves in winter, in decided contrast to the numerous species that comprise the flora of the mixed hardwoods.

Climate. The greatest climatic extremes on the earth's surface are believed to occur in the taiga at Verkhoyansk in northeastern Siberia (Figure 5-8). The average range of temperature totals 118°F from a mean of −58°F in January to 60°F in July, with an ex-

treme range of 187 degrees Fahrenheit from −93½°F in February, 1892, to 93½°F in July. During the few years records were kept, Oimyakon, 400 miles southeast of Verkhoyansk, was slightly colder on the average than the latter. The Mackenzie Valley of Canada and the Yukon Valley of Alaska have summer temperatures exceeding 90°F and winter temperatures that fall to −60°F or −70°F, giving an annual extreme range of more than 150 degrees Fahrenheit. Because of marine influence, the coniferous forest is found about 10 degrees farther north on west coasts than on east coasts of continents in the Northern Hemisphere. Only on the icecap in Antarctica have colder temperatures been recorded than in Siberia.

The taiga deteriorates northward, the trees becoming more and more stunted, until finally

Figure 10-3 A high-latitude meadow of the taiga in summer, surrounded by the dense evergreen forest. (Photograph by Mitchell G. Hanavan, used by permission of the U.S. Fish and Wildlife Service.)

the last spruce, birch, and willow disappear at the limit of tree growth and hardier plants like grass and herbs replace the forests. The last stunted trees may be shorter than a man, yet be one or two centuries old. The total rainfall required for the growth of conifers need not be so great as farther south, because the rate of evaporation is low and the growing season short. Most water from the snow of winter and the rain of summer remains available for use by trees.

Locally, in mountainous areas close to the ocean, very heavy snows may occur whose depth is measured in feet rather than inches. The great depth of snowfall in southeastern Alaska causes vast glaciers to form there, descending from mountains to the sea in a cloudy stormy region whose mean annual temperature is no colder than parts of New England. In other places in the coniferous forest the snowfall is only from one to a few feet in depth, but because of the cold the snow persists for many months.

In northerly latitudes the forests offer some advantages for travel during the winter cold. Ground is frozen, and men move freely everywhere on skis or snowshoes as well as on sleds pulled by dogs or by reindeer. Except where the few railroads have been built, summer travel is generally restricted to waterways, which are numerous in the glaciated regions. Airplanes equipped with pontoons in summer and skis in winter are useful for speedy travel.

With the arrival of summer, wild fowl migrate northward for nesting. Multitudes of wild flowers burst into bloom, trees put on new growth, and countless swarms of insects, especially mosquitoes, come into existence. Plant growth is very rapid because of the long hours of sunshine. Even wheat has matured in central Alaska; oats and barley, the hardier grains, and root crops can regularly be grown there. Much of the taiga has been glaciated, and lakes, ponds, and swamps abound. Fish, waterfowl, muskrats, and even larger creatures like moose and beaver get most of their food supply from ponds and swamps.

Forest Products.   Areas with adequate rainfall and up to three months of growing season may supply commercial timber, but those with limited precipitation or shorter growing season have only a stunted growth of trees, of value only for local fuel and possibly for paper pulp. Nevertheless, the taiga supplies a large share of the construction softwood lumber cut in the world and a greater part of the paper pulp. The best commercial stands of timber are located in the most favorable climate, along the west coasts and on the southern portion of the northern coniferous forests, where fortunately they are accessible.

Timber is cut mainly during winter in the commercial forests. Winter passes almost directly into summer, resulting in rapid melting of snow and consequent flooding of streams down which the logs, cut in winter and piled along the stream banks, are carried to the mills. Most of the forested region has numerous streams with power sites to supply the energy needed for the mills. Frequently sawmills and paper mills can be located on or near tidewater, allowing cheap and easy transportation of wood products to world markets. In Finland, which is easily accessible to European markets, 45 per cent of all workers in industry are employed in woodworking establishments: sawmills, plywood factories, planing mills, and pulp and paper mills.

Fire is often a hazard in the taiga; conifers become highly combustible during periods of drought, and once large-scale fires begin in these forests they are hard to extinguish. Large areas of the taiga in both the Old and the New World have been burned over. Following the fires, birch, aspen, and other broad-leaved trees form the beginnings of new forests. Conifers replace themselves very slowly; when a forest has been destroyed, a century or more may pass before it regains its former appearance.

Multitudes of fur-bearing animals are trapped during winter, and furs are exported to industrial regions of the middle latitudes. These furs and other animal products are the most valuable commodity coming from large

Figure 10-4   A modern homestead in the Matanuska Valley, Alaska. The land has been cleared and then planted in vegetables and grain. This type of human activity is relatively common on the northernmost frontier of the agricultural lands of the world. (Photograph by L. J. Palmer, used by permission of the U.S. Fish and Wildlife Service.)

areas of the northern forests. The lonely wilderness contains scattered trading posts at which the furs are collected.

Life in the Taiga. Much of the coniferous forest possesses only a poor leached soil, the so-called "podzol," which develops under the regional climatic and vegetation conditions. Field crops are limited to hardy grains like oats and barley for human use, and hay to supply the cattle. Dairy products customarily form the chief item sold from the farms. Among minor crops are potatoes, turnips, rutabagas and other root vegetables, peas, strawberries and numerous other small fruits, and cabbage or other leaf vegetables that mature in the short summer with its long periods of sunshine (Figure 10-4). The value of a farm is generally based on the amount of hay that can be raised to supply the dairy cows and other livestock throughout the winter.

Although millions of men live by agriculture in the taiga of Finland, Scandinavia, Soviet Russia, and Canada, the population is relatively small compared with that in more favored regions. Even trading towns are widely spaced. Because hard work supplies man with only the bare essentials of life and leaves little surplus for luxuries, the coniferous forests are unattractive to many. The population may be expected to increase slowly, but it seems unlikely that the northern forest will ever be extensively cleared and turned into productive farms.

Houses in northern forests are usually of wood, with log huts the common home in the remote places. In communities with heavy snowfall, houses are often built with steep roofs, from which snow can slip easily. Homes must be built to resist cold, with walls that are thick and often hollow (air being a poor conductor of heat), double windows, and other insulation. Some food is secured by hunting large game animals like deer and moose that usually band together in "yards" during the snowy season. In deep snow they have difficulty escaping from men who hunt on skis or snowshoes. Winter fishing may be done through holes cut in the ice.

In both northern Siberia and northern Canada, aboriginal peoples live in the coniferous forests and find their full support from hunting, fishing, and trapping, securing their food, clothing, furs for trade, and material for tents from such sources. Trapping supplies them with some necessary material for garments that will

Figure 10-5 Aerial view of Yellowknife, N.W.T., a frontier mining community in northern Canada, reached more easily by airplane than by other methods of transport. Note the thinly forested, glacially scoured landscape with its many lakes. (Photograph by the National Film Board of Canada.)

resist the cold. It also gives them furs which they exchange at trading posts for traps, imported foodstuffs, utensils, and other necessities. A trapper requires a large area for his string of traps, especially since the numbers of fur-bearing animals vary with their food supply from year to year.

In Canada, the Chippewa Indians represent a type of hunting forest tribe. In Siberia the Yakuts obtain their living similarly. The fur-trading posts, at which these natives deal with civilized man, may be scattered at distances of hundreds of miles, and in the forest wilderness they are generally built on the most accessible locations on the ocean or inland waterways from which natural routes diverge.

Modern development. Mining may bring a large influx of population to limited areas where ores occur (Figure 10-5). The Laurentian Upland, between the Great Lakes and Hudson Bay in Canada, is an important mining area in which mineral deposits have been discoverd even beyond the Arctic Circle. The southern portion of the Laurentian Upland is served by railroads; but to reach the Far North formerly took many weeks of continuous travel by steamboat and canoe. Except for dog sleds the remote mines and fur-trading posts were completely shut in during the winter. Now prospectors, mining engineers, and fur buyers fly to their stations, going by airplane in a single day over the forest wilderness that formerly would have required a month or more to cross. Airplanes are generally equipped with pontoons for landing on the numerous lakes in summer; in winter, skis are substituted for pontoons. Other mining regions are located in the taiga of the U.S.S.R. and Scandinavia. Mining development leads to only temporary occupance of forest land; when mines are worked out, the remote mining settlements will be abandoned.

THE TUNDRA

The Tundra Environment. The word *tundra* suggests a frozen treeless waste in winter, and even in summer the land displays only scanty stunted vegetation. Annual precipitation is light and snowfall is very small in amount because in extremely cold regions there is little atmospheric moisture to be condensed. Unattractive as this land sounds, with nearly nine months of winter, only two of summer, and about two weeks each for spring and autumn, people do live on the tundra in reasonable health, although the number of inhabitants is small because of scant resources. Seasons in these regions could as well be divided by light and darkness as by cold and warmth, since the presence or absence of the sun is the most important thing. The length of these periods lessens from the North Pole with its six-months day and six-months night to a single day at the Arctic Circle, yet as far south as 70° north latitude there is a period of no sun almost two months long in winter, whereas in summer continuous sunshine lasts for a similar period.

Polar climates generally are marked by temperature averages under 50°F for the warmest month (Figure 10-6). Vegetation begins to grow when the warmest month has a temperature higher than 40°F, but when the average for this month falls to freezing, only a polar desert like most of Greenland can exist. This is an extreme polar climate. Winter temperatures in polar regions are low but seldom reach the excessively low temperatures of continental interior regions, as at Verkhoyansk (Figure 5-8) in the taiga. Winter is notable for its extreme length. Snowfall is light, but strong winds cause drifts which last into June before they melt.

As length of day increases, winter suddenly disappears and summer comes to the tundra almost overnight. Flowers blossom; small berries mature. Ducks, geese, and other waterfowl migrate and nest along waterways and ponds, and mosquitoes, flies, butterflies, and other insects abound. In most of the tundra the ground thaws only on the surface and remains permanently frozen underneath. This causes poor drainage and produces a spongy swamp, or

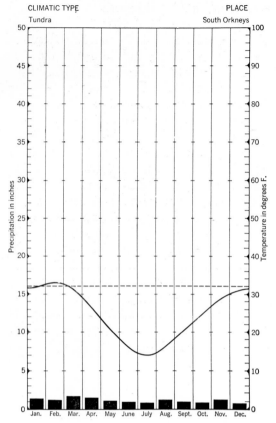

Figure 10-6 Climatic graph for South Orkneys. The high-latitude tundra lands experience very low temperatures throughout the year with most months having means lower than freezing. These temperatures are too low to permit the growth of trees. Precipitation occurs largely in the form of snow, but the total amount each season is small because the air is too cold to contain much moisture.

muskeg, where ideal conditions exist for breeding of mosquitoes (Figure 10-7). Swarms of mosquitoes then harass people, who may need to wear a headnet and gloves for protection.

During the short summer, the inhabitants prepare for the long winter. By the end of August ice forms on tundra ponds at night, and the first swirls of winter snow follow shortly. Trading ships hurry away to avoid being frozen into ice floes for the winter. The length of day rapidly decreases, and the long winter is again at hand.

The Reindeer and Tundra Life. In the Old World, in northern Scandinavia, Russia, and Siberia, live natives whose main support and livelihood is reindeer. These domestic animals, closely related to the caribou of North America, thrive under conditions that would quickly kill most other animals. Underneath skin and hair, a layer of fat protects a caribou or reindeer against cold and biting winds. It has broad cloven hoofs, useful for travel over snow and for pawing away the snow to secure reindeer moss and other feed. In fact, reindeer generally keep in better condition through the cold winter than in summer, when numerous biting insects make their lives so miserable that they can hardly graze in comfort.

The Laplander and the Siberian tundra tribes secure shelter, raiment, and food from herds of reindeer. Some reindeer are taught to draw sleds over the snow in winter, but as a rule they are not used for beasts of burden. Reindeer does may be milked. The animals not only supply ordinary meat but their internal organs furnish vitamins which in our latitudes would be obtained from vegetables or fruits. Reindeer hide furnishes natives with material for much of their clothing and for the tents in which they live.

Unless their lives have been modified by contact with higher cultures, the natives who keep reindeer are nomads and must move with their herds as required by conditions of feeding. Once the reindeer moss and other herbage has been thoroughly grazed, it may require two or three years before it recovers sufficiently to be grazed again. A herd of reindeer must have a very large grazing area, and it is not uncommon for the animals to roam from 20 to 30 miles a day in search of feed. Naturally the population of the tundra where the natives live with their herds is scanty. Nevertheless the numbers of people are greater and life is safer than in northern regions where reindeer do not exist.

The Laplanders in northern Norway (Figure 10-8), Sweden, and Finland have a much higher cultural development than natives of northern Siberia or Eskimos and Indians of

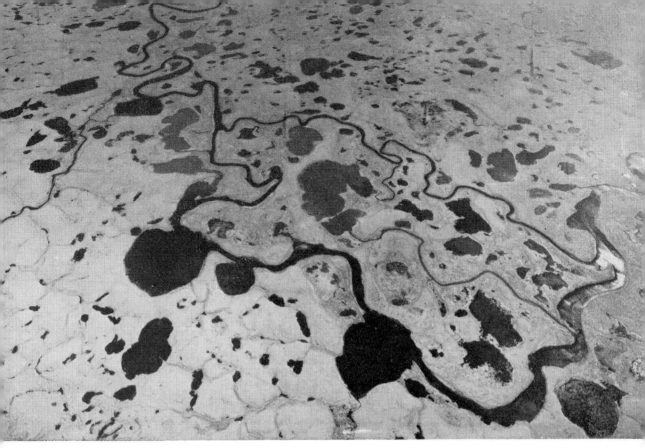

Figure 10-7   Tundra landscape of the Yukon-Kuskokwim Delta, western Alaska. Only scrub vegetation can live on these frozen muskeg plains. (Air Force photograph.)

polar North America. Laplanders migrate to the tundra in summer and back to the forests of the taiga in winter, but some occupy semi-permanent winter homes (Figure 10-9). There are also permanent schools in the forests, attended by the children during the winter season.

The Chukchi, a less advanced reindeer-breeding tribe of the tundra and taiga margin of northeastern Siberia, use reindeer to supply almost their entire needs. The tribe wanders with its reindeer herds over a range of thousands of square miles, the winter being spent where timber provides some shelter and the summer on the tundras which are relatively free from insect pests. A single native may own many hundreds of animals. Reindeer are slaughtered when they are needed for food, especially in autumn when their coats are in best condition for making clothing. A few roots and wild berries provide other foods.

In Alaska and northern Canada, the caribou once existed in herds of many millions and supplied food to both northern Indians and Eskimos. The caribou is really a wild reindeer that is somewhat larger than the domestic variety; the latter was once limited in its range to northern Eurasia. Caribou and reindeer can be interbred. By the introduction of high-powered rifles, the numbers of game animals were much reduced and in places the game was nearly exterminated, causing some natives to perish from starvation. To help this situation, reindeer were brought to Alaska (Figure 10-10) and more recently to Canada, and the living conditions of Indians and Eskimos who learned to handle these animals improved.

Indians of Tierra del Fuego.   Toward the southern tip of South America is an environment that does not invite civilized people. The climate is very stormy, rainy, and cold. In places forests clothe the lower parts of the

Figure 10-8 Lapps occupy tents during the brief summer of northern latitudes, because their dwelling must be readily portable to conform with their nomadic life. This Lapp tent is made of birch poles covered with canvas or sacking. (Photograph, courtesy of Eugene Van Cleef.)

Figure 10-9 Lapp nomads of northernmost Sweden and Finland depend on the reindeer for their subsistence. Many of their shelters must be temporary by necessity although their permanent dwellings may take the form of those shown in the background. (Photograph, courtesy of Eugene Van Cleef.)

mountains, which descend abruptly into the sea, and snow and ice cover the upper mountains most of the year. Occasional glaciers descend to sea level, furnishing conditions resembling those along the Gulf of Alaska. The Indians here never practiced agriculture and had no permanent homes. Each family used a boat to carry its members and their few possessions from place to place along the shore in search of food. The Onas and Yahgans living on Tierra del Fuego and the maze of other nearby islands wander along the shores, fiords, and islands and camp wherever shellfish (their staff of life) or other food may be available. These natives are rather a hardy race, but they have never advanced beyond a very low cultural level.

Although white miners, traders, and trappers have entered the region, not many care to bring their families and make permanent homes or remain long in a place that is so windy, cloudy, and rainy. Few primitive peoples can withstand the diseases and changes of food, clothes, and living conditions that follow contact with the white man. Most of the native peoples in the southern end of America have sadly declined in numbers, and some tribes have become entirely extinct. Since Europeans find the region so unattractive, the white population has not grown and the area is thinly inhabited.

The Eskimo. The Eskimo secures his living in one of the most formidable natural regions on earth, along the coasts of Greenland and the Arctic Ocean. No agriculture is possible, and almost no vegetable food is available. Only some places on the land have caribou and musk ox which can be killed for food. Of necessity most of the Eskimo food supply comes from the sea. Fortunately northern waters swarm with *plankton* (floating organisms) and other small forms of life on which fish, seal, walrus, and whales thrive.

The seal serves the Eskimo as the staff of life as the reindeer does for the Laplander. Sometimes many seals are secured at one time, especially during the breeding season. In winter, the animals must be hunted one by one and secured by patiently waiting for hours on the ice at a breathing hole, where the creature is speared when it appears. The thick layer of blubber that keeps the seal warm in winter supplies the Eskimo with a substitute for the starchy foods of warmer climates. He also burns seal oil for light and heat in his home. Walrus, polar bears, and whales are also captured. The arctic fox, ermine, and hare supply furs for clothing. Animal skins are both warmer and more waterproof than woven fabrics. Even white men traveling in the Arctic wear the Eskimo's skin boots, furry trousers, and windproof coats and parkas.

In summer, the Eskimo lives in a skin tent and in winter in a conical stone and sod house often built over a pit dug in the ground. When covered with snow, an Eskimo village is almost invisible. On hunting trips they build temporary hemispherical huts, called *igloos,* out of snow blocks. Eskimos have one domestic animal, the dog, used for pulling sleds in winter and to help in hunting—especially for polar bear. Originally the Eskimo made all his utensils of stone, bone, sinew, skins, and driftwood from the native environment. To an extraordinary degree the Eskimo shows how man can overcome handicaps of a poor and harsh environment by learning how to utilize fully the available food supply and raw materials.

Contact with civilized man is not entirely a blessing to the Eskimo. Tuberculosis and other diseases were introduced which proved deadly to the Eskimo who had little natural resistance to them. The general health of the Eskimo was better in their uncivilized condition than after they secured the white man's flour and other imported foods. Although the Eskimo benefits by trading furs for outboard motors, steel traps, and rifles which help in fishing and hunting, especially of marine animals, the use of rifles often so reduces the numbers of musk ox and caribou that inhabitants of villages depending on hunting large land animals suffer starvation. Dependence on trade for gasoline, stove oil, many manufactures, and even some imported food is dangerous to the Eskimo when fishing or fur trapping fails.

High-altitude Tundras. Tundra conditions may result from high altitude as well as high latitude. Thus the Plateau of Tibet lies just

Figure 10-10 Herd of reindeer in a corral near Nome, Alaska. (Photograph, courtesy of the U.S. Department of the Interior.)

Figure 10-11   Group of Kirghiz women living in the central part of Asia in the Russian Pamirs. Their dwelling, a yurt, appears at the left. They must wear heavy padded clothing in order to be comfortable in the continental climate which prevails in these mountains. (Photograph, courtesy of the American Museum of Natural History, New York.)

and widely distributed. During the short summer, a few of the people practice primitive agriculture in protected localities where irrigation water is available. More of the natives are semiroving stockmen or complete nomads; in either case they depend entirely upon herding for a livelihood.

Civilization in this cold desert can never advance as far as in more favored localities. Securing the bare essentials for existence takes so much time that people have little leisure in which to develop arts and literature (Figure 10-11). Some of the more ambitious and energetic people leave and seek homes in better environments. Those who remain must be contented with a meager diet and generally harsh conditions of life. Fuel is lacking, and the dried manure of animals must serve for cooking fires. Since houses can be warmed little with this fuel, the natives dress in quilted garments, furs, and skins. In Tibet nearly one-third of the inhabitants live in monasteries or nunneries and have not married. This custom helps keep the natural rate of population increase low; the food supply can maintain a population which remains nearly stationary, but if the number of inhabitants increased rapidly there would be insufficient food. Although the temperature of a cold desert is quite different from that of the hot desert, people nevertheless live under somewhat similar conditions. In both cases, the natives are largely nomadic and live on products of their herds. The usual food consists of milk, curds, or a sort of cheese, with meat being consumed only occasionally.

north of tropical India but is an entirely different world. Though the plateau is high, it is lower than the Himalaya Mountains, which shut off most of the monsoon rains from the south. Winters are long and severely cold. Because of altitude and position in the interior of the continent, Tibet and some other highlands in central Asia are cold deserts. Only animals especially adapted to these conditions can survive. In some interior deserts horses, mules, and Bactrian camels bear burdens, but in the highest and generally coldest localities the yak is the only burden bearer able to endure the harsh conditions. The population is very scanty

POLAR ICECAPS

The most forbidding and useless polar climate is that of the icecaps. Here the mean temperature of no month averages above 32°F and snowstorms may occur at any time of year. Only during a short period of the year when the sun shines constantly does air temperature rise enough to thaw some of the snow on top of the glacial ice. Temporary pools and streams of water may then exist. No large plants or animals and of course no human beings live permanently on icecaps, which are, therefore, more complete deserts than those of tropical location. Antarctica and all of Greenland except narrow coastal strips are covered with icecaps. Smaller caps are found in Iceland, Svalbard, South Georgia, and other polar islands. Some high mountains in lower latitudes also support permanent sheets of ice in southern Alaska, Canada, Scandinavia, and Tierra del Fuego.

Air aloft over the icecaps of Greenland and Antarctica is chilled by the ice and thereby becomes denser; a high-pressure area is built up. From this polar anticyclone, cold masses of air slip off toward lower latitudes, and meteorologists believe that the whirling cyclonic storms characteristic of midlatitudes are created when these cold air masses come in contact with masses of warm tropical air. Probably the coldest surface temperatures on earth occur on the high Antarctic icecap.

The two large polar icecaps cover high plateaus, possibly of a basin shape with ridges toward the plateau edge that help retain the ice sheets. Lowlands in the Arctic do not receive enough snow for development of glaciers, but plateaus and mountains can support them. Although the snow and ice line is much lower in Greenland than in mid-latitude and tropical regions, it reaches sea level only at certain bays in which the glacial ice descends valleys from the interior and breaks off to form icebergs (Figure 10-12). In summer the Labrador Current brings these icebergs southward until they melt in Atlantic waters. An international ice patrol, to which the United States belongs, guards steamer lanes and warns shipping by radio of the location of floating ice. Disasters like that of the *Titanic,* sunk in 1912 by collision with an iceberg with a loss of 1,500 people, can be thus avoided. No large ship has collided with an iceberg since the patrol was started. The use of radar equipment further increases protection against serious damage to shipping by these dangerous ice masses.

Gigantic flat icebergs break off from the Antarctic continental glacier along the edge of the ice shelf, which in places rests on the shallow sea floor.

During the International Geophysical Year

Figure 10-12   The snoutlike end of a glacier appears at the right, and the glacier has spawned many small ice floes and snowbergs. A larger glacier would break up into icebergs as it entered the sea. (Air Force photograph taken near Bache Peninsula on Ellesmere Island, Baffinland.)

(1957–1958), expeditions from many nations established bases on or around Antarctica to investigate oceanic, terrestrial, atmospheric, and celestial phenomena, together with all sorts of other scientifically important projects.

This enterprise led to widespread publicity about geographical conditions on the cold continent and increased public interest in seeking information about the southern region of the world.

SUMMARY

Climatic realms of high latitudes are particularly well developed in the Northern Hemisphere. These regions have an extreme continental climate, with very severe winters and short cool summers, although daytime periods are long in summer.

In the subpolar zone, conditions are good for growth of evergreen or coniferous forests, with some hardy broad-leaved trees like birch, aspen, and willow. In the Northern Hemisphere this forest region is called the taiga, and covers much of Canada and the Soviet Union. Here greater extremes of temperature occur between the warmest and coldest months than in any other climate. Human activity is largely directed toward exploitation of furs, mines, and forests. Agriculture is limited to hay, root crops, and hardy grains like oats, barley, and rye. Dairying is the most important animal industry. Population density decreases northward and is scanty on the tundra border.

In still higher latitudes, summer warmth is insufficient for tree growth, and the land surface appears as a treeless plain covered with dwarf plants, mosses, and lichens; this is the tundra with a climate too cold for crops or even trees. Very few people live in the region although some rely on reindeer for their sustenance or depend upon fish and game for food. Near both poles the sea and land remains ice-covered all year, and human beings are unable to find sufficient food from natural sources to support habitation permanently.

Outline
Subpolar continental climate or taiga
    Climate and vegetation
    Life in the taiga
Polar climate or tundra
    Climate and vegetation
    The reindeer people
    The Eskimo
High-altitude tundras
Polar icecaps

QUESTIONS

1. What is the effect of the short growing season on farming practices and the crops grown in southern Alaska?

2. Why is it possible to get wheat to ripen successfully in latitudes well north of Edmonton, Alberta?

3. Why is it difficult to ship wheat to Europe from Churchill on Hudson Bay, even though a railroad has been built to this point from the wheat-growing Prairie provinces of Canada?

4. Why, with all its forested land, does the taiga experience such scanty precipitation?

5. Why are northward-flowing streams like the Mackenzie and Ob Rivers particularly subject to flood conditions?

6. Why is agriculture possible on a limited scale in southern Alaska and not in similar latitudes in Labrador, Greenland, or Baffin Island?

7. Why are Eskimos hunters and fishermen?

RESEARCH TOPICS

1. Study the material presented in the text in connection with the Lapps and the Chukchi, and review the material on desert nomads. Then prepare a summary statement in which you attempt to reach satisfactory conclusions on this situation in which divergent causes lead to similarity in results.

2. Prepare a paper, not longer than one page, on any one of the following topics:

    a. Prospecting for uranium sources in northern Canada

    b. Development of iron mining in Labrador

    c. Fur sealing on the Pribilof Islands

    d. Problems of the migratory Lapp reindeer herders

SELECTED REFERENCES

Albright, W. D.: "Gardens of the Mackenzie," *Geographical Review,* 23:1–22, January, 1933.

———: "Crop Growth in High Latitudes," *Geographical Review,* 23:608–620, October, 1933.

Barnett, Lincoln: "The Arctic Barrens," *Life,* 36:90–109, June 7, 1954.

Freeman, O. W.: chapter on Alaska in William H. Haas (ed.), *The American Empire,* University of Chicago Press, Chicago, 1940, pp. 151–215.

Hart, John Fraser: *British Moorlands,* University of Georgia Press, Athens, 1955.

Herbert, C. H.: "The Development of Transportation in the Canadian North," *Canadian Geographical Journal,* 5:188–197, November, 1956.

Irwin, D. L.: "Agriculture in the Matanuska Valley of Alaska," *Scientific Monthly,* 60:203–212, March, 1945.

Kimble, George H. T.: *Geography of the Northlands,* American Geographical Society, New York, 1955.

Kratz, L. A.: "Cultural Progress of Iceland," *Journal of Geography,* 45:285–291, October, 1946.

Lloyd, Trevor, and Dorothy Good: *The North,* McGraw-Hill Book Company, Inc., for the American Geographical Society, New York, 1954.

Putnam, Donald F. (ed.): *Canadian Regions,* Thomas Y. Crowell Company, New York, 1952.

Rude, Gilbert T.: "Our Last Frontier: The Coast and Geodetic Survey's Work in Alaska," *Geographical Review,* 47:349–364, October, 1957.

Stanwell-Fletcher, Theodora C.: *The Tundra World,* Little, Brown & Company, Boston, 1952.

Stefansson, Vilhjalmur: *The Friendly Arctic,* rev. ed., The Macmillan Company, New York, 1943.

———: *Greenland,* Doubleday & Company, Inc., New York, 1942.

Stern, Peter M.: "Alaska," *Focus,* 4(1):1–6, September, 1953.

Valk, Hendrikus M. H. A. van der: *Economic Future of Canada,* McGraw-Hill Book Company, Inc., New York, 1954.

11. Natural Vegetation and Forestry

PLANTS AND THEIR DISTRIBUTION

FROM lowly grasses to towering trees, the vegetation cover of any given part of the world reflects not only plants that were present originally, but also subsequent effects of alteration in their natural environment. Upon the intervention of man, the plant cover usually undergoes further change resulting from the introduction of new species. Vegetation changes that follow affect the plant cover, often to its detriment. The botanist calls study of plants in relation to their physical environments *plant ecology*. In regions where man has not greatly destroyed or modified the natural vegetation, plants form a most obvious part of the environment (Figure 5-2). In general they reflect quite closely the sum total of all environmental factors: rainfall, sunshine, length of growing season, temperature, frost, soil, min-

eral content of the ground, drainage, windiness, among others. Water, light, and heat are especially important factors affecting plants.

Classification of plants. A common classification of plants divides them into trees, desert shrubs, and the succulent grasses and herbs. Another scheme groups plants by their relative resistance to drought: *xerophytes,* those most able to exist under drought conditions, *hydrophytes,* which thrive under wet conditions, and *mesophytes,* which grow under conditions of moderate moisture supply. Another method of classification groups plants according to susceptibility to frost and ability to withstand the cold of winter and short growing seasons.

Plants differ also in ability to grow in sunshine or shade. Casual observation shows that plants differ depending upon whether soil is well drained or waterlogged, whether it contains much soluble plant food or is poor and leached, whether it is impregnated with salt and other alkalies or free from such minerals.

The same type of plant may not always persist in the same localities. Plants occur in groups or associations, but after one association has occupied the ground a different association, which grows better under a greater degree of shade, thicker deposits of humus, or other natural conditions, usually succeeds the first.

Trees forming the different types of plant associations may be of unequal value to the lumberman. Thus Douglas fir, coming early in the development of forests in western Washington and Oregon, is more valuable than western hemlock and other trees that form the final, or climax, association of the region. The forester endeavors to encourage the reproduction and perpetuation of the more valuable species whether or not they are normal ones to be expected in the climax association.

Environmental factors. The plant complex in an association depends upon the particular local values of temperature, rainfall, soil permeability, soil fertility, length of growing season, depth and duration of snow cover (in middle and high latitudes), altitude, wind direction and velocity (in the case of air-borne seeds). Other items include intensity of sunlight, and temperature or heat.

One of the most important determinants of a plant association is the type of exposure. In the Northern Hemisphere, for example, certain types of plants require a southern exposure for best development; others cannot tolerate intensity of sunlight, evaporation of moisture, and other conditions associated with southern exposure. This accounts for the wide variation in plant associations that may be seen on southern and northern slopes of southern California mountains, in a semiarid climate. Contrasts are usually less clearly marked in humid climates.

Relation of Plants to Water Supply. In nature, plant habitats vary according to the amount of water available, from the salt oceans and fresh-water lakes to the driest rock surfaces in deserts. No plant can adapt itself for living under all these conditions, but each type becomes adapted to a certain water relationship from which it rarely departs. With decreasing dependence upon water, plants are classified as hydrophytes, mesophytes, and xerophytes, as previously noted.

Hydrophytes grow in ponds, streams, oceans, swamps, and wet meadows. They find it unnecessary to conserve water, and lack the structures which other plants possess to restrict evaporation. Leaves are usually large, and roots small and shallow. In floating plants the stem may lack supporting fibers. Besides the actual water plants, like algae, rushes, and lilies, the banana is a type of hydrophyte, since heavy rainfall is required for its successful growth.

Two hydrophytic trees are the mangrove and cypress. The former grows mainly in salt water along seacoasts. Its habitat is in shallow water, where it can put down a tangle of roots resembling stilts, supporting a scrubby trunk above the mud flats. The cypress, a valuable timber tree (Figure 5-13), grows in swamps in the southern United States.

In shallow lakes, a regular succession of plants may be observed. Submerged vegetation, *algae,* grows on the bed of the lake, then toward shore are seen semifloating pond lilies, followed by a zone of sedges and cattails. Next, on the swampy shores, are willows, alders, and meadow herbage that are tolerant of some flooding. Finally, where the ground is seldom flooded, hydrophytes are replaced by the usual forest trees and shrubs of the climatic realm.

Mesophytes include most familiar plants like the common trees, shrubs, and herbs that live in intermediate climates of moderate rainfall and temperature (Figure 11-5). They have few special features that reflect their environment. Roots are generally numerous and much branched. Foliage shows a heavy development, and the rate of water evaporation stands midway between that of hydrophytes and xerophytes. Areal distribution of mesophytes is limited by their ability to adapt themselves to climatic conditions in which cold or drought may be a principal limiting factor. Mesophytes are killed if standing water deprives the root system of air for a long time just as a long absence of water will cause the plant to die. This group includes both conifers and broadleaf trees. Some are evergreen, others deciduous. Although only their intermediate relationship to water determines their classifications, the characteristics of individual plants are greatly affected by many factors; among these are soils, length of growing season, extremes of temperature, rate of evaporation, and windiness.

Xerophytes live under drought conditions and have developed features that enable them to survive their harsh environment. Some xerophytes can complete the life cycle from germination to seed production in a short time on water from a single shower. This accounts for flower-carpeted deserts in bloom for a brief period after local showers. Desert plants may resist drought by accumulating water supplies that can be drawn upon during dry seasons; the barrel cactus is a well-known example (Figure 7-4).

Methods of plant adaptation to a small supply of water include:

1. Thickening of the tissues, leaving only a small surface from which evaporation can occur, as in the cacti.

2. Secretion of oil substances to reduce transpiration further.

3. Root systems vastly larger than the plant aboveground, which can gather moisture very quickly when it is available.

4. Leaves that are shed in the dry season or turn their edges to the sun or curl up in the heat.

5. Leaf surfaces protected against evaporation by fine hairs and the secretion of wax and resins.

6. Leaves modified to moisture-conserving thorns, which have the advantage that they protect the plant from being readily eaten by desert animals.

Light. Light is necessary to plant life because it furnishes energy for changing water and carbon dioxide into starch by the chlorophyll bodies of the leaves. This process is called *photosynthesis* (putting together by means of light). Plants react strongly to light differences. Leaves and stems of plants like the sunflower often turn with the light. Flowers and other parts of the plants open and close with different conditions of light. Some plants in shade tend to grow tall in order to reach the light, whereas in bright sunshine the same plants may be low and thick. Excessive light may destroy plant matter if it is too intense, but ordinarily it induces more rapid growth, as in the Far North where nearly continuous daylight lasts for several weeks, enabling vegetation to mature in the short growing season.

Plants that are shade resistant tend to form the climax plant associations in forest regions, since they germinate and grow to the exclusion of the sun-loving plants.

Heat. Plants differ markedly in need for heat. Each has an upper limit and a lower limit of endurable temperatures, and in addition, a certain optimum, or most favorable, temperature for growth. Often the finest-flavored fruit is grown near the colder limits of heat for the species. Thus many northern-grown vegetables are superior in quality to those coming from warmer parts of the world, and northern-grown garden seeds are preferred by many.

Other Factors of Plant Ecology. Wind has a material effect on both wild and cultivated plants. Sometimes windbreaks are used to protect growing plants from injury by strong and hot dry winds. On mountains or seacoasts that are exposed to severe wind conditions, tree growth may be limited or stunted. Excessive evaporation may injure plants, since the amount of water available for the plant may be insufficient to replace moisture as rapidly as it evaporates. Hot dry winds may, therefore, do much damage to growing crops in exposed locations.

Plants on bare rock and very stony ground

must survive with scant supplies of water because the rain runs off the ground so quickly. Lichens and short-lived annuals are the first plants to grow on barren rock. When humus has collected from decay of this simple vegetation, shrubs and trees then begin to invade the area and establish themselves, forming a normal vegetation cover. Soil is a major factor that influences plant growth. (The relation of soil quality to plant life will be discussed in Chapter 17.)

Plants as Environmental Indicators. Since vegetation is the product of conditions under which it grows, plants often provide a good indication of the occurrence of ground water, type of soil or subsoil, climate, and other factors of environment. Plants may indicate both natural conditions of environment and the use to which land may be put. The presence of bulrushes and cattails points to saturated soil conditions and consequent poor aeration. Grease-wood and other *halophytes* (salt-tolerant plants) suggest the presence of alkali in the soil. Cottonwood, willows, and mesquite indicate that ground water is fairly close to the surface.

Tall-grass prairies have abundant humus in the soil, coming from stems and roots of decaying grass. Thus grasslands are retentive of soil moisture and highly productive for agriculture, especially when planted to grains. Areas of scattered bunch grass store less moisture in the ground and generally indicate an average annual rainfall of less than 20 inches. Only with care can such lands be used for farming, and much damage has resulted from overgrazing and careless farming on these grasslands. Soils of both steppes and deserts originally covered with sagebrush and cactus may be highly productive when irrigated, but the presence of desert vegetation is an indicator that this land should not be used for farming without irrigation.

FORESTS

Forests, for their best development, require plenty of rain, preferably without prolonged droughts, a fairly long frost-free growing season, reasonable soil drainage, and absence of continuous strong winds. Long droughts injure trees and kill great numbers of them. When subjected to a well-defined wet-and-dry climate, trees generally shed leaves during the dry season and are otherwise modified in order to conserve plant moisture. The limit for poleward tree growth seems to be determined as much by the very cold dry winds of the long winters of high latitudes as by shortness of the growing season itself.

High mountains adjoining arid regions may have two *tree lines*—an upper one limited by cold wind and shortness of growing period (Figure 5-14) and a lower limit determined by lack of rain. Between these extremes, belts of vegetation on the mountain sides reflect the change in climate conditions that results from elevation, just as the much broader belts of vegetation on the lowlands extending from the hot tropical deserts to arctic wastes reflect climatic conditions resulting from latitude.

Man's Relation to Forests. Many men depend upon forests for their livelihood. At first primitive men hunted wild animals and gathered edible roots and berries in the woods. A few small groups of men, like Pygmies of the Ituri Forest in the Belgian Congo, Negritos in the remote forested mountains of Luzon, and Pygmies in interior New Guinea, still obtain their living in this way. People in tropical rain forests often make clearings for planting crops, and supplement their hunting by agriculture. The American Indians, in the eastern United States, also formerly raised corn beneath dead trees which they had killed by girdling. Sometimes animals are domesticated and a combination of livestock raising and subsistence farming is carried on, as in ancient Germany and Gaul, or today in parts of the Balkan Peninsula.

When commerce develops, forest people gather different natural forest products to exchange for the manufactured goods and luxuries they want. Among wild products are rubber, palm oil, Brazil nuts, and dyewoods of the tropical forest. Honey, wax, resins, turpentine, furs, ivory, perfumes, skins, drugs, and raw materials for varnish and tanning extract are other products gathered from forest lands and entering the world's commerce.

Forest industries.   In humid regions, the abundance of wood leads to widespread use of that material. Houses and other structures are built of it. Many forest people become skilled in making furniture, in wood carving, and in fabricating articles of wood: bowls, spoons, and other kitchenware, barrels, boxboards, shingles, and wooden rakes and handles for implements. Sometimes civilized forest dwellers develop special home industries which depend on skilled labor rather than expensive raw materials. An example is the manufacture of watches and other types of metalwares which require little material.

Animals in the forest economy.   The pasturage of livestock is a common industry of many forest regions, for although grass is not abundant, the forests provide some fodder and browse. After clearings have been made there is more feed for cattle and other domestic animals, and hay can be raised if needed for winter use. Milk cows and beeves are the most common domestic animals kept in forest regions. In general, sheep fare better on open plains, although these animals often graze in summer on meadows within mountain forests and on pastures above timber line. Goats are kept more commonly in hill regions of brush and open woods, like those of the Mediterranean climate, since they are good foragers and can utilize feed too poor for cattle and horses. Swine eat acorns and beechnuts in the Balkan forests and grub for roots and other food in the woods of the southern United States, but in most parts of the world pigs are not allowed to roam freely. A lack of concentrated feed, in combination with poor forest roads, causes oxen to be preferred over horses for draft purposes in "backwoods" parts of southeastern Europe in the Balkans and Carpathian Mountains.

In New England and the hilly parts of New York and Pennsylvania, dairying is a chief industry on land cleared of forest. Because these sections are well served by rail and highway, perishable products may be shipped to Boston, New York, Philadelphia and other cities. Regions less favored by swift transport often turn surplus milk into butter or cheese or preserve milk by manufacturing a condensed or powdered product. The Pacific Northwest, Wisconsin, and the St. Lawrence Valley, as well as the Dominion of New Zealand, offer examples of places where processing of milk is a common practice in areas where farms have replaced forests.

In some localities with cold winters fox and mink fur farms are successful.

Forests as barriers.   Since road building is more difficult in forests than in open country, forests handicap travel; hence wooded lands may be compared with more obvious barriers such as mountains or deserts. Most mountains support forests, and added difficulties of travel may result from the combination of trees, rocks, and steep slopes. In Germany the same word, *Wald,* is used for forests and mountains. The Black Forest (*Schwarzwald*) and the Bohemian Forest, for example, are understood to be mountains as well as forests.

Since communication is slow and soils are often poor, regional population density is low, and people of the forests live in isolated small groups. As a result, customs and culture tend to change more slowly than those of cities and fertile well-developed and populous lands.

Sometimes, forests provide refuge from invading armies for men of the surrounding plains. The Slavs in Russia fled to the forests to escape the Mongol horsemen of Genghis Khan and gain protection against these invaders of their land. Sometimes, forests offer shelter to political offenders, for example, the legendary Robin Hood in Sherwood Forest.

Trade centers usually appear in the larger forest clearings; often these settlements become

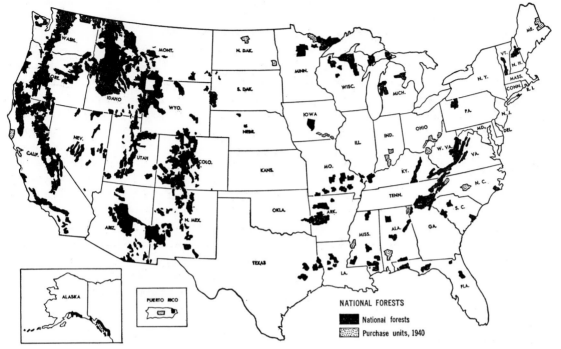

Figure 11-1   National forests in the United States. The majority of these forests are in the western United States, where government reserves of timber were uncut and the highest mountains are located. (Adapted from U.S. Forest Service.)

sites of local governments. In the days of poor transportation and isolation, such settlements might enjoy complete independence. Forested mountains of southern Germany during the Middle Ages sheltered hundreds of small, independent or semifree principalities, kingdoms, dukedoms, and the like. Not until modern transportation developed did such political units tend to consolidate.

Recreation.   Forests are favorite places for recreation. A considerable part of the more than 10 billion dollars which the people of the United States spend on recreation and travel each year pays for camping, fishing, hunting, and sight-seeing in forest regions. Over 25 million people annually have used 152 national forests in the United States for winter sports, hiking, riding, and picnicking as well as fishing, hunting, and camping. Another 50 million people drove through national forests on high-

ways provided by the government within their boundaries. Pleasant shade and higher humidity of wooded regions are especially appreciated during hot weather. Nearly every state in the Union has systems of wooded parks for use by citizens and visitors, and many cities, like Chicago, Cleveland, and Akron, also maintain extensive park tracts.

When left standing in parks, extraordinarily large trees may bring an area more revenue from tourists than it would have received if the trees had been cut down and used for lumber, Sequoia National Park in the Sierra Nevada, forests of redwoods in northwestern California, and the Olympic National Park in Washington with its giant fir, spruce, and cedar trees, attract thousands of tourists each year. The display of rhododendrons in the Great Smoky Mountains National Park also interests many visitors.

Figure 11-2   Excellent stand of ponderosa pine, Deschutes National Forest, Oregon. (Photograph by L. F. Ryan, courtesy of the U.S. Forest Service.)

FORESTS OF THE UNITED STATES

About 624 million acres, or one-third of the total land area of the United States, are now called forest land as compared with the original stand estimated to have covered 820 million acres. It is believed that 461 million acres are capable of producing timber of commercial quality either now or in future under proper management (Figure 11-2). The remaining 163 million acres are "noncommercial" forest land: mountaintops, desert fringes, chaparral and other scrub forests, mostly in the West and withdrawn for parks and other purposes. Of commercial forest land, about 205 million acres contain saw timber and four-fifths is forested with second growth (Figure 11-3). Cordwood areas total 95 million acres. About 86 million acres are in satisfactory stand of seedlings and saplings, but 75 million acres, or one-sixth of the whole, have only poor reproduction or are nonrestocking. Within all the above classifications, there is a total of 164 million acres of poorly stocked or denuded forest land. Any forest plan for the United States must consider the restocking of this unproductive land.

The total stand of saw timber in the United States is estimated to amount to about 1,968 billion board feet. (This unit is 1 foot square and 1 inch thick.) *Saw timber* includes trees 5 inches and larger in diameter at chest height. Thirty-one per cent of the standing timber of the United States is located in the Pacific Northwest, 28 per cent in the Southern states, 10 per cent in California, 21 per cent in the Northeastern and North Central states, and 10 per cent in the Rocky Mountain regions (Figure 11-4). The region having a mid-latitude west-coast marine climate occupies only 6 per cent of the entire forested area of the United States but contains almost a third of the remaining saw timber (Table 11-1). This situation results from the dense stands of

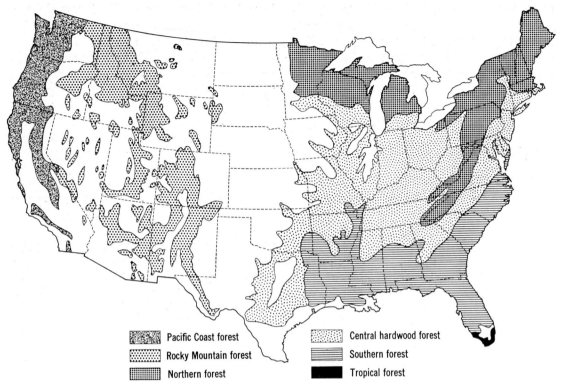

Legend:
- Pacific Coast forest
- Rocky Mountain forest
- Northern forest
- Central hardwood forest
- Southern forest
- Tropical forest

Figure 11-3   Principal forested types and areas of the United States.

large trees in this part of the country and the fact that access roads which facilitate logging have not been built into large areas of virgin timber.

Of the commercial forest land in the United States, 345 million acres (75 per cent) are privately owned and 116 million acres (25 per cent) are in public ownership. Commercial forests in private ownership contain nearly three-fifths of the standing saw timber. Large expanses of publicly owned saw timber are inaccessible and of little commercial use at present. They do protect mountain watersheds against excessive erosion, however. As roads are built into them, careful logging will utilize much of the mature saw timber that is now out of reach.

The largest block of publicly owned commercial forest land, 73 million acres, is included in the national forests, supervised by the Forest Service of the U.S. Department of Agriculture (Figure 11-2). Some 43 million acres lie within Indian reservations, state forests, and other publicly owned forests. Three-fourths of the publicly owned forests are in Western states.

Farm wood lots owned by about 3.2 million farmers account for 139 million acres of timber. This large total acreage comprises many small holdings. Half of the state of Pennsylvania is wooded, with most of the trees in farm wood lots. Other Eastern states also have large acreages in farm wood lots. More than half of the farm wood lots are used for pasture, however, and this interferes with proper reproduction of first-class timber.

Of the total commercial forest areas of the United States, the South has the highest acreage, 39.8 per cent, partly because the climate of that section favors rapid growth of trees. The Northeastern and Middle Atlantic states have 15.7 per cent of the forest acreage. Three Great Lake states (Michigan, Wisconsin, and Minnesota) have 11 per cent, and the

Central states (Ohio, Indiana, Kentucky, Illinois, Iowa, and Missouri) have 9.6 per cent. In the Central states, forest land is small because geographical conditions make agriculture the preferred use of the land; most of the remaining timber here is in farm wood lots. The Southern Rockies have 6.3 per cent, California, 3.5 per cent, and the Pacific Northwest, 10 per cent of the forest lands.

Hardwoods and softwoods. Trees may have broad leaves or needle leaves. In the United States these names are practically interchangeable with the expressions hardwood and softwood. Broad-leaved, or hardwood, trees may be deciduous and shed their leaves in the cold or the dry season, or they may be evergreens when growing in the tropics. Needle trees are usually evergreen except for a few species that shed leaves in winter, like the eastern tamarack and western larch.

TABLE 11-1. TIMBER STATISTICS OF THE UNITED STATES, 1953*

Region	Timber volume, 1953		All timber cut, 1952, million cubic feet	Timber mortality on commercial land, 1952, million cubic feet	1952 salvage, million cubic feet	Saw timber cut, 1952, million board feet
	All timber, billion cubic feet	Saw timber, billion board feet				
New England	24	51	500	298	Not	1,760
Middle Atlantic	34	74	470	233	avail-	1,800
Great Lake states	25	50	540	485	able by	1,240
Central states	25	83	400	102	local	1,810
Plains states	3	8	30	28	areas	90
Total, North	**111**	**266**	**1,940**	**1,146**	**150**	**6,700**
South Atlantic	34	107	1,460	95	Same	5,350
Southeast	48	139	2,410	314		9,410
West Gulf	32	111	1,190	220		4,840
Total, South	**114**	**357**	**5,060**	**629**	**240**	**19,600**
Pacific Northwest	146	749	2,390	747	Same	14,270
California	67	360	930	359		5,720
Northern Rockies	43	167	330	308		1,900
Southern Rockies	18	69	100	200		560
Total, West	**274**	**1,345**	**3,750**	**1,614**	**380**	**22,450**
Total, United States	**499**	**1,968**	**10,750**	**3,389**	**770**	**48,750**

Data for the Northern Rockies in Washington and Oregon are included with the Pacific Northwest.

Data for forests of the Colorado Plateau and the Great Basin are included with the Southern Rockies.

* U.S. Forest Service. One cubic foot equals 12 board feet. Second and third columns from *Timber Resources Review,* table 22, p. 44, 1955; fourth and seventh columns, *ibid.,* table 36, p. 62; fifth column, *ibid.,* table 4, p. 13; sixth column, *ibid.,* table 44, p. 75.

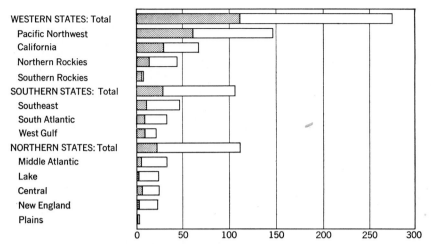

Figure 11-4   Total timber volume and saw timber (shaded), in billions of cubic feet, 1953. Data for Northern Rockies in Washington and Oregon included in the Pacific Northwest, data for Colorado Plateau and Great Plains included in the Southern Rockies. Total timber volume for all regions, 499 billion cubic feet; saw timber 164 billion cubic feet. (From Timber Resources Review, U.S. Forest Service, 1955, Table 22, p. 44.)

Expressed in terms of volume, that is, board feet, Western softwoods aggregate 1,345 billion board feet of saw timber, 68 per cent of the total for the country. Hardwoods east of the Great Plains account for 18 per cent, while Douglas fir of the Pacific Northwest represents 27 per cent of the volume of the nation's saw timber. It will be seen from the above figures that the volume of saw timber and acreage of forest land in a given region vary widely in different sections of the United States. For example, the area of Douglas fir timber is comparatively small but its volume is very large. In 1952 the annual production of saw timber was 48,750 million board feet.

Forest Regions of the United States. The United States originally was covered with virgin forests, grasslands, and other vegetation types reflecting natural conditions prevailing in different sections of the continent (Figure 11-3). Forests included both coniferous and deciduous trees. The principal forest regions of the United States and their dominant tree types are as follows:

Northern forest region.   This area extends from the coast of New England west across New York and around the upper Great Lakes and south to include the Appalachian Mountains. The forest is a mixture of conifers and hardwoods, with softwoods originally dominant in the northern part. White pine, hemlock, spruce, balsam fir, and cedar are among the principal conifers. There are considerable stands of hardwoods, including beech and maple, and several varieties of oak, birch, elm, ash, hickory, poplar, and walnut. The bulk of the virgin timber of the northern forest has been cut, and some land has been cleared for farming, but there is a large amount of second growth. Since it is near markets, this section, which has much nonagricultural land and favorable conditions for tree growth, should serve as one of the great permanent forest areas of the United States.

Central hardwoods.   This, the largest of the forest regions, includes the Piedmont area east of the Appalachian Mountains and the interior region west of those mountains. It extends across Ohio and the southern Great Lakes section to the treeless prairies of Iowa, south into northern Alabama, and southwest through Mis-

Figure 11-5 Large white oak trees in a virgin stand of hardwoods, Spring Mill State Park, Hoosier National Forest, Indiana. Stands of timber of this quality are difficult to find. (Photograph, courtesy of the U.S. Forest Service.)

souri, Arkansas, and eastern Oklahoma. The original forest consisted of mixed hardwoods of great commercial value, including oak (Figure 11-5), ash, elm, cherry, beech, maple, walnut, poplar, basswood and hickory, with red and black gums and sycamore as important trees in the southern portion. Hardwoods in Illinois and Iowa were largely restricted to bottomlands along streams, with interstream uplands chiefly covered by tall prairie grasses.

Much hardwood forest has been cleared from the fertile plains and rolling hills, to be replaced by productive farms. Many farms still maintain wood lots, which contain three-fourths of the remaining wooded acreage. The largest forest stands are in hilly sections. The hardwoods are valuable for the manufacture of such goods as furniture, interior finishing materials, and sports equipment.

Southern forest region.   This region extends from southeast Virginia to eastern Texas and includes all the Atlantic and Gulf Coastal Plains westward through Louisiana, southern

Arkansas, and the southeast corner of Missouri. Florida is also included except for the southern tip. Climatic conditions, with a long growing season and plenty of rainfall, favor rapid tree growth; hence the South is and should continue to be one of the most important timber producers of the United States (Figure 11-6).

The dominant forest trees growing here consist of different types of southern yellow pines, including longleaf, slash, and loblolly. Cypress, red gum, oak, sycamore, cottonwood, elm, and other trees grow along the moist river bottoms. Inland as the elevation mounts toward the Piedmont Plateau, the trees are a mixture of hardwoods with shortleaf and other pines. Longleaf and slash pine are sources of naval stores as well as timber. Southern pines are also used for the manufacture of kraft paper. Subtropical trees in southern Florida cover too small an area to be of commercial importance.

Plains.   On the semiarid Great Plains the only native trees grow in narrow corridors (gallery forests) of cottonwoods along flood-

Figure 11-6 Log train ready to dump logs into millpond at Crossett, Arkansas. (Note evidences of heavy use of hydroelectric power at this mill.) Burner at the left is used to dispose of wood waste. (Photograph by L. J. Prater, courtesy of the U.S. Forest Service.)

plains bordering the larger streams, and a few stunted junipers in the badlands. Because of greater rainfall, outlying ranges of the Rockies, like the Black Hills of South Dakota and several mountain masses in central Montana, support forest "islands" of lodgepole pine and other softwoods. In general, however, the Great Plains never had any considerable quantity of useful timber.

Rocky Mountains. Forests of this region extend from a point north of the Canadian border across the whole width of the United States and southward into Mexico; they can be divided conveniently along the southern boundary of Wyoming into northern and southern Rocky Mountain forests. The trees are limited mainly to rainy and snowy mountain slopes, high valleys, and elevated plateaus. Lower plateaus and valleys, like the surrounding plains, support merely grass, sagebrush, stunted cedars, or thorny brush.

The principal tree species in the Rocky Mountain and plateau country is the ponderosa, or western yellow pine, so drought-resistant that it can survive with a rainfall as low as 15 inches annually (Figure 11-2). Lodgepole and other pines, firs, and spruce dominate the higher mountains. The Northern Rockies, especially the mountains of Idaho, have important forests of western white pine mixed with larch (tamarack), firs, cedar, and other conifers.

West Coast. From the Cascade Range to the Pacific in western Washington and Oregon grows the Douglas fir forest. This contains the largest amount of virgin standing timber remaining in the country (Figure 9-3). Cedar, western hemlock, Sitka spruce, true firs, and some maple, aspen, and oak are associated with the Douglas fir. Climatic conditions are so favorable for forest growth that the board feet of timber per acre greatly exceeds that of other forest regions in the United States or Canada.

From the Oregon boundary southward to the Golden Gate occurs the redwood forest in a band only 25 to 50 miles wide, exposed to abundant rains and fogs of the Pacific. Inland forests of California are mainly sugar pine and other conifers in the Sierra Nevada and the highlands of the northern part of the state. On the western slopes of the southern Sierra are scattered groves of big trees, or sequoias.

FORESTRY

Successive Timber Exploitation in the United States. *The Northeast.* The utilization of forest resources depends primarily upon accessibility of the forests, the kind and character of the trees, available transportation to market, climatic conditions, and available labor supply.

During the colonial period and for nearly a century thereafter, the northeastern United States supplied most of the demand for softwood lumber. Here waterways gave access to virgin forests of white pine; logs were cut in winter and hauled over the snow to the banks of streams. In spring the logs were floated downstream with the floods and sawed into lumber in towns like Bangor or Augusta in Maine and many smaller places (Figure 11-7). Commercial white pine in the northeastern United States is practically gone; cutting spruce for pulpwood now constitutes the principal forest operation.

The Great Lake states. This section of the country became important for its lumber production following decline of the industry in New England, New York, and Pennsylvania after the Civil War. A magnificent stand of white pine covered the land tributary to the upper Great Lakes, and lumbermen migrated to Michigan, Wisconsin, and Minnesota. Numerous streams permitted rapid exploitation of forest resources, which were considered inexhaustible. Preferred locations for sawmills were at mouths of rivers entering the Great Lakes, and the lumber was distributed to consumers from Chicago or other lower lake ports. Rafts of logs went down the St. Croix and Wisconsin Rivers to the Mississippi and were sawed at river ports downstream to supply lumber for building the prairie towns. Saginaw, Bay City, and Muskegon in Michigan; Green Bay and Oshkosh in Wisconsin, and various towns in Minnesota were among centers from which came for a time the world's largest production of pine lumber.

Figure 11-7   Breaking a log jam in the rapids of the St. John River, Maine. (Photograph courtesy of the U.S. Forest Service.)

Supplies of timber about the upper Great Lakes were so accessible and exploitation so rapid and complete that the area was logged off in less than a half-century. The U.S. Forest Service estimates only 3 per cent of the saw timber of the Union is left in the Great Lakes region. Most of the original forest land has been devastated by careless logging and by forest fires. The pine is nearly gone, and large areas are nonrestocking or are covered with scrub oak and aspen. Here charred and decayed pine stumps show where the vanished forest stood.

Central hardwood forests. Cutting of this excellent timbered area began with the first settlement of the region, which lay between the forests of northern conifers and southern pines. The soil was fairly fertile, encouraging the clearing of land for agriculture; thus over wide areas most hardwood forest is cleared and only small remnants remain (Figure 11-5). Much of the hardwood region is now too important for general farming and specialty crops to permit reforestation, for hardwoods generally require much more time than softwoods to reach marketable size. Most of the trees left are in farm wood lots. In Ohio, Indiana, and Illinois, these often contain small amounts of hardwood timber of some commercial importance. These wood lots also provide supplies of firewood, mine props, railroad ties, fence posts, and some maple sugar and sirup. Northeastern Ohio farmers, like those of Vermont, regularly tap the maple "sugar bush" as a source of income from their wood lots.

This forest area provided valuable lumber for furniture, flooring, interior finishing, wagons, barrels, boats, and other wooden manufactured articles. Many woodworking plants were established near these supplies of timber. Among the furniture-making centers are the cities of Grand Rapids, Michigan, and Shelbyville, Indiana. Chicago, South Bend, Flint, and Detroit were famed for wagons and carriages long before automobiles were invented. Louisville, Kentucky, leads in manufacture of baseball bats; St. Louis makes bowling pins and alleys.

Further shift of the industry. Having exhausted much of the resources of the Great Lake states, the lumbermen moved southward to the virgin pine forests of the Gulf and Atlantic Coastal Plains and westward to the Pacific. Today the South and the West contain over 78 per cent of the remaining commercial timber of the United States. Water and rail transport make northeastern markets accessible to the South, but both the Rocky Mountains and the Pacific Coast areas are distant from large consuming centers.

The South. Conditions for lumbering in the South were different from those of the Great Lake states and New England. There was no snow to serve as roads in winter, but lumbering operations in the rather open forests of yellow pine could be carried on throughout the entire year. Level or rolling land favored the building of logging railroads and use of machinery (Figure 11-6). Mill towns developed both on the coast (Brunswick, Georgia) and at interior centers (Monroe, Louisiana). Furthermore the long growing season and abundant rainfall make posible rapid growth of trees and perpetuation of the industry. Unfortunately large areas of forests have been destructively cut with no thought of keeping them productive. Supplies of hardwood especially from Kentucky and Tennessee are used for furniture making, as at High Point and Gastonia, North Carolina. Furniture making is also of growing importance in Tennessee and Arkansas.

The West Coast. In the Douglas fir forest of the Northwest and the timberland of northern California climatic conditions are favorable both for growth of dense stands of large trees and for logging during most of the year. The enormous size of the firs, cedars, and redwoods led to use of machinery in logging operations (Figure 11-8). Railroads, trucks, donkey engines, spar trees, caterpillar tractors, and other loading devices are utilized to deliver logs to the mills. Here lumber is sawn at a faster rate than was ever known before. Sawmills are so large that a single plant equipped with band saws can cut twice as much lumber as did the 400 circular saws operating in all the mills of Bangor when in its prime.

In the Northwest the greatest lumber-sawing towns have the advantage of tidewater locations. Logs are brought by water, rail, and truck to mills from forested country inland as far as 100 miles away. Among the lumber-sawing ports are Tacoma, Seattle, Everett, Bellingham, Longview, and the Grays Harbor cities of Aberdeen and Hoquiam in Washington, Portland and Coos Bay in Oregon, and Eureka, California. Inland cities like Eugene, Bend, and Klamath Falls in Oregon and Lewiston, Idaho, are also important in the industry. Oregon, Washington, and California lead in output of lumber. Many pulp and paper mills utilize the spruce and some inferior woods for raw material. Waste from many sawmills is also used for pulp. Some of the best clear logs of Douglas fir are made into veneer and plywood, which find wide use in furniture and construction work.

Stand and Cut of Timber in the United States.
A survey of forest resources in the United States by the U.S. Forest Service showed that the total stand of timber in 1953 was 499 billion cubic feet, distributed as follows: 55 per cent in the West, 23 per cent in the South, and 22 per cent in the North and Northeast (Table 11-1). The stand of saw timber was 1,968 billion board feet, divided into about 80 per cent softwoods and 20 per cent hardwoods. This figure represents 40 per cent less standing saw timber than was reported in 1909, but 23 per cent more than for 1945. The lumber cut is about 48 billion board feet annually (Figure 11-9). The entire drain on the volume of all timber is over 10.7 million cubic feet. Of this, sawed lumber accounted for one-half, fuel wood for 16 per cent, pulpwood for 10 per cent, and ties, posts, poles, and miscellaneous items for 15 per cent. In 1952, insects killed 5 billion board feet of saw timber and fires about 1 billion board feet. In that year the total mortality on commercial forest land was estimated at nearly 3.4 million cubic feet of timber of which about a quarter was salvaged for sale.

The Forest Service estimates that under present conditions of growth and cutting our forests can grow only 80 per cent of the required stock to supply our future needs for timber by about the year 2000, although

Figure 11-8 Modern method of handling saw logs near Eureka, California. This is known as "cat (caterpillar) logging," and by this method it is possible to carry on lumbering in places far from rail or highway transport. (Photograph, courtesy of the Caterpillar Tractor Corporation.)

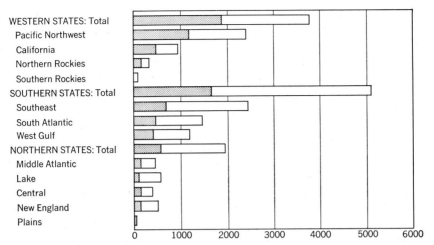

Figure 11-9   Total cut of timber and saw timber (shaded) in the United States, in millions of cubic feet, 1952. Data for the Northern Rockies in Washington and Oregon are included in the Pacific Northwest; data for Colorado Plateau and Great Plains included in Southern Rockies. Total cut in United States, 10,750 million cubic feet; total saw timber cut, 4,062 million cubic feet. (From Timber Resources Review, U.S. Forest Service, 1955, Table 36, p. 62.)

growth of timber nearly equalled the cut during the 1950s. This indicates urgent need for improved handling of our forests. Better management of privately owned forest resources in the South and the North is especially needed to ensure that those regions more nearly approach their growth capacity. About 13 per cent of the nation's commercial forest land is owned by industry and 27 per cent by government. These timberlands are managed best. For the conservationist, the largest problem is presented by the 60 per cent of forest land held by 4.5 million private owners, of whom 3.2 million are farmers. The situation regarding hardwoods, comprising 19 per cent of the nation's total stand of saw timber, is particularly serious because this type of forest grows so slowly. The hardwood forests are about evenly divided between the Northern and Southern states and are being depleted rapidly in both regions.

National Forests.   As an aid to the conservation of forests, the United States created the first forest reserve in 1891, but most national forests (as they were renamed in 1907) were established from the remaining areas of publicly owned forest land by President Theodore Roosevelt soon after 1900. Since the more accessible forest land had already passed into private ownership, most national forests were first located in remote mountain regions of the West. In 1911 Congress passed a law permitting the government to buy land; and by this method and by gift forest lands were acquired and national forests established in the White Mountains, Appalachians, and smaller areas in the Great Lake states and Ozarks.

Gross area of national forests in the 48 states is approximately 218 million acres, but not all the included land has commercial stands of timber because large areas of inferior tree types occur on high mountains within national forest boundaries. National forests include more than one-third of the forested area of the United States (Figure 11-1) but less than one-third of the standing timber. National forests in Alaska cover nearly 21 million acres and contain the best timber in the territory.

National forests were created "for the purpose of securing favorable conditions of waterflows, and to furnish a continuous supply of timber for the use and necessities of the citizens of the United States" (Act of June 4, 1897). By direction of the Secretary of Agriculture when national forests were placed under his administration in 1905, "all land is to be devoted to its most productive use for the permanent good of the whole people, and not for the temporary benefit of individuals or companies, . . . and where conflicting interests must be reconciled the question will always be decided from the standpoint of the greatest good of the greatest number in the long run."

National forests have multiple purposes and uses. They are a source of income, since timber is sold with the requirement that logging must be done in specified ways to ensure perpetuation of the forests and reduce fire hazards. There is a very close relationship between national forests and industrial, agricultural, and domestic consumers of water. Most great cities and irrigation projects of the Western states secure water from mountain areas included in the national forests. The Great Valley of California, Yakima and Wenatchee Valleys in Washington, and irrigated sections of southern Idaho and Utah are examples.

Forests have great value as protectors of watersheds; they help prevent floods and supply water for power and municipal use. In the East, national forests cover the crests of the Appalachians and White Mountains, which include the headwaters of many streams used for hydroelectric power and industrial and domestic supply. More than 1,000 cities and towns in the United States obtain all or most of their water from sources in national forests. Examples include Los Angeles, Denver, Ogden, Phoenix, Little Rock, and Portland, Oregon. By supervision and control over livestock national forests furnish much summer grazing for sheep and cattle, yet timber growth and watersheds are protected.

To an increasing degree, national forests have become summer playgrounds. There are 90,000 miles of streams in national forests, which provide some of the best fishing in the United States.

Timber Resources of the World. The continents have forest resources of great diversity as the result of such factors as climate, relief features, amount of former forested land now cleared for farming, extent of exploitation of forest resources, and differences in types of trees. Authorities differ widely in their estimates of forest areas of the world; estimates of the volume of timber differ even more, because detailed information is not available for many regions. According to the U.S. Forest Service, the forest area of the world is approximately 9,000 million acres (Table 11-2).

Lumber and other timber products are generally quite bulky and form important items for both domestic and foreign trade. This is readily understood, for sources of supply are often remote from consuming markets.

Softwoods. The taiga and forests located within the areas of west-coast marine climate are made up principally of softwoods; they supply large quantities of lumber and pulp-

TABLE   11-2.   WORLD   FOREST AREAS, *After U.S. Forest Service*

Areas	Per cent of total*
United States and Alaska	8.1
Canada, Newfoundland	9.3
Mexico, Central America, West Indies	2.4
South America	20.0
U.S.S.R., Europe, and Asia	26.2
Northern Europe	1.5
Western and Central Europe	0.7
Eastern Europe, except U.S.S.R.	0.8
Southern Europe	0.6
Middle East and North Africa	1.1
Central and South Africa	14.1
East Indies and Philippine Islands	5.1
Asia, except Middle East and U.S.S.R.	8.6
Australia, New Zealand, Pacific islands, and New Guinea	1.5
Total	**100.0**

* Total forest area, 9,000 million acres.

wood in North America and in Europe. Taiga lands of Siberia constitute an important reserve of softwood for lumber and pulpwood for export and future use in the Soviet Union. New Zealand, Tasmania, and southern Chile produce minor amounts of softwood, although true conifers are not native to the lands of the Southern Hemisphere. Humid warm temperate or subtropical regions, as in our own South and in parts of southeastern Brazil where the so-called "Paraná pine" grows, have extensive softwood forests. Softwoods also grow on the mountains of the Northern Hemisphere in instances where they extend into lower latitudes.

Foreign nations having large reserves of conifers, that is, softwood, are Canada, the U.S.S.R., both European and Asiatic, and Northern Europe around the Baltic Sea in Norway, Sweden, Germany, Poland, and Finland. Austria, Switzerland, and Romania also have extensive pine forests. Some softwood is available in Cuba, the Bahamas, and in the mountains of Mexico.

Temperate hardwoods. Land that supported hardwood forests in the midlatitudes generally possessed fertile soil and a favorable climate. In Western and Central Europe, the eastern United States, and northern China, as well as in Japan, Korea, Manchuria, and southeastern Siberia wide areas of this type of forest land have been cleared for agriculture. Hardwood is exported in some volume from the Balkan countries, especially Yugoslavia, and local supplies are cut in Western Europe. A little hardwood grows in the southern Andes. Australia produces only hardwood lumber, principally from various varieties of eucalyptus.

Tropical hardwoods. In the tropical rain forest many kinds of hardwood trees flourish, but logging is difficult and expensive. Heat and humidity make labor less efficient, trails and roads are difficult to clear through the tangle of vegetation, and much timber is remote from seaports and rivers (Figure 11-10). Species of trees having commercial value do not exist in solid stands as in the northern

Figure 11-10   Tractor hauling a large mahogany log in a tropical rain forest in Central America. (Photograph, courtesy of the Mahogany Association, Inc.)

coniferous forests but occur widely scattered, making it hard to find and cut desired timber. Some cabinet woods and other special timber —mahogany, rosewood, teak, and ebony— come from the tropics, but today most accessible commercial forests of the world are in midlatitudes of the Northern Hemisphere.

Tropical rain forests cover large areas and unquestionably contain much timber of species which have not been popularized. Furthermore tree growth is rapid, and it is possible that forests might be so managed as to increase reproduction of trees that are known to be useful and to reduce the number of undesirable trees. In future our own country may have to depend upon the tropics for much of our needs for hardwood. Hence, utilization of tropical hardwoods presents a challenge to lumbermen and users of wood.

World Resources and the United States Supply.   The estimated 9,000 million acres of the world's forested land is distributed among the continents in the following proportions: Asia, 28 per cent, South America, 28 per cent, North America, 19 per cent, Africa, 11 per cent, Europe, 10 per cent, and Australia, 4 per cent (Table 11-2). Of the world's forests, conifers, now being rapidly exploited, cover about 2,660 million acres, temperate hardwoods, 1,200 million acres, and tropical hard-woods, 3,640 million acres. Future expansion of the world supply of softwoods must depend on coniferous forests of the U.S.S.R. and on hardwoods in the tropical evergreen forests of South America and Africa.

The United States normally cuts as much lumber per year as the rest of the world combined, suggesting the rapidity with which our forest resources are being depleted. Yet if we get all commercial forest lands under good management and keep them productive, we can continue to produce on the present scale or at even a greater rate. Nevertheless, since annual drain on United States forests in most years exceeds annual growth, there is evident need to adopt a sound conservation policy for both public and private forest lands. The annual increase of nearly three million people a year in the United States, with the resulting demand for over one million new homes annually, makes conservation particularly necessary.

A forest program for the United States. A sound forest program for the United States involves both short-range and long-range activities oriented toward balancing national consumption and the growth of timber. At present there is sufficient forest land to grow all

the timber needed, provided that the forests are properly managed. Any effective forest program for our country must include the private lands, which comprise about 75 per cent of our 461 million acres of commercial forests. Only a start has been made in reaching the $3\frac{1}{2}$ million farm wood lot owners. Education and demonstration projects would be helpful in this field. Some states have substituted a severance tax for the usual system of taxes on land devoted to growing timber. This encourages both planting of trees and better handling of existing wood lots. Cooperative sustained-yield units may be the solution in certain areas. It may be desirable to establish benefit payments for forest conservation, as is done with soil conservation. Meanwhile and, as quickly as possible, some $3\frac{1}{4}$ million acres of publicly owned land that is partly or wholly denuded of forests should be brought into productive condition by planting.

Essential, too, is more effective protection against fires, insects, and diseases in forests. Certainly forest research and dissemination of information concerning forest problems will assist the development of forestry and utilization of forest products.

FOREST CONSERVATION

Natural Enemies of Forests. Many natural causes lead to depletion of forests, though man is the greatest destructive agent in the world today. In a condition of nature it is obvious that destruction by natural causes must balance the growth of timber in a mature forest. Among causes for losses are insects, fungus diseases, fire, wind, animals, winterkilling, and drought.

Insects. Damage wrought by insects in the forest is estimated to destroy timber worth many millions of dollars annually. In 1952 about 5 billion board feet of saw timber were killed by insects. All parts of the trees are subject to insect attack. Seeds may be eaten by maggots, cone beetles, and larvae of cer-

tain moths. Grubs, weevils, and beetles attack the seedling, sapling, and roots, bark, limbs, trunk, and foliage of both young and old forest trees. Wood borers work on sound trees by girdling the trunk in the inner bark (cambium layer) just under the outer bark. It has been estimated that, during outbreak periods between 1917 and 1943, the western pine beetle (Figure 11-11) has killed 25 billion board feet of pine timber. Losses were nearly equal to the cut of pine lumber for the period. The ponderosa, or western yellow pines, are most subject to attack by this pest.

Hardwood trees have their own insect enemies; locust borers wreak much harm in this type of tree. Caterpillars of the tussock moth, gypsy, browntail, and other moths, sawfly larvae, and adult beetles may injure both conifers and broadleaf trees by devouring foliage and thereby weakening trees and sometimes killing them. Aphids and various scales suck juices of plants and are special enemies of shade and fruit trees. Overmature trees and those damaged by fire or some other cause are easy prey for insects. Insects that kill trees increase the fire hazard and make tree reproduction and reforestation more difficult.

Insects preying on forests have natural enemies that normally keep them in check. These include mites, birds, rodents, other insects, and bacterial or fungus diseases. When a pest increases in numbers, its enemies also tend to increase and ultimately control it. Woodpeckers, nuthatches, and warblers are among the birds feeding upon eggs, larvae, scale, and other insects. Squirrels, shrews, and mice eat insects, especially in the hibernating pupal state. Sprays may help to control pests in cultivated or shade trees, and airplane spraying of forest trees has been done successfully. For example, in Idaho alone nearly 400,000 acres were sprayed against the tussock moth (Figure 11-12). In 1957 much of northern Vancouver Island, in western Canada, was sprayed to control the spruce bud worm and other pests. Cutting and burning of infested trees also helps prevent the spread of serious insect epidemics.

Tree diseases. Fungi work most havoc in mature forests although they serve a useful purpose in helping to cause decay of fallen timber that might otherwise accumulate to an extent that would increase the fire hazard and might interfere with natural reseeding. Fungi reproduce by means of spores carried by wind; they find entrance into trees especially through injured branches or broken bark. From these points of infestation the disease spreads until the wood is softened and decayed and becomes worthless for lumber.

Certain special diseases of trees, usually imported from abroad where the host species may have developed immunity, have proved very deadly when introduced into America.

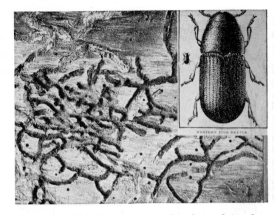

Figure 11-11   Western pine beetle and its damage to wood. This insect has caused great loss in the forests of the western United States. (Illustration, courtesy of the U.S. Forest Service.)

Figure 11-12   Spraying insecticides by aircraft to control forest pests in the northern Rocky Mountains. (Photograph, courtesy of the U.S. Forest Service.)

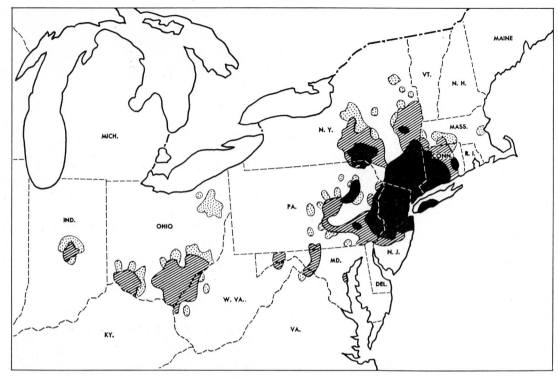

Figure 11-13   Extent of the Dutch elm disease infestation. Area quarantined in 1941 is shown in black (11,617 square miles). Diseased area in January, 1946, (23,659 square miles) is shown by hatching; diseased area in November, 1946, is shown by dots. (Adapted from American Forestry Association.)

One of these is the Dutch elm disease (Figure 11-13) for which no certain remedy is known although spraying is done against the little insects that are supposed to spread the disease. Another method is immediately to destroy all known elm trees infected with the disease in the hope that healthy elms will escape. Chestnut blight, another serious infestation, was introduced from the Orient into New York State in 1904. Unfortunately strict quarantine measures were not taken, with the result that practically all American chestnut trees have been killed from New England southward throughout its entire range (Figure 11-14).

Throughout the nation, a dangerous infection affects the white pine (Figure 11-15). This white pine blister rust has a peculiar life history. The disease does not spread directly from one infected pine tree to another, but only through an intermediate host, which must be a species of *Ribes,* usually the wild black currant and gooseberry. From these shrubs the spores again infect the white pine. Blister rust spreads only among pine trees having five needles in a bundle and does not affect the lodgepole or the yellow pine. The disease has spread throughout most of the range of five-needle pines in the east, north, and west. Attempts to control white pine blister rust provide for elimination of all wild currants or gooseberries in and near stands of white pine.

Damage by animals.   Animals grazing in the woods can damage both seedlings and older trees. Seedlings and young growth, especially of hardwoods, often are destroyed by browsing of horses, cattle, sheep, and goats. Animals may also trample out seedlings or break down young growth. In the South pigs root out and eat the inner bark of pine seedlings, and also consume seeds and nuts of trees, thereby preventing reproduction. Stock sometimes injure larger trees by nibbling at the bark. Trampling by stock may injure mature trees by exposing and wounding roots and by compacting soil so much that rain runs off instead of being absorbed. Domestic sheep and goats may also seriously damage woodlands. Regulation of grazing is essential if a forest stand is to remain productive very long. Some wild animals, notably the porcupine, injure trees by girdling the bark. Chipmunks, squirrels, and other rodents devour seeds, and beavers are sometimes destructive along streams.

Storms and other minor causes of forest injury. Other causes of natural destruction of forests include tornadoes and other windstorms and lightning. For example, a great "blowdown" in 1921 on the Olympic Peninsula caused a loss of at least 5 billion board feet of timber. The New England hurricane of 1938 blew down an estimated 13 billion board feet of timber. Destruction of trees by winds depends on many factors: the velocity and exposure to the wind, type, age, and health of the trees, condition of the soil, particularly if water-soaked, injuries owing to the process of gathering turpentine, weakness resulting from insect ravages or fungus growth, and size and depth of the root system. Lightning, ice storms, sudden changes from thaws to freezing temperatures, and extended drought may kill trees.

Forest Fires.   The most damaging of all destructive agents in the forests are fires. Fires destroy timber in all states of the Union, and the total number of fires may amount to over 100,000 in some years, with annual damage

Figure 11-14   Large chestnut tree killed by chestnut blight, standing in the Chattahoochee National Forest, Georgia. (Photograph, courtesy of the U.S. Forest Service.)

Figure 11-15   Diseased white pine seedling from a forest in Massachusetts. When blister rust attacks these trees, seedlings invariably die. (Photograph, courtesy of the U.S. Forest Service.)

of 30 million dollars or more. Some fires get completely out of control and have been known to burn over more than a million acres of forest land, destroying several billion board feet of timber in single "burns."

The worst fires generally come when weather conditions make their control almost impossible unless they are attacked immediately after they start. Hot, dry, windy weather furnishes ideal conditions for spread of fire. In many forested sections, when relative humidity falls below 20 per cent, forest-fire warnings are issued because low humidity causes litter on the forest floor to become highly combustible and fires will spread rapidly if started. Other factors to be considered in evaluating fire hazards include wind velocity and direction, length of time since the last rain, type of fuel available for the spreading fire, and the dryness of that fuel. When conditions indicating "fire weather" prevail, all clearing of land by fires and burning of brush and debris from logging should be halted. Likewise campfires and smoking in forests

should be prohibited except at designated campgrounds. In national forests and some private lands, lumbering operations are sometimes stopped until the dangerous weather condition has passed. In 1936 the terrible Tillamook fire in Oregon burned 6 billion board feet of lumber in two days. It was started by friction during logging operations, and it spread because of a hot dry wind through forests that were ordinarily too damp to burn easily. In 1952, fire destroyed about 1 billion board feet of saw timber.

It is easier to prevent fires than to extinguish them once they have begun. Fire-control measures begin with fire prevention. For once fire from any cause begins during the dry season, there is bound to be much combustible material in the woods that will feed the flames, especially after logging operations have left the ground covered with dead branches and discarded trunks of trees. This "slash" becomes very combustible when dry. In some national forest operations loggers are required to pile the tops and brush after cutting and where practicable to burn the refuse when it is too wet for fire to spread.

Causes of fires. Forest fires may occur from both natural and human causes, but 90 per cent are caused by man's carelessness or his intent and are, therefore, preventable. The principal natural cause of fires is lightning, especially in the western part of the United States where thunderstorms are not always accompanied by sufficient rain to extinguish fires started by lightning bolts. More than three hundred fires have been started in a single day in one national forest in Idaho; in one summer 14 per cent of the area of a forest of northeastern Washington and northwestern Idaho was burned over because of the spread of lightning fires. Nothing can be done to stop ignition of forests by lightning, but watchful care during the thunderstorm season may prevent excessive destruction. The building of roads and trails so that a fire can be reached quickly by a force of fire fighters aids in extinguishing or controlling fires before much damage is done. Fire fighters and supplies to aid them are sometimes transported by air and are dropped by means of parachutes.

Carelessness in burning brush by farmers during land-clearing operations is an important cause of fires. This combines with carelessness by campers and smokers to cause nearly one-third of all fires. In some sections, especially in the Southern states, it is the custom to burn off dry grass in the forest, in the belief that this practice will improve the quality of the grazing. Such ground fires have slight effect on mature trees, but by killing or injuring seedlings they may seriously affect natural reproduction of the forest. Fortunately some progress is being made in stopping this poor practice. Some fires are deliberately incendiary, set because of fancied wrongs, to make work in fire fighting, and for other reasons.

Ground and crown fires. Fires may not be hot enough to kill mature trees, especially those provided with thick bark, but even when fire is restricted to the ground, serious damage results. Ground fires kill seedlings and destroy undergrowth that helps to hold soil by retarding runoff after heavy rains. Forest leaves and other litter, which supply needed humus and help prevent undue erosion, are likewise destroyed by ground fires. Even if fire does not immediately kill a tree, it may leave injuries that allow the entrance of insects and disease-producing parasites and fungi, which will slowly kill the tree or weaken the wood. Soil deprived of humus and its covering of brush is subject to erosion. Its fertility and capacity to hold water are lessened by repeated burning. The value of the forest as a home for wild life is temporarily destroyed; many birds and game animals perish during fires, which also destroy the natural beauty of forests that make them attractive to campers and tourists.

When high winds occur during periods of low humidity, an entire forest may become ignited, from the litter on the ground to the treetops, producing what is called a crown fire (Figure 11-16). Crown fires totally destroy all small plants and animals; they kill even the largest trees that stand in the path of the flames. It may take many years before an area devastated by a crown fire can again support a worthwhile forest. Ground fires are fought by trenching or with water pumped by portable engines, but the only thing that will stop a crown fire is prolonged general rain, a shift in the wind, or the fire burning itself out to a place where no fresh fuel exists.

Protection against fire in forests. To help guard against forest fires, in all its national forests the government maintains a system of fire-lookout stations, placed on the highest peaks in mountainous areas or on tops of artificial towers on flat lands. When a fire is spotted, headquarters is notified by telephone. The best way to prevent great damage by forest fires is to get on the job quickly before the fire has a good start. Men and supplies to fight the fire are rushed to the site by roads and trails maintained for that purpose. Airplanes are also used for patrolling forest areas and locating fires. Sometimes men and supplies are dropped by parachutes from airplanes (Figure 11-17). Many private landholders and states cooperate in maintenance of fire-lookout service. Fire hazard in forests can be reduced by piling brush carefully after logging operations and allowing burning of debris and clearing of land only when the forests are too wet to make this hazardous.

Careless versus Selective Logging. Too frequently logging operations in the United States are conducted without regard for the future reproduction of forests. In cutting trees, sometimes a clean sweep is made of both mature and immature trees. *Careless logging* also causes unnecessary injury to forests, leaving the forest in poor condition for growth of more timber. Much timber also is wasted by such logging, which leaves about one-fourth by volume of a tree in the woods. Useful wood, for example, is sometimes left in very high stumps or in logs that are cut too short (Figure 11-18). Limbs and tops are generally wasted, though they would make fuel, but population centers are so far off that it is unprofitable to ship firewood out of the forest.

Selective logging. The forest can be made to reproduce itself economically by the use of good cutting methods. One way, for example, is selective logging, that is, cutting mature trees and leaving young growth and seed trees to grow into timber of better size. Small trees can seldom be logged and sawed at a profit. Their cutting is an unsound practice because they will grow more rapidly upon removal of mature and defective trees (Figure 11-19). European forestry, for example, generally uses the clean-cutting system, with planting. America must use more care in lumbering operations in order to perpetuate our forests. As possible remedies, a few states as well as some European nations require private owners to cut trees by approved logging methods, to ensure establishment of new growth. Sustained-yield timber management, already the practice in national forests of the United States, should be extended to all state forests and privately owned land.

Conservation of Timber Products. *Waste in mills.* Further waste occurs after a tree has been cut and sent to the sawmill, for there

sawdust, shavings, and slab wood are often thrown away or used only for fuel. Sometimes for lack of a market the wood waste is destroyed in enormous burners (Figure 9-4) merely to get rid of it. Progressive lumber mills have developed methods of reducing the amount of waste wood and have developed some ways of using it profitably. The use of thinner band saws in place of the old circular saw has reduced the amount of sawdust. Still there is an appalling amount of waste in many mills, where nearly one-third the volume of a log may be lost in sawing operations. Nevertheless the conversion of two-thirds of a log into lumber is better than the 50 per cent waste that was common practice some years ago. Much wood waste is being used also for numerous by-products.

Chemical preservatives and substitutes. Much timber is used for telephone and telegraph poles, railroad ties, mine props, fence posts, and pilings. For all these uses, timber will last longer if it is treated with creosote or some other wood preservative. Another way of conserving timber is to substitute brick, tile, or concrete for wood in constructing

Figure 11-16 Crown fire in Rhode Island woods. This hill slope will be a worthless expanse of dead or dying trees after the passage of the fire. (Photograph, courtesy of the U.S. Forest Service.)

buildings, bridges, and various other structures.

Reforestation. Where good logging practice is used, natural reproduction will perpetuate timber growth; but on lands denuded by improper logging or fire, planting may be necessary to restore the forest. Planting trees is practical from the economic standpoint at times, but it may often be too slow or expensive to attract private capital looking for investment. Hence much tree planting de-

Figure 11-17 Fighting a California forest fire, using helicopters for scouting and for transporting men, food, fire-fighting tools to inaccessible points. (Photograph, courtesy of the U.S. Forest Service.)

volves upon the government. In the northern United States, where it takes from seventy-five to a hundred years for a tree to become large enough for a saw log, an individual cannot ordinarily wait for financial returns from tree plantings.

In the Southern states, because of the length of the growing season and the abundant rainfall, pine trees grow very rapidly and may be cut for saw logs in as little as thirty years and for pulpwood in twenty years or less. Consequently reforestation in the South offers a good opportunity for investment. Artificial planting of trees and protection of naturally seeded ground from injury by fire and roaming livestock is an urgent necessity in Southern states, where natural conditions for growth of timber are among the most favorable of any in the nation.

Official regulations in national forests keep the number of grazing animals at a level that will not cause serious damage to young growth.

On privately owned land where woods are used for pasture, damage from overgrazing frequently occurs and greater control is needed.

Decline of Towns and Industries.   One result of unnecessary destruction of forests is the decay of towns dependent upon woodworking industries. Hundreds of sawmill towns in all parts of the once forested country have almost completely disappeared, and many others have sadly deteriorated upon closing of their mills. Yet with conservative methods of lumbering, the forests would have continued to yield a crop of timber annually; the abandoned towns could have remained prosperous sawmill centers indefinitely. A few companies are carrying on lumbering operations by methods that perpetuate the forest, and these set an example which should be followed by the rest of the woodworking industries.

Even furniture factories find it difficult to maintain themselves when they have ex-

Figure 11-18 Excessively wasteful logging operation in Oregon, in which too much lumber has been left to rot in the high stumps, and unmarketable timber has been left on the ground to form serious fire hazards. The center pole with its cables for hauling the logs appears in the distance. (Photograph, courtesy of the U.S. Forest Service.)

Figure 11-19   Many trees have been cut from each acre of this tract of 35-year-old loblolly pine in Virginia in order to thin the stand. The remaining trees will mature as valuable commercial timber. Some of the cuttings have been left on the ground, but these will be destroyed. (Photograph courtesy of the U.S. Forest Service.)

hausted the immediate supply of hardwoods and find it necessary to draw on distant supplies. Often factories in older lumbering districts are compelled to close and new factories that are near supplies of hardwood timber take their places. The veneer industry extends the usefulness of high-quality material by slicing valuable logs into thin pieces that are glued on the surface of cheaper woods.

SUMMARY

The relation of plants to their environment is plant ecology. Important natural factors affecting plants include water, light, and heat. Forests develop where rainfall is adequate and the growing season sufficiently long. Commercial forests of wide extent are found in regions with humid subtropical, humid continental, west-coast marine, or taiga climates, and it is in these parts of the world that many people depend upon products of the forest for fuel, industrial raw materials, shelter, and some food supplies. Tropical hardwood forests grow in the wet equatorial and parts of the monsoon regions.

The eastern United States was well provided with mixed forests of hard and softwoods, but increasing demand, as well as some careless exploitation, has removed its more valuable timber resources. Most of our commercial lumber is obtained from the Pacific Northwest and the South, and these supplies are being used rapidly. Large areas have been included in national forests on which timber is carefully cut. Some large private timber holdings are also well managed, so as to ensure continued lumber production.

Widespread removal of the forest cover was accomplished hundreds of years ago in well-populated parts of Northern and Western Europe, but in the taiga lands of the Soviet Union, Sweden, Finland, and also in Canada in the Western Hemisphere large untouched softwood resources remain for commercial use.

Besides careless lumbering, the world's forests are depleted by the ravages of tree diseases, insects, storms, and fire. Further extension of methods for conserving our forests is needed if future requirements for lumber are to be met. Marked progress toward fuller utilization of wood products has already been achieved.

Outline

Plants and their distribution

Classification of plants

Plant associations

Environmental factors

Water: hydrophytes, mesophytes, xerophytes

Light, heat, and others

Forests

Man's relation to forests

United States forests: area, timber volume

Forest regions of United States

Northern

Central hardwoods

Southern

Rocky Mountains

West Coast

Forestry

Changes in lumbering regions

Cut of timber

National forests: location and uses

Timber resources of the world

Softwoods

Temperate hardwoods

Tropical hardwoods

Forest conservation

Depletion: insects, diseases, etc.

Forest fires: cause and control

Careless logging and woodworking

Conservation methods

QUESTIONS

1. What specific attractions do most forests in midlatitudes offer the vacationist or tourist?

2. Why are most of our national forests located in the western United States?

3. In Figure 11-20, what advantages are apparent for the commercial lumbering operations that are necessary if this stand of timber is to be used at maturity?

4. Formulate a statement in which you summarize the geographical aspects of the photographs appearing in Figures 11-6, 11-8, 11-19, 11-20.

5. What important functions of forests, other than the production of lumber, can you suggest?

6. List five procedures in lumbering operations that are desirable from the viewpoint of the conservationist.

7. What change would appear in Figure 11-19 if selective logging had been practiced?

8. On the basis of a population of 165 million, how many acres of forested land does the United States have per capita?

Why is this figure deceiving?

9. What are the principal problems of lumbering in the wet equatorial lands?

10. Define "virgin forest."

11. What are the leading lumber-exporting nations of the world? The leading lumber-importing nations?

12. What relation does your answer to Question 11 bear to the total population of these nations?

13. What are some of the chemical products obtained from wood?

14. From the conservation standpoint, in what respects is it desirable to use wood rather than nonrenewable resources such as metals in manufacturing processes? In what ways is the reverse true?

15. Why should the recreational uses of some of our national forests, or considerable parts thereof, take precedence over other forest uses?

16. What must be done to convince the farm owner that forest conservation practices are desirable on his own small farm wood lot?

17. Why did forest conservation receive considerable national attention before most other phases of conservation?

18. Why has sustained-yield forestry come to be practiced more widely among paper pulp manufacturers than among lumber producers?

SELECTED REFERENCES

Allen, S. W.: *Introduction to American Forestry,* McGraw-Hill Book Company, Inc., New York, 1950.

American Forests: Monthly publication of the American Forestry Association, Washington.

Collingwood, G. H., and W. D. Brush: *Knowing Your Trees,* American Forestry Association, Washington, 1951.

Greeley, William B.: *Forests and Man,* Doubleday & Company, Inc., New York, 1951.

Haden-Guest, Stephen: *A World Geography of Forest Resources,* The Ronald Press Company, New York, 1956.

Holbrook, Stewart H: *Burning an Empire,* The Macmillan Company, New York, 1952.

Kittredge, Joseph: *Forest Influences,* McGraw-Hill Book Company, Inc., New York, 1948.

Lane, Ferdinand C.: *The Story of Trees,* Doubleday & Company, Inc., New York, 1952.

Marsh, R. D., and W. H. Gibbons: "Forest Resource Conservation, 1940," U.S. Department of Agriculture Yearbook, Washington, 1941.

Mobley, Mayor D.: *Forestry in the South,* T. E. Smith, Atlanta, Ga., 1956.

Panshin, Alexis J.: *Forest Products: Their Sources, Production, and Utilization,* McGraw-Hill Book Company, Inc., New York, 1950.

Smith, Guy-Harold, (ed.): *Conservation of Natural Resources,* John Wiley & Sons, Inc., New York, 1950, chaps. 5, 10, 11.

Smith, J. Russell: *Tree Crops: A Permanent Agriculture,* The Devin-Adair Company, New York, 1950.

Stewart, George R.: *Fire,* Random House, Inc., New York, 1948 (a novel on forest fires).

U.S. Department of Agriculture: Yearbook, *Trees,* Washington, 1949.

Whitaker, J. Russell, and Edward A. Ackerman: *American Resources,* Harcourt, Brace and Company, New York, 1951, chaps. 11–14.

Zon, R., and William N. Sparhawk: *Forest Resources of the World,* 2 vols., McGraw-Hill Book Company, Inc., New York, 1923.

NOTE: The Superintendent of Documents, Washington, will furnish a list of publications on different aspects of forest conservation. U.S. Forest Service, Department of Agriculture, Washington, will supply a list of recent publications on request.

12. The Changing Face of the Earth

VARIATIONS in the surface of the earth have resulted from natural forces working slowly but steadily for countless ages. The same forces affecting the earth today, seemingly insignificant in themselves, can bring about vast changes if given the millions of years available in the geologic past. In general the natural features of the earth's surface result from unending but intermittent conflict between forces tending to elevate, distort, or build up the land and others continually striving to reduce all irregular surfaces to featureless plains.

The arrival of man complicated the operation of many natural agencies, since many of his activities, including cultivation of soil, destruction of grass and forests, and construction of dams and ditches, hasten or delay the various forces that affect the land surface.

The Magnitude of Surface Features. A convenient classification of surface features of the earth is based on their descending order of magnitude. Features of greatest size are the vast depressions occupied by the oceans and the enormous elevated blocks of the continents. Authorities differ in their recognition of the number of ocean basins and continents. Those accepted generally include the Pacific, Indian, North Atlantic, South Atlantic, and Arctic Basins; the continents include Eurasia, Africa, North and South America, Australia, and Antarctica.

Major relief features are divided into those of a second order of magnitude. These include the cordilleras of associated mountain ranges (the Andes, Himalayas, Rockies), large plains and basins (North European Plain, Great Plains, Congo Basin), plateaus (Tibet,

Colorado), oceanic troughs or *deeps* (south of the Aleutians, parallel to the west coast of South America), and submarine plateaus (North Atlantic). Land features of the second order form the dominant framework of the continents (Figure 12-1). The ocean troughs typically are elongated depressions which usually have their trends parallel to mountainous coasts and chains of islands. Submarine plateaus are usually found near the middle of an ocean basin. These contrast with the *continental shelf* which adjoins each continent and results from the flooding of its shallow edges by the sea.

The third order of surface features in descending size and importance on the land areas includes mountain ridges, individual peaks, hills, tablelands, valleys, lakes, and small plains. Although submarine canyons, submarine volcanoes, and banks are among marine features affecting the contour of the sea bottom, in general the ocean floor is smoother than the land because the forces causing changes in the relief of the land are more effective than those working beneath the sea. Both large and small landforms result from interaction of forces that elevate or depress, build up or tear down the earth's surface. The final natural landscape that develops depends on many factors, such as type and hardness of rock, climate, and vegetation, as well as the character of the original surface features.

For most people, the significance of the third order of surface features of the land areas is easier to perceive than vast expanses of continent or ocean basin. Relatively few people are privileged to travel great distances on the face of the earth; millions rarely see farther than the horizon of their own small plain or the confines of their mountain valley. To be sure, modern improvements in transportation are changing this situation.

Forces Affecting Landforms.   Forces originating within the earth, causing structural changes or deformation of the crust, are termed *tectonic*. Of these the forces of *diastrophism* bend, fold, and break the earth's crust. Another term is *vulcanism,* which is concerned with movement of molten rock underground or its eruption above the earth's surface. Tectonic forces produce inequalities on the earth's surface, such as uplifts or depressions. If as a result of such movements there should be a break (fault) in the rocks an earthquake is the result.

The forces of *gradation* (lowering of land surfaces by erosion and gravitation) oppose tectonic movements and tend to level off inequalities of the land. The chief agents of gradation are running water, ground water, wind, glaciers, and waves. Rocks are first broken or otherwise prepared for removal from their original position; the material is transported and is finally deposited elsewhere. Leveling of the earth's inequalities by gradation is accomplished by *degradation* (removal of material) and *aggradation* (deposition of transported debris). These forces, both constructional and destructional, which affect earth features will be discussed in more detail later in this chapter.

Classes of Rocks.   The solid portion of the earth is known as the *lithosphere*. Its outer part, roughly a few miles thick, called the *crust*, consists of various kinds of rocks and is quite well known to man. Little is known about the interior of the earth, on the other hand, because it has not been visited at any great depth. Rocks of the earth's crust are divided into three classes: igneous, sedimentary, and metamorphic.

Igneous rocks were once molten material that has solidified, and are divided into *intrusive* and *extrusive* types. Molten rocks that emerged and cooled quickly on the earth's surface, like lava and volcanic ash, are called *extrusive*. Lava contains various gases, including water and sulfur compounds, and many gas-bubble holes, similar to those found in light bread, are left in the rock of those lavas that cooled quickly. Pumice and scoria are types of these lavas. Sometimes lava on cooling forms a natural glass, called *obsidian*. The

American Indians made excellent arrowheads from such material. When some force, usually that of expanding steam, blows volcanic rocks into fine dust, the product is called *volcanic ash.* This material, thrown out by explosive eruptions of volcanoes, may be transported many miles by the winds and deposited in some distant place as a layer of soil material upon the ground.

Igneous rocks that cooled slowly far below the earth's surface are called *intrusive,* and their characteristics and position distinguish them from extrusive lavas. The molten mass, or *magma,* of intrusive igneous rocks remained liquid for a long time, possibly thousands of years, because its location far underground prevented rapid loss of heat. This slow cooling gave minerals composing the magma time to combine into granules and relatively large and definitely shaped crystals; hence intrusive igneous rock such as granite has a coarsely granular appearance. Although formed far below the surface, intrusive rocks may be exposed today on top of the ground as the result of removal of overlying rock by natural forces of degradation.

Sedimentary rocks were formed from materials deposited in water or on land by streams, winds, glaciers, plants, or animals. Thus fine mud or clay solidified into shale. Sand became sandstone. Gravel formed conglomerate. Limy ooze and shells made the limestone, and peat provided raw material for coal. Because sediments are commonly deposited in beds and layers, sedimentary rocks usually show distinct layers, or *strata,* and hence are often called *stratified rocks.*

Metamorphic rocks were once of igneous and sedimentary origin but have been changed by heat, pressure, and the deposit of material from solution; their present characteristics are therefore far different from those they first possessed. Metamorphic rocks are generally crystalline and harder than the original material of which they were formed. Thus shale, sandstone, and limestone become respectively slate, quartzite, and marble. These metamorphosed rocks not only are usually harder than the original sedimentary rocks, but pressures and tensions to which the rocks have been subjected have caused formation of many fractures or planes that permit easy splitting. This characteristic is useful in slate and permits slate shingles and blackboards to be manufactured with relatively little difficult. *Schist* and *gneiss* are banded metamorphic rocks that have been subjected to such great changes that it is difficult to determine the original rock material with certainty. Pressure exerted upon them was so great that minerals of different types formed layers or bands at right angles to the direction of the force.

Chapter 19 on mineral resources will deal with the relationship between occurrences of minerals of economic importance and the kinds of rocks.

Rock Weathering.   People speak of the "everlasting hills," but no rocks are so hard and resistant that they cannot be broken and worn away by natural forces. A process called *weathering* breaks rocks and changes their character. The weathering process is carried on by mechanical and chemical agents. Cracks in rock surfaces serve as convenient points of attack by both agents of weathering. Gradually the firm bedrock changes toward the surface into broken and partly decomposed fragments called *mantle rock.*

Mechanical agents merely break rocks apart or physically disintegrate them. Disintegration may occur after rapid changes of temperature have split rocks by expansion and contraction. Expansion of water freezing in cracks and expansion of growing plant roots may produce disintegration of rock masses. Boulders roll downhill by force of gravity and may be broken. Glaciers and debris carried by running water, wind, and waves have great abrasive power. The explosive force of volcanic eruptions may shatter rock into bits. Animals and man often bring about rock disintegration by their activities.

Chemical agents actually change the substances of the rock materials, producing decay or decomposition. This may come from solu-

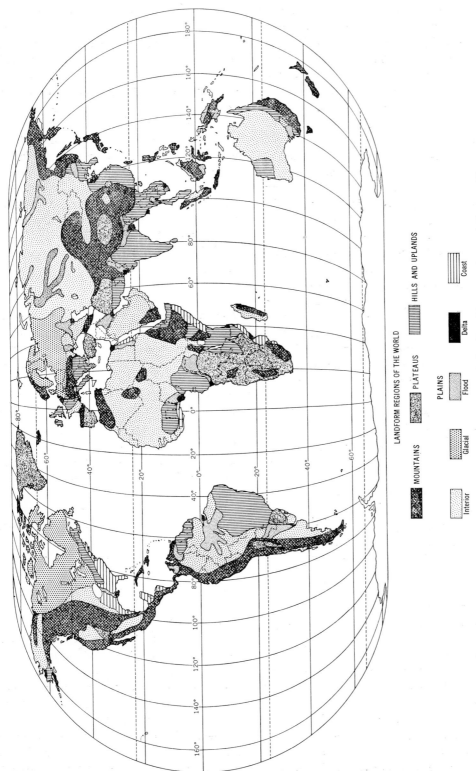

LANDFORM REGIONS OF THE WORLD

MOUNTAINS

PLATEAUS

HILLS AND UPLANDS

PLAINS

Interior

Glacial

Flood

Delta

Coast

Figure 12-1 Landform regions of the world.

tion by ground water of cement that binds rock particles together, or from softening and crumbling of rocks when softer and looser compounds are formed from the original substances. A familiar example might be the slaking of lime, in which quicklime, which is fairly solid, combines with water and makes a crumbly substance. Oxygen, water, and carbon dioxide are atmospheric agents for chemical weathering, subjecting rocks to the processes of oxidation, hydration, and carbonation, respectively. Rusting of iron is a common example of oxidation and hydration. Typical green stains on the outcrop of copper-bearing veins result from carbonation and hydration. Volcanic gases, humic acids from decaying organic matter, and certain bacteria are other agents causing decay of rocks.

The term *soil* is applied to the mixture of weathered rock and organic materials in which plants grow. Soil is known as *residual* when it forms from weathering of bedrock in its place of origin or as *transported* when carried and deposited by any agent. Transported soils are therefore unrelated to underlying rock material. Soil contains humus and other organic material in addition to weathered rock and transported debris. Quantities of earthworms, nematodes, bacteria, and other living organisms affect its physical and chemical structure. The uses and types of soil and conservation of soil will be discussed in Chapter 17.

EROSION

The wearing away of rocks or the denudation of the earth's surface is called *erosion*. Agents of erosion include running water, ground water, glaciers, wind, and waves.* These agents can pick up, transport, and deposit weathered material; and they also possess tools, i.e, stones and rock fragments carried by the erosive agents, by means of which exposed bedrock is abraded. Transported material can be reduced in size by abrasion, and some agents are effective in sorting debris before it is deposited. Given sufficient time, the simple processes of weathering and erosion produce profound changes on the earth's surface. Even high mountain masses covering thousands of square miles may be reduced to lowlands by erosion. Geologists give the name *peneplain* (almost a plain) to these gently rolling plains, which are the final product of all gradational activity.

Stream Erosion. Running water comes from runoff accompanying rainfall, from melting snowbanks and ice fields, and from springs fed by underground water. When rain comes or snow melts, sheets of water creep and trickle down any slope. Soon little rills develop (Figure 12-2). These lead into small gullies and then into large gullies, until finally they all join some trunk stream. If fed at its source by a spring, it may be permanent. If there is not a permanent source, the stream will be intermittent.

Streams tend slowly and constantly to deepen, widen, and lengthen their valleys. The broadening and lengthening process extends to the divides of neighboring streams, but continued modification of the valleys is always in progress. In doing this the running water scours material from the stream bed and undermines the banks where it is swiftest on the outside of a river bend. Clear water, however, has little mechanical power to wear away bedrock, and the actual work is done by tools the stream carries—sand and even finer silt.

The character and structure of bedrock have much to do with the arrangement of drainage systems. In the folded Appalachian Mountains the rivers occupy valleys that were eroded from weak rocks between parallel ridges of resistant rock material. Alternation

* In this chapter, the discussion of erosion will be limited to the work of running water, ground water, and wind. The work of waves will be described in Chap. 16 on coast lines and islands. Most of that on glaciers is divided between Chap. 13 on plains and Chap. 14 on mountains.

of hard and soft rocks resulted from folding of mountains and rocks which that region has experienced. The drainage systems that result have a *trellis* arrangement. On the Great Plains the strata lie nearly flat and are generally uniform in character, and as a result the river systems that develop take on a branching pattern. This *dendritic* drainage, named for its many treelike branches, is in strong contrast to the trellis pattern of drainage in folded mountains, where parallel ridges and valleys alternate. Dendritic drainage also is the characteristic pattern of most of the Appalachian plateaus where stratified rocks have been eroded after uplift that only slightly deformed or warped them.

In general dendritic drainage systems develop where there is no rock control on stream flow and also in areas of unconsolidated materials. Other arrangements of drainage are found under these circumstances:

1. Layers of rocks which are inclined from the horizontal vary in resistance to erosion.

2. Bedrock is partly dissolved by water solutions.

3. Deposits made by glaciers, volcanoes, wind, and other agents have modified the former drainage pattern.

Streams transport material in suspension, in solution, and by pushing or rolling it along the stream bed. Many little whirls or eddies of water in flowing streams help the current to pick up and carry rock fragments. Such material may soon be dropped, but the process is repeated and debris from the land finally reaches the ocean. Tributaries bring part of their suspended material to a main stream, particularly in times of heavy rainfall.

The amount of load carried in suspension by a river mainly depends on the volume and velocity of the stream, the kind and size of weathered material available, vegetation cover preventing soil erosion, and the character of the stream bed. Even a relatively clear stream carries some material in solution, as is evident from the residue after river water has evaporated. Large rivers like the Yangtze Kiang may carry sediment into the ocean by

hundreds of millions of tons annually. The Mississippi River alone transports nearly a million tons of silt into the Gulf of Mexico each day. Authorities estimate this amounts to some 400 million cubic yards of sand, silt, and mud carried to its mouth every year.

Near the source of a stream most rock fragments have angular shapes. Then as the rock fragments are carried downstream, abrasion wears away the sharp edges. Even large boulders become rounded and reduced in size until the largest stones left are the size of gravel. Finally, rivers may carry only sand, silt, and clay, the larger stones having been destroyed by abrasion or left behind upstream.

Waterfalls. Waterfalls are a significant factor affecting the development of water power, locations of hydroelectric plants, and establishment of mills and factories. They also affect trade, since they limit the use of rivers for navigation. Waterfalls are usually caused by outcrops of resistant rock in the beds of

Figure 12-2 Small gullies on a plowed hillside field. Silt eroded from the slope has accumulated to form alluvial fans on a miniature scale at the mouth of each gully. The same process occurs on a large scale at the mouths of many mountain canyons. (Photograph, courtesy of the U.S. Soil Conservation Service.)

streams. (Figure 12-3). With continued erosion the falls retreat upstream or sometimes degenerate into rapids. Waterfalls can retain their vertical drop while retreating upstream when a resistant top layer of rock is eroded less rapidly than underlying weaker rocks. Thus the resistant layer is undermined and breaks off at intervals, and the position of the falls moves headward up the stream channel. This sapping situation prevails at Niagara Falls.

Cycles of Erosion. Both rivers and regions pass through a life history or *cycle of erosion* whose stages a famous physiographer, William Morris Davis, named youth, maturity, and old age.

The river cycle. Youthful streams are swift and usually straight with relatively few tributaries. They actively deepen their beds toward a base level determined by the surface of the body of water into which they flow, or temporarily, by a ledge of rock or other obstruction. Occurrence of rapids, waterfalls, and lakes along the course of young rivers is further evidence of immaturity, because such features disappear as erosion progresses. Valleys of youthful streams are narrow and V-shaped. They may be deep and steep-walled canyons and very difficult to cross. Like overgrown gullies, young streams are eroding headward upstream and expanding their drainage basins. Young, swift rivers which flow through narrow gorges offer favorable sites for dams, and many such locations have been developed for power production.

Mature streams have nearly attained base level, and are no longer vigorously eroding

Figure 12-3 Lower falls of the Yellowstone River, 308 feet high. The canyon is eroded in a lava plateau covering most of Yellowstone National Park. The location of the falls is determined by the presence of a dike of resistant rock material. (Photograph, courtesy of the Northern Pacific Railway.)

their beds. The number of tributaries usually increases. Rapids are few, and waterfalls and lakes nearly disappear. Valleys are broad, with gentler slopes than in youth. The rivers begin to *meander* (flow in great curves), and develop valley flats or floodplains (Figure 12-4). A floodplain is covered during high water, hence the name, and is formed partly by undercutting on the outside of bends and partly from deposition on the inside of meanders. Large mature rivers may be valuable for navigation, and their valleys used for farming.

In old age, streams reach base level. Valleys are very broad and divides are low. As valleys widen and divides lower, streams are absorbed and consolidated, and the number of rivers becomes fewer. Rounded hills of the most resistant rock, called *monadnocks,* may rise above valley floors as remnants of erosion. Old-age rivers are sluggish and may carry more material in solution than in suspension. They meander widely across the plain, and "oxbow" cutoffs or lakes (Figures 12-4 and 12-5) occur where the current in flood cuts through the narrow neck between two curves. Large rivers in old age are commonly used for navigation.

Different sections along a stream may have differing local base levels. Sometimes a section will be in maturity or old age, while upstream or downstream there may be swift parts of the river that have not yet reached base level. Furthermore, uplifts of land or removal of a temporary obstruction that slowed the erosion process may permit active erosion to be renewed. A stretch of the river in maturity or old age may then again assume characteristics of youth. This phenomenon is called *rejuvenation.*

Regional cycle of erosion. In the *youthful* stage, the work of erosion has just begun. Streams are comparatively few, valleys are narrow, and since divides (interfluves) are broad and poorly drained, lakes and swamps are common (Figure 12-6A). In *maturity* the rivers and their tributaries have eroded headward until the whole region is well drained

and completely dissected. Little original upland remains; hence stream divides tend to be narrow (Figure 12-6B, C). Major streams are approaching base level and developing meanders and floodplains. There is an abundance of tributaries. The lakes and swamps of youthful regions have disappeared. During maturity the maximum difference in elevation in any stage of the cycle of erosion exists between the ridge tops of the interfluves and the valley floor. In *old age,* valleys are very broad, and divides have been so reduced by erosion that the region has become a peneplain (Figure 12-6D). Streams have reached base level, and

Figure 12-4 Stream meanders and an oxbow lake.

A. The stream has reached a stage of maturity in which it flows almost at grade. Large swinging meanders have developed in its floodplain, and the neck of the middle meander is nearly cut through by the undercutting of the current at X.

B. *Here the stream channel has been straightened naturally. The current has cut through the neck at* X, *leaving the former channel as a semicircular oxbow lake detached from the main channel.*

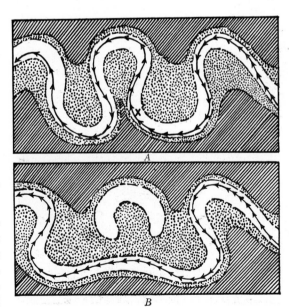

A

B

their number is less than in maturity. Oxbow lakes and scars of former river meanders may indent the wide floodplain of rivers. A few monadnocks may stand above the general level of the peneplain.

In youthful regions, man can best live on the broad flat interfluves; the valleys are too narrow for occupancy. In mature regions, farmers till the river flats and gentler lower slopes of the valleys. The steeper upper slopes and narrow ridges of the interfluves are usually left in forest or used for pasture. In old-age regions, man can move freely across the peneplain. Chief handicaps are the broad rivers that require long bridges or ferries, and the poor drainage of the floodplain.

Deposition of Load.   If fully loaded, streams deposit their sediment whenever decreased velocity or declining volume of flow lessens their capacity to carry material. Such deposits frequently are made at bases of slopes, along river courses, and at mouths of rivers. Running water thoroughly sorts the debris it carries. The largest and heaviest stones are dropped first, followed in order by gravel, sand, and mud.

Deposition at bases of slopes. When a heav-

ily loaded stream has its capacity to carry material in suspension suddenly reduced, as when its velocity is decreased by lessening of slope, conditions for deposition are favorable. Thus *alluvial cones*, or *fans*, of coarse debris are deposited at mouths of hillside gullies where they debouch to gentler slopes (Figure 12-7). Mountain torrents also encounter a sudden change in slope where they leave mountains and flow out on broad plains. This reduces the carrying power of floodwaters; the streams are thus forced to deposit great fans. These frequently coalesce to form compound alluvial fans or slopes, sometimes called *alluvial piedmonts* because of their location at the foot of mountains.

Where coarse material predominates, these piedmonts and fans are unsuited for crops, but the fine material makes excellent farm land (Figure 12-7). Rapid shifts in direction and change in velocity of the currents cause the sediments of alluvial fans to change rapidly as to size and weight of material. Shifting of the currents, which occurs during the deposition of torrential fans and coarse bars in rivers, causes sudden changes in direction and inclination of the layers of debris. This arrangement is known as *cross-bedding*.

Figure 12-5   Meanders, oxbow lakes, cutoffs, and meander scars of the Koyukuk River plain in west central Alaska. Note the light-colored alluvial deposits on the sides of the stream opposite the undercut slopes. This tundra landscape supports few people. (Photograph by U.S. Air Force.)

Deposition along rivers. Wherever the velocity of the stream decreases, deposits are made along rivers carrying material in suspension. The resulting mudbanks and bars of gravel and sand are located in quiet water in the lee of some obstruction, on the inside of meanders, or along banks of streams during floods. On a floodplain the banks may be built higher than the surface distant from the stream to form *natural levees.* Sometimes a river becomes so overloaded with sediment that material is deposited in the stream bed itself, clogging the channel and forming a "braided" stream of many shifting courses (Figure 12-8), like the channel of the Platte River. Streams depositing debris in their beds are said to be *aggrading,* in contrast to the normal condition in which a river is *degrading* (lowering) its valley by erosion.

Deposition near mouths of rivers. Deltas

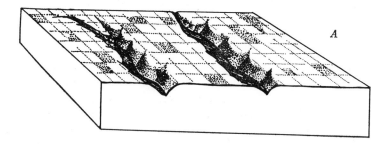

Figure 12-6 Evolution of a landscape through four stages of its degradation by natural agencies: A. Region in youth showing wide, flat interstream areas. Erosion is active by swift, rather straight streams which occupy narrow V-shaped valleys.

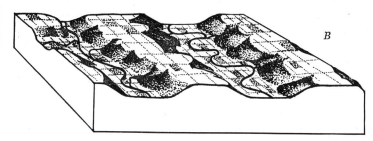

B. Region in early maturity. Note that much of the area of upland interfluves has been destroyed by erosion; streams have developed meanders and floodplains.

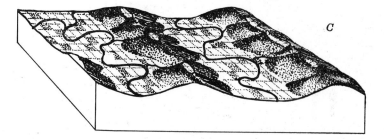

C. Region in late maturity with meandering, sluggish flowing streams. Only small remnants of the former upland remain.

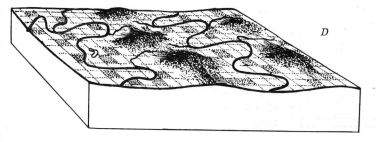

D. Region in old age. Relief is low and gently rolling with only a few island-like hills called monadnocks *left after erosion of the old upland. Streams flow slowly in wide meanders, and oxbow lakes may occur on the broad floodplain.*

occur at river mouths when streams carrying much sediment flow into quiet bodies of water and are forced to deposit their loads where the velocity is suddenly checked. If strong tides or currents are present, however, deposits are distributed alongshore or are carried into deep water, and no delta is formed. In a delta the deposition of material in the stream bed causes a river channel to divide. By repetition of the process, numerous *distributaries* fed from the main river are formed in the delta, and the channels constantly shift as deposits are made, making the lower delta regions somewhat difficult for occupance.

Sediments in deltas tend to become compact, a process which causes sinking of the ground sometimes below sea level. Frequent shifting of shore lines and distributaries and rankness of shallow water vegetation often make it difficult to distinguish land from water in a delta.

Special Features in Valleys. If a broad-floored valley of depositional or erosional origin is elevated, or if its stream for any reason renews its downward cutting, it would be clear that remnants of the old floodplain would remain above the new valley floor. These flat areas, records of higher past levels of a river,

Figure 12-7 Typical southern California view, showing the crop zoning of the alluvial piedmont at the base of the San Gabriel Mountains. View toward the north, with the snow-covered mountain range, topped by an ancient peneplain surface, forming the sky line. At the foot of the mountains the orange and lemon groves descend to the low-lands, where the dark trees are replaced by the bare limbs of deciduous fruit trees and vineyards in the middle distance. In the foreground slope, crop zoning is repeated, with the lower edge of the citrus grove sharply delimited by low temperatures. Contour irrigation and planting of orange trees in the immediate foreground. (Photograph, courtesy of the Los Angeles County Chamber of Commerce.)

are called *river terraces*. After a river has developed a meandering course across a floodplain, uplift of the land may force the stream to renew downcutting in its bed, producing the phenomenon of entrenched meanders. Since meanders are characteristic of late maturity or old age, when they have become incised in narrow youthful valleys, the region and the stream have been rejuvenated.

If a stream has cut through a mountain ridge, the resulting gorge is termed a *water gap,* or narrows. This may happen from headward erosion by a vigorous river or by overflow of an impounded lake. Another cause is an uplift of the ground occurring in a river bed, the movement being so slow that the river can cut downward as fast as the ground is raised. Occasionally drainage changes leave an abandoned water gap; the pass that remains is called a *wind gap.*

Ground Water.   The term *ground water* refers to water underground, which is derived mainly from rain that sinks into the earth. The amount of this "sink off" depends largely on the slope, character of soil and bedrock, natural vegetation, crops, and methods of cultivation. It is also affected by quantity and character of rainfall, since water of a long gentle rain may sink in whereas that of a cloudburst may nearly all run off.

Water held near the surface of the ground in tiny openings or capillary spaces between soil grains and rock particles is utilized by plants. Its conservation in semiarid climates is highly important to farmers. In dry-land farming the surface cracks and capillary tubes through which precious moisture evaporates are broken by cultivation. This covers the ground with a clod and dust mulch that interferes with the escape of water, thereby retaining needed moisture in the ground for the use of crops. A rough cloddy surface is now recommended to "dry farmers," since a fine dust mulch allows soil to blow too easily.

Rain water that sinks below the surface soil continues sinking until it is impeded by some impervious earth or rock (Figure 12-9). Above this, small openings in the pervious material are impregnated with water. The upper level to which these openings are filled is called the *water table.* Wells dug or drilled below the lowest level of the water table reach a permanent supply of water; if a valley has been

Figure 12-8   Stewart, British Columbia, a small isolated settlement located on the delta of a braided stream that enters the head of a fiord. This town is almost wholly lacking in productive hinterland. (Air Force photograph.)

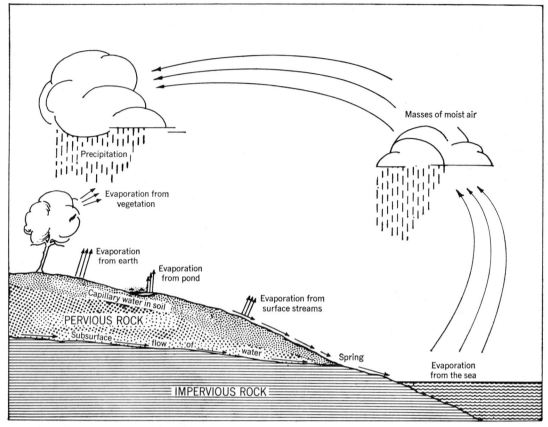

Figure 12-9   Normal movement of moisture on the earth's surface. Moisture is returned to the sea by both underground and surface flow; then it is evaporated into the air, returned to the land by air movements, and precipitated over land.

eroded to this depth, seeps and springs result. On a hillside the common location for springs is determined by the outcrop of an impervious bed or rock above which water is retained until it can slowly seep out.

Simple natural conditions account for artesian wells. For example, a pervious stratum, like gravel or sandstone, may lie between two impervious beds. Then if the pervious rock is exposed at some high elevation where water seeps into it, the impervious beds of rock hold water under pressure in the pervious material. When the pervious stratum, called an *aquifer,* is tapped by a drilled well whose outlet lies below the water level in that stratum, a flow of artesian water results. If the well outlet is higher up the slope, however, water may rise only part way to the surface. A natural orifice leading from the underground supply may feed a large spring of steady flow, unaffected by drought years that would dry up an ordinary hillside spring. Springs and artesian water supplies are important factors in the location of homes and towns in regions of water scarcity. In Queensland, Australia, the Great Artesian Basin supplies water to thousands of stock ranches that depend upon this subterranean supply.

When ground water percolates through soil and rocks, it may dissolve and carry away considerable amounts of soluble minerals. Limestone is soluble in water containing carbon dioxide, a gas derived from decaying organic matter. This carbon-laden water, seeping through cracks in limestone, enlarges the openings until large caves are formed. Water dripping into these caverns may evaporate and deposit its dissolved limestone, forming beautiful icicle-like stalactites on the roof of the cave, bulbous stalagmites on the floor, and other deposits (Figure 12-10). Springs sometimes deposit lime, iron, and other compounds at the surface; cracks in rocks are often filled with minerals deposited by ground water. Rich veins and ore pockets in most mines were formed in this way.

In areas where limestone is the principal rock so many cavities have been formed by solution that drainage is mostly underground instead of on the surface. Sinkholes also are developed by enlargement of surface openings into the underground drainage and by collapse of portions of the roofs of caves. Such a region of caves, sinkholes, and subterranean streams is called a *karst* region, being named after a typical area near the head of the Adriatic Sea. Beds of salt and gypsum are dissolved also by ground water. An example is the Pecos River valley in New Mexico where this process has formed many sinks.

Ground water is a potent factor in causation of landslides and soil slumps on steep slopes. Often when soil and certain rocks like shale become water-soaked, they become so slippery that masses of material slip and slide downhill. On plowed hilly land in the spring many little landslips may be seen. Highways may be blocked and houses damaged by landslides where the equilibrium of the ground has been disturbed by construction work. Sometimes in mountains very large landslides occur which may destroy much of a village or dam a river to form a lake.

Ground water may be heated by coming in contact with uncooled masses of magma or rocks heated by friction along an active fault or warmed in some other way. Such water emerges above ground to make hot springs or steam vents. Spouting hot springs which erupt at intervals are called *geysers*. Notable geysers are found in Yellowstone Park, New Zealand, and Iceland. The source of heat for geysers is believed to be from underground masses of hot lava.

The Work of Wind. In dry climates where there is little vegetation and moisture to hold the soil, winds become important agents of

Figure 12-10 Stalactites and stalagmites in Carlsbad Caverns, New Mexico. (Photograph by R. V. Davis, used by permission of the U.S. Geological Survey.)

erosion and may cause soil to blow and drift. Careless farming methods and overgrazing by livestock may destroy the grass cover protecting the ground and allow the wind to do great damage to soil. Topsoil from whole farms has moved with the wind during a single dust storm on the Great Plains (Figure 9-9).

Wind-blown sand hurled against rock cliffs removes the weaker portions and etches the most resistant parts into relief. When wind erodes weak rock from beneath resistant layers or masses, the result is odd shapes among which are the "mushroom" rocks shown in Figure 12-11. Winds carrying sand may abrade, erode, and polish boulders and exposures of bedrock. Faces of cliffs are sometimes pitted from the effect of wind-blown sand; stones may be beveled and polished by the same action. Glass in exposed lighthouses has had to be replaced because of grinding by the natural sandblast.

Sand may be blown into heaps or dunes by wind. Material for dunes may come from the weathering of sandstone or other suitable bedrock, but more commonly it is brought in by temporary floods and streams. Sand for dunes is also left on shore by rivers and by the waves of lakes or oceans. When dry, sand is subject to the work of winds, and dunes begin to form, especially to leeward of obstructions. Once started, sand dunes move in the direction of prevailing winds and sometimes bury forests, fields, and houses in their paths. The control of moving dunes is a difficult task best accomplished by plants, especially those with creeping roots, which cover, protect from the wind, and bind together the moving particles. Sand dunes are widely distributed in deserts but are common also in quite humid regions as along the Atlantic or Gulf seacoasts and the shores of large lakes like Lake Michigan.

In northwestern Nebraska is a sandhill region where dunes cover 20,000 square miles, probably the largest such area in the United States. Sand grains in dunes are well rounded from mutual abrasion resulting from their movement by the wind. Ripple marks made by wind generally mark the surface of dunes. If wind-deposited sand later becomes solid rock, the rock shows cross-bedding similar to

Figure 12-11 Mushroom rock in Death Valley, California, formed by a combination of rock weathering and wind erosion. Desert landscapes of this type are almost entirely lacking in vegetation throughout most of the year. (Photograph by Frashers Photos, Pomona, California.)

that made by swift-running water because winds, like stream currents, shift their directions from time to time.

Strong winds may blow dust in great quantities from deserts and dry steppes. Where winds are prevalently in one direction, dust is dropped to leeward of deserts in regions having sufficient rainfall to support a good growth of grass. The grass prevents the wind from moving the particles again, and dust accumulates. These dust deposits, called *loess,* are particularly important in China east of the Gobi, in parts of the Columbia Basin, and in the Mississippi and Missouri Valleys. Some so-called "loess" in humid regions may have been deposited by running water. Frequently loess is found beyond the outside margin of former continental glaciers, and this probably was derived from fine outwash or rock flour deposited by melting ice.

Loess soils are inherently fertile, but once the sod of semiarid grasslands is broken, cultivation must be done carefully, or drifting of soil by winds will occur in dry years. During the 1930s, damage was done in parts of the Great Plains by giant dust storms that moved millions of tons of fine material. Drifting soil is best controlled by planting certain fodder crops and reestablishing a cover of grass. Improved tillage practices also minimize soil movement by wind.

Glaciers.   Glaciers consist of moving masses of ice formed on land from compacted snow. They are agents of degradation in high mountains of midlatitudes, and they even descend to sea level in snowy regions like the coast of Alaska and from cold plateaus like Greenland and Antarctica. In the past, continental gla-

ciers covered North America well into the United States and extended over most of northwestern Europe and parts of Siberia (Figure 12-1).

Glaciers develop where snowfall exceeds the rate of melting and evaporation. By pressure, partial melting, and refreezing, snow is transformed into ice. When the ice has movement, it becomes a glacier. Glaciers move down slopes and outward from their source until melting equals the rate of advance. The movement varies from a fraction of an inch to many feet per day, the latter being recorded for some glaciers in Greenland. Moving glaciers secure debris from surfaces over which they move and in addition material is worn or falls from the cliffs around them. This transported material is dropped when the ice melts. Many rocks are found on the surface of glaciers, exposed there by melting of snow and ice which once covered them. Crevasses in the ice occur as the result of movement over irregularities and enlargement of the cracks by melting. Melting takes place all through a glacier. Some melt water runs off from the upper surface; some collects beneath the ice, emerging from a tunnel at the lower end of the glacier in the form of a large river. The water of glacier-fed rivers has a milky appearance from its load of silt (Figure 12-8), which it obtains by pulverizing the rock and forming *rock flour.*

The two main types of glaciers are continental and mountain. Continental glaciers so changed the surfaces of the northern half of North America and Eurasia that their effects will be described under glacial plains in Chapter 13. Mountain glaciers, which had profound effects on the relief features developed in mountains, will be described in Chapter 14.

DIASTROPHISM

Geologists apply the term *diastrophism* (movements in the earth's crust) to processes of mountain building, rock folding, earthquakes, and uplift and down-warping in general. All land surfaces would be reduced by denudation to peneplains and finally wave ac-

tion would truncate the last land above sea level until nothing would be seen except water, if it were not for counteracting forces which elevate parts of the earth's crust and thereby offset the work of weathering and erosion. High mountains, broad plateaus, and extensive plains result from the slow action of internal forces that heave up large land masses. Since geologic time includes millions of years, it is sufficient for these profound changes to occur.

Earth Movements. When compressive forces develop in the earth, they exert the greatest effects where the crust is weakest. Zones of weakness may develop in the interior of land masses but are most common along edges of continents, where thick beds of sediments have collected. Here compression may crush the sediments together, fold them into high mountains, and sometimes produce breaks, or faults, in the earth's crust. Thus rugged mountain ranges frequently parallel coast lines. Movements along fault lines cause most earthquakes. Sometimes volcanoes break out along fault zones. The Pacific Ocean is nearly surrounded by rugged chains of mountains with numerous volcanoes, from the southern tip of South America through North America via the Aleutian Islands to Kamchatka and Japan, and thence through volcanic and mountainous islands to New Zealand. In addition to uplifts of the land, sinking of blocks of the earth's crust also occurs.

Sea shells and marine fossils which have been found far inland and even near summits of high mountains are evidence of the uplift of land. Further evidence of uplift appears in beaches, terraces, wave-cut cliffs, and other coastal phenomena clearly visible high above the ocean along rising coasts like the Pacific Coast of North and South America. On the other hand, sinking of the land causes "drowning" of rivers, changing them to wide-mouthed estuaries in which trees and man-made structures have sometimes been submerged. Changes of level in the interior of continents have taken place frequently but are less evident than along the coasts.

Earthquakes. Earthquakes may accompany volcanic eruptions, but more often they result from strong earth stresses that crush, bend, or break the rocks. Movements of rocks underground, usually for only a slight distance, cause vibrations of the earth which are transmitted to the outer crust. Most earthquakes can be detected only by a delicate instrument called the *seismograph,* but occasionally severe shocks occur which cause much loss of life and property and which produce important changes on the earth's surface. It should be noted that the earthquake does not make a fault or break in the rocks but is itself the result of such movement.

From the earthquake focus, or place of occurrence, compression waves pass outward in all directions. Some waves move along the crust of the earth, others through the interior directly from the focus. The speed and character of earthquake waves depend on the density and elasticity of the material transmitting the vibrations. By comparing the time of arrival of two sets of waves on a seismograph, the approximate distance to the source of the earthquake and sometimes its depth can be calculated. The term *seismic* is used to refer to earthquake phenomena. Seismic areas of the world are shown in Figure 12-12.

Earthquakes may be very damaging to life and property if they affect well-populated areas, especially cities. Regions of active mountain uplift are most apt to have earthquakes, although probably no part of the earth's surface can be considered entirely free of seismic danger. In Europe the island of Sicily and the southern part of the Italian peninsula have been much afflicted with earthquakes during recent centuries. In 1783 over 30,000 people perished in this region; again in 1908 a terrible shock destroyed the city of Messina, killing over 76,000 persons.

Japan, interior China, India, Chile, Central America, and southern California are other regions where earthquakes have occurred with some frequency. Noteworthy earthquakes killed several hundred thousand people in Kansu and Shansi Provinces in China in December, 1920, and destroyed Lisbon, Portugal, in 1755. Japan was afflicted in 1703, 1858,

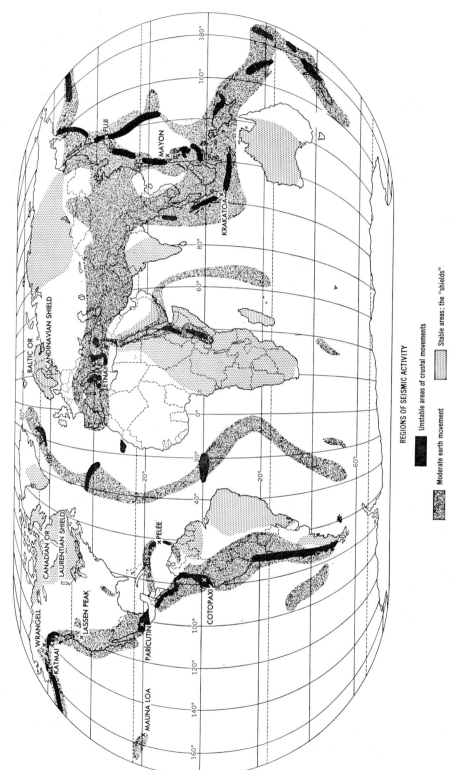

REGIONS OF SEISMIC ACTIVITY

■ Unstable areas of crustal movements

▨ Moderate earth movement

▦ Stable areas: the "shields"

Figure 12-12   Regions of seismic activity.

Figure 12-13   Effects of an earthquake on poorly constructed buildings at Brawley, California.

1896, and in 1923, when some hundreds of thousands were killed or injured at Tokyo and Yokohama.

In the United States a movement along the San Andreas fault in 1906 did much damage at San Francisco and in that vicinity. Another slight earthquake was experienced there in 1957. At Long Beach, California, in 1933, and later at Brawley, numerous buildings constructed of masonry were seriously damaged by a fairly severe quake. Earthquakes sometimes occur far from mountains, as at New

Madrid in southeastern Missouri in 1811 and at Charleston, South Carolina, in 1886.

Earthquakes at sea or close to shore may produce high *tsunamis* or earthquake waves, misnamed "tidal" waves, that drown many persons and damage shipping and longshore property. Earthquake damage depends a great deal on the type of building construction in the afflicted area. At Long Beach and Brawley only poorly constructed buildings were seriously damaged by a fairly severe quake (Figure 12-13). Solid stone and brick structures are easily destroyed, whereas frame buildings, if properly tied together, resist earthquakes very well, as do structures of reinforced concrete and steel. Buildings can be constructed to resist earthquake damage, and this should always be done in regions where shocks may be expected. City buildings should be as nearly fireproof as possible, since fire may account for much loss of life and property, as at Tokyo in 1923. In cities emergency reservoirs should be built to provide water for fire protection and domestic supply if the pipes bringing water happen to be broken by the quake, as at San Francisco in 1906, when fire following the earthquake destroyed more property than the quake itself.

VULCANISM

Volcanoes. Like earthquakes, volcanoes occur along lines of weakness in the earth's crust; some well-known volcanoes are shown in Figure 12-12. From a geologic standpoint vulcanism produces swift changes of the earth's surface. The ultimate source of magma (molten rock) probably lies many miles beneath the surface of the earth, and the exact cause of the formation of magma is uncertain. Single eruptions have formed cinder cones hundreds of feet high. Parícutin in Mexico first erupted in a cornfield in 1943; within two years it had attained an altitude greater than 1,000 feet and had destroyed several villages and many farms.

Some of the world's most active volcanoes are in Alaska, especially throughout the Aleu-

tian Islands. One of these is Pavlof, which had over a dozen eruptions between 1910 and 1945. Another is Shishaldin, nearly 10,000 feet in elevation, with eight great eruptions between 1901 and 1946. In Italy, Vesuvius and Etna have erupted many times in the present century. Because of its history, Vesuvius, near Naples, is the best-known volcano in the world. After a long period of quiescence, eruptions of Vesuvius in A.D. 79 destroyed the cities of Pompeii and Herculaneum. There are three active volcanoes in Hawaii, with Kilauea and Mauna Loa experiencing eruptions every few years.

Volcanoes are common in the lesser islands of the West Indies, in equatorial East Africa, and on the island of Java. Remote ocean is-

Figure 12-14 Recently formed cinder cone in Lassen Volcanic National Park, California. Between the horsemen and the cone is a deposit of volcanic ash and lava, with evidences of a renewal of vegetation cover beginning to appear. (Courtesy of Lassen Volcanic National Park authorities and the National Park Service.)

lands like St. Helena and Mauritius are generally volcanic. There are even volcanoes in Iceland and Antarctica. There are said to be about 2,000 volcanic islands in the Pacific and many that have been reduced to shoals from wave erosion. The map (Figure 12-12) shows that an active seismic and volcanic area nearly surrounds the Pacific in the shape of a large horseshoe. Another important area extends through the Mediterranean Sea to southern Asia.

Large areas of the earth's surface are covered with rocks of volcanic origin. Sometimes vast quantities of molten lava emerge from long fissures in the ground to cover old surface features with flows that cool one above another until the lava deposits have built large plateaus. The Columbia Basin, the Deccan in India, much of southeastern Brazil, and east central Africa were formed in this manner. The Cascade Range is built mostly of volcanic material.

The only volcano in the United States proper known to have been active since the middle of the nineteenth century is Lassen Peak in the Cascades of northern California; it erupted in 1914 and 1915. Indians reported eruptions of St. Helens and perhaps other peaks in the Cascades early in the last century, and within 1,000 years there have probably been eruptions in southern Idaho, central Oregon, and possibly in California (Figure 12-14).

Various materials come from volcanoes. Lava, gas, and different sizes of fragmental material varying from fine ash to huge boulders are blown out during eruptions (Figure 12-15). Volcanoes that produce mainly lava during eruption have rather gentle slopes, like Mauna Loa in Hawaii, but those that give off explosive debris form steep-sided cinder cones. The eruption of ash and cinders is most common toward the end of a period of vulcanism. Often a big volcano formed mainly of lava is surrounded by several satellite cinder cones resulting from the last volcanic activity in that region. Sometimes hot and poisonous gases are given off during eruptions, like that

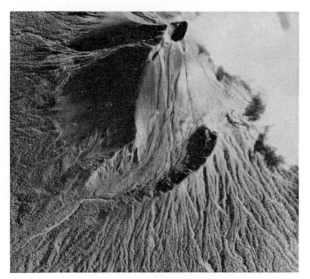

Figure 12-15   Fresh lava flow on the slopes of an active volcano on the island of New Britain. (Photograph by U.S. Air Force.)

of Mt. Pelée in the island of Martinique in 1902, which destroyed the city of St. Pierre, killing 28,000 people.

Volcanoes occasionally suffer tremendous explosions, probably resulting from the accumulation underground of superheated steam which literally blows away the upper part of the mountain. Krakatoa (Figure 12-12), between Java and Sumatra, was blown to pieces in this manner in 1883. The Mount Katmai eruption in Alaska in 1911 and possibly in part the formation of Crater Lake in Oregon during prehistoric times represent other examples of this type of explosive eruption.

Volcanic eruptions often destroy human life, but where they are not too dangerous they may attract tourists, as do Kilauea volcano in Hawaii, Lassen Peak, and Vesuvius. More important is the relatively rapid decay of most

volcanic rocks, producing very fertile soils in tropical regions. As a result, volcanic islands like Java can support large numbers of people by agriculture and have sufficient quantities of agricultural produce for export. The plantations of Hawaii, Fiji, and Mauritius also are favored by their volcanic soils.

Lava rock outside the tropics decays slowly, and areas of recent lava flow may be so rough, with very thin soil and little vegetation, that small use can be made of them. The Modoc Lava Beds in northern California and the Craters of the Moon in central Idaho are examples of recent lava flows. Very rough recent flows are sometimes called malpais (literally "bad country") by the Mexicans in the Southwest.

Intrusions of Igneous Rock.   Various names are applied to the different forms of intrusive molten rock that has solidified underground. Fillings of cracks in bedrock are called *dikes.* Dome-shaped intrusions with a flat base are *laccoliths,* some of which form mountains in the western United States; very large intrusions forming the cores of some mountain ranges are called *batholiths.*

Metals are commonly associated with intrusions of igneous rock deep underground. Many metal-mining districts of the world are located in ancient areas of vulcanism, exposed at the surface by erosion of former overlying rocks. Diamond deposits in South Africa were formed in intrusive "pipes" of lava. Some building stone, like granite, is of intrusive igneous origin.

Intrusive rocks are often harder than adjacent rocks of other character, and so may be left to form resistant rock ridges, flat-topped buttes and mesas, and other elevations after less resistant rocks have been eroded.

SUMMARY

In descending order, surface features vary from (1) continents and ocean basins, (2) mountain systems and cordilleras, large plains, plateaus, and submarine plateaus, to (3) peaks, hills, valleys, lakes, and other minor features. Surface features result from movements of the earth's

crust, erosion by running water, ground water, winds, glaciers, and waves, and the deposition of transported debris.

Rocks are classified as igneous, sedimentary, and metamorphic.

Weathering may consist of mechanical disintegration of pieces of rock into smaller fragments, caused by temperature changes, frost work, abrasion, or plant roots. Chemical weathering or decomposition results from interaction of rocks with water, oxygen, carbon dioxide, acids from decay, and fumes from volcanoes. Weathered rock fragments are the materials from which soil is developed (Chapter 17), and the weathering process prepares materials for removal by erosion and solution.

Stream erosion deepens, broadens, and lengthens valleys. Streams transport material by suspension, solution, and rolling. Erosion of stream beds and material brought in by rain and tributaries provide streams with their loads. The load carried by running water depends on the volume and velocity of the stream, character of the stream bed, and size of materials to be carried. Both rivers and regions pass through a cycle of erosion. A region whose landscape is in a youthful stage is characterized by many lakes and swamps, valleys are narrow, and streams have many rapids or falls. In maturity, a region is well drained and dissected; divides between valleys are narrow but the valleys themselves are wide, and the major streams have reached base level and have developed flat floodplains on which they flow in meandering courses. In maturity the maximum difference in elevation has developed between valley floors and the summit hills and ridges. In a stage of old age, streams swing widely across broad valleys that have slight slope, and uplands have been reduced to peneplains above which may rise a few remnants of erosion called monadnocks. The cycle of erosion may be interrupted and a region may be rejuvenated by uplift after reaching an older stage.

Special features developed by streams are waterfalls, meanders, oxbow cutoffs, terraces, and water and wind gaps.

Wind erosion is active in dry regions and along seashores and rivers where sand and dust are available and winds are strong. Dunes and loess deposits are among those made by the wind.

Ground water carrying carbon dioxide in solution can dissolve limestone to make caves, sinkholes, and karst regions. Deposits are often made by ground water.

Glaciers develop when annual snowfall over many years exceeds the rate of melting. They may be continental or of the mountain type.

Waves and currents erode coasts and also form extensive deposits along shores.

Long-continued faulting and folding of rocks may cause mountain ranges, depressed basins, and other earth features. The associated earth movements are a common cause of earthquakes. Volcanoes develop along lines of weakness in the crust and from them may come eruptions of molten lava and cinders, or other blown-out materials. Igneous intrusions are significant features often associated with mountain uplift.

Outline

Surface features vary in magnitude
Definitions
    Tectonic
    Vulcanism
    Diastrophism
    Degradation
    Aggradation
Classes of rocks: igneous, sedimentary, metamorphic
Rock weathering: disintegration, decomposition
Stream erosion
    Relation to volume and velocity
    Transportation
    Cycle of erosion: youth, maturity, old age
    Deposition of load
Ground water
    Source and factors affecting
    Caves, karst regions, and deposits
Work of wind
    Erosion and deposition
    Dunes, loess
Glaciers: formation and types
Diastrophisms
    Definition and examples of earth movements
    Earthquakes
Vulcanism
    Location of volcanic regions
    Origin and effects of volcanic eruptions
    Intrusions of igneous rock

QUESTIONS

1. Why do valleys usually have finer and more fertile soil than adjacent hilly land?

2. Why do roadways often follow river valleys?

3. What forces of erosion are most effective in arid climates?

4. What processes of weathering are important in your locality?

5. Along a coast, what evidence would you seek to indicate that the coast has risen or sunk?

6. What methods have you seen used to control erosion by (*a*) running water, (*b*) wind, or (*c*) wave actions.

7. Of the landforms mapped in Figure 12-1,
 a. Which are smallest in area?
 b. Which are most useful to man?
 c. Which are found in the Northern Hemisphere?
 d. Which are related to marine climates?
 e. Which are related to continental climatic realms?

8. What are some of the desirable aspects of volcanic activity?

9. Why are dunes better developed on the east side of Lake Michigan than along its western shore?

10. What are factors determining the depth to which wells are drilled in order to obtain a permanent flow of water?

11. Why are artesian wells regarded as a form of valuable property?

12. What natural conditions provide the Colorado River with a very large load of silt?

13. What factors determine the size and length of a valley glacier?

14. Assuming the snowfall is equal on all sides of a mountain peak, in the northern midlatitudes where would you expect to find the lowest snow line?

15. What are the characteristics of the most useful streams in your locality?

SELECTED REFERENCES

Barnett, Lincoln: "The Face of the Land," *Life,* 34:86–109, Apr. 13, 1953.

Coleman, S. N.: *Volcanoes, New and Old,* The John Day Company, Inc., New York, 1946.

Cotton, Charles A.: *Geomorphology,* John Wiley & Sons, Inc., New York, 1947.

————: *Landscape as Developed by the Processes of Normal Erosion,* John Wiley & Sons, Inc., New York, 1949.

Finch, Vernor C., Glenn T. Trewartha, A. H. Robinson, and E. H. Hammond: *Elements of Geography,* 4th ed. McGraw-Hill Book Company, Inc., New York, 1957, pp. 208–230.

Heck, Nicholas H.: *Earthquakes,* Princeton University Press, Princeton, 1936.

————: "A New Map of Earthquake Distribution," *Geographical Review,* 25:125–130, January, 1935.

Leet, Don: "Earthquakes," *Annals of the American Academy of Political and Social Science,* 309:36–41, January, 1957.

Lobeck, A. K.: *Geomorphology: An Introduction to the Study of Landscapes,* McGraw-Hill Book Company, Inc., New York, 1939.

Stamp, L. Dudley: *The Earth's Crust,* Crown Publishers, Inc., New York, 1951.

Strahler, Arthur N.: *Physical Geography,* John Wiley & Sons, Inc., New York, 1951.

Sturgis, Samuel D.: "Floods," *Annals of the American Academy of Political and Social Science,* 309:15–22, January, 1957.

Thornbury, William D.: *Principles of Geomorphology,* John Wiley & Sons, Inc., New York, 1954.

Visher, S. S.: "Climate and Geomorphology: Some Comparisons between Regions," *Journal of Geomorphology,* 14:54–64, February, 1941.

von Engeln, O. D.: *Geomorphology,* The Macmillan Company, New York, 1942.

13. Plains

and Plateaus

PLAINS

PLAINS are the most important landform from the human point of view, for most of the world's inhabitants live on lowlands. Only in the tropics are plateaus or mountains preferred to lowlands because of better health conditions and attractive coolness. Plains vary widely in origin, size, altitude, climate, and natural vegetation. Most have a rolling surface, but local relief should not exceed a few hundred feet difference in elevation if a region is to be called a plain. The truly level and nearly level plains are usually comparatively small. In altitude the Great Plains of North America are actually higher than the Appalachian Plateau; they even rise above most of the Appalachian mountain ridges and summits. Yet because of its low relief, we call the area a plain, even though the land surface rises gradually toward

the Rockies until its elevation may exceed 6,000 feet.

Plains are formed in different ways, but primarily they are caused by erosion and deposition or a combination of both as described in the preceding chapter. Level plains with fertile deposits include river floodplains and deltas and lacustrine plains which are the beds of former lakes. Glaciers so profoundly modified the surface of much of Canada, northeastern United States, and Northern Europe that the term *glacial plains* is appropriate. Peneplains result from the prolonged erosion of highlands which reduced them to gently rolling surfaces. Generally lowlands near the ocean are called *coastal plains* and those toward the center of a continent, *interior plains*. But however formed or wherever located, plains have similar characteristics over most of their extent. The word *plain* in many cases is a synonym for uniformity.

Advantages of Plains.   Fertile, well-watered plains are favorable for agriculture and support large populations in our modern world. Usually the building of waterways, railways, and highways is cheap since it does not present the problems of opening transportation routes into and across rugged mountains. Road building is so easy that in the interior United States, highways are nearly always located on section lines (Figure 1-10), arbitrarily following meridians and parallels, instead of being forced to occupy the easiest natural routes, as in more broken areas. Farming on a plain has many advantages: nearly all the land can be tilled, erosion is reduced to a minimum, machinery can be used to advantage, and transportation is no problem. For these reasons such favorably located areas are intensively used. In Europe, the United States, and Canada nearly 90 per cent of the population live on midlatitude lowlands. All great commercial crops of the world like wheat, corn, and rice are grown chiefly on plains.

Plains often contain valuable minerals. Fuels (coal, petroleum, and natural gas) are widely distributed on plains. Many of these occurrences have contributed to the growth of population centers nearby. Building stone and clay for brick, drainpipe, and other clay products, cement materials, and material needed for road building are also commonly found.

Primitive Life on Plains.   A primitive society located on grass-covered steppes that lack natural barriers for defense is often peculiarly vulnerable to enemy attack unless the inhabitants themselves are good warriors. Warlike horsemen can quickly overrun even the most extensive of interior grasslands. Thus during the Middle Ages Mongols under Genghis Khan and Kublai Khan conquered all the open country from China to Poland. Agricultural utilization of the great steppes of Russia was left until a much later time when farm populations had increased in numbers and ability to defend themselves. Forested parts of Europe were little affected by invaders, on the other hand, since horsemen are repelled and not attracted by forests.

Civilization seems to have early developed on river plains like those of Egypt, Iraq, and the Wei River area in China. Deserts or mountains afforded some protection against invasion; hence agriculturists enjoyed safety and time in which they could peacefully develop their arts. These lowlands were naturally dry and required irrigation, especially for wetland crops like rice, yet individual efforts were unequal to the task of developing water supplies, building ditches, and leveling or otherwise preparing land for crops. To secure the needed cooperation of all inhabitants government tended to be established to organize protective measures. Increased production allowed large landowners to enjoy more leisure and the niceties and luxuries of living. So civilization, with its arts and sciences developed. Plains of the Ganges and the great rivers of China are examples of early development. Forests had to be cleared from part of those plains as advancing farming peoples occupied the lowlands and dispossessed or absorbed more primitive tribes who lived in the forests. Where plains have been occupied by a succession of invaders, as in the Ganges Valley, there is usually found a mixture of races, languages, and cultures.

Development of Civilization on Plains.   In ancient times rather small plains, well protected by natural barriers against invasion and yet open to receive ideas and commerce by water routes or defensible land routes, were among favored areas in which came many of the advancements in civilization. Examples include the Syrian coast and the plains, valleys, and islands of Greece.

Much of the lowland area of northwestern Europe was covered by forests, and its population lived in small clearings so isolated that contacts with the outside world were few and advancement was slow. In ancient times, the cost of transportation of bulky products like wheat across extensive plains was too high for export crops unless waterways were available. In our own day, great plains are easily cultivated with modern machinery, and railways can supplement water transport in bringing products of farms to the export markets.

Improved weapons and superior political organization enabled agricultural peoples of the plains to protect themselves from the warlike but less numerous nomads. These factors also helped the strongest tribal or racial group to develop the idea of nationality until it dominated large plains like those of Russia and northern Germany. For, if part of such a plain is occupied by a weaker group of people, they may be subject to attack by stronger neighbors, and their history will be one of continuous warfare and boundary changes; it was under such circumstances that Poland disappeared for over a century from the map of Europe.

Ease of political expansion on plains. A great open plain is an encouragement to expand territorially. Mountains and forests of the eastern United States required a century and a half to be crossed by the English colonists; but once open plains had been reached where natural barriers were few, expansion over the remaining distance to the Pacific—more than twice the distance from the Atlantic to the grasslands—took only a generation. Although the western mountains are higher than those of the East, much of the intermountain country and plateaus was treeless, and routes were often available around or between the ranges. The first explorers and traders did not arouse much antagonism on the part of the Indians so early crossings were generally unopposed. The arrival of buffalo hunters, cattlemen, and farmers was often bitterly fought.

Farming population tends to be evenly distributed over tillable plains, whereas in mountainous regions the people are crowded into the small areas available for cultivation, giving very uneven distribution of population. Of course there are many great cities on plains and such urban clusters cause uneven distribu-

tion of the total population in contrast with the evenness of the rural population.

The size and richness of the plains area of a nation in large measure determine that country's ultimate relative importance among other nations of the world. Hence nations often have tried to extend their political control over plains. Transportation and communication are easy on plains, the inhabitants tend to lead similar lives, that is, to have a general similarity in cultural conditions. Contacts with each other lead to increased knowledge and the best utilization of available resources.

River Floodplains. Silt-covered river floodplains are of particular importance to man. In these locations (Figure 12-1) are found some of the world's most fertile soils, easy transportation, and prime sites for cities.

River floodplains are formed when running water deposits part of its load of sediment because its current is retarded. In times of flood, rivers overflow banks on either side of their channels and may cover most of the valley flats alongside the stream, where deposits of silt, gravel, mud, sand, and other material are laid down. Floodwaters themselves are disadvantageous to human residence on floodplains, but replenishment of the soils of the plains compensates in part for damage by floodwaters.

Deposition of material occurs first immediately along the banks of most large streams; in this location the river forms low banks called *natural levees* which rise above the general level of the lower land away from the river. In themselves, natural levees are inconspicuous features; but when they are surmounted by strong banks of artificial levees (Figure 13-1) built for the specific purpose of confining the worst of the floods within the natural river channel, they provide considerable protection against flood damage. Natural and artificial levees are usually paralleled by low swamps known as the "back swamp line." These poorly drained areas receive river water seepage through the levees and may also receive the waters of tributaries of the main stream that are unable to take their natural course because of interference by the levees. Back swamps are usually serious problems for people who farm floodplains, for they provide breeding places for insects and may become a serious menace to the health of residents.

A typical example of the condition described above may be found along the boundary of the states of Mississippi and Louisiana, where the Yazoo River, flowing into the Mississippi River from the east, is forced to run parallel to the main stream for many miles before it finally joins the Mississippi below the city of Vicksburg (Figure 13-2). Low ground between the Mississippi levees and the Yazoo is marked by numerous swamps and lakes; where drainage is possible, this land is very fertile and produces excellent cotton and other crops. This bottomland is also superior for pastures. The swamps and lakes often are semicircular in form and represent abandoned stream channels of the Yazoo River. Lakes of this type are known as *oxbow lakes,* and they are characteristic features of many river floodplains.

It is apparent that a low, level river plain will offer slight resistance to changes that may occur in the channel of the river, for natural and even artificial levees often fail to keep the river within bounds in flood time. When the gradient (rate of drop) of the stream is slight, the channel may undergo numerous changes within the course of a single year. One conspicuous result of changes in the channels is the presence of wide-swinging river bends known as *meanders.* They are relatively unstable features of the landscape and may be almost entirely eliminated in a single season if the river channel cuts across the neck of these meanders and leaves them as oxbow lakes. Meandering streams are difficult to navigate because of the many bends where the current shifts; they are many miles longer than streams whose channels are straight. Furthermore, meandering streams are often shallow and must be dredged to maintain adequate depth for shipping. The side-to-side swing of river meanders tends to erode the valley laterally and so widen it; such valleys often are marked by high bluffs on either side of the river, but

Figure 13-1 Flood condition at Leland, Mississippi, during the great flood of 1927. Livestock and people have taken refuge from flood waters on the highest ground along the line of the rail embankment; this has been reinforced as a levee by dumping large amounts of soil in foreground. (Photograph used by permission of the U.S. Weather Bureau.)

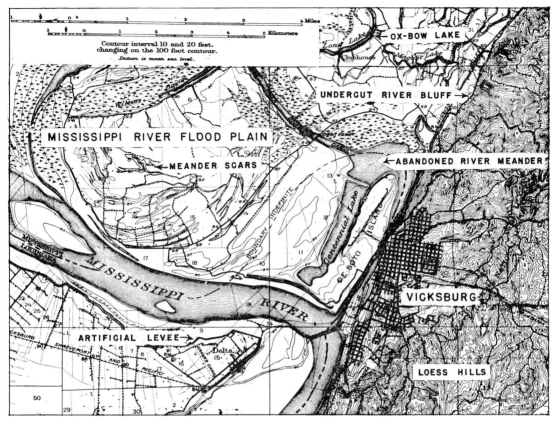

Figure 13-2   Part of Vicksburg, Mississippi, contour map published by the U.S. Geological Survey. Note the relationship of the city to the nearby floodplain and the commanding location overlooking the river bend.

at some distance from it. Conditions along the Mississippi floodplain follow this pattern.

The Danube, Volga, Po, and Elbe Rivers in Europe, the Ganges, Yangtze, and Yellow Rivers in Asia, and the Mississippi, Sacramento, and San Joaquin Rivers in the United States are some of the many streams of the world having floodplains that support large populations. This comes from the very great fertility of the soil in combination with favorable climatic conditions. Even small alluvial plains situated in favorable climates are very densely populated and support large cities as well as many rural residents. Japan's river plains serve as excellent examples, because the majority of the inhabitants of that nation live on fertile fluvial and alluvial plains, many of which are small in extent.

Floodplains of rivers which flow through deserts may, through the skilled use of irrigation, support dense populations of farming people and many large cities. The Nile Valley, the land of Iraq (Mesopotamia) between the Tigris and Euphrates Rivers, and most populous of all, the plains irrigated from the Indus River, are noteworthy developments in deserts.

Even when rivers flow through highlands and have cut deep canyons, some local floodplains usually exist, and such occupance as is possible centers at these little strips and parcels of level land. The Columbia and Colorado Rivers have these characteristics. Mountain sections of many rivers like the Yangtze and Brahmaputra in Asia and the Rhine also enjoy small arable stretches of alluvial ground.

Figure 13-3   Dutch windmill used for drainage of polder lands near Domburg, Zeeland. Neat hedges separate the fields and paths in this orderly rural landscape. Windmills are now being replaced by pumping apparatus to drain the land more easily and quickly. (Photograph, courtesy of the American Museum of Natural History, New York.)

In addition the lower courses of these rivers have formed famous alluvial plains.

Nevertheless, if climatic conditions do not foster agriculture or other activities, many floodplains contribute little to human welfare. The river plain of the Mackenzie in northern Canada, for example, is situated so far north that it is extremely unattractive for farming; it is occupied by very few people in relation to its vast extent. Other floodplains that are too cold for the support of many human beings are found along northward-flowing streams of the northern part of Siberia, the Lena, Ob, and Yenisei.

Delta Plains. Deltas form at mouths of muddy rivers flowing into quiet bodies of water at the seaward extremities of river floodplains. The Nile Delta, the type location, is triangular, and thus the name of the Greek letter has been given to all similar deposits, despite the fact that few of them are triangular in shape. Delta lands consist of the richest soil washed from surfaces farther upstream. In spite of severe drainage problems, deltas often form productive and populous farming regions, especially on some located in Europe, Asia, and North America. Familiar examples of deltas include those of the Rhine (Figure 13-3), Mississippi, Volga, Rhone, Ganges, Tigris, Yangtze, Mekong, and Hwang Ho. Deltas under a desert climate, like those of the Nile and the Colorado, may become very productive when irrigated by water taken from nearby rivers. Since deltas are low in relief and subject to flooding, dikes are needed to protect farms and cities from inundation. Like coastal plains and river floodplains, deltas are often swampy and subject to poor drainage (Figure 13-4), in which case they are nearly unpopulated, like the delta of the Orinoco. Delta lands of the Mississippi and Rhone are difficult to reclaim and are less used for farming than higher land.

Because they are productive of agricultural wealth and are situated at entrances to great river plains, delta communities frequently emerge as cities of some size and importance. Major cities whose locations are related to delta plains include Cairo; New Orleans; Barranquilla and Cartagena, Colombia; Venice; Marseille; Amsterdam; Astrakhan; Calcutta; Rangoon; Basra; Karachi; Shanghai; and Canton.

Delta cities sometimes have special problems, and the conditions that prevail at New Orleans are typical of many. Originally, with its drainage basin largely forested, the Mississippi sent down annual floods that were not unduly destructive. Recently, however, with much former forest cleared and swamps drained, the volume of floodwater has increased. The river has become increasingly difficult to control and has threatened the safety of residents of New Orleans many times. The city was barely saved from destruction in the great flood of 1927. It has been completely ringed by levees and equipped with pumping plants to lift excess rain water and sewage out of the center of the saucer in which it is located. Residents of New Orleans must construct an expensive plant to purify the water supply for the city, and fight a number of threats of epidemic diseases when the drainage problem around the city becomes serious. In this delta city it is difficult to find adequate material for building roads or to discover a solid foundation for business structures and approaches to the river bridge. Few other major American cities have had to face geographical problems like those imposed upon New Orleans.

Lake Plains.   When lakes are filled with sediment and peat or disappear through evaporation or drainage they leave in their old beds a plain of silt and plant remains that may afford very fertile farm land. If the plain is too swampy for cultivation, farmers may dig drainage ditches to reclaim the land for agriculture. The Red River Valley in Minnesota and the

eastern Dakotas is a good example of the value of lacustrine (lake bed) farmlands, since a large deep lake that once extended into Manitoba occupied this region during the last glacial period. This former lake, called Lake Agassiz, once overflowed southeastward through the Minnesota River to the Mississippi. Other former lake beds occupy lands south of Lake Erie and Lake Ontario, areas around Great Salt Lake, Death Valley, and the Takla Makan in central Asia. Former glaciated regions contain thousands of little plains that are sites of former ponds or lakes now filled or drained. These constitute some of the best farmland in these parts of Europe and America (Figure 13-5).

Alluvial Piedmont Plains.   Running water flowing from higher lands may deposit material in the form of alluvial fans and cones at mouths of valleys or canyons where the gradient of the stream bed changes abruptly. These alluvial deposits may coalesce until they combine to form wide alluvial slopes or compound

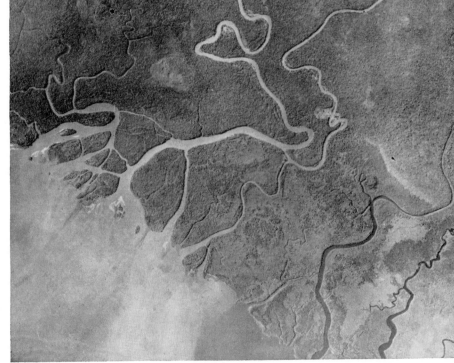

Figure 13-4 A tropical delta: the mouth of the Pogo, or Waponngaa, River as it enters Geelvink Bay, New Guinea. Note the dense rain forest vegetation cover merging with the coastal swamps. The larger stream is heavily burdened with silt that is carried some distance into the bay; the smaller stream remains relatively clear. (Air Force photograph.)

Figure 13-5 Specialty farming of onions on reclaimed muck soils of a former glacial lake at Elba, New York. Other crops grown on this fertile soil include potatoes, lettuce, carrots, beets, and spinach. Farm labor comes from Jamaica to work in these fields. (Photograph used by permission of the U.S. Department of Agriculture.)

alluvial fans extending far out from a mountain range (Figure 12-7). When these plains occur at bases of mountains, they are known as alluvial piedmont plains, as described in an earlier chapter. Typical alluvial piedmont plains are found on the eastern side of the Great Valley of California, the northern side of the Po River plain, the eastern slope of the plains of Iraq, the northern side of the Indus and Ganges River plains, and the western slope of the Wasatch Range in Utah. These alluvial plains merge by imperceptible degrees with fluvial deposits like those along the Sacramento and San Joaquin Rivers in California. Alluvial plains are generally fertile and when well watered, by either natural rainfall or irrigation, may support great numbers of people, as in India. As a rule, alluvial plains of this type are limited to arid or semiarid climates, with the notable exception of the great piedmont at the southern base of the Himalayas, in a humid monsoon region.

Peneplains. With time, agents of erosion, like running water and wind, will completely reduce rugged mountains and high plateaus to gently rolling surfaces called *peneplains,* as described in Chapter 12. True peneplains have few prominent relief features, and only a few rounded hills may break the monotonous flatness of their landscape; but such are rarely found, although most of Western Australia and much of Canada west and south of Hudson Bay are probable examples of uplifted peneplains. Many partial examples occur widely distributed throughout the United States and the world, where rivers have locally reduced a higher level to a lowland.

Erosion plains are located in regions in which uplands have been so reduced as to form a plain with a rolling surface, or low hills whose difference in elevation does not exceed a few hundred feet. On most erosion plains, bedrock is deeply weathered and is often covered with good soil; these facts make such plains desirable places for occupance where the land is climatically suitable. When well watered, the deeply weathered soil of erosional plains is highly suited for agriculture and will support a large population. Such plains occupy much of western France and part of southern Germany. The Bluegrass region of Kentucky and the Nashville Basin in Tennessee are examples in the United States. Erosional plains are not always well populated. They may be of rough relief even if differences in elevation are small, or soil may be thin or poor, like the rim surrounding the Bluegrass region. They may be too dry for agriculture, like Western and central Australia, or too cold, like much of interior Alaska and northern Canada. Any plain, whether of erosional or other origin, must have suitable climate, soil, and relief before it can be utilized for agriculture to any considerable extent.

Coastal Plains. Coastal plains represent former sea floors that have been recently uplifted. On the Atlantic and Gulf Coastal Plains the bedrock is often soft and loosely consolidated where the plains are of recent origin. Soil may be sandy and poor, but men farm even inferior lands here because cultivation is easy and markets in seaport cities are accessible. Terraces are common features of coastal plains, each level representing a renewed uplift of the land. Low hills may break the surface of the coastal plain where somewhat harder bedrock appears. These outcrops result where bedrock dips toward the sea somewhat more steeply than the slope of the land itself. The resulting landform presents a steep slope inland and a gentle slope seaward and has been named a *cuesta*. These cuestas develop on sandstone strata and are common phenomena of the Atlantic Coastal Plain; they present an interesting contrast to the more fertile areas developed on weak rocks between the more resistant beds.

Residents of coastal plains often face problems of poor drainage, and swamps are usual features of the landscape near the shores of these plains. For this reason mosquitoes that breed in stagnant pools and transmit malaria are often encountered in warm coastal plain areas as well as in inland marshes.

Among well-known coastal plains of the world are those facing the North Sea and south of the Baltic Sea in Northern Europe, the Campania between Rome and the Tyrrhenian Sea, the narrow shelf along the Malabar and Coromandel Coasts of India, the peninsula of Yucatan, and the coastal plain along the Atlantic Ocean and Gulf of Mexico in the United States.

The Atlantic and Gulf Coastal Plain of this country is rich agriculturally and important commercially. A large variety of crops, including vegetables, fruit, peanuts, tobacco, and cotton, is grown. Forest resources are important, and the many seaports serve both the interior and the coastal plain itself.

The chief rivers of coastal plains are usually navigable, and seaports are often located near their mouths. Hundreds of such ports have been founded, including Savannah, Georgia; New Orleans; Hamburg in Germany; and Le Havre and Bordeaux in France.

The Fall Line. Since the rocks of coastal plains are relatively soft, streams that rise in an interior upland of resistant rock usually have falls and rapids at the contact between the hard rocks of the upland and weaker rocks of the coastal plain.

Along the Atlantic Coast the contact between hard crystalline rock of the Piedmont Plateau and the Atlantic Coastal Plain, called the *Fall Line,* is a feature easily traceable from New Jersey to Alabama (Figure 13-6). The Fall Line determines the head of navigation on many streams and furnishes water power for manufacturing; this in turn leads to establishment of many towns and cities. Among centers whose locations are in part determined by their position on the Fall Line are Newark, Trenton, Philadelphia, Wilmington, Baltimore, Washington, Richmond, Raleigh, Columbia, Augusta, and Macon.

A similar fall line traverses central Germany, marking the contact between older harder rocks of south Germany and the young weak rocks of the coastal plain in the northern part of that country.

Occupance of Interior Plains. Some of the most extensive and useful plains on the face of

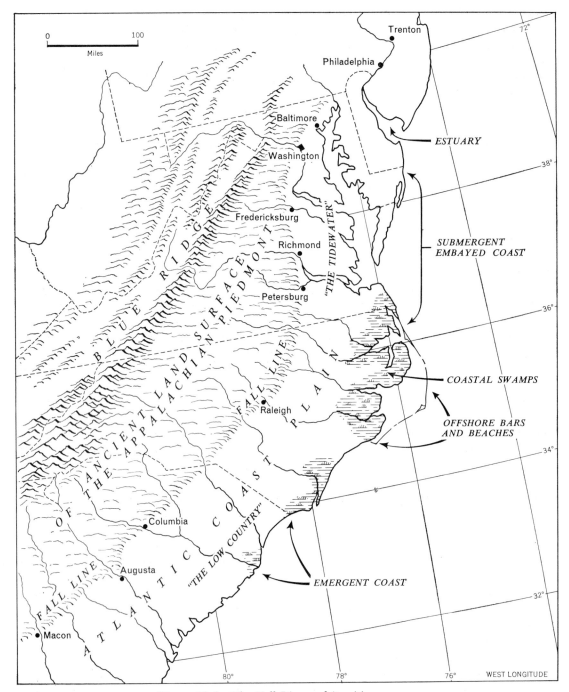

Figure 13-6   The Fall Line and its cities.

the earth occupy the interior of continents. An example is the interior lowlands and the Great Plains of North America. The great European plain stretching from the North Sea inland into Russia is another. In South America a vast lowland or plain extends from west Argentina north into eastern Bolivia, Paraguay, and interior Brazil.

Interior plains have various origins and the term refers to their location only. Erosion of once higher land accounts for some interior plains like Australia and parts of Canada. Marine shells which are found in the bedrock of many inland plains in Europe and America prove those areas were once at the bottom of the sea. Other interior plains are in areas where debris has been dumped by prehistoric rivers and glaciers and so left the land with small differences in relief. Those parts of the great European plain and central United States which receive adequate rainfall include great areas of fertile land, support many large cities with their associated industries, and constitute some of the most important economic regions on earth. In contrast, some other interior plains, like the Llanos of central Venezuela and southern Colombia, the Sudan region of Africa, southwestern Siberia with other parts of inland Asia, are seas of grass, devoted to grazing of wild game and domestic cattle. They are peopled with scant numbers of hunters and herdsmen. These plains are difficult to reach from the sea, and perhaps because of their isolation the inhabitants have been slow to advance in culture and economic development.

In general, since interior plains are characterized by low relief, they present relatively few obstacles to modern methods of transportation. Those plains which have soil and climate favorable to settlement and economic development are generally well served with railroads and highways. Interior plains, as well as other areas located in middle and high latitudes toward centers of continental land masses, usually experience very severe climatic conditions. Influence of the sea air seldom reaches great distances into the hearts of continents. Severe climate prevents some crops from being grown and so handicaps the inhabitants.

The lack of pronounced relief features on interior plains was an advantage to the United States and Canadian governments when they divided large tracts of land on the basis of rectangular surveys. The cultural landscape evolving on lands divided by these surveys is different in appearance from that of the countryside of the eastern United States, where other schemes for land division were established.

Plains are readily invaded by modern mechanized armies; this occurred in Poland in 1940 and happened repeatedly in the days of cavalry and foot soldiers, but the vast extent of plains of a country like the Soviet Union lends itself readily to military defense, for it leaves room to maneuver and to retreat to the interior without suffering disastrous defeat. This plan was followed by the Russians during the Napoleonic wars and more recently in their retreat to Stalingrad in World War II; when the communications of the invading armies were greatly extended, the Russians successfully counterattacked.

Glacial Plains. Ages ago, gigantic ice sheets accumulated in North America, Northern Europe, and other parts of the earth which were then experiencing very low temperatures. In North America, these continental glaciers extended southward as far as Long Island, northern New Jersey, Pennsylvania, central Ohio, Illinois, and Iowa. Then the ice front extended west to about the Missouri River, which it roughly followed to the Rocky Mountains. Ice also invaded the northern part of the state of Washington.

The moving ice sheets materially modified the natural landscape of these regions. Debris called *drift* or *till* was deposited on the surface of the land when the glacier melted away. Valleys were sometimes filled with debris, thereby reducing an original steep relief to a less rugged condition. In other places, lobes of the ice sheet gouged out vast quantities of material from ancient river valleys and dumped it in elongated heaps around the excavated basin. When the ice melted, some of these depressions were occupied by lakes, the greatest example marked by the Great Lakes of North America.

Heaps of material deposited at the end of a melting glacier usually formed long, irregular, hilly ridges called *terminal moraines.* Such moraines have hummocky, rough surfaces often covered with boulders, both small and big. Where glacial deposits are very stony, there is interference with agriculture. On the whole, however, the effect of the glaciers was to reduce the topography, leaving it smoother than it was originally. An example of a hilly region made less rugged by glaciers planing off hilltops and filling valleys is in northeastern Ohio. Here the hilly lands of the Appalachian Plateau were leveled by erosion and deposits from the continental glacier.

When the ice melted, quantities of sand, silt, and gravel were deposited to form gently sloping outwash plains (Figure 13-7). As the ice melted away, it dumped at random boulders, clay, rock flour, and other material it contained, forming the so-called *glacial till* which covers the whole country in the northeastern United States. This debris often filled old valleys and compelled complete readjustments of drainage lines.

A region in southwestern Wisconsin and adjacent corners of southeastern Minnesota, northwest Illinois, and northeastern Iowa was never covered by any ice sheet. This is known as the *driftless area;* here there is rugged relief and much less good farmland than in adjoining glaciated regions. Similar hilly lands of inferior

Figure 13-7 Landscape features near the front of a retreating glacier: F, *ice front,* LM, *lateral moraine,* MM, *medial moraine,* TM, *terminal moraine,* K, *kettleholes remaining after detached pieces of ice have melted,* T, *glacial till,* B, *bedrock.*

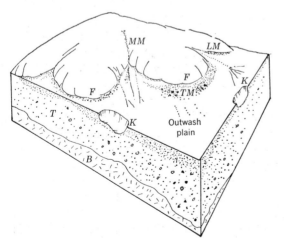

value for farming are found in southern parts of Ohio, Indiana, and Illinois beyond the limits reached by glaciers.

Parts of Canada and many New England hills lost much of their soil by glacial erosion. Areas of northwestern Europe also suffered. Glacial erosion removed much of the soil in Scandinavia and Scotland. Finland, too, was affected.

In general, glaciated parts of the continents form plains of less relief than before glaciation, though they display much minor irregularity of surface. As far as the United States is concerned, continental glaciers benefited man by reducing relief, bringing in some material of high fertility, creating lakes useful for transportation and other purposes, causing many waterfalls and other power sites, and depositing sand, gravel, and clay of value for construction materials.

Glaciers of continental extent secured most of their load from local sources, though they also carried some boulders hundreds of miles from Canada. In New England and northern Wisconsin, where bedrock is hard, the glacial till is very stony and cultivation of soil is difficult; around the lower Great Lakes the till was largely derived from weak, easily weathered rock, and the land is easier to plow and develop into farms.

Continental glaciation is the cause for tens of thousands of lakes. Uneven dumping of glacial debris made dams or left basins. Big masses of ice were surrounded by deposited material and lakes filled the hollows when the ice melted. The largest glacial lakes were formed either by dams from the ice itself or in part by glacial erosion of weak rocks. The limits of these former lakes are determined by the presence of abandoned beaches, sand dunes, wave-cut cliffs, terraces, exposed deltas, and sand bars. In these temporary lakes layers of silt and clay were deposited. Shallow glacial lakes soon filled with peat and silt and became some of the swamps that are characteristic of glacial plains. Some swamps and glacial lake beds when drained make very fertile and productive farmland (Figure 13-5), although other lake beds are sandy and so of limited use. Among the first group are the beds of extinct glacial lakes or "muck lands" in northern Ohio. High-value truck crops are grown here, and the price of such land is usually far above that of adjoining farms not located on former lake beds.

Great volumes of glacial meltwater sorted, transported, and redeposited material from the end of the melting ice. These are called *glacio-fluvial deposits* and are well sorted and even stratified. Glacial floodwaters deposited the re-worked material to form *outwash plains* in front of continental ice sheets (Figure 13-7). These provide a source of commercial supplies of sands and gravels. If deposits occur relatively near construction jobs, they are much used for concrete and other building materials.

Blocking by glacial deposits of former river systems has caused many drainage changes. For example, much of the drainage now tribu-tary to the upper Ohio River once flowed into the ancestral St. Lawrence Basin. In North America most of the portages used by fur traders between the Great Lakes and the Ohio and Mississippi Rivers follow abandoned glacial meltwater spillways. In Europe the ca-nals connecting the rivers which cross the northern plain of Germany usually follow sim-ilar deserted channels occupied by rivers in the glacial period.

Glaciated regions have the characteristics of youth in the cycle of erosion. Insufficient time has elapsed since the glacial period for drainage systems to become well established and relief features to reach maturity. The many lakes and swamps show that drainage is not yet stabilized. Rapids and waterfalls were created when glacial deposits filled former valleys and forced streams to seek new courses. Where the water dropped over a cliff, as at Niagara, a waterfall resulted; cascades, rapids, and newly eroded narrow gorges are likewise character-istics of regions formerly occupied by conti-nental glaciers. Many of the waterfalls and other sites have been developed for power and account for the location of numerous factories and mill towns.

Changing Occupance of Plains. The vegeta-tion which covers plains affects their occupance and their economic development. Open steppes

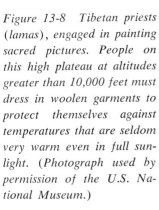

Figure 13-8 Tibetan priests (lamas), engaged in painting sacred pictures. People on this high plateau at altitudes greater than 10,000 feet must dress in woolen garments to protect themselves against temperatures that are seldom very warm even in full sun-light. (Photograph used by permission of the U.S. Na-tional Museum.)

are easily occupied and crossed whereas dense forests, extensive marshes, and deserts often impede movement of peoples. In forested regions, the first arteries for travel and trade are usually the rivers. Explorers long ago penetrated essentially all parts of the Andes, but considerable forested parts of interior Brazil away from the rivers are still virtually unknown.

Originally plains with suitable climate supported dense forests (Figure 5-1). In the east central United States and in Western Europe the lowlands were covered with hardwood trees growing in excellent soils. Once these regions were sparsely populated by primitive farmers and hunters. Today the forests have been largely cleared away; the land has been brought under cultivation and supports a much larger population. In colder parts of Northern Europe, Asia, and America, the climate is harsh and soils are inferior. These areas naturally are less useful for crops and support only sparse populations. Likewise tropical forested plains in Africa and South America have more repressive effects and support few people. Difficulty in clearing the land of trees is among the handicaps slowing up settlement and utilization of plains covered by tropical rain forests.

Plains of the great interior semiarid steppes have been previously described in Chapter 9.

PLATEAUS

Plateaus resemble mountains in elevation but plains in their comparative levelness. Technically a plateau is an extensive flattish area that has been uplifted without essential deformation. Plateaus are somewhat more difficult of access than plains because they often are reached by an abrupt ascent and are crossed by deep canyons. Resulting isolation may lead to greater conservatism among their inhabitants. Thus the plateau of Judea retained the Hebrew religion in its most pure form while the more fertile lowlands broke away from strict religious observances as a result of more contacts with foreigners.

Figure 13-9   The city of Taxco, in the interior highlands of the Mexican plateau.

Figure 13-10   A Bolivian Indian woman of La Paz. Note the very heavy woolen garments that are necessary in the high altitudes of this plateau. (Photograph used by permisson of R. J. Baker, Honolulu.)

In middle latitudes high plateaus may have harsh, almost polar climates as in Tibet (Figure 13-8) and Turkestan (Figure 13-11). Here man struggles against the severities of climate and ekes out a scanty existence by stock raising and a little agriculture carried on in the more protected places. In an equal area in the same latitudes in the lowlands of China Proper, nearly half a billion people live. In the southwestern United States, the high Colorado plateaus have more rain and support forests and lush meadows, whereas lower altitudes around them are desertlike in character. Here altitude is an advantage for the lumberman, rancher, and dairy farmer. The Colorado Plateau also supplies much of the water for irrigation by which numbers of people have conquered part of the nearby desert.

The Appalachian Plateau is in a mature stage of erosion. Comparatively little of the original gently rolling surface remains. Erosion has made it into such a hilly region that only the general uniformity in elevation of the hills, ridges, and other flattish summits prove that a plateau exists.

In the tropics, plateaus are usually preferred to lowlands for human activity, since the climate is less enervating. Thus the plateaus of southeastern Brazil, the Deccan in India, highlands of Central America, and Mexico (Figure 13-9) and high plateaus of northwestern South America in Peru, Bolivia (Figure 13-10), Colombia, and Ecuador are favored parts of those countries.

Except in the tropics, plateaus are generally less desirable for human use than plains. Canyons often isolate the level land, making it difficult to transport produce, and causing the same backwardness among inhabitants that is characteristic of people in isolated mountain regions. Interior plateaus of Asia—the Pamirs (Figure 13-11), Tibet, and Afghanistan—are typical representatives of this landscape and its peoples. The great canyons that cross the Colorado Plateau are almost impassable barriers to travel, though communication is easy on the broad tablelands between the canyons.

Since plateaus are thus usually less suited

Figure 13-11   Sarikol tribesmen in the Pamir district of Chinese Turkestan. Note the warm padded clothing and heavy felted hats which are needed for comfort in this continental environment. (Photograph, courtesy of the American Museum of Natural History, New York.)

for occupance by man than lowlands, they support fewer inhabitants than plains if the latter are humid and not mere desert. Grazing and forestry are the principal human occupations on plateaus of the world. They are unsuitable for farming outside the tropics; seldom do they have large cities. Those found there are industrial centers supported by mineral resources or transportation facilities. Nevertheless elevations like the Appalachian Plateau contribute important quantities of coal, oil, natural gas, and building materials for man's use.

Pueblo Indians. In the arid American Southwest, because of the high altitude the deserts of the Colorado Plateau experience colder winters than the nearby tropical deserts which are at lower elevations. Here two types of Indians lived side by side, the Pueblo Indians and the nomads. The nomads, like the Apaches, were mostly hunters and gatherers, and rarely planted corn. They were feared enemies of the sedentary Indians.

The Pueblo Indians once occupied the entire plateau country, but before the arrival of the white man their numbers and importance declined. Many ruined cliff dwellings and abandoned Pueblo villages show the large area they formerly occupied.

Existing village sites are located on the tops of nearly inaccessible buttes or mesas (tablelands) for protection (Figure 13-12). Villages consist of one or more community houses generally of stone and adobe brick with wood used only for roofs, ladders, door frames or other

openings, and the doors themselves. Each family has its own rooms, and structures are sometimes four or five stories high.

Pueblo Indians support themselves almost entirely by agriculture. Corn and beans, with squash and other gourds, are principal crops. Formerly these Indians made superior pottery and other utensils; today some of them still make pottery or silver and turquoise jewelry for sale to tourists. Little game can be hunted, since the Indians live in permanent locations, and animals within convenient hunting distance are few. Water is a problem. Rains furnish part of the supply, but women laboriously carry most of the water in jars up the steep and rocky trails from distant springs. Water is reserved mainly for cooking and drinking; little can be used extravagantly, for washing, and none for growing ornamental plants about the village.

Some Indians practice irrigation on a small scale from springs or tiny streams, but most of their crops are raised by flood irrigation. Corn is planted in a sandy alluvial fan at the mouth of a dry wash or canyon coming down from the mountains or plateaus. The rainy season in Arizona and western New Mexico comes in July and August, mostly in the form of heavy local thunderstorms. As a rule, sufficient water is retained from the preceding winter in the sandy soil to germinate the planted kernels of corn, but not enough of such water is present to mature the crop. The Indians depend upon summer rains to grow the needed supply of food. Their religion and ceremonies, including

Figure 13-12　The Pueblo Indians built their community houses of stone and adobe on isolated hills for protection against more warlike tribes. These Indians raised corn, beans, squash, and other crops in the sandy soils of nearby bottomlands where flood irrigation supplemented the light variable rains of the Colorado Plateau region. (Photograph by Frashers Photos, Pomona, California.)

the so-called "snake dance," are efforts to propitiate the god of rain so that crops will be good and food plentiful.

The Pueblo Indians often have two or more years' food supply in their large storehouses.

Hence the tribe is not completely dependent upon uncertain rains of any one particular year but can count upon what it has put aside from surplus produced in good years for use during unfavorable times.

SUMMARY

Plains, of which there are a number of types, provide the most acceptable type of environment for the largest part of the world's population. Plains in general have the greatest extent of soils favorable for farming, thus providing sufficient quantities of food for supporting large populations. Furthermore, most plains offer few serious obstacles to travel. Floodplains, delta plains, lake or coastal plains, and some glacial plains provide good soils and transportation advantages. It is in these favored locations that the world's largest cities flourish. It is essential, however, that climatic conditions be favorable for crop growth, or plains will not be capable of greatest development for human use. Some plains with a wet equatorial climate are too hot, humid, and densely forested to attract large populations. Dry, grass-covered plains or steppes are used chiefly for grazing, the herders often being nomads.

Plateau surfaces resemble plains, but the added feature of altitude makes them generally less useful, except in tropical latitudes where the plateau may be preferred for human residence, since low altitudes in the tropics are relatively unsuited to support many people.

Outline

Origin and appearance of plains

Occupance of plains

   Under primitive conditions

   Development of civilization and political expansion

Types of plains

   Floodplains, deltas, lake, and alluvial piedmonts

   Peneplains

   Coastal plains

   Interior plains

   Glacial plains

Changing occupance

Plateaus: characteristics and occupance

QUESTIONS

1. Why are not all plains densely populated?

2. Why are plains of midlatitudes more generally useful than those of low and high latitudes?

3. Compile a list of large cities whose sites are related to (*a*) deltas, (*b*) floodplains, (*c*) coastal plains.

4. How many of the world's large river plains open toward enclosed seas?

What disadvantages do they experience over plains that open toward the open sea?

5. What large river plains are unfavorably located because of a climate that is unsuitable for the support of large populations?

6. Among the world's large deltas, which are most useful?

7. How are coastal plains distinguished from interior plains? Can you suggest a second contrast?

8. List at least six problems that face the people of most delta cities.

9. What advantages has a city located on a large fertile plain with regard to commerce and manufacturing?

10. Why are there few densely populated plateaus?

11. Why are equatorial plateaus well peopled?

RESEARCH TOPICS

1. The Mississippi and the Mackenzie are large streams. They are nearly the same length; both flow through wide lowlands, and have well-developed deltas. Account for the difference in human population within their valleys.

2. Outline the handicaps that face river transportation on the St. Lawrence, the Ganges, the Volga, the Missouri, the Columbia, the Mississippi, and the Amazon Rivers.

3. Prepare a study not longer than one page in which you develop as fully as possible the human life that is characteristic of one of these interior plains: campos of western Brazil, the Llanos, Bohemia, the Gobi, the Chaco.

4. Using the resources of your local library, prepare a one-page paper in which you develop arguments for and against this proposition: "Resolved, that the losses of life and the expense of flood protection in the lower Mississippi Valley have been greater than the benefits derived from the cultivation and occupation of the land."

SELECTED REFERENCES

Clements, Frederic E.: "Climatic Cycles and Human Populations in the Great Plains," *Scientific Monthly,* 47:193–210, September, 1938.

Cressey, George B.: *The Basis of Soviet Strength,* McGraw-Hill Book Company, Inc., New York, 1945.

Freeman, O. W., and H. H. Martin: *The Pacific Northwest,* John Wiley & Sons, Inc., New York, 1954, chap. 5.

Garland, John H. (ed.): *The North American Midwest,* John Wiley & Sons, Inc., New York, 1955.

Gregory, H. E.: "The Navajo Country . . ." U.S. Geological Survey Water Supply Paper 380, Washington, 1916.

————: "Geology and Geography of the Zion Park Region, Utah and Arizona," U.S. Geological Survey Professional Paper 220, Washington, 1952.

Haas, W. H.: "The Plateau Indian of South America," *Journal of Geography,* 45:243–253, 1946.

Hargreaves, Mary W.: *Dry Farming in the Great Plains, 1900–1925,* Harvard University Press, Cambridge, 1957.

Parkins, A. E.: *The South: Its Economic-Geographic Development,* John Wiley & Sons, Inc., New York, 1938.

Putnam, Donald F. (ed.): *Canadian Regions,* Thomas Y. Crowell Company, New York, 1952, chaps. 6–18.

Russell, R. J.: "Geomorphology of the Rhone Delta," *Annals of the Association of American Geographers,* 32:149–254, June, 1942.

————, F. B. Kniffen, and others: "The Lower Mississippi Delta," Department of Conservation, Louisiana Geological Survey, Jan. 1, 1936.

Stevens, George P.: "Agricultural Methods in the Lower Nile Valley and Delta of Egypt," *Journal of Geography,* 46:327–337, December, 1947.

Sykes, Godfrey: *The Colorado Delta,* American Geographical Society, New York, 1937.

Webb, Walter P.: *The Great Plains,* Oxford University Press, New York, 1944.

14. Mountains
and Hills

MOUNTAINS are earth features of greater relief than hills; their surfaces normally have less level land than plateaus or plains. Whether a particular area will be called hilly or mountainous is determined both by actual elevation and by comparison with the height and steepness of neighboring land features. Mountains and hills affect men in numerous ways which interest the geographer. Their beauty, use for recreation and health, industries, and influence on routes of trade or travel, as well as the irregular distribution of their population, make the study of mountains an important part of geography.

MOUNTAINS

Origin of Mountains. Details of the origin of particular mountains concern geologists particularly; but the matter becomes of geographical importance if mountains originating in different ways have diverse effects upon human affairs. Types of mountains include those formed by folding, faulting, intrusion of igneous rock, volcanic activity, and intense erosion of high plateaus. As mentioned in a preceding chapter, a cordillera is "the whole system of mountain ranges, groups, ridges, and peaks" (the Rocky Mountains, Andes, and Himalayas are excellent examples of extensive cordilleras). Mountain chains and ranges may rise separately from others, but often the boundary that divides them is only a valley or even a somewhat arbitrary line, as among the so-called "mountain ranges" of northern Idaho. The highest summits are generally given individual names like Pikes Peak or Mt. Shasta. Even the term "hills" is sometimes applied to a mountain group like the Black Hills in South Dakota, which are really mountains.

Folded mountains usually consist of long parallel ranges or ridges. Valleys in folded mountains at first occupy the downfolds, as in the Jura Mountains west of the Alps. Sometimes prolonged erosion of folded mountains modifies the location of the ridges. This occurs when upfolded rocks and weaker strata are removed faster than other bedrock, until finally valleys come to occupy the outcrops of weaker rocks, with more resistant beds forming mountain ridges (Figure 14-1). These conditions prevail in the Appalachian Mountains. In folded mountains where trends of the folds are parallel, transport follows the elongated valleys between ridges rather easily, but human travel across such mountains is very difficult because of the many ridges and rivers that are encountered.

Faults (breaks in the earth's crust) are common causes of mountain uplift. Where faulting has occurred recently, geologically speaking, the face of the upraised mountain block rises abruptly from the plains at its base without intermediate foothills. The Front Range of the Rockies in Glacier Park, the east front of the Sierra Nevada (Figure 14-2), and the western face of the Wasatch Range in Utah are the result of faulting. These mountain escarpments are difficult to cross and form important barriers to transportation. Main routes of travel generally follow deeply eroded canyons that cut across the high faulted mountains, thus avoiding steep fault slopes wherever possible. Isolated fault blocks sometimes have been uplifted to form islandlike mountain masses rising above surrounding valleys and plains, like the basin ranges of Nevada.

Igneous intrusions. Sometimes gigantic masses of molten rock have intruded other rock materials and produced vast upheavals on the earth's surface. The heart of many mountain ranges like the Sierra Nevada, the Rockies of central Idaho, and the Pacific Coast

Figure 14-1   Hogback ridges along the southwestern border of Algeria. A hogback is made of resistant rock and results from erosion of beds of weaker rock in places where the strata are steeply inclined. Note the desert character of the landscape and the evidences of erosion in this dry climate. (Air Force photograph.)

Figure 14-2 Eastward face of the Sierra Nevada with the Alabama Hills in the middle distance. The highest point on the sky line in the center of the picture is Mt. Whitney. Note the deep dissection of the face of the escarpment and the extensive development of alluvial fans and cones at the base of the escarpment. The floor of Owens Valley appears in the foreground.

Range of Canada consists of great intrusions (batholiths) of granite. Intrusive rock usually resists erosion and often forms mountain summits after more easily eroded rocks that once covered and surrounded the intrusions have been removed. Intrusions also may cause separate peaks or isolated mountain groups like the Judith Mountains of central Montana and the Henry Mountains of Utah.

Volcanoes have helped form many mountains. Sometimes the lava flows build up a broad plateaulike mountain range like the southern Cascades in Oregon, or broad domes like Mauna Kea and Mauna Loa in Hawaii. More frequently volcanoes form individual piles or cones of lava and explosive volcanic debris. These sometimes occur as isolated peaks but more often in rows built up along a line of fracture in the earth's crust. Smaller parasitic cones may surround a major volcano. Lava domes have comparatively gentle slopes. In contrast, volcanoes formed of cinders or a mixture of lava and cinders are generally steep-sided cones like Fuji in Japan, Mt. Vesuvius near Naples, or Lassen Peak in northern California.

Plateau erosion. When a high plateau has been deeply trenched by valleys until little of the original level summit surface remains, the region resembles a mountain area in its effects on travel and occupance. A dissected high plateau region of this type occurs in northern Idaho and adjacent parts of Montana and Washington. When eroded plateaus have been so reduced that only remnants of the original surface remain perched on the ridge summits, relief may be sufficiently rugged so that they are regarded as hill lands rather than as plateaus. This has occurred in the case of the Ozarks and the so-called Allegheny and Cumberland Plateaus in the United States and in some other hill regions. Usually dissection of the plateau demands a long period of geologic time in order to reach maturity. The Appalachian Plateau is an excellent example of such a mature region. At some future time the divides between rivers will be lowered by erosion, valleys will become very broad, and finally what was once a high plateau may be reduced to a gently rolling plain or peneplain.

The method by which rivers develop water gaps through ridges was mentioned in the discussion on erosion in Chapter 12. In a maturely dissected plateau or in mountain systems formed mainly by elongated ridges, lines of travel follow the rivers. The location of the water gaps governs major routes of trade. In the Appalachian region, the Indians discovered the trail, which was perhaps first made by buffalo and deer. Then it was blazed by fur trader and frontiersman. Next it was widened for use by the Conestoga wagon of the emigrant, and finally it was followed by railroads and paved highways. Valleys, water gaps, and other passes in maturely eroded mountains of southern and southwestern Germany have exercised a similar influence upon the settlement and routes of commerce in that area.

Cycle of Erosion in Mountains. No sooner has a mountain region begun to be elevated above its surroundings than it is attacked by forces of erosion that tend to level it. In the resulting cycle of erosion, the different characteristics for the stages of youth, maturity, and old age grade into each other by insensible degrees.

In youth, mountain streams have carved narrow deep gorges, and there is very little level land on which man can live. Streams are too swift and too much interrupted by falls and rapids to use for navigation. Youthful streams may be developed for power, but unless such rivers happen to be situated near enough to cities to make transmission of power profitable, there is little use for the energy because of the small population in mountains. Human settlements avoid the gloomy chasms and usually occupy the divides between rivers. Rarely is there much good land for farming, and indeed the land may reach such high elevations as to be

climatically unsuited for agriculture. On steep slopes soil is thin and poor chiefly because of the rapidity with which erosion may remove the finer particles. Usually few people live in young mountains because they are repelled by the narrow valleys with limited areas of tillable land, scanty soil, short growing season, and dense forests. Grazing and forest industries, however, may be of some importance.

When a mountain region has reached maturity, little of its original upland surface remains. Divides are narrow ridges, useless for occupance. The larger rivers have begun to develop floodplains, and it is on these and the gentler lower slopes of the mountains that settlements are located. Upper slopes may provide timber and summer grazing for livestock. Population is widely scattered, since families can find support only on the small plots of available land.

In time, even high mountains attain old age, and the once rugged land is reduced to a peneplain. Then rivers are easily navigable and the erosional plain of slight relief can be crossed or cultivated almost everywhere. A few monadnocks, the erosion-resistant roots of ancient ranges, remain as proof that the vanished mountains ever existed.

In an arid climate mountains also pass through a cycle of erosion but debris eroded from uplands by torrential floods is dropped around bases of the mountains where it forms extensive alluvial piedmont plains. Mountains thus disappear in part from erosion by water and wind, and in part from filling of adjacent lowlands by debris coming from the mountains themselves.

Mountain Glaciers. When snowfall exceeds the rate of melting year after year, the snow first changes to a granular condition and finally into snow ice. Mountain glaciers are formed at high altitudes from this consolidation of snow into ice, occupying upper parts of valleys in high mountains. Some are even found in very high mountains near the equator, as in the Andes. Away from the equator glaciers descend to successively lower elevations until, in

Alaska and Tierra del Fuego, some even reach sea level. Many scenic features in mountains like the Alps and Rockies result from glaciers.

Glaciers profoundly affect mountain valleys they occupy by grinding off loose and weathered rock material, polishing bedrock surfaces, transporting rock debris, and finally dropping the material into irregular heaps and ridges called *moraines,* wherever the ice melts. Glaciers work headward toward their sources and often excavate the valley head into a steep-walled semicircular amphitheater, or *cirque.* Glaciers sometimes gouge the floor of the cirque irregularly, leaving depressions in the bedrock which subsequently may be occupied by rock-basin lakes (Figure 14-4). Farther down their valleys, glaciers usually deposit large *terminal moraines.* Glacial gouging and deposition of debris frequently form lake basins (Figure 14-3) that add to the beauty of the scenery. Deposits of stones and smaller debris along the sides of glaciers, including those on the ice itself, are known as *lateral moraines* (Figure 14-4). If two lateral moraines join they form a *medial moraine.*

The surface of a glacier toward the end of summer, when the snow has melted under a summer sun, always appears dirty from rock debris that has fallen from cliffs above or has been scoured by abrasion of bedrock or in other ways. The ice melts on top and within the glacier as well as at the end. When passing over irregularities in the valley, the glacier usually develops great cracks called crevasses, which serve as conduits to lead meltwater into a massive channel under the ice, from which a full-fledged river emerges at the lower end of the glacier. This stream is loaded with finely ground rock which gives the water a typical milky appearance. Much of this debris is deposited in front of the melting ice down the valley, producing extensive valley fills.

Former glaciation. In the past, glaciers were much more extensive, and many mountain valleys show evidence of this prehistoric ice at work. Today glaciers in mountains may be only small remnants of larger ones. Nonetheless, glaciated valleys can be easily recognized. Moving glacial ice erodes the ends of all projecting ridges and spurs and thus by

Figure 14-3 Lake Ellen Wilson (*upper left*) and Lincoln Lake (*lower right*) in the Northern Rocky Mountains. These glacially formed lakes occupy the valley of a former active glacier whose ancient cirque appears in the distance at the left near Gunsight Pass. (*Photograph, courtesy of Glacier National Park authorities and the National Park Service.*)

Figure 14-4   Sperry Glacier in Glacier National Park occupies a cirque. The lines crossing the ice indicate that the glacier moves more rapidly at the center than at the sides. Note how the rock sediments at the right of the picture have been crumpled, twisted, and mashed together by the enormous pressure exerted when the mountains were being formed. Small faults can be seen on the face of the cliff at the right. A lateral moraine appears at the side of the ice in the lower left corner. (Photograph by Hileman, courtesy of the Great Northern Railway.)

cutting off lower parts of mountain spurs changes a normal V-shaped valley formed by stream erosion into a broader U-shaped valley (Figure 14-6) having smooth slopes and a straightened course. Tributary valleys often end high above this new valley floor which was lowered by glacial erosion. From these hanging valleys, waterfalls may plunge into the main valley, as at Yosemite Falls. The rock walls lack soil and may be almost devoid of vegetation.

Outwash deposits and moraines are useful where they are not too stony for agriculture. Above the level reached by valley glaciers, upper parts of mountain spurs may have been little affected by glacial erosion. Here are meadows of value for grazing. The Swiss call such mountain meadows *alps,* a name now applied to the entire mountain system.

Mountains as Barriers. Mountains may be barriers to travel, to commerce, to invasion, and to rainfall and temperature. The barrier effect of mountains depends on their height and length and the arrangement of the ridges, as well as on the altitude, character, and number of passes that penetrate them.

Mountains may cause so much precipitation on their windward slopes that deserts occupy most of the land to leeward, as the desert of Nevada lies east of the Sierra in the prevailing westerly winds. Mountains like the Alps may protect land to the south against freezing Arctic air from the north, thereby allowing the production of subtropical crops like oranges on protected slopes much farther from the equator than would be possible otherwise. By their effect on climate, mountains often interfere with the spread of natural vegetation and animal life.

Mountain ranges sometimes make naturally marked boundaries when they are high and rugged enough to form good barriers. The Pyrenees separate France and Spain, but neither the political nor the social boundaries always coincide with the main divide of the range. Actually the Pyrenees possess a particular type of pastoral economy which is present in both nations. Mountains of Scandinavia form a natural barrier between Norway and Sweden, as do the Bitter Root Mountains between Idaho and Montana.

When forested, mountains are more difficult to cross with wagons than are bare ranges of similar height. Thus the Appalachians are comparatively low, but their densely forested ridges formed an important barrier against western exploration and settlement from the

Virginia and Carolina colonies until passes had been located and trails or roads established through the woods.

Mountain Passes. When mountains are barriers against travel and trade, passes through the obstruction are of paramount importance. The utility of a pass depends upon its latitude, its elevation above the lower land at either end, length of time in which it is free of snow and open to travel, roughness or other difficulty presented by the terrain, and the type of area it joins. To be widely used, a pass should connect important settled regions.

Passes in Europe. In Europe the Alps rise high above the plains of northern Italy, and passes afford the only means of reaching northwestern Europe by land. Cities thrive at the ends of passes, from which trade routes diverge and goods are distributed. Thus Turin has connections through the Mont Cenis Tunnel to Lyon, France; from Milan the long Simplon Tunnel offers access to Central Europe. The St. Gotthard route is occupied by a

Figure 14-5 Seaward end of Columbia Glacier near Valdez, Alaska. Note the extensive development of medial and lateral moraines and the icebergs in the foreground. (Air Force photograph.)

railroad which has been tunneled under the pass. The historic St. Bernard Pass has now lost some of its former importance because tunnels through the Alps are occupied by railroads that transport most of the freight, passengers, and mail. Some passes are of great historic interest. The Brenner Pass, for example lies north of Venice and affords a comparatively easy route from the Adriatic Sea into Austria, Germany, and the Baltic coasts (Figure 14-7). Between the North German Plain and the Danube Basin lies the Moravian Gate.

Passes in Asia.   The highest mountain barrier on earth is the Himalaya range north of India. The most important route from the northwest into Pakistan and India comes from Afghanistan through the Khyber Pass. This route from the earliest times to the present has provided the path for invasion of the Indian peninsula by fierce nomads from steppes and deserts of central Asia, attracted by the wealth and fertility of India. Passes north and northeast of India are so very high or otherwise difficult that they have served as routes for only a few hardy traders. Large armies have invaded India only from the northwest where passes are lower and easier. Two important passes from China are the Nankow Pass leading from Mongolia west of Peking and that from the Wei Basin into the Tarim Basin— the Jade Gate.

Routes related to the Rocky Mountains.   In the western United States, both the Rocky Mountains and Sierra Nevada–Cascade ranges are formidable barriers to transportation. Railroads have sometimes been built around the mountains, as the Santa Fe and Southern Pacific swing south of the Rockies. The Northern Rockies have few east-west trending valleys; thus all transcontinental railroads crossing Montana come together at Spokane at the western end of the only easy route (Figure 24-6). Denver was handicapped because passes west of that city are so high and so often blocked by heavy snow that railroads found construction costly and operation difficult. Railroads, therefore, built lines northward from Denver through the open country of Wyoming or southward to the Grand Canyon of the Arkansas River, avoiding the more difficult routes across the high Rockies. Finally Denver itself, impelled

Figure 14-6 A glacially scoured U-shaped valley in California. (Photograph by F. E. Matthes, used by permission of the U.S. Geological Survey.)

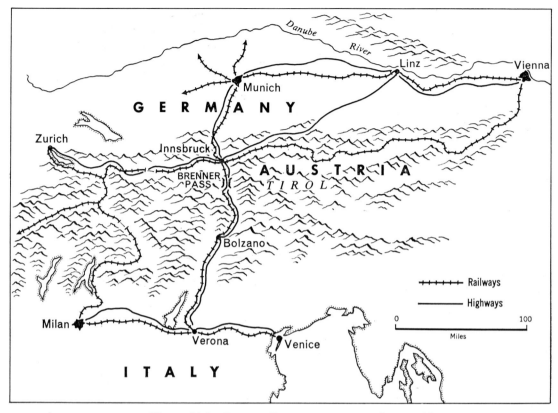

Figure 14-7   Brenner Pass as a transportation corridor.

by the need of overcoming the natural handicaps to transportation, helped raise funds to tunnel through the Rockies west of the city, thus saving 173 miles of travel between Denver and Salt Lake City. The longest railroad tunnel (nearly 7½ miles) in the United States is that of the Great Northern Railway in the Cascade Mountains of Washington, built to eliminate steep grades and danger from snowslides.

Occupance of Mountains. Mountains appear to be excellent natural boundaries, although actually they serve infrequently as political boundaries. The continental divide of the Andes Mountains, for example, is utilized as a national boundary only for part of its length between Argentina and Chile.

Mountains and hills may serve, however, as places of refuge. Defeated peoples often find shelter in mountains and hills after an invader has driven them from fertile lowlands.

Thus the original Britons sought refuge in the mountains of Wales and Scotland and the rocky peninsula of Cornwall. The Basques, one of the oldest peoples of Europe, live in the Pyrenees on both sides of the political boundary between France and Spain. Other descendants of very ancient inhabitants of Europe are found in Albania.

Because of lack of resources, mountain people have difficulty making a living and in the past often raided nearby fertile lands for cattle and grain. Thus for many years the English border lands suffered from raids by the Welsh and Scots. The Christians in Spain, defeated by Moslem invaders, fled to the Pyrenees. From this haven for centuries they harassed the lowlands occupied by the Moors and gradually regained their ancestral land from the invaders, completing the conquest late in the fifteenth century. Afghans and other "hill" peoples of the Himalayas have been troublesome neighbors for the plainsmen of the Ganges-Indus lowlands for centuries. Sometimes mountain peoples, united under a good leader, are able to conquer larger populations living on nearby lowlands. Thus mountain dwellers in the highlands north and northeast of Iraq have emerged from their homeland several times in history and conquered less warlike agriculturists of the plains.

Mountain and hill people at home.   The activities of mountain people often reflect the conditions of their environment. Houses are built of available native materials, usually stone or wood. In forested snowy mountains the house is made of logs with a steep roof to shed snow. Often less steep roofs are covered with stones so that high winds will not destroy the structure (Figure 14-8). In mountains around the Mediterranean and in the high Andes where timber is scarce, stone houses are more common. Often mountain people find it difficult to raise or make products for sale. Some mountain communities specialize in carving wood, or making toys, laces, clocks, and other goods which utilize local labor and skills. Materials used are mainly of local origin or if imported, are usually cheap or of small weight and volume. In Germany 90 per cent of the clockmakers are residents of the Black Forest region. Improvements in transportation may make it cheaper to import grains required for food in which case the mountain grain fields may be abandoned or used for hay.

The Southern highlanders.   The inhabitants of the southern Appalachians long lived in isolation. Nearly all are descended from English, Scottish and Irish ancestors, since few later immigrants cared to enter the mountains. For more than a century, difficulties of transportation compelled the people to live an isolated, self-sufficient life in remote mountain homes where lack of outside contact allowed traditional ways of life to continue. Archaic English words in common use before the Revolutionary War survived for many years among these people, although such remnants of the past are now disappearing from the Appalachian region. Until relatively recently, however,

pioneer conditions lingered. Houses were built of logs by the residents themselves. Members of the family made most furniture and other daily needs. Women once wove their own cloth from home-grown wool and flax. Furs and leather made from the skins of domestic animals were commonly used for clothes and shoes.

Generally mountain people, whether in the United States or abroad, raise a variety of crops instead of specializing in one or two things; with poor transportation, trade is difficult and food is produced for sustenance and not for sale. Until modern highways and railroads began to penetrate the mountains, and schools and hospitals were established, people lived largely without education, medical aid, or effective government.

With the construction of highways, the establishment of schools, and the resulting increased contact with the outside world, old customs

Figure 14-8 A typical house of the hill and mountain lands of southern Germany. Note the wide, overhanging eaves and the use of heavy rocks to protect the low-pitched roof from high winds and sliding snows.

Figure 14-9   Palomar Mountain observatory, San Diego County, California, at an altitude of 6,126 feet. This structure houses the 200-inch telescope. The site was selected because of the exceptional clarity of the air and the distance from city lights which might interfere with nighttime observations.

and culture decline, and mountain people assimilate themselves and their ways to those followed by the general population. Such changes have now taken place over most of the southern highlands of the United States.

Mountain regions may become overpopulated and men and women leave their homes to earn a living in nearby lowlands and cities. During the nineteenth century many Scottish Highlanders moved to the industrial cities of Great Britain or emigrated abroad. Certain villages in the Italian and French Alps have lost more than half their population since 1900. The hilly Appalachian Plateau, southern Appalachian Mountains, and the Ozarks in a similar way have supplied labor to industrial cities and more favored farmlands in the United States.

Mountain Countries. Politically isolated mountains frequently contain small independent states. Because it is difficult for invaders to move into mountain masses, nature helps the inhabitants defend their properties. Thus in Europe the tiny independent countries of Andorra, Liechtenstein, and San Marino are in rugged mountain regions. Most Swiss live in valleys and lower land rather than in the high Alps, although the mountainous character of the country aided the cantons in their movement toward independence and in defense against outsiders. Nepal and Bhutan on the southern slopes of the Himalayas occupy regions that are difficult to penetrate, and thus they remain independent political entities. Even where a mountainous area has not separated from a lowland with which it may be associated, political friction frequently results from different problems in the two areas.

Mountain Climates. Mountains affect climate in several ways, and they may have climates that are distinctly different from those on adjacent lowlands. They sometimes also separate regions with quite different climates on either side of a mountain barrier.

Temperature. Insolation received by mountains differs from that of neighboring lowlands:

1. Less density and greater purity of air in higher altitudes permit passage of more of the sun's radiation (Figure 14-9).

2. Rays of light that are oblique on lowlands fall directly on slopes of highlands facing the sun.

Highlands may receive more insolation than neighboring lowlands, but average temperatures decrease with elevation largely because the less dense air allows rapid loss of heat by radiation from highlands (Figure 14-10). In mountain valleys sunny slopes are preferred to shady slopes for farms and places of residence. The shaded slopes are generally used for forests and pasture lands.

Mountain peaks usually are exposed to strong winds but mountain valleys and leeward lowlands may be protected from severe winds. Long valleys often control wind direction locally, since winds blow with least resistance up and down the valleys. Convectional day-and-night movements of air, called *mountain and valley breezes,* commonly occur in mountains, as described in Chapter 4.

Temperatures among high mountains may be too low at night to permit growth of any but hardy plants. Likewise some valley floors and lowlands may experience late frosts in spring and early frosts in autumn, resulting in a growing season too short for fruits. On hillsides between frosty lowlands and cool uplands, however, there may be a thermal belt having a long growing season suitable for growing fruit. These belts may be only a mile or two wide, lying between differences in elevation of only a few hundreds of feet, but within their narrow zone relative freedom from frost is experienced. Familiar examples of such thermal belts are found in North Carolina east of the Appalachians, in foothills of the Sierra Nevada along the San Joaquin and Sacramento Valleys, and along the southern slopes of the Alps. They are particularly associated with the presence of piedmont alluvial plains (Figure 12-7), though any foothill location may have this so-called "frostless belt."

Citrus fruits mature along shores of mountain lakes in northern Italy on the southern slopes of the Alps, for example, at Lake Maggiore which is in the latitude of Michigan. Although the lakes help prevent frost, growing of citrus fruits in this northerly location is made possible in part by the protection the mountain masses afford against cold winds from the interior of the continent. In a similar way the Himalayas protect the plains of northern India from invasion of cold air masses from interior Asia. High mountains lying north of Florida would be of great benefit to that state, since they would protect the peninsula entirely from frost, and tropical products could be raised everywhere in the area.

Rainfall. Mountains exert most important climatic effects when their length extends at right angles to prevailing wind directions. Thus the Sierra Nevada and Cascades stretch hundreds of miles across the path of prevailing westerly winds in their latitudes. Exceedingly heavy rains and snows occur on westward slopes of these ranges, but winds descending to the eastward have lost moisture and become drying desert winds. Mountains rising in the zone of the trade winds display astonishing

differences in rainfall distribution between windward and leeward slopes (Figures 5-1 and 12-1). Thus the summit of Kauai, one of the Hawaiian group, has rainfall of nearly 450 inches a year, decreasing to less than 20 inches over the crest, 20 miles westward down the mountain slope.

As a result of rainfall differences, windward sides of mountains often support dense forests, whereas grasslands and even scanty desert vegetation may appear on leeward sides. On the western face of the Cascades, great forests

Figure 14-10 Climatic graph for Bogotá, Colombia. Weather stations located at high altitudes in low latitudes usually have remarkably even temperature means throughout the year—an isothermal condition that tends to provide a monotonous temperature. This, however, is offset by considerable daily (diurnal) range with warm daytime and below-normal nighttime temperatures for their latitude. Precipitation, either as rain or snow, is variable in amount.

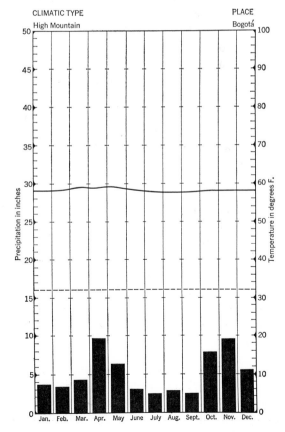

support very important lumbering operations. East of the mountains, agriculture predominates, with grain raised by dry-farming methods. Fruits and alfalfa are produced by irrigation, and livestock is grazed on land unfit for farming. Water for power, municipal supply, and irrigation often is derived from mountains. The relationship of mountains to water resources will be discussed in Chapter 20.

Latitude and Altitude Factors. Uses of mountains depend to a considerable degree upon latitude. In midlatitudes the greatest number of people live on plains and lowlands in which the growing season is longer than at higher elevations. There are only five cities—Denver, El Paso, Salt Lake City, Spokane, and Albuquerque—of more than 100,000 people between the Pacific Coast and cities of the humid interior lowlands of the United States. Yet this area includes nearly 40 per cent of the total extent of the country. Of course, dryness helps explain the small population in the western interior. Three out of five persons in the United States live below 1,000 feet in elevation, although nearly three-fourths of the nation lies above this altitude.

In Europe also, great cities are nearly all on seacoasts or plains that are under 1,000 feet in elevation. Madrid and Munich are the most populous exceptions. In Asia most Chinese and Japanese live on deltas and floodplains of rivers. Mountains in mid-latitude zones, then, support only a scanty population. Because most residents of these mountains live in the valleys there is great disparity in distribution of population in mountain areas. Even in wet-and-dry tropical monsoon climates like India, one-third of the population lives in deltas and valleys of the Ganges River alone.

In the rainy tropics, an entirely different situation prevails. Tropical lowlands are so hot and humid, so densely forested, and so plagued with insect pests and disease that men choose to live on high plateaus and mountains. Important Indian civilizations developed in mountains and plateaus whose climate was tempered by altitude in Mexico, Colombia, and Peru, located within the tropics. Except for coastal seaports, all great cities of tropical America are situated on plateaus or in high mountain valleys. In Ecuador, Peru, and Bolivia men prefer to live at elevations of 7,000 to 12,000 feet; for example, Quito lies 9,350 feet and La Paz over 12,000 feet above sea level. Temporary huts of shepherds have been found at elevations exceeding 17,000 feet. Such elevations in high latitudes are utterly useless because they lie above the snow line.

In high latitudes only the lowlands find use by man, because mountains are generally covered with snow fields and glaciers. Sometimes it is asserted that in the tropics between sea level and the tops of snow-capped mountains, one can find every climate corresponding to those which would be experienced in going from the equator to polar regions. With reference to average temperature this is true, but equatorial highlands lack the extreme range in temperature between winter and summer of high latitudes; only moderate changes occur in daily temperatures throughout the year. A snow-capped mountain in equatorial Africa, then, has somewhat different climate from that of glacier-covered mountains of Alaska and Greenland, even if average temperatures are about the same.

Snow line. Permanent snow fields begin at altitudes around 18,000 feet under the equatorial sun and may descend to sea level in polar regions. Height of the snow line depends upon the amount of snowfall and rate of evaporation. The latter is affected by temperature, amount of sunshine, cloudiness, and wind movement, as well as by the direction of exposure to the sun.

HILLS

Hills merge with mountains and plateaus at their upper limits and with plains on their lower borders. Since relief features of hills partly resemble those of both mountains and plains, their occupance and use likewise fall at an intermediate position between human activi-

Figure 14-11   Wheat fields of the Pacific Northwest, with harvest under way by four combine harvesters. This is large-scale farming. (Photograph by Brubaker Aerial Surveys, used by permission of the Leonard Delano Studios, Portland, Oregon.)

ties of higher and lower landforms. In general, regions with local relief ranging from 300 to 500 feet or more between valley bottom and hilltop are considered hilly; when the magnitude of difference in elevation greatly exceeds 1,000 feet, the region is usually called mountainous if rugged, or a plateau if its upper surfaces are level to rolling (Figure 14-11). Local custom and authorities both differ so widely on terminology that no hard and fast definition of hill lands can be offered.

Origin.   Hills commonly result from erosion of uplands that may have been mountains at one time or from erosion of plateaus or plains of sufficient height that their reduction will result in a difference of local relief, as described above. Only remnants of the original surface remain undissected. In once mountainous regions the hill stage can be expected in late maturity when mountain summits are much reduced in elevation. In a plateau the region is called hilly when in maturity the valleys crossing the area have become so wide that slopes rather than the original surface dominate the landscape. In general the same conditions would be true of plains, provided that the original plain was of such elevation that local

relief developed there by erosion attained a difference in elevation of several hundred feet. Otherwise an eroded plain of this type would still be considered a plain.

Human Relationships to Hill Land.   Much of what has been said of mountains is also true of hill lands, although on a reduced scale. Hills lack sufficient altitude to become significant climatic barriers but ruggedness of surface hampers farming as well as the construction of railroad and highway networks. Hill people sometimes live in an environment as isolated as that of mountain people. Hilly land situated in humid climates originally had an excellent forest cover; the utilization of such forests is still of great importance to residents of these regions. Grazing and subsistence farming occupy many people.

Hills may provide protection when defense is needed. They are invaded with difficulty by warlike neighbors, although this was not true of the hilly Ardennes region of Belgium and France during early days of the German invasion in the Second World War.

Usually, hill lands do not supply their residents with sufficient raw materials or minerals to foster extensive manufacturing or to accumulate any large amounts of wealth. Some of the Balkan peoples, the Irish who live in the western counties of Eire, and Italians who dwell in the hilly Apennines are barely able to make a decent living for themselves; their living standards are noticeably lower than those of people in more fertile and productive lowlands nearby. When hill country does possess some resource that the outside world considers valuable enough to exploit then hill people may have a source of additional income. Hill regions of West Virginia and western Pennsylvania and eastern Kentucky, for example, have valuable beds of bituminous coal that afforded employment when mines were placed in operation. These coal beds outcrop on hillsides; and in many places, therefore, coal can be mined by entering from a side hill along some creek whose valley has truncated the coal stratum. Tunnels driven in from these hillsides are cheaper than sinking a vertical shaft, and the coal thus mined can be delivered by gravity conveyors directly to railroads in the valleys below the mine entrance.

Erosional processes by which hill lands are formed through dissection usually remove soils as they develop on hilltops and slopes, and running water may wash these soils away rapidly. Thus slopes and summits normally lack soil of any great depth, and meager soils that remain in place on the slopes are usually of low fertility. As a result, many hill farmers have small incomes and poor living conditions. Nevertheless some hilly regions do have excellent high-quality soils and here farming operations are successful. This is true in the Palouse Hills of eastern Washington (Figure 14-11), the loess hills of northern China, and some hilly areas of central Europe.

In hilly parts of New England, Pennsylvania, and other states near substantial city markets, dairying is the leading occupation for the farmers. Abundant rainfall makes good grazing even on rather thin and poor

soils, so that a living can be made on moderate-sized farms. Both cattle and sheep are also raised for market. Favored by large markets, the poultry industry is important too.

Unless great care is used in farm practices, hill farms are more subject to damaging effects of rain-water erosion than lands with lower angles of slope. In too many cases, both in this country and abroad, farmland of hill regions has suffered severe erosion (Figure 14-12). This matter becomes the more serious when it is remembered that the original extent of good farmland in most hill sections is small and that loss of soil increases farmers' difficulties. Some hill lands near the southern Appalachians, the Mediterranean Sea, and northern China have been made almost worthless by serious soil erosion.

In hill regions, principal towns and villages are often located at valley confluences or at ends of passes that traverse the rough country. Thus few large cities are found in hilly country. Yet often there are a great number of small trade centers as in Pennsylvania. Steep grades and poor roads in early years of settlement probably were factors in founding many hamlets as was also the occurrence of coal deposits. Possibly Pennsylvania has more little country villages and small settlements than any other state.

Railways and highways are typically crooked in hill country in strong contrast to the straight transportation routes usual on plains. Moreover building railways and highways among hills and mountains requires many cuts, fills, bridges, and even tunnels. This makes construction expensive and limits the number of roads and rail lines that a region can support. Generally transportation costs are high. Furthermore the irregular distribution of people makes it harder to serve all of them with the transportation they need.

In fair weather airplanes readily fly above

Figure 14-12   Effects of soil erosion on the appearance of a once-prosperous Ohio farm. Neglect of proper principles of cultivation has caused bankruptcy of many farms of this type. Topsoil of the pasture behind the barn has been completely removed by erosion, and there is little topsoil remaining on the cultivated fields. (Photograph, courtesy of the U.S. Soil Conservation Service.)

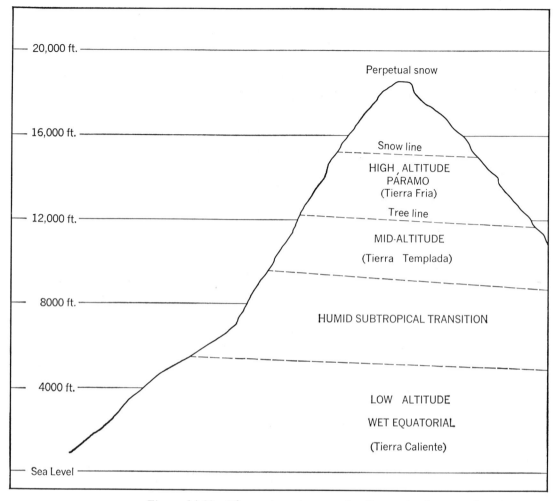

Figure 14-13   The zoning of mountain climates in the central Andes.

mountain areas which make land transportation slow and difficult. But when fogs, clouds, and storms envelop mountain summits transportation by air becomes a serious problem.

UTILIZATION OF MOUNTAINS AND HILLS

Forests. Most mountains and many hills support forests of considerable extent. This was suggested in Chapter 11, where it was pointed out that the place name, Schwarzwald, signified both mountain country and forested country. The same condition prevails in the use of some other names; Transylvania, a wooded and mountainous section of Romania, was the name applied to that region, and in the United States the name Pennsylvania signifies not only the original owner's name but the fact that much of that state was forested.

Zones of vegetation. Frequently a zonal arrangement of vegetation, ranging from lower elevations to mountaintops, can be recognized, but the character of the vegetation changes slowly from one zone to another, depending upon increase of altitude (Figure 14-13). It may also vary widely as the result of differences in type of bedrock, soil, relief, or exposure to winds. Temperature, rainfall, and length of growing season are only a few of many factors that affect types of vegetation. In deserts there is an upper and a lower tree limit, the former determined principally by temperature, the latter by rainfall. Thus belts of forested land may surround high mountains, as in the Great Basin of Nevada and Utah which rise from steppes or treeless plateaus to summits of alpine meadows.

Vegetation zones may have their own peculiar species and varieties of animal and insect life, as is illustrated by the summits of many mountains in the United States; here at the heights the plant life and insects are similar to those living along the shores of Hudson Bay. Toward the upper limit of growth, trees become dwarfed and sometimes assume grotesque shapes (Figure 5-14). A tree whose age is measured in centuries may stand only a few feet high, though its branches may spread widely over the ground. Such trees are buried in many feet of snow in winter and experience a growing season that lasts only a few weeks in summer.

The tree line. On some mountains the tree line will be higher on the windward side because of heavier rainfall in that quarter. Usually the tree line is lower on northern slopes of mountains in the Northern Hemisphere. This is because of the greater slant of the sun's rays on the shadier northern slope which results in less insolation and melting of snow than on the south side.

Summits of many mountains are free of tree growth. This may result from exposure to wind and to very sudden temperature changes, especially on sunny southern slopes of northern mountains. Variation in elevation of the tree line in the Alps is from 5,000 to 8,000 feet; the 3,000-foot difference is partly the result of temperature contrasts, different exposure to the sun, duration of snow cover, and amount of rainfall. Other factors include ground-water conditions, soil depth, and rate of evaporation. Even the character of the bedrock is important. Trees generally extend to higher altitudes on soils that have been formed from granite than on those formed from limestone, since the latter allow rapid seepage of ground water. Plants on mountain meadows grow quickly after the snow melts; they must mature in the brief summer and on the small amount of water that they can secure from the very pervious rocky soil. In this they resemble plants on the Arctic tundras.

Forests and Water Conservation. The relation between forests and the consumer of water is very close. A map of irrigation districts of the western United States (Figure 20-13) shows that practically all secure their water supply from forested mountains. It is well known that erosion of steep mountain slopes becomes very rapid when forests have been destroyed by fire, careless lumbering operations, or overgrazing. Increased runoff sweeps the scanty soil away, making reforestation very difficult. In addition, coarse debris may be dropped on tillable land in the valleys. Rapid runoff, by reducing the supply of ground water, may cause springs to dry up and streams to cease to flow except during intermittent floods. Examples of the terrible results of deforestation in mountains can be found in northern China and in many mountains adjoining the Mediterranean.

In the western United States, adjacent valleys—one forested and the other devastated by fire—have many times shown the expected results after heavy rains in each drainage basin; destructive floods have come from the deforested area while the forested valley has had its emergent stream remain clear and nearly normal in flow. The forest with its accumulated debris slowed the runoff and prevented erosion, and the emerging stream was relatively clear without any destructive flood; whereas in the deforested area, rainfall ran off so quickly that little water sank into the ground. In addition to flood damage, the stream was filled with coarse debris which, when deposited, covered and ruined fertile arable land along its lower course.

Snowbanks under cover of trees melt more slowly than those in treeless places, and thus they prolong the flow of streams and the period of irrigation. Profitable farming operations in deserts adjacent to mountains and in mountain valleys generally necessitate the preservation of forests. The relationship between mountains and the water resources used for power, irrigation, and municipal supply will be included in Chapter 20.

Logging costs. Forests in mountains are relatively inaccessible, and lumbering operations are somewhat more costly than on lowlands. When more accessible forest resources have been exhausted, however, supplies in mountains begin to be used. This utilization is proper if care is used in logging so that, by selection, only mature trees are cut and young growth is left as protection against excessive runoff and as a provision for future tree growth.

Agriculture.   The absence of large areas of level fertile land usually makes the problem of raising a food supply one of considerable difficulty in hills and mountains. First the most nearly level land along streams will be cleared and cultivated. Then the more level hilltops will be farmed if they are not too high, and gentler slopes on the shoulders of hills. Finally even steep hillsides, with slopes as great as 30 to 40 degrees, may be cultivated. On these slopes, erosion will be so rapid that a field will produce crops for only three or four years, then is abandoned and more land cleared. Such practices naturally result in great harm to forests and ultimately to the downstream portion of the drainage basin.

Sometimes people who need more cropland laboriously terrace mountainsides and farm narrow terraces whose soil is supported by rock walls, as in the vineyards along the slopes of the Rhine Gorge. Terraced *huertas,* as the Spaniards call their vineyards and orchards, cling to the steep Mediterranean coast near Valencia. Even primitive peoples may raise crops in remote mountains on terraces. An earlier chapter has described how certain Ma-

lay tribes in interior Luzon grow rice in this way. Little terracing has been done in the United States, primarily because this nation has great areas of land and economic pressure has not yet compelled us to use these methods of conservation.

Livestock Industry.   Lack of tillable land and considerable areas of available grassland in mountains generally encourage the livestock industry. Furthermore, animals can be driven to market over poor trails on which it is impractical to haul farm products. Cattle have another advantage in that they produce both meat and dairy products. Limiting factors in the complete utilization of mountain grasslands are the long period of winter feeding required in cold weather and the scarcity of land available for raising hay. To conserve land for hay and other crops, in many parts of Europe dairy cows are stall fed and seldom graze in pastures.

Dairying in the Alps.   Formerly, and to some extent today in the Alps, the inhabitants occupied three or four houses at various times of the year. The winter house was in a valley where animals were fed conveniently. Another house in the lower alp pastures was used in late spring, and a house in the high mountain pastures was occupied in July, August, and September (Figure 14-14). Distances from high pastures to the home village made the return of animals each day, as well as transportation of the milk itself, highly impractical. Herders and dairymen accompanied herds to the high pastures and there made the cows' and goats' milk into cheese, which was then brought down for consumption in the lowlands. This periodical movement is called *transhumance.* Some villagers remained at home to gather hay, grain, and fruit crops cultivated in the valley.

It should be noted that transhumance utilizes permanently built houses, whereas the nomad uses a portable house or tent. In modern Switzerland, immature and beef animals are taken to the mountains, but milk cows or

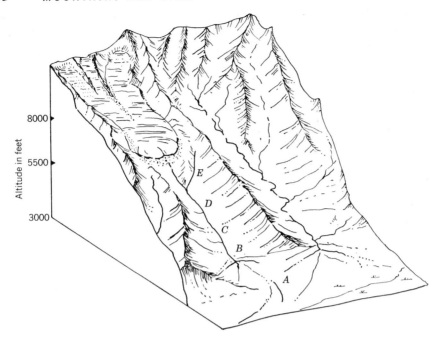

Figure 14-14   Transhumance in the western Alps.

A. *Meadow lands, pastured at all seasons. No permanent village at the lowest levels because of flood and frost threats.*

B. *Vineyards cultivated in April and May. Permanent year-round village settlements making extensive use of hydroelectric power.*

C. *Grain fields, sown with rye, oats, and a little wheat. Permanent villages. Most of the cultivation is done in May.*

D. *Villages, or* montagnettes, *occupied during June, July, and August. Small fields of potatoes are characteristic of farming at this altitude.*

E. *Temporary dwellings, or* montagnes, *occupied by mid-June. Hay is cut in the mountain meadows (alps), and grazing continues until October 1 when the cattle are returned to A. There is no agriculture or tillage at this altitude. (After R. Blanchard.)*

goats are kept at lower levels. As a result, less cheese is now made in the high Alps. Most cheese for export or consumption is produced in plants in the accessible valleys, showing how, with improvement of transportation, utilization of resources may also change.

Livestock in the western United States. In the western United States, flocks of sheep and herds of beef cattle are commonly pastured during summer in mountain meadows (Figure 14-15); in winter they feed upon available wild range and hay in the lowlands. The ani-

mals are accompanied by a few herders, whose movement represents a modified form of transhumance, without the permanent mountain hut of some European herders. This type of transhumance is common practice along the California coast south of San Francisco and Monterey, where descendants of Italian-Swiss dairymen still take cattle to upper pastures where they can find green forage during dry summers. Sheep and goats may be preferred over cattle in some mountain regions, since they utilize less nutritious herbage

Figure 14-15 Flock of sheep pastured in the Blue Mountains of eastern Oregon. This view is typical of many pasture lands and ranges throughout the semiarid western United States.

and crop the plants nearer the ground than cattle.

Tourism.　Recently it has become fashionable for lowlanders to visit mountains for health and pleasure. Large hotels and entire towns have been established to cater to summer and winter tourists and health seekers (Figure 14-16). St. Moritz, Lake Placid, Banff, Sun Valley, and Colorado Springs are a few examples. Tourists spend millions of dollars annually in Switzerland. Thousands of Swiss people earn their livings by catering to visitors. Resorts

need not be particularly high in altitude, but they must offer some special attraction derived either from the characteristics of mountain scenery or from the pleasant summer temperatures that may be found in mountains. Resorts on Mount Rainier and Mt. Hood, for example, appeal to tourists by impressive scenery, accessible glaciers, mountain forests, clear atmosphere, and cool summer temperatures.

Minerals.　Some mountains, especially those containing intrusive igneous rocks, have important mineral deposits. Others formed of sedimentary rock may contain coal. Utilization of these mineral resources may lead to development of large local centers of population in places where otherwise only a few herders might find support. Most western cities at high elevation in the mountains—Butte, Leadville, Bingham—are mining towns. Hundreds of smaller settlements are scattered through the western mountains of the United States. A mining town is generally a short-lived settlement. After a few years, or a few generations at the most, the mines are worked out and the community associated with them becomes a ghost town unless some other means of support can be developed.

Figure 14-16 Eastern face of the Teton range, Wyoming, and Jackson Lake. The pyramid peaks were shaped partly by glacial erosion. (Photograph by C. D. Walcott, used by permission of the U.S. Geological Survey.)

In Europe several mountain ranges have important mineral deposits, notably the Ural Mountains in the Soviet Union, and mountains of southern Germany. The Erz Gebirge, or Ore Mountains, along the borders of Saxony and Czechoslovakia have contributed mineral wealth to this part of Europe for several centuries although some ore deposits have been exhausted. This part of Europe, with mineral resources of less importance than formerly, is marked by many small communities from which people have emigrated to busier regions after the decline in mining. Other examples of highly mineralized mountains are the Andes of Bolivia, Chile, and Peru, many mountain ranges in Southeast Asia and Siberia, and the Rocky Mountains of the United States and western Canada. In contrast important metal deposits have not been found in the Alps, Pyrenees, and Himalayas. The subject of minerals will be discussed further in Chapter 19.

SUMMARY

Mountains are less capable than plains of supporting many people, but they do provide many resources, as well as variety of scenic features. Mountains are formed by uplift resulting from folding and faulting of the earth's crust, volcanoes and intrusions of igneous rock, and erosion of high plateaus. Depending on origin and erosion history, mountains appear as long ridges, jagged peaks, great scarps along fault planes, and jumbles of summits and valleys. The chief agents of erosion in mountains are running water and glaciers. Mountain glaciers were formerly more extensive than now and were effective agents in shaping existing surface features.

The presence of high mountains may interfere with freedom of human movement, whether by land or air. Therefore it is common practice to seek the lowest routes through rugged terrain, using passes and corridors to penetrate mountainous areas or to move across highland barriers.

In the ascent of highlands, climatic zones with successively lower temperatures correspond roughly to the climatic regions that occur at sea level in the successively higher latitudes poleward from the equator. Each of these climatic zones on mountain slopes has its appropriate type of natural vegetation and crops that can be grown until temperatures are too frosty for plants just below the snow line on the higher peaks.

Human economies in mountains and hills usually include mining, grazing, or forestry, and sometimes the generation of hydroelectric power and the tourist industry.

Hill lands, with altitudes lower than those of mountains, may show different types of economic development. Agriculture may be more practicable on hill lands if erosion of soils has not stripped slopes of their cultivable ground. Difficulties of transportation through hills and mountains often lead to conditions of isolation.

Outline

Origin of mountains
Cycle of river erosion in mountains
Mountain glaciers and characteristics
   Effects on scenic features
Mountains as barriers
   Passes and routes of travel
Occupance
Climates
   Zones of climate and vegetation
   Relation to latitude and altitude
Origin of hills
Human activities and relationships
   Transportation
Utilization of mountains and hills
   Forests, tree line
   Water conservation
   Farming, dairying, and livestock
   Touring
   Minerals

QUESTIONS

1. Compare the problems of a city built on hills with those of one located on a plain.

2. Why are most boulders in the beds of mountain streams larger than those of the lowlands?

3. Why are mountain streams generally clear of silt and mud?

4. Why is intensive cultivation of mountain slopes carried on in southern Italy and almost none in southern California?

5. In what four ways does high altitude affect climate?

6. In what parts of the world are mountain regions preferred to lowlands as places of human residence?

7. Refer to Figure 14-2, then answer these questions:

What natural agent is partly responsible for the deep dissection of the rock materials of the mountain face?

What was the source of the materials that formed the alluvial piedmont?

Is this a region capable of supporting a large population?

In what cycle of erosion do these mountains appear to be?

In what stage of development is the floor of Owens Valley?

8. After studying Figure 14-5, answer the following questions:

What is the glacier producing as it meets the sea?

What are the curving dark lines at the left of the photograph?

What is the heavy dark line extending into the distance?

If this glacier scours the land below sea level, what shore feature will result?

9. What are some of the features or characteristics of mountain regions that attract tourists or vacationists?

10. List several of the world's most important mountain passes. What regions or nations do they connect? Name a city whose location is related to the traffic through each pass.

11. What is the maximum difference in elevation on the earth's surface? What fraction or proportion of the earth's diameter does this figure represent?

12. Name the outstanding mountain ranges and the highest peaks in your state. If such elevated areas do not exist, what is the closest mountainous region to your home?

13. Account for the abundance of waterfalls in mountain streams.

14. Find out from your instructor the approximate elevation above sea level for your city, and calculate the fraction of the earth's diameter that this represents.

15. Locate the city of Quito, capital of Ecuador, and the city of Pará (Belém) near the mouth of the Amazon. You will note that the two cities are essentially in the same latitude.

Since this is true, would they experience a vertical sun at noon every day in the year?

Would they experience the same temperature at noon every day in the year?

Would they have approximately similar vegetation conditions?

Would they have noon at the same time each day?

Would their residents follow similar human economies?

SELECTED REFERENCES

Atwood W. W.: *The Rocky Mountains,* Vanguard Press, Inc., New York, 1945.

Bowman, Isaiah: *The Andes of Southern Peru,* The American Geographical Society, New York, 1916.

Gray, George W.: "Life at High Altitudes," *Scientific American,* 194:59–68, December, 1955.

Hunt, Sir John: *The Conquest of Everest,* E. P. Dutton & Co., Inc., New York, 1954.

Ives, Ronald L.: "Population Changes in a Mountain County (Grand County, Colorado), "*Economic Geography,* 18:298–306, July, 1942.

Lobeck, Armin K.: *Geomorphology: An Introduction to the Study of Landscapes,* McGraw-Hill Book Company, Inc., New York, 1939.

McConnell, W. R.: "Switzerland and Austria: A Study in the Use of Natural Environment," *Journal of Geography,* 45:337–346, December, 1946.

Peattie, Roderick: *Mountain Geography,* Harvard University Press, Cambridge, 1936.

————: *The Great Smokies and the Blue Ridge: The Story of the Southern Appalachians,* Vanguard Press, Inc., New York, 1943.

Pugh, L. G. C., and M. P. Ward: "Some Effects of High Altitude on Man," *Alpine Journal,* 61:507–520, 1957.

von Engeln, O. D.: *Geomorphology, Systematic and Regional,* The Macmillan Company, New York, 1942.

White, C. Langdon: "Storm Clouds over the Andes," *Scientific Monthly,* 70:306–316, May, 1950.

15. The Oceans

THE ocean possesses great uniformity of conditions, compared with the diversity of environment that prevails on land. It exerts much the same influence upon man all over the world wherever he comes in contact with the salt seas; there life appears to have developed first and migrated from that environment to the land.

Oceans cover three-fourths of the earth's surface, and land areas occupy only one-fourth; but without the ocean as a source of rain, life on land would be nearly impossible. Oceans present barriers to the spread of plants, animals, and man and prevent their movement to other lands far distant from their original homes, yet oceans also transport some life forms by floating in favoring cur-

rents and serve as a highway for man's vessels.

Oceans temper the climate of the lands, further the movement of commerce, and supply food, several minerals, and some raw materials for manufacture.

The sea has served as a route for the migration of man and has carried explorers and traders with new ideas and cultures to all seacoasts of the earth. It has profoundly affected the development and expansion of nations, the course of history, and the prospects of the earth's inhabitants. Yet as a whole the ocean is still one of the earth's great mysteries since its life and the features of its floor are among the least-known parts of our global environment.

OCEANOGRAPHY

The term *oceanography* is applied to the study of the oceans, their waters, and their floors.

The World Ocean. Land areas lack continuity on the earth, but the ocean completely encircles the globe and separates and surrounds the continents and islands. Parts of the ocean form enormous basins separated from each other by shallow water, broad straits, continents, and islands. The larger oceanic basins are the North and South Atlantic, the Indian, and the comparatively small Arctic, along with the big Pacific Basin. The so-called Antarctic Ocean is merely the waters south of the Pacific, Indian, and Atlantic Oceans surrounding the continent of Antarctica; it does not occupy an oceanic depression. This southern ocean, however, forms the only continuous band of water encircling the earth without change of latitude.

According to the usual separation of the world ocean, the five seas cover some 142 million square miles, of which nearly half is included in the Pacific. Most of the rest of the waters are included in the Atlantic and Indian Oceans. Some 10 million square miles consists of water that has spilled over onto the continental margins, covering the land to a depth of a few hundred feet. A gradually sloping platform, the continental shelf, extends out until the ocean bed begins to deepen rapidly in its drop to the oceanic depths.

Sometimes offshore islands, projecting peninsulas, and other irregularities of coast line partially separate seas from the main oceans. Such seas characterize much of the coasts of Europe, Asia, and eastern Middle America. Examples include the Mediterranean Sea, Gulf of Mexico, and Bering Sea. The ocean contains enough water to cover the entire surface of the earth to a depth of about 2 miles. However, since land is exposed on about one-fourth of the earth's surface, the actual depth of the ocean averages about 2½ miles.

The most profound ocean depths occur in elongated troughs called *deeps,* which are generally parallel to and not far distant from recently uplifted mountainous coasts or chains of islands. The uplift of the land and depression of the sea floor may be associated in origin. Some geologists hold that the depression of the oceanic deep is preliminary to the process of mountain-building. Deeps in the Pacific lie off Japan, south of the Aleutian Islands, east of the Philippines, east of Guam, and near the Tonga Islands. Depths exceeding 6 miles have been recorded east of the Philippines and off the island of Guam. In the Atlantic the greatest depth is about 5 miles, located in a trough north of Puerto Rico.

Centers of ocean basins are never as deep as troughs lying comparatively near the shores. About midway in the Atlantic Ocean the Mid-Atlantic Ridge extends from the North Atlantic to the South Atlantic for a length of several thousand miles. Large underwater platforms on which water is much shallower than in most of the ocean are called *submarine plateaus.* The relief of the ocean floor is far from being uniform. Nevertheless, although explorations on the floor of the ocean have found many irregularities it is generally thought to be smoother than the exposed surface of the land. Volcanic eruptions and folding of rocks produce large inequalities on the ocean floor. Sometimes canyons and other erosion forms developed on land are submerged subsequently below the sea. Thus the Hudson River channel continues below sea level toward the edge of the continental shelf. Many oceanic canyons also exist off the California coast, and flat-topped submarine peaks called *seamounts* occur in numbers in the Pacific.

Sediment brought by rivers and other agents from the continents is usually deposited near shore in shallow waters of the continental shelf. The material is well sorted by the water; coarse debris is dropped near shore, and successively finer sediment is carried outward toward deeper water. Continental shelves, especially the shallow areas called "banks," are favored places for multitudes of fish. The ocean bottom in deep water receives little but oozes composed mainly of the remains of marine animals and plants.

Chemicals. Ocean water contains some of practically every material found on land. Even millions of pounds of gold are said to exist in sea water in a very finely divided state. Common salt is the most abundant dissolved substance, over 14 million billion tons of it existing in solution. This is sufficient salt to make a layer 400 feet thick over the earth. Much lime carbonate is brought into the sea by rivers, but it is steadily absorbed to make the shells and skeletons of sea life, so that the percentage of the substance in the oceans is much smaller than that of salt. Ocean water always contains some air, the coldest water usually containing the most, since solubility of gases decreases with increase of temperature. This dissolved air provides oxygen for all sea life except some large mammals like whales and seals.

Pressure.   Sea water has a slightly greater density than fresh water because of its mineral content. One cubic foot of sea water weighs about 64 pounds, compared with 62½ pounds for fresh water. Pressures in ocean depths become enormous. Pressure at a depth of one mile exceeds one ton per square inch, and at the greatest depth the pressure is nearly six tons for every square inch. These great pressures do not affect sea life, since external pressure is balanced by the internal pressure of organisms. A deep-sea fish brought rapidly to the surface, however, is distorted by expansion of its internal air made possible by reduced pressure. Likewise any body not perfectly solid lowered to the depths of the

ocean, would be compressed into the smallest possible space. Inasmuch as water is practically incompressible, density of water on the bottom of the ocean is little more than that at the surface. Hence any object that is heavier than water at the surface will sink to the bottom of the sea.

Temperature.   The surface temperature of ocean water varies with latitude, being about 80°F near the equator. At 40° north or south latitude it has an average temperature of nearly 60°F and is near freezing in polar regions. Since water increases in density with decrease in temperature (to a few degrees of its freezing point), water on the bottom of the sea is near the temperature of greatest density for salt water and averages from 30 to 40°F from polar to equatorial regions. Vertical movements of ocean water result from differences in temperature, cold water sinking and forcing the lighter warm water to rise. If a nearly enclosed sea has a shallow entrance like that of the Mediterranean or the Red Sea, no cold water can enter below the temperature at the depth of the entrance. Therefore temperatures on the bottoms of these seas are no colder than the water which enters the shallow straits of Gibraltar or Bab el Mandeb.

OCEAN CURRENTS

Although the absolute cause of ocean currents has not been definitely agreed upon, they probably result from movements of water caused by the drag exerted by prevailing winds, combined with effects of the earth's rotation and the position of land masses which deflect them. Vertical movements of ocean water may result from temperature changes, evaporation, and influx of fresh water from rivers and other sources. Lateral movements of sea water, which make up the greatest oceanic currents, seem to be the result of the trade winds and prevailing westerlies (Figure 15-1).

Both the northeast and southeast trades cause ocean currents and by their steady

movements set up a slow drift of water toward the equator, flowing at a rate of perhaps 25 miles a day. Rotation of the earth causes both winds and ocean currents to be deflected to the right in the Northern Hemisphere and to the left in the Southern Hemisphere. As the equator is approached, the wind blows nearly from the east, and the currents drift westward until they reach a continental land mass. Then the equatorial drift is deflected away from the equator by the position of the continent and by rotation of the earth. It then moves north or south into the prevailing westerlies which blow the waters eastward until another continental mass is reached. There

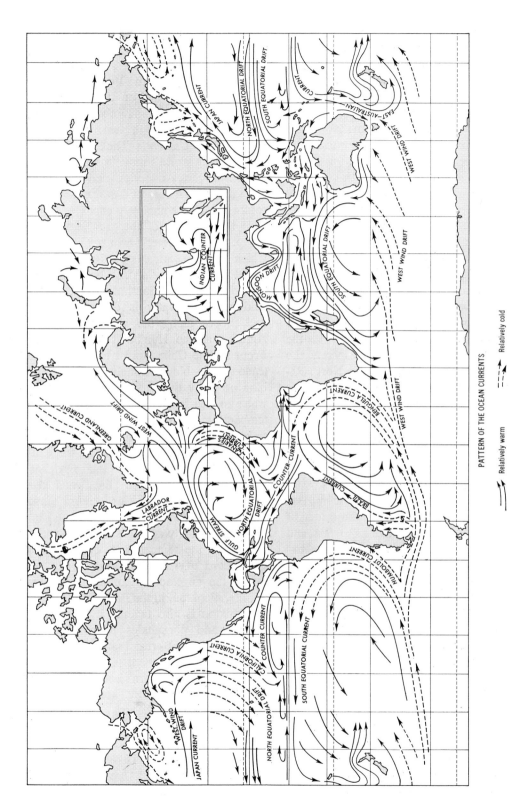

PATTERN OF THE OCEAN CURRENTS

Relatively warm   Relatively cold

Figure 15-1 Pattern of the ocean currents.

the earth's rotation, deflecting objects to the right or to the left, combines with the outline of the continent to deflect the currents equatorward back to the trade winds which provide renewed energy to keep up the oceanic drift.

In the Northern Hemisphere, the North Atlantic and North Pacific Drifts move in a clockwise direction; in the Southern Hemisphere, the motion of the South Atlantic, South Pacific, and South Indian ocean drifts is counterclockwise.

In both hemispheres water moves from east to west in the trade winds and from west to east in the prevailing westerlies. These ocean drifts are gigantic eddies, thousands of miles in extent, around which water is moved with a velocity of perhaps 10 to 25 miles per day. Sometimes special names are applied to parts of these drifts. The Japan Current in the northern Pacific, for example, is merely the northern and western portion of the North Pacific Drift. This part of the drift is warm because the water comes from equatorial regions, where it was warmed as it flowed for a distance of nearly a thousand miles beneath the tropical sun. A floating object might take from one to two years to complete the circuit of the North Pacific Drift.

In the North Atlantic Drift, a comparatively calm area that occurs near the center of the big eddy is called the Sargasso Sea and was described by Columbus and other explorers. Seaweed and other floating objects are somewhat more abundant in the Sargasso Sea than in the ocean currents, but most of the popular tales concerning this "sea" have little basis in fact.

Cold Currents. Where winds blow offshore, the surface water, which is warmer than that in the depths, is carried away, allowing colder water to well up in its place. The cold temperature of continents along leeward coasts comes partly from the cold currents. These are chilled by the rise of cold water from below as well as by an actual movement of cold surface water from polar regions. Thus in the latitudes of the trade winds we have cold currents on the west coasts of continents, as the California Current off that state, the Canaries Current off northwestern Africa, the Benguela Current off Southwest Africa, and off the southwest coast of South America, the Humboldt or Peru Current (both names are in use).

The Peru Current. The Peru Current is probably the world's most important cold current. Between Antarctica and the southern extremities of Africa and South America, the southern ocean completely encircles the earth. This is the realm of the "roaring forties" in the prevailing westerly winds (Figure 15-1), which set up an eastward-moving current called the *west wind drift*. When this impinges on the continent of South America, part of the cold southern water is deflected northward and moves along the west coast of South America as the Humboldt or Peru Current. From middle Chile almost to the equator the trade winds blow strongly offshore and by blowing away the surface waters, allow cold water to rise from the depths. Hence the low temperature of this region, considering its latitude, results from the effects of this cold current. It extends north as far as the equator, bathing the shores of the Galápagos Islands, which lie exactly on the "line," and keeping temperatures of those islands more moderate than tropical.

Since solubility of a gas in water varies inversely as the temperature, cold water contains more oxygen than warm water, which favors the development of abundant floating sea life, plankton, in the Peru Current. Growth of plankton is also favored by abundance of nitrates and phosphates in cold up-welling water. Myriads of crustaceans and other small sea creatures feed on plankton, and vast schools of fish in turn feed on the smaller creatures. Attracted by abundant fish and other food, sea birds and sea lions abound along the western shores of South America. Many birds nest on small desert islands off the coast of Peru (Figure 16-11), where through centuries their refuse has accumulated to depths of more than a hundred feet, slowly forming a material called *guano*. This guano contains a high percentage of phosphates and nitrates and is very valuable fertilizer. During a half century, Peru sold 375 million dollars' worth of guano to world markets. The birds are now well protected in their nesting places, and guano beds are worked only at intervals of several years, with precautions taken to protect the wealth-producing flocks which probably are the most valuable wild marine birds in the world.

The Benguela Current. The Benguela Current off southwestern Africa closely resembles the Peru Current. Both are cold, both are south of the equator and flow northward to within a few degrees of the line, and both are located off a desert coast. In both currents are found islands to which birds resort and deposit guano, though the African deposits were not well protected and are no longer highly productive. The influence of these currents in lowering coastal temperatures is similar; the port of Swakopmund in Southwest Africa has an average temperature ranging from 55°F in September to 63°F in March and is reported as having the lowest average temperature for its latitude in the world (Figure 15-2).

Cold currents in the westerlies. In the prevailing westerlies, cold currents hug eastern coasts of continents partly because the rotation of the earth deflects anything moving toward the equator to the west. The best known of these currents is the southward-flowing Labrador Current off northeastern North America, and the Kamchatka Current off Siberia. A similar stream, the Falkland Current, is found on the eastern coast of South America off Argentina, but Africa does not extend far enough south to have such a current.

In both the Labrador Current and the Kamchatka Current abundant plankton and associated food are available for fish. Some of the most important fishing grounds in the world are along the banks of Newfoundland and near Japan and the Siberian coast. The Labrador Current by bringing floating ice-

bergs south from the glaciers of Greenland endangers shipping lanes from America to Western Europe. Danger from icebergs is increased by the prevalence of fogs near the contact of the cold Labrador Current and the warm Gulf Stream.

Warm Currents. *The Gulf Stream.* The Gulf Stream is the most famous and important warm current on earth. A curious fact about this current extending across the North Atlantic is that much water of the Gulf Stream actually comes from the South Atlantic Ocean. The southeast trades cause a drift of water toward equatorial South America, and this drift is divided by the angle of South America made by Cape São Roque, part of the water

Figure 15-2 Climatic graph for Swakopmund, Southwest Africa. A low-latitude trade-wind desert station where temperatures are modified by the presence of a cool ocean current off-shore.

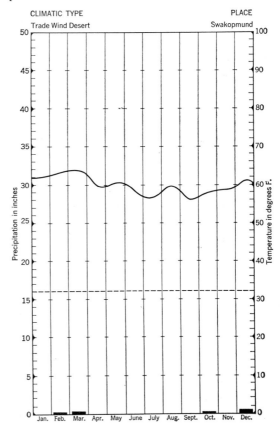

being deflected northward across the equator into the Caribbean Sea. From here it flows into the Gulf of Mexico and finally out through the Straits of Florida into the Atlantic Ocean. The narrow channel between Cuba and Florida acts like the nozzle of a hose and forces the water to flow swiftly through it with a velocity as high as 4 or 5 miles per hour.

On leaving the Straits of Florida, the Gulf Stream is several hundred feet deep and about a hundred miles wide. Flowing northeasterly toward Europe, it spreads out and finally divides, one portion turning east to join the North Atlantic Drift off Europe. Another part continues northward along the coast of Norway to the Kola Peninsula and Murmansk coast of the Soviet Union, keeping those coasts ice-free in winter even within the Arctic Circle. Still another branch wanders off toward Iceland and disappears in Arctic seas. The warm Gulf Stream modifies the temperature of northwestern Europe in winter, although the

land there would have a mild oceanic climate anyway since it lies on a windward coast in the prevailing westerlies. Nevertheless the Gulf Stream raises the average winter temperature in Western Europe at least a few degrees. Off the United States the edge of the Gulf Stream is well defined by a "cold wall," and water temperatures may change by 10 degrees within a mile or two.

Warm currents in the oceanic drifts. Warm currents exist where the drifting water comes from the tropics into naturally colder regions. The warm current loses heat from the water as it moves into colder climates; but because it is warmer by contrast than the usual surface temperatures for poleward latitudes, it will be called a warm current. The Japan Current and Brazil Current are examples, and the former is really the northern part of the North Pacific Drift. Conversely, a cold current in the tropics may be warmer than a warm current toward the polar seas.

TIDES

Cause of Tides. Although tides can be entirely explained only with the aid of higher mathematics, the gravitational effect of the moon is an important factor in causing tides. The side of the earth toward the moon is nearer that body than the rest of the earth. Since the moon's gravitational pull is greater on the side toward it than for the rest of the earth, water tends to move toward the moon. On the opposite side of the earth, the effect of the gravitational pull of the moon is less than for any other portion of the earth because of greater distance to the moon; hence there is a tendency to pull the earth away from the water on the far side, producing another "bulge," or tide wave (Figure 15-3).

In reality high tides rarely coincide with the greatest altitude of the moon. This results both from the configuration of the coasts, and from the fact that tides move from the horizontal pull of the moon and that the sideways pull is zero when that body is overhead. That is, tidal movements, or the ebb and flow of tides, re-

sult from the horizontal rather than the vertical component of the moon's gravitational force of attraction.

Tide periods. Since tides result mainly from the attraction of the moon, periods between high tides are controlled by the revolution of our satellite. During half the time from moonrise to moonset, about twelve hours and twenty-five minutes, there is a tidal surge in one direction until the moon passes the vertical and the horizonal force ceases; then the surge begins in the opposite direction. Ideally, along a coast for six hours and twelve minutes the tide flows, and then for an equal length of time it ebbs. However, coastal configuration plays an important role in the movement and times of tides.

On a globe covered entirely with water, the two waves would follow the movements of the moon. Modification of tides results from continents and islands which cause deflection of tides and may also change the time of high and low tides so that flow and ebb do not correspond with the theoretical periods. Tides require a large body of water in which to develop. Even the Great Lakes are too small for the tidal range to exceed 2 inches.

Because the moon rises about fifty minutes later each day, high tides are separated in theory by twelve hours and twenty-five minutes in time. This time interval holds approximately for the Atlantic Ocean. In some other parts of the world like the North Pacific coasts, the flood tide meets the ebb tide in such a way that they cancel each other. In still other places the two crests coincide to make one high tide, and the two troughs join making one low tide each day. All kinds of mixed tides and gradations occur. Between the two extreme types of twice each day and once each day, all kinds of mixed tides and gradations occur. Some localities, like Tahiti, have practically no tides.

Spring and neap tides. The sun modifies the effect of the moon on tides. The two bodies act together during new and full moon to cause spring tides of greatest range. During the first and third lunar quarters, however, they act at right angles to each other, the sun neutralizing part of the effect of the moon, and neap tides result, with a minimum range from high to low tide. Though the sun has the mass of 26 million moons and gravity depends directly on the masses involved, the moon has over twice the effect of the sun in producing tides because the moon is only about one three-hundred-and-eightieth as far from the earth as the sun is.

Effects of Tides. When tides enter a long shallow estuary that narrows inland, water piles up higher toward the head of the bay, thus causing a great range between high and low tide. This occurs in the Bay of Fundy, with an extreme tidal range of 50 feet, and at Cook Inlet, Alaska, which experiences a tidal range of 40 feet. Large tidal ranges in a harbor make it so difficult for ships to load cargoes that floating docks become necessary. When tides enter a bottle-shaped bay like those at San Francisco or Liverpool, the water spreads out and the height of the tide is reduced from that on the coast outside the bay.

Height, character, and time of the tides obviously affect the availability of inlets for navigation. Tides increase the depth of water in shallow harbors and over the shallow entrances of some harbors, thus making ports available during high tide; they scour out entrances of inlets, remove wastes dumped into the sea from cities, distribute mud and silt brought to the ocean by rivers, modify the contour of shore lines, and affect the human

Figure 15-3 The tides. When the moon and sun are aligned on the same side of the earth, as in A, or when they are on opposite sides of the earth, as in B, they cause spring tides. Tidal conditions shown in B follow those of A by about two weeks. The moon is nearer the earth than the sun; hence its tidal effect is about double that of the sun despite their disparity in size. Conditions that prevail when low, or neap, tides occur are shown in C, when the sun and moon affect the earth from different directions. About two weeks after the position shown in C, the moon will be on the opposite side of the earth, and neap tides will be repeated.

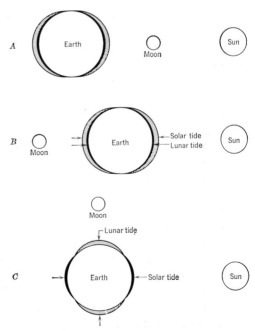

use of coasts in many other ways. Thus far little practical use has been made of tidal power, although development of hydroelectricity would be possible at certain places of large tidal range, like Passamaquoddy Bay in northeastern Maine.

SUMMARY

Oceans serve as convenient and economical routes for shipment of goods. They also greatly modify temperatures of the lands, especially on windward coasts, and supply most of the rain that falls. Conditions within the seas themselves —warm or cold currents, tides, and waves—may retard or advance the use of the sea by man. Fisheries for food and other materials are locally important.

Circulation of the ocean water is started as a drift by the prevailing westerlies and trade winds. Then the currents are deflected by the continents which bar them and further deflected by the rotation of the earth. The net result is a huge clockwise moving eddy in the North Atlantic and North Pacific Oceans; the corresponding eddy in the South Atlantic, Pacific and Indian Oceans circulates counterclockwise. Cold and warm currents are significant factors in modifying coastal climates.

The tides, caused primarily by the attractions of the moon and sun, are important along coasts where they affect many human activities.

Outline
Oceans and their extent
  Human relationships
  Deposits and chemicals
  Pressures and temperature
Ocean currents
  Origin
  Cold currents: Peru, Labrador, etc.
  Warm currents: Gulf Stream, Japan, etc.
Tides
  Cause and characteristics
  Effects

QUESTIONS

1. Name some seafoods that are available in local markets, and investigate their probable domestic and foreign sources.

2. Why do ocean trade routes often converge at the mouths of large rivers?

3. Since a great-circle route is the shortest distance between terminal points on the globe, why do some shipping routes diverge from this preferred course?

4. What determines whether a current is called "warm" or "cold"?

5. After you have studied Figure 15-1 answer the following questions:

Why are floats from Japanese fishing nets sometimes found on the coast of Oregon?

Is the Gulf Stream moving in a clockwise or a counterclockwise direction? Why?

Why are no ocean currents indicated in the Mediterranean Sea?

Why are bottles cast adrift off the coast of California sometimes found on the beaches of Luzon?

6. Why was it easier for Columbus to reach the West Indies than Cape Cod?

7. What part of the world is most affected by the temperatures of the Gulf Stream?

8. Why are isotherms affected less by ocean currents in the Southern Hemisphere than they are in the Northern Hemisphere?

9. Why are the cold Labrador and Kamchatka Currents on the eastern sides of continents, whereas the Peru Current, also cold, is on the western side of South America?

10. Why is sea water salty?

11. How do tides make it easier for shipping to use harbors? In most harbors, how great a tidal range is regarded as satisfactory?

12. By whom are tide tables regularly used?

SELECTED REFERENCES

Barnett, Lincoln: "The Miracle of the Sea," *Life,* 34:58–80, Feb. 9, 1953.

————: "Creatures of the Sea," *Life,* 35:79–106, Nov. 30, 1953.

————: "The Coral Reef," *Life,* 36:74–83, Feb. 8, 1954.

Bauer, H. A.: "A World Map of Tides," *Geographical Review,* 25:259–270, April, 1933.

Blanchard, W. O.: "The Narrow Seas," *Journal of Geography,* 50:221–230, September, 1951.

Carson, Rachel: *The Sea Around Us,* Oxford University Press, New York, 1951.

————: *The Edge of the Sea,* Houghton Mifflin Company, Boston, 1955.

Coker, R. E.: *The Great and Wide Sea,* University of North Carolina Press, Chapel Hill, 1947.

Douglas, John Scott: *The Story of the Oceans,* F. Muller, London, 1953.

Jones, O. T.: "The Floor of the Ocean," *Geographical Journal,* 103:125–128, March, 1944.

Marmer, H. A.: *The Tide,* Appleton-Century-Crofts, Inc., New York, 1926.

————: *The Sea,* Appleton-Century-Crofts, Inc., New York, 1930.

National Research Council: *Physics of the Earth,* vol. V, *Oceanography,* National Academy of Sciences Bulletin 85, Washington, 1932.

Ryther, John H.: "The Sargasso Sea," *Scientific American,* 194:98–104, January, 1956.

Sverdrup, H. U.: *Oceanography for Meteorologists,* Prentice-Hall, Inc., Englewood Cliffs, N.J., 1942.

————, M. W. Johnson, and R. H. Fleming: *The Oceans: Their Physics, Chemistry and General Biology,* Prentice-Hall, Inc., Englewood Cliffs, N.J., 1942.

Whitney, P. C.: "Elementary Facts about the Tide," *Journal of Geography,* 34:102–108, March, 1935.

Williamson, J. A.: *The Ocean in English History,* Oxford University Press, New York, 1942.

16. Coast Lines and Islands

COASTS are zones of transition from land to sea, and they partake of the characteristics of both environments. Coastal inhabitants are simultaneously attracted and repelled by the sea. Natives in need of food are attracted because of fish, shellfish, and other marine life. These may provide a more certain and abundant food supply than that which is afforded inland, if the land is barren of wildlife or too mountainous for farming. Lacking seaworthy craft, men were at first frightened by the rough open sea and had to learn seamanship in calm waters of protected bays and harbors. After learning how to build safer boats, they ventured farther into the ocean and finally developed into capable seafaring people.

Waves and Their Work. Waves cause erosion along shore lines, make deposits along or near shores, affect the use of ports by shipping, and are of concern to the fishing industry and many other human activities. Waves sometimes damage ships at sea, but their most effective locale is along the shores. To a less degree the shores of lakes are affected also by wave work.

Waves are caused by frictional drag of wind on the water surface and move in the same direction as the wind. Only the waveform advances, the water particles themselves merely moving in small orbits. Thus a floating object allows waves to pass underneath as it rises and falls.

In shallows, the bottom of a wave is slowed by friction and its crest advances faster. The crest overturns and rolls forward to form surf or breakers. The *swash* resulting from forward motion of the water carries sand and gravel, which are forceful tools for shore erosion at the base of cliffs. Underneath the breakers is

Figure 16-1 Wave erosion along the coast of Kelley's Island in Lake Erie has produced these steep cliffs and the balanced rock and the cave. (Photograph by the Ohio Department of Highways.)

the backwash or "undertow" made by water pouring back down the sloping beach. This backwash transports material from the shores out into the sea where the load may be deposited. Also effective on exposed cliffs are direct blows delivered by great compression and expansion of air in cliff-face cavities. Constant motion of water on the beach causes sand and stones to rub together, quickly rounding angular fragments and ultimately wearing away even the hardest rocks.

Most work of erosion along coasts is done by big waves which crash onto shores during great storms. Wave erosion is most effective on exposed islands, cliffs, and headlands. In narrow channels, currents often effectively aid waves in the work of erosion.

Wave erosion is particularly rapid on some coasts (Figure 16-1), especially where the earth materials have small resistance. At Cape Cod and along the chalk cliffs of England, the shore line retreats several feet each year from attacks by waves. It has been estimated that

the southern shore of Lake Erie has retreated on the average about 6 feet each year under the wave battering it receives during storm periods. Wave erosion develops steep cliffs and in bedrock erodes picturesque wave-carved caves and arches (Figure 16-2). *Stacks* or chimneylike rocks of resistant material are left offshore as the shore line retreats. Waves cut inland most rapidly where rocks are weakest, or where the waves and currents work most effectively. This differential erosion may create many little coves.

Along protected coves, across entrances of calm bays, and in quiet waters generally, longshore currents tend to deposit debris eroded from exposed locations. The net effect of waves and currents is to destroy projections along coasts and to deposit much of the eroded material in calm waters between headlands. The resulting bar or barrier beach may separate the bay between the headlands from the ocean, thus forming a lagoon. If strong currents are present, the bar will grow across the

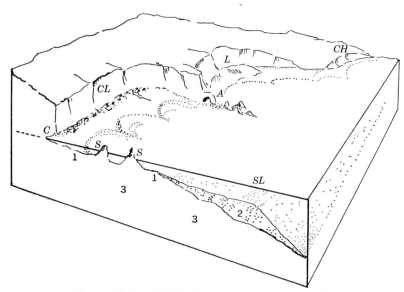

Figure 16-2   A high shore line of erosion, with its associated features: SL, *sea level, 1, wave-eroded terrace, 2, wave-deposited terrace, 3, bedrock;* S,S, *chimneys or stacks,* C, *seacave,* CL, *wave-cut sea cliff,* A, *arched rock,* L, *landslide where waves undercut cliff;* CH, *cliffed headland.*

bay principally in the direction that the current moves (Figure 16-3*C*). In the course of time a lagoon may be filled with silt and plant remains, forming first a tidal marsh and then solid ground (Figure 16-3*C*).

Offshore bars develop where storm waves break on low-lying coasts. Along the Carolina and Texas shore line these offshore deposits form long, narrow islands. Between the sandy islands and the mainland are large "sounds" or lagoons. Charts of coastal waters must be revised every few years because of shifting coast lines produced by wave erosion and formation of bars in new locations.

Shallow coastal waters, often located in large lagoons, sounds, estuaries, and bays, frequently afford excellent feeding grounds for fish and shellfish.

Deposits along coasts supplement the effect of erosion in modifying coast lines. Waves sort material well, leaving boulders on the beaches in swift water, "shingle" in less swift water, then sand, and finally mud. Offshore the same sorting action occurs. Hence near the coast the moving water drops the coarse material, farther out the sand, then the silt and mud; and finally the smallest particles of limy ooze reach the ocean floor. When these sorted materials become consolidated, the sedimentary rocks —conglomerate, sandstone, shale, and limestone—are formed in that order outward from shore. The combined effect of erosion and deposition along coasts is to develop a gentle slope partly above and partly below the usual sea level. If the land then rises relative to the sea, the old sea bottom forms an ocean terrace.

COAST LINES

Coast lines are generally of two contrasting types. Where land has risen or emerged relative to the sea, coast lines usually are regular and there are few good harbors. Where land has sunk or submerged relative to the sea, coasts are "drowned" and are very irregular in form (Figure 16-3*B*).

Emergent or Regular Coasts.   Rising coasts may be high and steep where uplift of land has been rapid but are low and generally sandy where uplift was slow and of less degree. Sandy coasts, incidentally, provide excellent bathing beaches which have enjoyed great development as summer resorts during the last half century. Atlantic City, Deauville, and Biarritz are examples of popular seaside cities. Expansion of highways and increased use of the automobile largely account for growth of beach resorts.

Pauses of considerable length may occur during the process of uplift of coasts. Then the beaches and wave-cut terraces formed at a former sea level are elevated. These raised ocean terraces are striking features of some elevated coasts (Figure 16-4). An example is the coast of Oregon where ocean terraces appear at different heights like giant steps cut on the face of mountains.

Drowned or Submerged Coasts.   When land sinks below sea level, the valleys become sounds, straits, or inlets. Isolated hills become islands; ridges form peninsulas. A "drowned" coast has an abundance of harbors. Coasts of New England, Chesapeake Bay, and Puget Sound, and most coasts in Western Europe represent examples of submerged coasts. Their protected waters provide superior places for learning the handling of boats, and irregular coasts are, therefore, training grounds and homes of fishermen and sailors. "Drowning" of the lowland during past geologic time may leave so little land suitable for tillage that few opportunities for farming are available. To make a living, men often are forced to turn to the sea.

Mountainous coasts that have been strongly glaciated may have many fiords. These are coastal valleys that appear to have been over-deepened by ice erosion below sea level and then invaded by ocean water when the glacier melted. Some fiords penetrate many miles into the mountains (Figure 12-8). Fiord coasts are found in Norway, Alaska, southwestern New Zealand, and southern Chile. Cliff walls of fiords are generally bare rock with very little soil and usually so steep that cultivation is

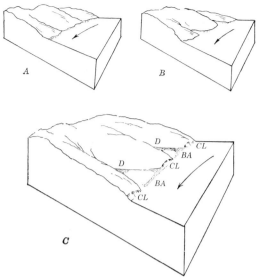

Figure 16-3   Coastal modification by erosion and deposition: A, original unmodified shore line; B, submergence and "drowning" of stream mouths and coastal lowlands, forming estuaries; C, advanced shore line condition, with deltas (D) *deposited in estuaries, wave-cut sea cliffs* (CL), *and bars* (BA) *deposited by ocean currents across estuaries. Arrow shows direction of ocean current.*

impossible; even forest growth is difficult. Only limited amounts of land for cultivation are supplied by occasional gentler slopes and the fans and deltas formed by torrential streams. Farming on Norway's coast and in southeastern Alaska is greatly handicapped by this lack of any considerable area of farmland. Frequently the largest stream tributary to a fiord enters at its head and there sediment is deposited to form a delta. Fishing villages in fiords are often built near the head rather than the mouth of the fiords. This permits inhabitants to build on more level land and affords a better chance to supplement fishing by gardening and dairying.

Where mountain ridges descend into the ocean at nearly right angles to the coast, a *ria* coast develops. These inlets somewhat resemble fiords, but are unglaciated. The word ria comes from this type of coast in northwestern Spain at El Ferrol, Vigo, and other ports. The eastern side of the Adriatic Sea has a similar

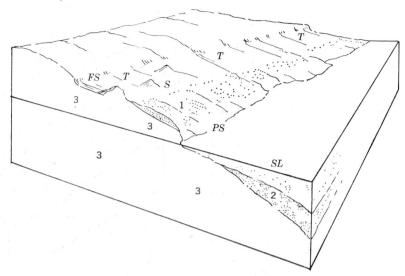

Figure 16-4 Uplifted ocean terrace an emergent coast: T, *raised terrace,* S, *stacks,* FS, *former shore,* PS, *present shore;* SL *level of sea,* 1, *raised wave-deposited terrace,* 2, *submerged wave-deposited terrace,* 3, *bedrock.*

coast. Rias usually form splendid protected harbors, but access inland may be so difficult over the mountains that fine harbors support only insignificant villages.

HARBORS AND SEAPORTS

Although harbors and ports are both situated on coasts, they have distinct meanings. *Harbors* are places of shelter for ships. *Seaports* are the city sites used by ships. Ports, where feasible, utilize harbors, and the largest seaport cities are generally located on good harbors. If there are products to ship and no harbor is available, however, a port may be located in places with very little protection. Such landing places are called *roadsteads*.

Origin of Harbors. Harbors may be formed in many different ways. Besides the harbors of "drowned" coasts, the fiords and rias aforementioned, harbors may result from deposition. Sand bars, when built above sea level by the work of wave and wind, may partly enclose a lagoon which will form a harbor. The cities of Erie on Lake Erie, Duluth on Lake Superior, Port Angeles in Washington, and San Diego in California occupy this type of harbor site. Spits, hooks, and barrier beaches have formed other harbors like Provincetown, Galveston, Miami, and Durban. Coral reefs may constitute the protecting barrier, as in the harbors of Honolulu, Hawaii; Suva, Fiji; and certain coral atolls in the South Pacific. Lava flows and glacial moraines have at times created barriers that protect harbors. Sometimes volcanic craters form deep landlocked harbors when one side is breached by wave erosion, as at Pago Pago in Samoa, or when land has sunk, flooding the crater, as Aden in the southwest Arabian Peninsula and Christchurch, New Zealand. Sometimes a block of the earth's crust sinks below sea level. Some of the best harbors have been formed in this manner, including San Francisco and Rio de Janeiro. Offshore islands may protect a harbor from excessive wave action, as at Boston and Los Angeles. River mouths make good harbors (Figure 16-5), and often afford easy access to the interior unless the river has sand bars or a delta that may interfere with navi-

Figure 16-5   Waterfront scene in the harbor of Portsmouth, New Hampshire. This port on a glacially scoured coast formerly handled much of New England's shipping; today it is a favorite spot of tourists. (Photograph by Douglas Armsden.)

gation. Philadelphia, New Orleans, Shanghai, and London are among many examples of seaport cities near mouths of rivers.

Functions of Seaports.   Seaports have varied functions. Some like Southampton and Cherbourg are primarily passenger ports. Others are naval bases like Portsmouth; Toulon, France; Bremerton, Washington; and Pearl Harbor, Hawaii. A few cater to pleasure cruises like Hamilton, Bermuda, or Nassau, Bahamas. Some are ferry terminals, like Key West, Florida, or Calais, France. Major cities like New York, Hamburg or Marseille are dual-purpose ports for passengers and freight. However, the business of most seaports is the transfer of freight between land and ocean routes. Passengers may be served, but are generally subordinate to the handling of freight.

The business of many ports is primarily the export of raw materials. Examples include Abadan, Iran, which ships petroleum; Coos Bay, Oregon, lumber and paper; Narvik, Norway, iron ore; and Tampa, Florida, phosphate rock.

General-cargo ports handle a great variety of goods including manufactures, semiprocessed commodities, foodstuffs, and raw materials. Valuable goods are packaged and a cargo will be composed of a great many different articles. Cheap materials move in bulk, often in entire shiploads.

Entrepôt ports receive goods from other seaports and distribute them to other markets. Commodities may come by shipload or carload and go out in broken lots or less than a carload. London is such a great entrepôt; it receives goods from all over the world and ships them to almost every seaport. Hong Kong is another example. To lessen the formalities involved in import duties some ports have a section called a "free port" where goods are stored. If reexported they pay no duty, but if sold for domestic use the required duty is collected. Hamburg has a successful free port.

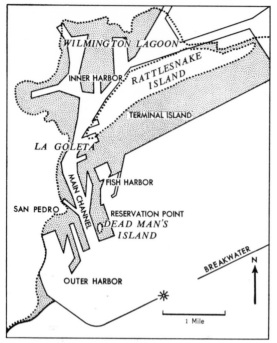

Figure 16-6   Los Angeles harbor in 1868 (dotted lines and italicized names) and in 1956 (solid lines). Note the extensive changes brought about by human activity. Filled land, largely from dredged material, is indicated by stippling.

Importance of the Hinterland.   Usefulness of harbors is in direct proportion to the productiveness of their hinterlands. A good harbor alone is not sufficient for development of a great seaport. To be most useful a harbor must be needed for the movement of goods. Magnificent harbors in Alaska, in Labrador, and in southern Chile are little used because their hinterlands are undeveloped, lack resources, or are not readily accessible, and hence produce little for export. On the other hand, coasts without any good harbors will be provided with seaports if important quantities of goods are to be shipped out. Under these conditions, breakwaters will be built. Shallow bays will be dredged to create harbors like that of Los Angeles, which originally was merely an anchorage. Dredging and the addition of breakwaters and piers made an artificial harbor (Figure 16-6) that completely altered the original character of the shore line.

Even the great port of Buenos Aires is largely artificial.

Where no harbor exists ships remain offshore from the landing place (roadstead). Goods and passengers move to and from the port by lighters or rowboats. At the poorest locations they are landed through the surf onto the beach without the use of a wharf. Roadsteads are dangerous for ships in storms because they offer no protection from winds and waves. Examples are found on coasts of northern Chile and western Peru, the east coast of Madagascar, the coast of Patagonia, and the anchorage off Nome, Alaska. Generally the landing selected has access to the interior by some valley or pass that governs the natural trade route. For example, the regular coast line of western Africa has few harbors; hence ships must use roadsteads where landings are made near accessible routes inland.

If a great city is to develop as a seaport, the character of its hinterland is of more importance than the quality of its harbor. It is possible to change the physical character of the harbor, but it is almost impossible to make major changes in the type of products that the hinterland provides for export. The largest cities in existence, New York and London, have excellent harbors combined with first-class communication with rich and extensive hinterlands.

Coasts with poor hinterlands.   If coasts are isolated or unhealthy, lacking ports for trade or otherwise difficult of access, inhabitants may be little affected by proximity of the sea. The Arctic coast of Canada and Siberia, the Mosquito Coast of Central America, and the whole of northern Australia are examples of relatively poor coasts.

The Baltic states are wooded, swampy, cold countries with poor soils and few resources except timber. These coastal areas, to the Slavs, were less attractive for farming than more fertile areas inland, and they were left for a time to the Finns, Letts, Estonians, and Lithuanians. Later, however, when Russia felt the need for better outlets to the Baltic Sea, political control over much of the coastal area was secured.

Pirate coasts. Where people could not produce goods to exchange for food and other supplies, or where the location was unproductive or poor for trade, the inhabitants sometimes turned to piracy when population outgrew facilities for earning a living. Certain mountain coasts—the eastern shore of the Adriatic Sea and the hilly coast of Liguria (west of the modern Genoa) in Roman times, Norway in the Middle Ages, and the Barbary Coast in the Napoleonic period—offer examples. Today surplus man power may emigrate from these coasts, find work as sailors, or as in Norway, build ships and carry goods for other nations.

Desirable Characteristics of a Harbor.

An ideal harbor would be of good size, thoroughly protected from storms, with deep water close to shore, a firm sandy bottom for anchorage of ships, and freedom from troublesome silting problems. It should be free from dangerous reefs and shallows and without fog, ice, strong winds, or dangerous currents or shifting sand bars. There should be little tidal range, although entrance to shallow harbors may be facilitated at high tide by a range of 6 or 8 feet between tidal extremes. At the same time, there should be sufficient tidal scour to prevent stagnation of harbor waters. The entrance channel should be large, fairly straight, and deep enough to make approach both easy and safe. Suitable building sites should be available for the seaport city and there should be routes tapping the hinterland. Few harbors, of course, approach this ideal combination of natural factors.

The ideal ocean port, in addition to a superior harbor with as many of the favorable features named above as possible, should have adequate facilities for handling freight and passengers, a location on principal world trade routes, and an easily accessible hinterland that both produces and consumes goods.

Aids to navigation. To aid navigation, governments have carefully surveyed and published charts of coasts and coastal waters, built lighthouses, and installed buoys and lights to mark channels. They also maintain fog warnings, issue weather forecasts, print tide tables, and provide other navigation aids as well as lifesaving stations in case of disaster.

New York.

Among the world's ocean ports, New York has ranked first in value of trade for many years. Reasons for its importance are partly natural and partly human. The harbor has a long frontage with deep water near shore, and it lies convenient to the relatively short North Atlantic route to Europe. It was built at the mouth of an easy route inland via the Hudson River (Figure 24-4) and the Mohawk and Genesee Valleys to the Great Lakes and Mississippi Valley. It has a small tidal range and little trouble with fog or ice. It is generally free of currents, shoals, and other obstructions. New York handles between 40 and 50 per cent of all foreign trade of the United States. Twelve lines of railroads reach the harbor, although only three terminals are situated on Manhattan Island itself. To handle the enormous transfers of freight, great numbers of piers, wharves, and warehouses, tugboats, lighters, and floating elevators have been built and equipped with modern machinery. Both private enterprise, as at Bush Terminal, and the municipality, as at Staten Island, have constructed special piers and warehouses for use by shipping firms. Furthermore New York is a great manufacturing center with nearly a million employees and provides a large consuming market in the 13 million inhabitants of the city and vicinity.

Changes in Ports.

When modern trade routes differ from those of the past, a port may lose its importance. Thus Venice, once a highly important trading city, now is insignificant as a port and has dwindled to little more than a tourist attraction. Bruges, great port and industrial town in the Middle Ages, is unimportant today, partly because large boats cannot use the silted shallow channel from the sea. In colonial days, Bristol and Plymouth were leading English ports; with the Industrial Revolution, new ports like Liverpool, Newcastle, and Hull, which serve iron, coal, and textile regions in central England, expanded faster. Old ports, such as Exeter in southwest England, having few expanding industries did not advance as rapidly as those that now serve the newer industrialized regions. An example from New England is the city of New Bedford which turned to textile manufacture after the decline of whaling, for which it had been a leading seaport.

Modern dredging machinery may change inland cities into seaports when it is used to construct ship canals like those from Liverpool to Manchester and from Galveston Bay to Houston. By dredging and building breakwaters, poor natural harbors have been made into safe convenient modern ports where a natural haven was lacking and a rich hinterland needed an outlet. A few among many possible examples include Cherbourg, Callao, and Dakar.

In modern times increased draft of ocean vessels compelled the building of outports on deeper water than available at the site of the original port. On rivers this may be downstream from the old seaport located upstream at the former head of ocean navigation. Thus Bremen has its Bremerhaven and Hamburg its Cuxhaven.

Construction of the Suez and Panama Canals shortened some ocean trade routes and changed the relative importance of certain seaports. Magallanes (Punta Arenas) on the Strait of Magellan, and Port Stanley in the Falkland Islands declined when many ships used the Panama Canal instead of the route around South America. St. Helena and Mauritius declined as ports of call after the building of the Suez. On the other hand, Aden, Port Said, Bombay, Los Angeles, and Panama increased their commerce upon completion of the canals.

OCEAN INDUSTRIES

Cities in ancient Phoenicia and Greece controlled only small areas of productive soil suited for growing food. Hence it was found necessary to import grain and other supplies. To pay for these the people turned to manufacturing, exchanging cloth, glass, pottery, and metalwares for foodstuffs and raw materials available elsewhere. To those distant and often undeveloped regions the merchants brought their culture along with their goods. From such small beginnings have grown the vast fleets presently used for commerce; this will be described in Chapter 22. Regions where the presence of the ocean affected development of coastal industries are New England, Norway, and several other coasts that are involved in the fishing industry.

New England. When population of a coastal land expands beyond the land's capacity to support its people, they migrate elsewhere, or turn to manufacturing or the sea. Farming in New England was of a subsistence type, and even in the colonial period some residents turned to fishing, home manufac-

tures, and trade for a living. Excellent harbors (Figure 16-5), abundant timber for shipping, and available goods for export—cured fish, lumber, rum, and small manufactures—stimulated development of shipping. In the 1840s, clipper ships, which were the fastest sailing vessels known, were built in New England and the American flag was seen in every foreign port. The invention of steam and the ironhulled boat was advantageous to Great Britain which had an important iron industry. This brought a decline in numbers of New England trading ships, which were made of wood and used sail. New Englanders also entered the whaling industry and until the Civil War led the world in catching whales. Whaling declined when the discovery of petroleum brought down the price of whale oil and the opening of the West offered other opportunities for investment.

Norway. At present the Norwegians, only 2 per cent of whose land is tilled and many of whom therefore turned to the sea for their living, dominate whaling, catching the creatures mainly in the antarctic seas (Figure 16-7). Whale oil now is used for soap and margarine while the remainder of the carcass is ground into fertilizer.

Much of the world's carrying trade is carried by Norwegian vessels, some of which rarely visit their home ports. Norwegians are leaders, too, in fishing in waters of northwestern Europe. Some fish are used for food in Norway but large quantities are exported, especially to Spain and other countries of Southern Europe.

The Fishing Industry. The life of the sea has been utilized by man for food and other materials since the dawn of history. Great piles of clamshells along the shores of San Francisco Bay and elsewhere show how Indians and other primitive men depended on the sea for food. Polynesians living on islands in the tropical "South Seas" depend greatly on fish and other seafood to supplement their diet of coconuts, breadfruit, and starchy roots. Although fish are abundant in the tropics, the great numbers of different species of fish are more noticeable than the numbers of any one species.

Commercial fisheries of the world are located where fish find abundant food (usually plankton). Usually the industry is based on comparatively few species of fish, present, however, in vast schools. Generally the shallow waters, a few hundred feet deep, on submarine banks and continental shelves in the cool temperate regions constitute the important fishing areas. Primitive people using canoes or small boats must be near their fishing grounds, but commercial fishermen have greater mobility in their large seaworthy vessels. Such fishing boats permit voyages of many hundreds or even thousands of miles from home ports to the banks or regions sought. French fishermen from Brittany regularly sail for summer fishing off Iceland and to the Grand Banks of Newfoundland. Other important fishing areas include Georges Bank and others off New England, coastal waters from California to Alaska, the Dogger Bank in the North Sea, coasts of Japan and

Figure 16-7 Commercial whaling vessel operating off the coast of South Georgia in Antarctic waters. The harpoon gun is mounted conspicuously on the bow, and the vessel has a whale in tow. (Photograph, courtesy of the American Museum of Natural History, New York.)

Kamchatka, the Sea of Okhotsk, and waters near Norway and Iceland (Figure 23-1).

In the United States salmon are among the most valuable fish. They are secured from the Columbia River (Figure 23-3), Puget Sound, and coastal Alaskan waters. This migratory fish is taken in vast numbers as it ascends fresh-water streams to spawn and is sold fresh, frozen, canned, and smoked. Seattle, Bellingham, Prince Rupert, Ketchikan, and Juneau are centers for canning, freezing, and shipping salmon.

When fish are to be sold fresh, many home ports of commercial fishermen are near large cities. Gloucester, Boston, and New York are important Eastern markets for cod, herring, mackerel, haddock, and other fish taken in the open sea. San Diego and Los Angeles pack tuna (Figure 16-8), and Monterey cans pilchard ("sardines"). Grimsby and Yarmouth, England; Bergen, Trondheim, and Stavanger, Norway; Hakodate, Japan; and Brest, France, are among foreign fishing centers. Herring is the most valuable fish caught off the northern European coast.

Often fishermen live along sterile coasts of rock and sand where the land has few re-

sources and man of necessity depends on the sea for livelihood. Fishing is hard dangerous work and only hardy and resourceful people succeed in the industry. Fishermen are among the most capable sailors in the world. Until recently, most fish were caught from small sailboats even in the stormy open Atlantic. At present motorboats and steam trawlers are used, or at least an auxiliary engine is added to help the sails. These larger modern boats are independent of the winds and are safer. They carry cargoes of fish to market more quickly and regularly than sailing ships. Modern improvements in freezing and shipping fresh fish fillets to inland markets have aided the industry.

Shore fisheries mainly produce lobsters, crabs, clams, and oysters. Matagorda Bay, in Texas, and the Mississippi Delta are centers of shrimp fisheries. Shallow estuaries and protected coastal waters and lagoons are favored homes for shellfish. Since the numbers of these coastal species can be seriously depleted by overfishing, the fisheries are protected by closed seasons, restrictions on size of catch, and other conservation measures. Also some shallow protected coastal waters may be leased by individuals from the state for the planting and raising of oysters. Chesapeake Bay, Long Island Sound, Puget Sound, and parts of the Gulf Coast are important in oyster culture in the United States.

Minor products from the ocean. Whales, seals, fur seals (really a sea lion), pearls, pearl shell, and ambergris (used in the manufacture of perfumes) are among other useful sea products (Figure 16-9). Varieties of seaweed are frequently eaten and supply vitamins and minerals in the diet of the Japanese and many other coastal people.

Figure 16-8 Preparing tuna for canning in a modern cannery. The fish are caught by hook and line, steam pressure-cooked, and filleted before being placed in cans. (Photograph, courtesy of Tuna Research Foundation and Rotkin, P.F.I.)

Figure 16-9   Fur seal rookery on shore of Pribilof Islands, Alaska. (Photograph by F. B. Scheffer, used by permission of U.S. Fish and Wildlife Service.)

Salt is often made by solar evaporation of sea water. Recently other minerals such as bromine, used in ethyl gasoline, have been recovered from the ocean. Magnesium, a light metal, is also extracted from sea water. Sometimes potash and iodine are produced from kelp or seaweed.

ISLANDS

Islands form an interesting field for geographic study because their isolation by surrounding water from all other land masses has fostered development of many peculiar plants, as well as flightless birds and other oddities.

The many thousands of islands in the world may be divided into offshore islands, lying close to continents with which they may have at one time been connected, and remote oceanic islands located hundreds and even thousands of miles from other lands. Isolated oceanic islands are mostly of two types: volcanic and coral. Oceanic islands rarely contain sedimentary or crystalline rocks. The two main islands of New Zealand, 1,200 miles from Australia, are exceptions. At one time in the remote past they may have been connected with some continent.

Volcanic Islands.   Volcanic islands are built up from depths of the sea, where some zone of weakness in the earth's crust allowed lava eruptions to break forth as submarine outpourings, until finally the eruptive material formed cones above sea level and created islands. Great volcanoes in Hawaii, two of which exceed 13,000 feet above sea level, have been built up from oceanic depths nearly three miles below the surface (Figure 22-1). Probably more than 90 per cent of the mountain mass of Hawaii is below sea level. Volcanoes built of ash and pumice may be quickly destroyed by wave erosion, as in the case of the Bogoslof volcano in the Aleutian Islands, which has appeared and disappeared as the result of eruptions and erosion more than once in historic times. Volcanic isles composed even of hard lava may ultimately

Figure 16-10 One of the Arenas Cays off the northwest coast of Yucatan. This small island was formed as a reef. Note the heavy surf in foreground; reefs of this type are hazards to navigation. Vegetation is barely beginning to grow at the far end of the cay. (Air Force photograph.)

be entirely truncated by waves. Then only a submarine bank will be left as evidence that an island once existed. Many volcanic islands have great cliffs on their windward sides as the result of wave erosion.

Coral Islands. Sea animals, called corals, include hundreds of different species, but from the standpoint of island formation, the reef-forming corals are most important. These flourish in tropical waters whose temperature rarely drops below 65°F, where currents bring supplies of food to the animals, and where depth does not exceed 200 or 300 feet. The Bahamas, Bermuda, and the Florida Keys are familiar examples of coral islands (Figure 16-10).

In the Pacific curious ringlike islands, called *atolls,* have been built by lime-secreting animals. Charles Darwin believed that coral atolls were formed when the volcano-studded tropical Pacific underwent progressive sinking of the oceanic floor on which the mountains stood. He thought that coral atolls began as fringing reefs along the shores of volcanic cones and that, as the cones sank, the fringing reefs became barrier reefs with a lagoon separating the land and the reef. Finally the volcano sank below the sea, but the reef had been built up as rapidly as sinking occurred; when the last land disappeared, the reef was left as a narrow roughly circular island with a broad shallow lagoon in its center.

Sir James Murray believed that coral atolls resulted when coral grew up to sea level from deposits built on any submarine bank and that wind and waves then heaped up the coral sand a few feet high to make the island. A truncated volcano could easily form a suitable bank. Corals grow only where they receive food easily from currents, which would be on the outside of a shallow bank, making an island of circular shape. Other scientists have felt that some atolls are formed both as Darwin and as Murray suggested, with others perhaps created in a still different manner. In size, atolls vary from a few miles in diameter up to nearly 100 miles, and they are commonly of oval shape.

Whatever their origin, coral atolls are usually broken up into a number of islets. Since the land is only a few feet above sea level, sometimes waves completely wash over it. The work of waves and wind breaks the coral and heaps the sand to form scanty soil in which coconuts and a few other plants will grow. The lagoon and adjacent shallow seas contain shellfish, seaweed, and many varieties of fish. All these are used for food by the inhabitants, who live mostly on the products of the coconut and what they obtain from the sea.

To the Polynesians living in the South Pacific, the coconut is as important as the date palm to the Arab. The tree furnishes the timber with which they support their houses and build their canoes. Leaves are useful for thatch, for making mats, and for fuel. Covering of the nuts is used for making mats, sails, and cordage; the nut itself furnishes both food and drink. The meat may be dried, and an edible and otherwise useful oil may be pressed from the dried product, called *copra.* The leafy crown of the coconut may be used for salad, and the sap may be fermented for drinking purposes.

Offshore or Continental Islands. These are believed to have been a part of the adjacent continents at one time; they have similar plants and wildlife still. Large islands situated near productive and developed mainlands are favorably located for carrying on commerce. Island merchants often act as middlemen between mainland ports and more distant foreign regions. Great Britain and Japan are the most important nations located on large offshore islands near a populous continent with many resources. Great Britain is well supplied with coal and iron and during the nineteenth century led the world in industrial development. Protection from invasion lessened loss of manpower and destruction in war and permitted trade to develop more freely.

Small islands near mainlands are usually part of the territory of strong continental powers, since such islands are too small to form self-defending nations. However, a naval power sometimes occupies strategic islands near other countries; Malta controlled by the United Kingdom is an example.

Islands, especially where surrounded by swift currents, are difficult to escape from and may be used for prisons, like Alcatraz in San Francisco Bay.

Strategic Islands. Because islands are isolated and may be the only land within a thousand miles or more, they may be of strategic and economic importance. Naval powers value islands highly for bases and fueling stations. Hawaii is an excellent example of an important naval base and fueling and supply station at the crossroads of the North Pacific. Islands also serve as bases for transoceanic airplane routes. Thus American aircraft utilize islands along routes between San Francisco and Asiatic ports, stops being made at Hawaii, Wake, Guam, and Manila. Flights from the Seattle-Tacoma airport to Japan are usually made without stops on a great-circle route, although some flights land in southern Alaska for refueling. On the route from Honolulu to Australia, aircraft use islands like Canton, Fiji, and Samoa. Bermuda and the Azores are island stops between New York and Lisbon and Iceland is used for refueling on the North Atlantic air lane. Even tiny remote islands have high strategic value since the development of airplanes.

When ocean commerce moved on sailing ships, the Falkland Islands were a convenient refitting point for ships that had a rough passage around Cape Horn. For vessels carrying goods in the trade between Europe and China, islands like Ascension and St. Helena in the Atlantic and Mauritius and Réunion in the Indian Ocean were useful sources of fresh food, water, and other stores. During Second World War, Ascension was developed into a major airplane base on the route to Africa.

Islands lying off a populous mainland are often preferred as trading centers, since they are convenient for receiving and reshipping goods from both the mainland and more distant ports. Such a trade center is called an *entrepôt*. Hong Kong and Singapore in Asia and London in England are examples of island entrepôts.

Island Life. Because of their isolation, islands may possess unique examples of plant and animal life that have developed or survived there. Australia, islandlike in its isolation, presents an outstanding example of this, for the continent was separated from Asia when only marsupials (pouched animals) existed and before more complexly organized carnivores and grazing mammals like cattle or deer had evolved. Hence, except for a wild dog introduced by the Australian "blackfellow," native Australian animals were all primitive like the kangaroo, wombat, koala, and platypus, or duckbill, the last an egg-laying mammal.

Remote islands like Hawaii or New Zealand and the maze of isles between these extremes in the Pacific contained no native wild mammals except the bat, which could fly, and the rat, which might be carried inadvertently by Polynesian sailors. Bird life, however, was abundant.

Birds. Sometimes, before the arrival of man and other enemies, large birds ceased to

Figure 16-11 Pelicans and cormorants nesting along the desert coast of Peru. (Photograph, courtesy of the American Museum of Natural History, New York.)

fly after arriving at some island; then their wings atrophied and they became birds of a terrestrial, running type. The moas of New Zealand, emu and cassowary of Australia, the extinct dodo of Mauritius, and the dinornis of Madagascar are examples. Some diving birds that nest on isolated islands and inaccessible coasts also have lost the power of flight. When such islands are discovered by man, the birds, from whose fat bodies an oil can be extracted, are so easily killed for this product that they are greatly reduced in number or even exterminated, like the great auk. The albatross and other birds that obtain their living from the sea commonly nest on the ground and seek remote oceanic islands for breeding places. Kure and Laysan Islands in Hawaii, and Wake Island are examples. Sometimes nesting grounds of birds are raided by hunters seeking skins and feathers. The Guano Islands off the coast of Peru and some other islands serve as nesting places for large numbers of birds (Figure 16-11). As has been mentioned, if such islands are arid the bird refuse accumulates and can be mined as the valuable fertilizer, guano. If the climate of these islands were rainy, the guano would be washed away.

Mammals and reptiles. Man has exterminated sea elephants and fur seals along mainland coasts and those animals now survive only by using breeding grounds on isolated islands. Different species of sea elephant use South Georgia in the South Atlantic and Guadalupe Island off Lower California, and fur seals use the Pribilof Islands. A South Pacific fur seal, once common on the Juan Fernández group, is now almost extinct.

In the Galápagos Islands (the name signifies "tortoise" in Spanish), each island has its own species of huge land tortoise, but the seagoing form is common to the entire group of islands. Isolation accounts for their different evolution. One island having five volcanoes, once separated by water but now joined, has five species of tortoise.

Various lizards have sometimes been preserved on islands after dying out elsewhere. A lizard found only on one small volcanic island off the coast of New Zealand possesses three eyes for some time after birth. Monitor lizards 10 to 15 feet in length exist on one island in the East Indies. Large lizards also are found in the Galápagos Islands. One species of these is seagoing; others live only on land.

Plants. Isolated oceanic islands generally show few species of plants, since not many types can be carried far over salt water. Winds and birds carry seeds of a few types, and fewer still may float. Nearly every tropical Pacific island has pandanus and coconut trees, but it is believed that viability of the seed is soon lost in salt water and that most of these trees were carried by Polynesian migrants and planted on newly discovered isles. Some islands have unique species of plants, like Australia with its eucalypts, Norfolk Island with its "pine" tree, and Lord Howe Island, which supplies seeds for growing indoors the common ornamental palm (*Howea belmoreana*).

Human Relationships. *Isolation and health.* Peoples on isolated islands develop certain characteristics as the result of their environment. Population tends toward uniformity in appearance and culture because of repeated intermarriage between inhabitants. Free from contact with the outside world and the diseases epidemic there, island peoples are healthy. In the Pacific area the Polynesians had no contagious or infectious diseases; hence they had never developed any immunity to such sickness. When these islanders were brought into contact with Europeans, introduced diseases like tuberculosis, influenza, smallpox, measles, and blood infections carried off the people at a shocking rate. The population of the Marquesas Islands declined from over 100,000 to less than 3,000 in a century and a half. It is estimated that since 1800 the native population of Polynesia, Australia, and Melanesia has declined by at least three-fourths. Several high islands in the Marquesas group and numerous low atolls have lost all native people. Such shocking decrease in population was partly the result of the inability of many natives to compete successfully with the newcomers whose culture was the stronger.

Population density. With their limited space, islands tend toward overpopulation if the birth rate continues at a normal increase and if freedom from local wars, invasion, and disease protects those born from sudden death. Some islands have an extraordinary density of population. Puerto Rico has almost as many people as the state of Washington, which is nearly twelve times larger. Barbados supports nearly 227,000 people on only 166 square miles, a density of about 1,370 per square mile. Bermuda has 40,000 people on only 22 square miles, part of which is wasteland. Jamaica's 1,500,000 people have only 4,410 square miles, much of which is mountainous. Haiti is also very mountainous, yet in its 10,714 square miles over 3,100,000 people attempt to earn a living. Another remarkable example of large population is Java, which has over 50 million people living on 51,000 square miles of rugged terrain—a density of nearly 1,000 per square mile. Although the Javanese live by farming, population density is exceeded only by that of small industrial regions like Belgium or parts of England and the fertile lowlands in China, India, or Egypt. Yet Java's population is increasing, though only unremitting toil can wring a living from the limited areas of moderately rich volcanic soil and other available resources.

In Madeira and the Azores the mountains have been laboriously terraced to raise grapes, fruits, and other foodstuffs. Farming is largely handwork, and earnest endeavor is needed to earn a living. Every available square foot of ground seems under cultivation.

Landless laborers on overpopulated islands may suffer from unemployment. Sometimes these agricultural laborers emigrate to better-favored lands. An example is found in the tens of thousands of Puerto Ricans who have migrated to New York City. Generally labor from well-populated islands is accustomed to work hard and can survive strong competition. Thus Barbados Negroes helped build the Panama Canal. Jamaica Negroes help cut sugar cane in Cuba and some have emigrated to Great Britain. Thousands of Filipinos migrated to Hawaii.

Racial survival. If islands are sterile, very stormy, rocky, or otherwise unattractive for human habitation, they may be left to those willing to eke out an existence there. As a result, old languages and cultures sometimes endure there. Residents of the little Aran Islands west of Ireland speak almost pure Gaelic, for example; the Hebrides and other islands off the Scottish coast support similar remnants of original Scots. Balearic Islanders speak the purest Catalan.

Breeds of livestock. Sometimes man has developed new breeds of domestic animals on isolated islands. If fodder is in short supply, selection produces small ponies rather than large horses. Thus the Shetland pony developed in the Shetland Islands. In the same way the Channel Islands had little grass and needed small cows that would furnish very rich milk. By selection, dairymen on Jersey Island and Guernsey Island developed the dairy breeds that bear those names.

Plantations. Since islands are readily reached by modern steamships and easily dominated from abroad because of relatively small indigenous populations, they are often chosen as sites for plantation enterprises when climate and other factors encourage production of marketable commodities. Thus Cuba, Puerto

Rico, Trinidad, Hawaii, Java, the Philippines, the Fiji Islands, and Mauritius grow most of the world's sugar cane. Much cacao (cocoa beans) comes from São Thomé in the Gulf of Guinea and from Trinidad. Coffee is grown in Java and Puerto Rico, tea in Java and Ceylon, rubber in Indonesia, cloves in Zanzi-bar, vanilla in Tahiti, and cinchona, the source of quinine, in Java. When indigenous labor is insufficient, immigrant workers are brought into plantation islands; these may become racial melting pots like Hawaii, or have two communities living separately, side by side, as do the Fijians and Indians (Hindus) in Fiji.

SUMMARY

The most useful coasts for commerce are those that have good harbors and productive hinter-lands. Ports should have facilities for handling goods efficiently and be advantageously located with reference to large populations. The hinter-land should have adequate transportation to dis-tribute goods from abroad and to ship commodi-ties readily to ports and harbors. As a rule, sub-mergent coasts offer satisfactory conditions for development, since numerous indentations pro-vide excellent sites for harbors. Yet even a coast with good harbors will seldom be visited by ships if the harbors, like those on the coast of southern Chile, lie far from usual paths of ocean trade and lack productive hinterlands.

Fishing is important along many coasts, espe-cially those near good fishing grounds, or those where the land is infertile, rugged, or with a cli-mate too severe for successful farming, as in Ice-land, Norway, or Newfoundland.

Since very early in human history, islands have served those who travel by sea. They made ocean travel easier by providing convenient locations to replenish fuel and food or to repair ships. With islands and coasts as steppingstones across the sea, it was possible to travel great distances in small vessels without the risks accompanying long-distance voyages. In modern times, islands have become increasingly important strategically.

In peace, islands served first as coaling stations and then as halting places on transoceanic air routes. In war, islands may be strongly fortified bastions during maritime and aerial conflict.

Outline
Transition character of coasts
Waves and their character
Coast lines
    Submergent or drowned, irregular
    Emergent, usually regular
    Wave erosion and deposition
Origin of harbors
    Importance of hinterland
    Roadsteads
    Coasts with poor hinterlands
Desirable characteristics of harbors
    Aids to navigation
Changes in usefulness of ports
Ocean industries
    New England and Norway
    Fishing: deep-sea and shore
    Minor products
Origin of oceanic islands: volcanic, coral
Important offshore islands
Strategic islands
Island life
    Birds, plants, etc.
    Human relationships

QUESTIONS

1. Select one of the following islands, and state reasons for its particular usefulness: Ceylon, Ber-muda, Malta.

2. Study the photograph of Stewart, B.C., Fig-ure 12-8 and analyze the advantages and disad-vantages of this type of coastal settlement.

3. What are desirable characteristics of a har-bor?

4. Name several improvements by which man aids navigation along coasts.

5. What type of coast would you enjoy for a va-cation? Why?

6. Why are atolls found only in low latitudes?

7. By means of an atlas if necessary find where the following islands are located, Newfoundland,

Sicily, Azores, Crete, Iceland, The Faeroes, Okinawa, Rhodes, Formosa, Madagascar, Tasmania, Hawaii, Cuba, Sumatra.

8. Study the character of each of the following coastal zones, and underscore those regions that exhibit the features of a submergent coast: Oregon, Dalmatia, Riviera, Peloponnesus, British Columbia, Malabar, Normandy, Calabria, Florida, Yucatan, Arakan, Denmark, Norway, Lower California, Nova Scotia, southern Chile, the Netherlands.

9. Which of the above submergent coasts have also have been affected by glacial action? What is a fiord?

10. Which of the above submergent coasts are utilized extensively as bases for the fishing industry?

11. Locate the following seaports and mention an export of importance for each: Houston, Duluth, Oporto, Tampico, Antofagasta, Narvik, São Paulo.

12. How has the geography of Japan favored the development of commercial fisheries?

13. Where are most important commercial fisheries located in the Northern Hemisphere?

14. What inventions have given importance to remote oceanic islands in recent years?

SELECTED REFERENCES

Cumberland, Kenneth J.: *Southwest Pacific,* McGraw-Hill Book Company, Inc., New York, 1956.

Daniel, Hawthorne: *The Islands of the Pacific,* G. P. Putnam's Sons, New York, 1943.

Freeman, Otis W.: "The Pacific Island World," *Journal of Geography,* 44:16–30, January, 1945.

———— (ed.): *Geography of the Pacific,* John Wiley & Sons, Inc., New York, 1951.

Johnson, Douglas W.: *The New England Acadian Shoreline,* John Wiley & Sons, New York, 1925.

————: *Shore Processes and Shoreline Development,* John Wiley & Sons, New York, 1919.

Marmer, H. A.: "Is the Atlantic Coast Sinking? The Evidence from the Tide," *Geographical Review,* 38:652–657, October, 1948.

Minikin, R. R.: *Coast Erosion and Protection: Studies in Causes and Remedies,* Chapman & Hall, Ltd., London, 1952.

Murphy, R. C.: "Oceanography of the Peruvian Littoral with Reference to the Abundance and Distribution of Marine Life," *Geographical Review,* 13:64–85, January, 1923.

Robson, R. W. (compiler): *Pacific Islands Handbook: North American Edition, 1944,* The Macmillan Company, New York, 1945.

Spoehr, Alexander: "The Marshall Islands and Transpacific Aviation," *Geographical Review,* 36:447–451, July, 1946.

Stewart, John Q.: *Coasts, Waves, and Weather,* Ginn & Company, Boston, 1945.

Taylor, Griffith: *Australia,* Methuen & Co., Ltd., London, 1949.

17. Soils and Soil Conservation

SOILS constitute one of the most important factors in geography. Compared with the whole volume of the earth, soils form but a small film from a few inches to several feet in depth on the surface, yet this relatively thin layer produces nearly the entire food supply of man. Warlike invasions and peaceful migrations have occurred almost numberless times during human history, when man began his search for areas of fertile soil. Possession of a large area of productive soil is a very advantageous factor which has favored growth of population and development of many nations. The west-ward expansion of the United States was largely dominated by the need and desire for more fertile farmland.

In the past, peoples and kingdoms have risen and attained great importance in the civilized world, only to decline in numbers and influence, partly because of careless destruction of soils by erosion, deforestation, overgrazing, and improper farming. Examples include parts of Syria and certain other lands near the Mediterranean, as well as some worked-out and eroded lands in the "Old South" and portions of the loess hills of northern China.

SOILS

Origin of Soil. Soils have a very complex origin and result from the interaction of many different factors. One might list as most important of these: the type of parent material from which the soil was formed, rainfall, temperature, and other climatic influences, natural vegetation, relief of the land, drainage, animal organisms living in the soil, bacteria, and finally, the length of time during which the various factors have worked together to create the soil cover. Decay and disintegration of bedrock furnish the original material of which soils are made. Weathered fragments, called *mantle rock,* form the basal material from which develop *residual soils,* which are formed in place. Soil may also be derived from transported material deposited by running water, glaciers, winds, and waves. Residual soil changes vertically from the bedrock through broken mantle rock into the subsoil and surface soil, but a transported soil may differ entirely in character from the bedrock over which it lies. Obviously, the original character of soil will be determined by the material from which it is derived, but other agencies may cause a soil to change its original character so greatly that, after a long time, similar soils may develop from entirely different bedrock or different soil types develop from similar bedrock. In general, soils in which parent material dominates are youthful; soils materially modified by various agencies are mature.

Humid and Arid Soils. The most important factor affecting soil character is that of climate. In well-drained ground, there is steady downward percolation of water in areas of abundant precipitation. This ground water contains a weak solution of carbon dioxide, obtained from decaying organic material. Such a solution can dissolve and carry away lime and other salts in the ground. Thus in a region of abundant rainfall and good drainage the soil becomes *leached.* In regions of deficient precipitation the rain water penetrates but a few feet underground. There lime and other salts dissolved in the water are deposited in soil when the water evaporates, building up a zone of lime accumulation from one to several feet beneath the surface. When present in a dense layer, this zone may be called *hardpan* and by the Spaniards *caliche.*

A modern classification of soils divides them into *pedalfers,* formed under humid conditions, and *pedocals,* formed under arid and semiarid conditions. The word pedalfer is derived from

Ped for soil, Al for aluminum and Fe for iron. These chemicals are characteristic of leached soils. Lime (calcium carbonate) is characteristic of arid soils. In the United States the line separating pedalfers from pedocals runs from northwestern Minnesota to Corpus Christi, Texas. East of this line, mature soils without exception are pedalfers formed under humid climatic conditions. West of the line, pedocals predominate, and pedalfers occur only in the rainier areas, especially in the Pacific Northwest.

Soil Horizons and Maturity. Soils go through a series of changes by which the original freshly accumulated rock material becomes greatly altered. This finally results in development of zones, or horizons, in the soil, each having its own characteristics and each differing markedly from the unchanged material beneath (Figure 17-1). When this stage has

Figure 17-1 Soil profile (hypothetical) showing principal soil horizons developed under humid conditions. Not all horizons are found in all soil types.

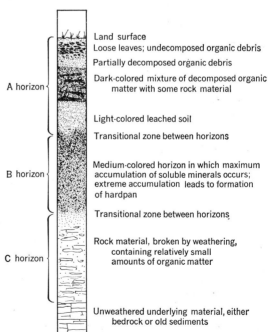

Land surface
Loose leaves; undecomposed organic debris
Partially decomposed organic debris
Dark-colored mixture of decomposed organic matter with some rock material

Light-colored leached soil
Transitional zone between horizons

Medium-colored horizon in which maximum accumulation of soluble minerals occurs; extreme accumulation leads to formation of hardpan

Transitional zone between horizons

Rock material, broken by weathering, containing relatively small amounts of organic matter

Unweathered underlying material, either bedrock or old sediments

A horizon
B horizon
C horizon

been reached, soil is said to have attained maturity. Soil scientists (pedologists) call topsoil the A horizon, subsoil the B horizon, and the slightly changed mantle-rock material the C horizon. Soils are classified by the character of these different horizons: their composition and color, size of soil particles or texture of soil materials—sand, loam, or clay—and structure, which depends upon arrangement of soil particles.

Soils that are waterlogged most of the year or impregnated with alkali do not develop normal characteristics or profile of a mature soil, since stagnant water prevents normal leaching and weathering. Neither do soils on steep slopes develop mature characteristics, because excessive erosion removes the soil before it has a chance to attain maturity.

Effects of Plants and Animal Organisms on Soil. Natural vegetation is another important factor in soil formation. Where climate favors growth of tall prairie grass and herbs, the abundant stems, leaves, and roots furnish rich humus which gives soils a dark color like those of the prairies of Illinois, soil of the Red River Valley, and the famous black soils in Texas and Russia. Various animal organisms, such as earthworms, also live in soil and by their activities change dead vegetable matter into soluble nutrients for plant life; furthermore, earthworms have a material effect on soil structure or aggregation of soil particles. Bacteria, fungi, and other lower forms of life produce most important effects in formation of soil by helping decay of organic matter, development of humus, and formation of soluble compounds that plants can use for food.

Leaves from hardwood forests are rather readily incorporated in the ground by bacterial action and generally produce more productive soil than that which develops on ground covered with coniferous needle leaves, which contain too much pitch to decay readily and become incorporated in soil.

Life History of Soils. Soils pass through a life cycle. Those which have been formed recently

are said to be in the stage of infancy. Youthful soils are characteristic of floodplains and recent deposits of both lava and volcanic ash. Such young soils, even in a rainy climate, are likely to contain desirable plant nutrients which make them fertile, since the leaching action of percolating rain water has not had time to dissolve the soluble salts used by plants. Mature soils are those in which the effects of rainfall, natural vegetation, biological life, and other factors have developed certain acquired characteristics, rather than those originally derived by the soil from its parent material. Mature soil is in equilibrium with its environment, and hence is subject to little natural change, although many mature soils have been modified beyond all comprehension by human activities. Since mature soils are end products of all the numerous factors acting upon them, they occur mainly on level plains and plateaus, where erosion has small opportunity to disturb soil-forming processes, and rarely in hilly or mountainous regions where erosion is active. The actual type of soil developed in such places depends upon all the factors that joined to produce the change and the time that elapsed while these factors were operative.

Generally the A horizon is richest in organic matter, since most roots and the greater part of the humus are found there, along with most of the organic life. This normally gives the A horizon a darker color than the B horizon (Figure 17-2). As humus decays, nitrates and potash are released in a soluble form that plants can use. The A horizon is not always fertile; for example, soil that is formed under the climatic conditions supporting the coniferous forests of the Northern Hemisphere tends to be so leached that the lower part of the A horizon consists of a gray sand lacking in fertility. This soil was named *podzol* by the Russians.

Texture and Structure. Important physical properties of soils are texture and structure. These affect absorption and retention of water and hence are factors in growth of crops and natural vegetation.

Soil texture is concerned with size of particles of the soil. Some soils are largely coarse gravel and broken rock, whereas others, in order of increasing fineness of particles, consist largely of sand, silt, or clay. Coarse soils permit rapid percolation of water, and generally in this case the natural vegetation should be of a drought-resistant nature. Exceptions occur when rainfall is excessive or where the water table is close to the surface. Fine soils are highly retentive of water, in the case of clay, to such a degree that during wet seasons plowing and cultivating soil become difficult. Because of the large total of surface areas afforded by fine particles, silt and clay soils provide more accessible and extensive ground water for plants than do gravel or sand. Mixtures of fine and coarse materials may form desirable soils; one of these, called *loam,* is formed from sand, silt, and clay. Very small particles of clay are sometimes said to be of colloidal size, but the term also includes colloids of organic origin. Mixed with the minerals or rock particles are colloids, organic remains, living organisms, water, and substances in solution; together these help determine the texture and other characteristics of the soil.

Another important factor affecting plant growth is availability of water in the soil. Soil texture helps to determine how readily plants can obtain this water. Sands, silts, and clays differ in their retention of water because of differences in the film tension that holds the water to the soil particles.

Air is present in soil and is necessary for the growth of organisms forming humus from raw vegetable matter; it also performs other functions to prepare the food materials in soil for plants. Water may occupy the openings between soil particles. If it moves freely downward, it is called *gravitational water.* This feeds springs, wells, and artesian flows. That which is held in small openings is called *capillary water* and is the chief source of supply for plants. Since capillary water may evaporate, its retention for use by crops is the basis for "dry-farming" methods. Water that tightly adheres to soil particles is called *hygroscopic*

Figure 17-2   Road cut in the Palos Verdes Hills, southern California, showing the sharp contrast between bedrock (C horizon) and residual soil (A horizon). In this case the B horizon is almost entirely lacking. The short-grass vegetation cover of these hills is typical of the drier parts of the Mediterranean climatic lands. (Photograph by Anton Wagner.)

and has negligible movement in the ground.

Structure is the arrangement of soil particles; it affects the penetration and movement of water and availability of soil nutrients to plants. In a good soil structure the particles are joined to form granules or floccules that favor the necessary circulation of air and water. Granules may themselves be arranged in various ways. Soil structures may be granular, crumb, columnar, prismatic, platy, or irregular, angular, fragmental material. Soil structure suited for plant growth may be injured by wrong methods of tillage, by exhaustion of humus and lime, and by other abuses. The pore space of a well-aggregated loam soil is 35 to 50 per cent. When this pore space has been reduced by cultivation and in other ways, the entrance and movement of air and water are limited and the soil may then become dense, thus reducing crop production. Loss of humus following continuous cropping and failure to return crop residues to the soil frequently results in serious deterioration of soil structure. An example is found on farms where

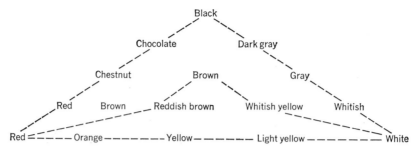

Figure 17-3   Soil-color relationships. Note how the different colors blend.

wheat has been grown continuously and the straw removed or burned. This often allows the drifting and blowing away of soil particles because of lack of humus. Humus serves to hold the soil in well-aggregated form and helps to prevent erosion. Farm systems should be oriented toward maintaining desired soil structure.

Color of soil is a minor characteristic that helps to indicate soil origin and fertility (Figure 17-3). The blackness of soil usually is in proportion to the humus content, produced by organisms from decaying plant material. Red and yellow colors reflect the presence of minerals, usually iron in some form. Reddish-colored laterite is a common tropical soil resulting from rapid oxidation processes, leaching of other minerals faster than iron, and lack of organic matter that insects and agents of decay rapidly destroy. Light-colored soils may be the result of leaching in cool rainy climates. Other light-gray–colored soils occur in deserts where scarcity of plant life means that humus is unavailable. Some desert soils contain an excess of alkaline salts, which inhibit the growth of most vegetation. Excess alkali also injures soil structure to an extent that farming is handicapped.

Soil Types in the United States. In the United States there exist thousands of different soil types having characteristics by which they can be distinguished from each other. The outstanding mature soil groups in this country, however, can be reduced to eight (Figure 17-4). Those formed under humid conditions, the pedalfers or non-lime-accumulating soils,

are the podzols, gray-brown forest soils, red-yellow forest soils, and the prairie soils. The leading types of pedocals formed outside the forested areas are the black earth, dark-brown earth, light-brown earth, and the gray desert soils. Other soils are undifferentiated types of the mountainous regions, swampy areas, and the sand hills of Nebraska and similar areas. Different phases of the soil types are recognized, depending on texture, structure, and chemical composition, especially whether they are lime-accumulating (pedocals) or non-lime-accumulating (pedalfers).

The Pedalfers: non-lime-accumulating Types. *Podzols* are badly leached soils that develop typically in parts of northern Michigan, northern Wisconsin, northeastern Minnesota, and northern Maine. Somewhat similar soils are also developed on pervious gravels and sandy deposits in rainier parts of the Pacific Northwest. The largest extent of podzol soil appears as a broad belt occupied by the taiga of Northern Europe, Asia, and North America. Podzols generally develop under a cover of conifers. They are so thoroughly leached that their resulting low fertility makes them unattractive for farming. The topsoil (A horizon) has lost most of the soluble plant nutrients; the subsoil (B horizon), although also low in fertility, may actually be more fertile (Figure 17-5*A*). Agriculture is usually of slight importance in regions with podzols; lumbering, fishing, trapping, or mining are the main industries. Farm crops are often of a subsistence character for local consumption; they include oats, barley, rye, potatoes, and root vegetables.

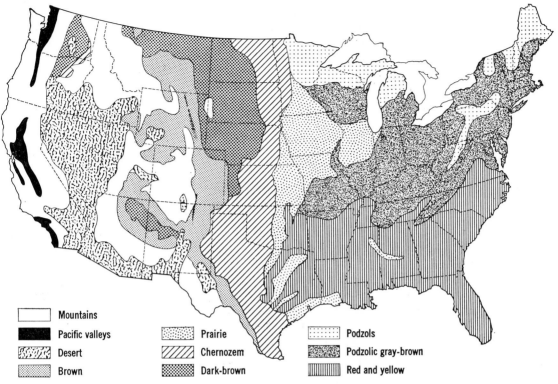

Legend:

- ☐ Mountains
- ■ Pacific valleys
- ▨ Desert
- ▦ Brown
- ⬚ Prairie
- ⧄ Chernozem
- ▧ Dark-brown
- ⋮ Podzols
- ▨ Podzolic gray-brown
- ▥ Red and yellow

Figure 17-4   Principal soil types of the United States.

Since hay can usually be grown with some success, exports coming from the farms may consist largely of dairy products. Many farmers, unable to make an adequate living on podzolic soils, have abandoned their farms and deserted large areas once cleared for cultivation, as in parts of northern Michigan.

Gray-brown forest soil has developed in rainy midlatitudes, where the principal trees consisted of broad-leaved species. These forest soils cover the northeastern United States east of the prairies from the Ozarks and southern Wisconsin to Virginia and southern New England. This soil group has a lower acid content than podzols, is less leached, and can retain water better. The soil is reasonably high in humus, and the A horizon is brown in color, with the B horizon of lighter color and rather compact structure (Figure 17-5*B*). When care is used in cultivation, gray-brown soils are productive and easily tilled. Except in regions too rugged for farming, most of these soils

have been cleared of forests and turned into productive farmland. By rotation of crops, their fertility can be maintained, especially where a crop of clover is plowed under every three or four years. A large variety of crops is raised on these soils, from wheat, corn, small and large fruit, and tobacco, to fodder crops for livestock.

Red and yellow forest soils are characteristic of the southeastern United States and have developed under rather high rainfall conditions, long growing seasons, and hot summers. Various species of pine trees form the dominant native vegetation, but oaks and other hardwoods frequently occur. In general the soils show evidence of considerable leaching, since winters are too mild for freezing the ground and ground-water percolation continues throughout the year. The yellowish phase is especially leached. This soil is developed in a rainy climate and long growing season under a vegetation cover of southern pines and hardwoods.

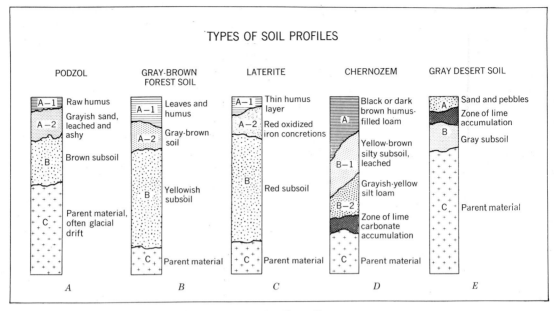

TYPES OF SOIL PROFILES

PODZOL

A-1 Raw humus
A-2 Grayish sand, leached and ashy
B Brown subsoil
C Parent material, often glacial drift

GRAY-BROWN FOREST SOIL

A-1 Leaves and humus
A-2 Gray-brown soil
B Yellowish subsoil
C Parent material

LATERITE

A-1 Thin humus layer
A-2 Red oxidized iron concretions
B Red subsoil
C Parent material

CHERNOZEM

A Black or dark brown humus-filled loam
B-1 Yellow-brown silty subsoil, leached
B-2 Grayish-yellow silt loam
Zone of lime carbonate accumulation
C Parent material

GRAY DESERT SOIL

A Sand and pebbles
Zone of lime accumulation
B Gray subsoil
C Parent material

A   B   C   D   E

Figure 17-5   Types of soil profiles.

The redder soils are more often associated with deciduous trees. These soils are easily cultivated, but fertility is low and poor practices may soon exhaust their productivity, as large areas of abandoned farmland in the South attest. By application of chemical fertilizers, specialty crops like fruits and vegetables for the Northern market as well as cotton or tobacco are sometimes raised even on the poor soil. The South is a very large consumer of commercial fertilizer. Production of peanuts, field peas, and other legumes in rotation with crops that exhaust the soil has also proved advantageous to Southern agriculture. Widespread changes in the farm economy of the South are demonstrating that productivity of yellow and red soils can be improved.

Where cultivated fields are too hilly, heavy rainfall causes very destructive gullying and sheet erosion on areas of light yellow to red soil. Better cultivation practices and a scientific crop-rotation system are being used to build up many of these soils. In many parts of the South especially on sloping land, pastures and planted grasses for livestock are replacing row crops in areas of depleted soils.

Lateritic soils.   In the tropics, a deeply weathered reddish soil develops under conditions of heavy rainfall, high temperatures, and dense forest growth (Figure 17-5C). These soils, called *laterites,* characterize the tropics and are generally of low fertility because of excessive leaching. Some forest soils in the southeastern United States resemble laterites and may be termed lateritic. Laterites consist largely of aluminum and iron oxides which have accumulated, and these soils are red in color because of high iron content.

Brazil, central Africa, and southeastern Asia have large areas of laterite soils, requiring extensive use of fertilizers to maintain good crop yields if they are used for agriculture. Some lateritic soils formed from volcanic materials are comparatively fertile because continuing decay of the lavas restores the minerals needed by plant life. This is the case in parts of Hawaii and in Java.

Prairie soil.   Among the most fertile soils formed under humid conditions are those developed on nearly level grassy plains and slightly rolling prairies of Illinois, Iowa, and adjacent humid prairie regions. Black prairie soils are rich in humus, retentive of moisture, deep, and productive; and by means of crop rotation and prevention of erosion, their fertility can be maintained almost indefinitely. These deep rich prairie earth soils are among the most fertile farmlands in America. The Corn Belt in part and much of the Winter Wheat Belt occupy land covered with this soil group. The large farming population that this soil supports is further evidence of its fertility. Manure from the large number of farm animals raised constitutes an important element in maintaining fertility.

Black prairie soils of Texas and Oklahoma are the most important cotton lands of those two states and produce more than double the yield per acre of the leached yellow and red soil of the coastal plain. Certain youthful soils in the floodplains and delta of the Yazoo and Mississippi Rivers are deep and highly fertile, since alluvial materials of which they are composed are too recent in origin to have suffered leaching; hence they still have great productive capacity. Those in the famous "Black Belt" of Alabama and Mississippi are residual, however, and owe their excellence to underlying limestone from which they were formed.

Pedocals: Lime-accumulating Soil Types.

Chernozem soil or the black earth is among the most productive grain land in use by man. These soils develop on prairies having adequate but not excessive rainfall, where natural conditions favor growth of grass rather than trees (Figure 17-5D). Such soils belong with the semiarid pedocal type because they possess a zone of carbonate accumulation a few feet below the surface of the ground. Chernozem soils in Russia often have a thickness of from 4 to 6 feet of topsoil extending over large areas. In the United States, the black portion of the soil is usually only from 1 to 2 feet in thickness. These chernozems occur in a zone extending from the Red River Valley in western Minnesota and eastern North Dakota southward through Kansas and central Texas. They also occur in the Far West and include the excellent Palouse soil of eastern Washington and adjacent regions used for wheat production.

Formerly devoted to livestock, chernozem soils have proved so good for wheat and other grains that farmers have usually replaced stockmen, and former grazing land has been changed into productive farms. Crops naturally vary with the length of the growing season. On the Great Plains, spring wheat occupies the black soils of the Dakotas, whereas winter wheat is the principal crop for such lands in Nebraska and Kansas, with winter wheat, sorghum, and cotton in Oklahoma and Texas.

Brown earth soils. Adjoining the chernozem soils, where precipitation is less and tall prairie grasses are replaced by short grass and bunch grass, occur the brown earth soils which have both dark or reddish-brown and light-brown phases. These soils occupy most of eastern Montana and western parts of the Dakotas and Kansas as far south as Oklahoma and the "panhandle" of Texas. They also occur in those parts of the Columbia Basin between the Cascades and Rocky Mountains in areas having a precipitation of about 10 to 15 inches annually. These soils originally supported short grasses and in a state of nature afforded excellent grazing for cattle and sheep. When first cultivated, crops of wheat are generally successful on light-brown soil, but the humus that binds the soil particles is soon exhausted, and then in dry seasons the soil may drift away with the wind. Once it was common practice to burn off straw after harvest to make plowing easier, but this is now seldom done because it was found that plowing under the wheat stubble helps to maintain humus needed by the soil. This and other improved methods of tillage have reclaimed much of the "blow land" on these light soils (Figure 17-8).

Gray desert soil. This generally develops on less than 10 inches of rainfall and is gray because of lack of humus materials (Figure 17-5E). The zone of lime accumulation is thick and nearer the surface than in the case of light-brown and black pedocal soils. Only under exceptional circumstances can gray desert soils be cultivated for wheat and other crops without irrigation, and attempts to farm such areas have universally resulted in failure, as is evident from the many abandoned farms on the gray soil of south central Oregon, southern Idaho, and the driest part of the Columbia Basin in Washington.

Desert soils, though low in humus, have not had much of the soluble salts leached by rain water; desert soils may, therefore, become very productive when irrigated. Without irrigation, the chief dependence is on grazing, and only a few stockmen can be supported since the herds can obtain forage from sparse vegetation only if large areas per animal are available. Often 40 to 80 acres per steer are required in dry-land areas, in contrast to several animals to the acre on a well-watered meadow in the humid eastern United States.

Utilization of Soil. Although in the United States only about one-sixth of the labor force is engaged in agriculture because of mechanization of farming, the proportion of farmers rises to about 80 per cent in many nonindustrialized countries. In the aggregate, more of the world's people directly depend for a living on agriculture than on any other industry, so use of soils for farming is most significant. Proper land utilization requires selection of crops best adapted to different soils, development of farming methods to maintain productiveness of land for agriculture, and handling of grazing and forest land so that these resources are not quickly depleted.

The plants best for any given set of geographic factors may be determined by experimentation with many types of plants in various soils and under different climatic conditions. Sometimes new plants developed by plant-breeding experiments provide improved varieties better adapted to conditions than any previously available. Of course, under certain market conditions, it may pay to raise a crop in areas not ideally suited for its production, as in the case of berries and vegetables that are grown near large cities where they can be marketed at a profit. Some tomatoes and other sorts of produce are grown in hothouses near city markets during winter. Some nations, greatly in need of a particular crop such as

sugar beets, may try to stimulate uneconomic production by high protective tariffs on imports, payment of bonuses, or some other form of subsidy.

Soil Maintenance. Plants secure minerals for their growth from the soil. Steady planting of any staple crop year after year exhausts soil nutrients and results in decreased crop yields. Though rotating crops usually helps temporarily since different plants have somewhat different food requirements, ultimately most soils become so depleted by steady cropping that yields decrease. Then farming becomes unprofitable and farms may be abandoned.

The Soil Conservation Service estimates that erosion on sloping lands takes away fertility elements five to twenty times faster than depletion by cropping. With change in the farm system, soil fertility can be maintained and even increased. Commercial fertilizer may be added to enrich soil and increase crop yields. This is practicable only when greater output brings a return equal to or above the cost of fertilizer, since most staples must sell at low prices. Animal manure, wood ashes, crop residues, and other organic wastes add needed nutrients to soils. Crop rotations should include green manure and meadow containing such legumes as alfalfa and clover, which have nitrogen-fixing bacteria on their roots and thus improve the soil while producing useful fodder and food crops.

Because different soils require different handling, the successful farmer must scientifically study his soil and manage soil and water in a way that will produce a comfortable living while maintaining soil fertility for use by future generations. Reckless exploitation of soil by depleting, cropping, and erosion, followed by land abandonment and local depopulation must cease if the United States is to remain a great and prosperous nation, since soils are the most fundamental resource of our land.

Land and National Development. To control considerable areas of productive land is an obvious advantage for any nation. Although some countries now import much of their food-stuffs, paying for them by profits from trade and industry, in many cases an area of fertile land was the nucleus around which such nations grew and in which its people developed their culture. The Paris Basin in France, the lowlands of Great Britain, the reclaimed marshland of the Netherlands, and the Po Valley in northern Italy are among many examples from the countries of Europe. Although the United States expanded westward from the stony hills of New England and sandy tidewater Virginia, the heart of the country is situated in the fer-tile Middle West which has great blocks of good soil in a humid region where the growing season is long enough for wheat, corn, and many other crops.

About 4 billion acres of arable land are available now to the world's farmers, although part of it is only of poor to medium quality. The world population is more than 2.5 billion; less than 2 acres of tilled land are available for the support of one person. The need to maintain soil fertility and prevent erosion and other causes of soil depletion is apparent if the people of the world are to be fed.

SOIL CONSERVATION

Soil Erosion.   Conservation of soils is recognized as essential to the maintenance of standards of living and culture in any region whose economy is based on farming. Where through carelessness and neglect, soil has been allowed to wash away, as in some areas tributary to the Yellow River in China, sections once densely peopled are depopulated and in almost a desert condition. Even in the United States, where farming has been carried on a comparatively short time, it is estimated that 50 million acres of land have been so badly washed that they have become of negligible use for agriculture. Nearly 100 million acres more have suffered severe damage from erosion. This is especially important, since it requires many years for soil to be rehabilitated after serious abuse.

Forms of Erosion.   The agents of soil erosion are chiefly running water and the wind. Erosion of soil by running water takes several forms, among them: sheet erosion, gullying, and lateral erosion by streams. Sheet erosion,

Figure 17-6 Typical sheet erosion on northern Idaho burned-over forest lands. This unprotected soil washes rapidly. Reforestation and grass seeding would restabilize these badly burned areas. (Photograph, courtesy of the U.S. Soil Conservation Service.)

Figure 17-7   Severe washing in winter-wheat land in the foothills of the Blue Mountains of Oregon. A 48-hour wash from a 40-acre drainage area on a 5 per cent slope cut this gully 8 feet and 15 feet wide. (Photograph by J. G. James, courtesy of the U.S. Soil Conservation Service.)

the repeated removal of a thin layer of soil from the top of the ground, resembles the skimming of cream from a pan of milk, since the richest soil is usually on the surface (Figure 17-6). Sheet erosion is insidious, for most farmers hardly realize that their fields are being damaged. Gully erosion results from runoff in myriads of little drainage channels that unite and finally wear a deep gully; by growing headward, this may so divide a field that tillage is difficult (Figure 17-7). Streams often destroy farmland by lateral erosion, which undermines banks and allows soil to slide into the water. In times of flood, a river like the Missouri may destroy half a cornfield at a stroke.

Wind erosion usually begins when soils in dry regions like the Great Plains have had their structure destroyed by unwise cultivation or have had their surface protection removed by overgrazing. Once the process is started, blowholes are excavated by wind, and dunes travel to leeward with the air currents, creating a damaging condition that is difficult to control (Figure 17-8).

Factors Affecting Erosion.   Soil erosion is most rapid on sloping land subject to heavy rainfall, especially when the rain is torrential. In a

state of nature, trees, shrubs, grass, and decaying plant litter help absorb the rain impact energy and retard runoff so that erosion is not rapid enough to do damage. Early settlers on the Atlantic Coast remarked on the clarity of the streams; only after the land had been cut over and cultivated did erosion give the streams the muddy look they have today.

The custom of plowing and of cultivating up and down slopes instead of along contours promotes erosion. Destruction of vegetation by livestock and creation of paths and ruts may concentrate the runoff and lead to gully formation. The type of soil also influences runoff and resulting erosion, since some soils are more absorbent, permeable, and resistant to erosion than others. Erosion is a special problem in hilly parts of the Piedmont Plateau and rolling lands included in the coastal plain from Virginia through the Carolinas, as well as in Alabama, Georgia, and Mississippi. It is also serious on cleared areas of the Appalachian Plateau regions, glacial hills around the Great Lakes, and sloping land surrounding the Ozarks. Severe soil erosion is affecting many farms in the Corn Belt, partly because of tillage methods and insufficient rotation of crops. Areas in southern California have been very severely damaged by erosion, as have parts of the intermountain wheat sections of Washington and Oregon.

Effects of Erosion.   If erosion occurs on hilly land, the topsoil is removed first from the brow of the hills and steeper slopes where soil is thinnest and therefore most needed. It is deposited on bottomlands, where the fertile soils need enrichment least. Some fine soil is carried away downstream. After several years of such erosion, only the clay subsoil remains on the hill summits, and the farming of such slopes has become unprofitable even if gullying has not destroyed its usefulness for agriculture earlier. In some parts of the country these eroded hilltops are known as "balds."

When gullying begins, infertile and stony subsoil is washed away and may be dumped on fertile bottomland, thus completing the

Figure 17-8 Irrigated land (upper left) and unirrigated land (right) in the Gila River basin of Arizona. Undeveloped desert land, almost barren of vegetation cover, must be watered before it can become productive. Along the irrigation canals, there is enough seepage to maintain more plant life. Wind erosion on this unwatered land is a serious problem. (Photograph, courtesy of the U.S. Soil Conservation Service.)

ruin of a region. In addition, heavy rains fill streams and reservoirs with silt from the washing. In this way, channels and reservoirs used for irrigation often have their storage capacity lessened. Several reservoirs in the Piedmont in the southern United States are so filled with silt that they have become useless. Reservoirs on the Rio Grande project which have been in operation only forty years have already lost over one-third of their storage capacity from silting. Sudden floods from eroding land may fill culverts and cover highways and bury gardens under worthless debris. Altogether it seems probable that more than 3 billion tons of the best and most fertile soils are lost from the fields of America each year.

Wind Erosion. Wind erosion causes grave destruction of soil resources in regions of deficient rainfall. Originally semiarid land had a sufficient cover of grass and other herbage; this held its soil in place, and the wind did negligible damage. When the grass cover is

destroyed by overgrazing or the plow, the land is maladjusted to the natural conditions and damage by wind erosion occurs. Continued cultivation of former grasslands breaks down soil structure and produces a fine dust, easily moved by winds. The finest-powdered particles, usually the most fertile part of the soil, may be carried so high and far by strong winds that this material is entirely lost to the afflicted region. Coarser fragments may be rolled and drifted by wind to form heaps of sand and other relatively infertile deposits that may cover growing crops, adjacent fields, and even buildings.

During the summer of 1934, which was a dry season on the Great Plains, a series of dust storms carried material from their southern portion entirely across the United States and deposited millions of tons of dust, really topsoil from formerly productive land, over the northeastern United States. Within the drought-stricken areas from which the dust came, the sun was literally blotted out at mid-

Figure 17-9 Strip cropping to control soil erosion is shown in the background with a grass-covered waterway separating strips of planted corn in foreground. Measures to control soil erosion will save this farm from the losses apparent in Figure 14-9. (Photographed in the Muskingum Valley of Ohio. Courtesy of the U.S. Soil Conservation Service.)

day. The dust was not only very unpleasant to the afflicted settlers but severely damaging to human and animal life (Figure 9-9). Topsoil of whole fields was sometimes blown away to plow depth; growing crops were literally blown out of the ground. In the worst cases, farm implements and even buildings were wholly or partly buried under heaps of sand and dust. The experience of these "dry black blizzards" brought home to the entire population of the United States the necessity for proper control of wind erosion.

Control of Erosion. Protective measures for conserving soil have been developed by the Soil Conservation Service and various other

agencies. For example, contour cultivation and the building of terraces on sloping land helps to prevent runoff and will increase the amount of ground water available for plants. If sheet erosion or gullying has removed most of the topsoil, the area is planted to grass and trees that will bind the soil particles together and build up the soil.

Planting of grass may suffice to hold the soil and will supply grazing. In the Southern states a legume, lespedeza, is very successful in stopping erosion on eroded land and providing fodder. It also builds up the nitrogen content of the soil, thereby helping to restore it for agriculture. Soil-conservation measures that result in the use of grass and legumes will lead to greater diversification in the cash-crop regions, by encouraging dairying and livestock production. Gullies sloped and planted to grass or trees will stop erosion and help rebuild the depleted land. Sometimes crops are planted in strips along the contour, alternating hay with cultivated crops at close enough intervals to check any tendency for erosion to carry material down the slope (Figure 17-9).

On the public range in the Western states, both deficient water supply and erosion by water and wind have become serious problems, brought about by overgrazing. Stock-

men formerly paid nothing to use publicly owned grassland, and many were in the habit of abusing the natural fodder it provided. Finally by the Taylor Grazing Act of the middle 1930s, Congress created range districts in which rights to graze are leased by stockmen. Consequent reduction in the number of animals pastured gave grass and other plants a chance to reseed; experience shows this has increased the carrying capacity of the open grasslands, besides preventing much damage formerly done by erosion. Increasing the plant cover will slow up the runoff and help to replenish the depleted supply of stock water.

Efforts to control movement of soil by the wind and to reseed injured parts of the Great Plains to grass and other plants that will hold soil particles and prevent drifting and erosion have been largely successful. Trees were planted for windbreaks on the plains to reduce wind velocity, decrease evaporation of soil moisture, and help prevent soil movement. Although some windbreaks have been successful, it has been concluded that most of the Great Plains is not suited to tree growth and that other control measures should be adopted. Among methods used to reduce wind erosion are:

1. Cultivation of soil in strips at right an-

Figure 17-10 Strip farming in southern Idaho. These long strips of wheat and fallow land help prevent soil erosion by breaking the force of storm runoff waters. (Photograph, courtesy of the Soil Conservation Service.)

gles to the prevailing wind so that only comparatively narrow surfaces are exposed to wind action (Figure 17-10).

2. Addition of straw, manure, and other refuse to the soil to help prevent the wind from getting a start.

3. Change in methods of cultivating wheat from plowing the ground to disking or subsurface tillage.

4. Leaving a rough clod mulch and unburned stubble mulch, as in dry farming, instead of forming a dust mulch and burning off the straw.

5. Seeding grain by the furrow method, with stubble residues on the surface, whereby moving sand is deposited in the depressions before any extensive erosion occurs.

6. Reseeding of overgrazed, wind-eroded, and otherwise abandoned land. In humid regions trees may be planted to help break the force of the wind.

Farmland Situation in the United States. In the United States there are 460 million acres of potentially good cropland. Some 80 to 100 million acres of this need drainage, irrigation, clearing of woodland, or other labor before they can be used for crops. Of total arable land in the United States, only 70 million acres of the best land lie level enough so that no protection against erosion is required. Control of soil erosion is among our country's most pressing problems and it must be solved if we expect to maintain present high living standards. It is estimated that 100 million acres of our land are being farmed by methods that will conserve soil. Farmers should consider themselves trustees of their land; they should adopt accepted practices for preventing erosion and so help pass the land down to their successors in better condition than that in which they received it.

SUMMARY

Soil is formed from the rock materials of which the earth's crust is made mixed with decaying plant and animal matter and a variety of living organisms. Soils vary widely in ability to support plant life. Among the factors affecting that ability are the nature of the parent rock, presence or absence of moisture, prevailing temperature conditions, and slope of land. Soils may be lime-accumulating (pedocals) or non-lime-accumulating (pedalfers); they may be mature or recently formed. Soil color varies according to the conditions of soil formation. The soil mantle may be stratified, with differing soil horizons, or it may be uniform throughout. Soil textures and structures also vary greatly from place to place. Soils in the United States include podzols, gray-brown forest soils, red-yellow types, prairie, chernozems, chestnut-brown, brown, and gray desert soils. Laterite is a typical mature soil in humid tropics.

Soil erosion results from improper cultivation methods that expose soil to wearing by water and blowing by wind. Among other abuses, one might note attempts to farm slopes that are too steep and unwise burning of plant cover. Soil is also depleted by steady cropping. Methods for conservation of soils include application of fertilizers, use of stable manure or green manure crops, contour cultivation, strip farming, seeding to grass or legumes, rotation of crops, and plowing under of plant litter.

Outline
Soils: origin and characteristics
Soil types in the United States
   Pedalfers
   Pedocals
Utilization of soils
Soil maintenance
Land and national development
Soil conservation
Erosion
   Forms and effects of water erosion
   Wind erosion
Controls
Farmland situation in the United States

QUESTIONS

1. What principal soil groups occur in your locality?

2. How do farmers in your neighborhood correct undesirable soil conditions?

3. How may depleted soils be restored to fertility?
How can their productiveness be maintained?

4. Where has soil erosion occurred in your locality, and how can this damage be repaired?

5. In which climatic realms would the soils tend to become pedocals? Pedalfers?

6. In spite of limited fertility, why are pedalfers more generally useful for agriculture than pedocals?

7. What soil conditions result from each of the following:
Steep slope and small annual precipitation

Poor drainage conditions and slight annual rainfall
Excessive humus and low winter temperatures
Torrential rainfall, no dry season, and dense vegetation cover
Hardpan layer in the B horizon, combined with low annual rainfall

8. In your locality, how is soil productivity apparent in the quality of (*a*) farm structures, (*b*) highways, (*c*) types of transport.

9. Which is the more important factor in the formation of a mature soil: climate or parent rock material? Why?

10. Why do grassland soils contain two to four times as much organic matter as most forest soils?

11. What geographical conditions combine to render northwestern Europe relatively immune from serious soil gullying?

SELECTED REFERENCES

Archer, Sellers G.: *Soil Conservation,* University of Nebraska Press, Lincoln, 1956.

Bennett, H. H.: *Our American Land: The Story of Its Abuse and Its Conservation,* U.S. Soil Conservation Service Miscellaneous Publication 596, Washington, 1946.

————: *Elements of Soil Conservation,* McGraw-Hill Book Company, Inc., New York, 1947.

Dale, Tom: *Topsoil and Civilization,* University of Oklahoma Press, Norman, 1955.

Hyams, Edward S.: *Soil and Civilization,* Thames and Hudson, New York, 1952.

Jacks, Graham V.: *Soil,* Philosophical Library, Inc., New York, 1954.

Kellogg, Charles: *The Soils That Support Us: An Introduction to the Study of Soils and Their Use by Men,* The Macmillan Company, New York, 1941.

————: "Conflicting Doctrines about Soils," *Scientific Monthly,* 66:475–487, June, 1948.

Marbut, C. F.: *Atlas of American Agriculture,* Part 3, *Soils of the United States,* U.S. Department of Agriculture, Washington, 1935.

Mohr, E. C. J.: *Tropical Soils,* Interscience Publishers, Inc., New York, 1954.

Pendleton, R. L.: "Laterite and Its Structural Uses in Thailand and Cambodia," *Geographical Review,* 31:177–202, April, 1941.

Person, H. S.: *Little Waters,* U.S. Soil Conservation Service, Washington, 1936.

Robinson, Gilbert W.: *Soils: Their Origin, Constitution and Classification,* John Wiley & Sons, Inc., New York, 1951.

Sears, Paul B.: *Deserts on the March,* University of Oklahoma Press, Norman, 1935.

Thompson, Louis M.: *Soils and Soil Fertility,* McGraw-Hill Book Company, Inc., New York, 1952.

U.S. Department of Agriculture: Yearbook, *Soils and Men,* Washington, 1938.

U.S. Department of Agriculture: Yearbook, *Soil,* Washington, 1957.

Veatch, J. O.: "The Geographic Significance of the Soil Type," *Annals of the Association of American Geographers,* 40:84–88, March, 1950.

Whitaker, J. R.: "Sequence and Equilibrium in Destruction and Conservation of Natural Resources," *Annals of the Association of American Geographers,* 31:129–144, June, 1941.

White, Gilbert F.: *Human Adjustments to Floods: A Geographical Approach to the Flood Problem in the United States,* University of Chicago Press, Chicago, 1945.

NOTE: Numerous publications of the U.S. Department of Agriculture, as well as those of the U.S. Soil Conservation Service, are helpful in investigating the geography of soils. Many state experiment stations and extension services of state agricultural colleges also provide useful publications in this field.

18. Agriculture

AGRICULTURE is basic to the development of civilization. Hunters, fishermen, and gatherers of wild products tend to remain primitive. Nomadic herders must subordinate their activities to the necessities of their animals; hence, their participation in civilization is generally predatory, as has been pointed out in Chapters 7 and 13. Only an economy based on farming can produce the reliable surplus, security, and leisure needed for cultural progress.

In modern times, many nations have become so industrialized that large numbers of their people live in cities. Ultimately, however, both commerce and industry depend upon agriculture (Figure 23-1) to a major degree. Without the farmer, factory workers and other city dwellers could not be fed, many raw materials like cotton would be lacking, and an important market for the products of

urban industry would be lost. Thus a very close relation exists between the prosperity of cities and that of the rural districts tributary to them; and it is a commonplace to state that cities generally grow in proportion to their hinterlands.

Factors Affecting Agriculture: Land. Several natural and human factors influence utilization of land for agriculture. Soil, rainfall, length of growing season, topographic condition, and location with respect to transportation and markets are among the natural factors affecting agriculture. Before crops can be raised, men must work the land and some land requires much labor: it must be drained, irrigated, or cleared of forest before plowing and planting. Not all land can be tilled—in some areas, only a low percentage is arable, whereas 90 per cent of Belgium or Iowa can be used for crops. Houses, roads, fences, and other works of man may reduce the cultivated acreage. Plants that are available for domestication and improvement, or those that have been introduced by man, also help determine farm crops and farming systems. Systems of landholding, markets, technology and other human activities are also factors affecting agricultural practices.

Density of population and requirements for food crops affect the amount of arable land that is planted to crops. In parts of the Ganges Delta in the province of Bengal, now divided between India and Pakistan, more than 1,000 people per square mile derive support directly from the land, and every bit of soil is cultivated. Similar conditions are found in China and Japan. In contrast, New Zealand, with fertile soil and a favorable climate but only 2 million inhabitants in an area double the size of New York State, uses only 3 per cent of its area for crops and keeps most of its arable land in permanent pasture.

Climate is an important factor in determining the kinds of crops that are raised. Examples include the farms of New England whose cleared land is largely in hay and pasture; the Great Plains, where half the land in a single county may be planted to wheat; a Wyoming ranch, with 99 per cent pasture and 1 per cent hay; and intensively used irrigated land near Los Angeles, devoted to fruit and truck crops. Farming as it is related to conditions in the different climatic regions has been discussed in preceding chapters.

Human Adaptation and Agriculture.   Peoples vary in the food they prefer and the methods of farming that they follow. Different peoples in the same environment may exert quite different effects on the land; thus Manchuria has a climate similar to that of the Dakotas, but the intensity of cultivation is far different. Whereas the farmer in Dakota tills hundreds of acres with machinery, his Chinese counterpart in Manchuria handles a few acres with primitive implements. Western France and England are separated only by the narrow

English Channel, but methods of farming and the organization of rural life are so different that even the appearance of the two landscapes is affected. Systems of agriculture adopted by different peoples vary greatly. By trial and error, man finds those crops which will produce best in the local environment, and in general, he works out a system of farming reasonably well adapted to conditions.

Density of population in a given area may also determine the type of farming that is undertaken. Until the recent introduction of collective farms, the traditional Chinese system of agriculture was characterized by intense cultivation of small farms, in some provinces averaging only 1 to 5 acres per farmer. Chinese agriculture began in the semiarid Wei Ho Valley, which requires irrigation. From their beginning around Sian over five thousand years ago, the Chinese have increased to nearly 600 million people, who may speak different languages and dialects but nevertheless have a similar cultural life in the areas they occupy. Although dependence on rice in southern China changes to reliance on wheat, millet, and grain sorghum in the northern portion, the people use the same intensive methods of farming with only simple implements.

Some people adapt themselves readily to different environmental conditions; others succeed more easily when they emigrate to regions which have an environment similar to that of the old home. Thus settlement of New England and the Middle Colonies by the English was furthered by the fact that the climate resembled Great Britain's sufficiently so that many familiar crops could be raised and livestock kept as in England. English and Scotch sheepherders and dairymen have transferred activities successfully to a similar climatic region in New Zealand, and settlers from the British Isles have populated southeastern and southwestern Australia. On the other hand, Britishers can be found living in many different environments in the world where they often succeed very well in adapting themselves to local conditions.

Italians, with their experience in caring for vineyards and the various Mediterranean fruit trees, succeed well in California, where the climate is similar to that in their Mediterranean homes. Italians and Poles, who are accustomed to hand labor, succeed in the cultivation of market gardens in New York, New Jersey, and the Connecticut Valley. Other examples of good adjustment of immigrant farmers to regions of similar climate include the Finns in northeastern Minnesota, Scandinavians in the Northern states from the Great Lakes to Puget Sound, and the Germans who helped promote dairying in Wisconsin after it had been introduced by settlers from New England and New York.

Agricultural Patterns. Distribution of land used for farming varies widely, depending on factors like relief features, soil, drainage, and local climatic differences. In mountains and eroded plateaus, cultivation is restricted to narrow strips and little plots. In parts of the Great Lakes states, the glacial deposits, lakes, and swamps cause a very patchy pattern of tilled land. In contrast are the fertile lands of the Mississippi Valley and southern Russia, where for miles the land is all productive. In the arid West of our country or in the equally dry Indus Valley in Pakistan, great differences are seen on adjoining plots of land, depending on whether the ground is irrigated or is still untamed desert.

Land included in farms has different uses: tilled crops, orchards, pasture, wood lots, buildings, and lanes. The various uses of the different fields and types of crops raised have marked effects on the cultural landscape, whose appearance changes with the season.

Subsistence Agriculture. Almost all farming operations can be classified into subsistence, cash-crop, and diversified-farming systems. Hundreds of millions of people in the world obtain their chief support on farms from which they secure practically everything they wear, eat, or otherwise consume. Although today it is rare to find an American farmer who does not buy many things he does not produce, the great masses of human beings in China, India, Africa, and Indonesia raise most of what they need and buy comparatively little. Corn-producing American Indians before the days of Columbus were even more self-sufficient, perhaps. Some of the Pueblo Indians of the Southwest and many natives in Latin America, including Indians of the Amazon Valley, still produce nearly all they use. It should not be assumed that all subsistence farms are on a primitive economic level, however. If soil and climate are favorable for agriculture, a subsistence farmer may be well fed, well clothed, and comfortably housed.

In colonial New England, farmers were almost wholly self-sufficient, raising wheat for flour, corn for meal, and buckwheat for hot cakes. Grains were ground by a local mill operated by water power. Maple trees were tapped for sap from which sirup and sugar were made. New Englanders fattened hogs and cured bacon, hams, and salt pork; they tanned leather for shoes made by itinerant shoemakers, and cut their own fuel. Local mills sawed trees into lumber for houses and barns. A prosperous farmer might have an actual cash income of only $20 or $30 per year, yet he needed to buy almost nothing. Women carded wool, spun yarn, and wove homegrown flax and wool into clothing for the entire family. Stockings, mittens, caps, sweaters, and other garments were made from wool. Furs of animals were utilized also. Food, clothing, fuel, and shelter all came from a few acres of New England hillside.

Today New England farms that once produced a surprising variety of goods may grow only hay and a little fruit, with fresh milk and cream the chief source of income, helped by sale of apples and poultry products or by income from tourists. Much corn, bran, and other concentrated feed for cattle and chickens is imported. On many farms in the United States today, the tendency is to specialize on one or more cash crops or on dairying, poultry, or other animal products. Consequently, more farmers are dependent upon the market, variations of prices, demands for products, and fluctuations in industry than in the "good old days." On other farms, for example in the South, the tendency is toward diversification which lessens the risk involved in specializing on one product.

Hundreds of millions of peasant farmers in Asia and Africa live by subsistence agriculture. Poor transportation and other handicaps, sometimes reinforced by custom, compel them to continue the practice. Handling tiny plots of ground by primitive farming methods (Figure 6-5), the peasant by steady application is able to raise barely enough food to maintain himself and his family. Clothing is homemade, and there is little variety in food. Because these farmers have little to sell, they cannot get money to buy. Resulting low standards of living deny such subsistence farmers what American families consider ordinary comforts.

Intensive versus Extensive Agriculture. In general, agriculture can be classified as intensive or extensive. In the United States intensive farming is characteristic of market gardens near large cities, truck and small fruit farms of the Southern states which supply the Northern market in winter and early spring, much irrigated land in the arid West, and fruit orchards nearly everywhere. In densely populated lands nearly all agriculture is intensive (Figure 8-6) because cheap efficient labor abounds.

Intensive agriculture seeks the greatest possible output from a small plot of ground. The expenditure of labor necessary is possible in the United States only when high-priced crops like tobacco and fruits are produced, but in China, India, and Java, where the press of population on the land is very great and workers not crops are surplus, human energy is fully expendable and most crops are grown by intensive methods. Where land is hilly and fields are small or there is a demand for specialty crops like fruit and vegetables that take much human labor, intensive agricultural methods are also found. Such methods may not be economical. Although Belgium grows

nearly twice as much wheat per acre as does the United States, the cost of producing a bushel of wheat by the great expenditure of human energy in Belgium is higher than for raising wheat by machinery in the United States.

In extensive agriculture (Figure 9-8), the farmer seeks to produce the greatest amount of food per unit of manpower rather than per unit of land area. This may lead to somewhat careless methods of farming, and yields per acre will be less than where land is intensively farmed. Nevertheless, by use of power equipment, costs of producing food may actually be less in a land of high wages where machinery is used than in a land of low wages where hand methods prevail. Thus rice is grown in California, Texas, Louisiana, and Arkansas at less cost per bushel than in China or Japan, yet wages in America are many times those paid in the Orient. Extensive agriculture cannot be carried on in all locations. It is best adapted to open plains or gently rolling topography, lacking in dense populations.

Sometimes the system of land ownership has a material effect upon land utilization. For example, the wheat-growing section of Argentina is of crescent shape inland from Buenos Aires. Most land within a hundred miles of Buenos Aires is in stock farms rather than in grain, although soil and climate are usually favorable for wheat and corn. Drainage conditions are poor and rain at harvest is more frequent than farther west, but, the situation cannot be fully explained without noting that this land is held in very large estates. Owners can secure sufficient income with less risk by producing beef cattle, mutton, and wool than by growing grain. They are, therefore, little interested in buying machinery, plowing land, and producing crops for sale.

Agricultural specialization. Although specialization on one crop sometimes leads to larger incomes and higher standards of living, the producer suffers if prices fall or the specialty crop fails. Many farmers, even when they practice diversification, often depend on one product for the major part of their income.

Thus we have the cotton farmer in Arizona, the wheat farmer of the Great Plains, the apple grower of the Northwest, and the fruit ranch producer of California and Florida; even the cattleman or sheepman is likely to specialize on one breed of animal.

Although different soils and climates which are best adapted to certain plants further the growing of crops in well-suited areas, other factors also affect their production. For example, skills developed by specialist farmers may ensure better quality and improved yields even if the environment is not ideal for a certain crop. Great distance to market may reduce the net returns to the producer in an optimum environment. Furthermore, reliance upon one crop is undesirable, since adverse climatic conditions and harmful insect pests and diseases may destroy the single crop or overproduction may prevent its profitable marketing. Reasonable diversification certainly offers less risk than single-crop production.

Diversified farming. Diversified farming is common in the central United States and Western Europe. It exhausts the soil less, because different crops remove different proportions of plant nutrients. Then, too, under diversified farming methods, dairy cattle, pigs, poultry, and other animals are kept, and much hay and grain raised on a farm is consumed by the animals. Their manure goes back to enrich the land, and the farmer gets most of his income from the sale of beef cattle, hogs, calves, wool, lambs, milk, eggs, and poultry.

Among other significant features of this type of farming are (1) growing of legumes or other soil-building crops and (2) well-developed systems of crop rotation. Clover and other fodder crops are fed to livestock, and the soil fertility is maintained by these green-manure crops in addition to the animal product. If a farmer practicing mixed farming raises grain for sale, it is probably a side issue; and failure of grain, apples, or any one commercial product will not mean complete economic loss. Recently in the Middle West there has been a large expansion in the growing of soybeans, which have proved a good rotation crop in this region.

The proprietor of a farm where large numbers of animals are kept is confined to his home more closely than the producer of a single crop. A cotton or wheat grower of the Great Plains may work only a hundred days each year to get his crop grown. It may not be as profitable when he sells it, but he actually works only from one-third to one-fourth of a year, whereas farmers using diversified agriculture are busy at some task at least part of every day in the year.

Plantation agriculture. Man seeks first to provide food for his own needs and for those of his immediate family, tribe, or clan. This involves relatively small planted areas, no larger than an individual and his relatives can work comfortably. In contrast with diversified or subsistence agriculture, one-crop farming may be carried to extremes and reach a scale that resembles factory production.

Some parts of the world are adapted to large-scale but often intensive cultivation of products which have an export market. This is particularly true of tropical and subtropical lands, where trees are so large and numerous that people must work together in order to develop a tract of land for production of commercial crops. Such combined effort, under some form of compulsion results in large landholdings. Such large farms or plantations also require intricate financing, special types of implements for cultivation, and an elaborate and expensive system of transport for sending commodities to market. A labor force is also needed that may mount to thousands of men.

As an economic enterprise, the plantation system is especially well adapted to tropical regions, producing marketable surpluses of foods or other goods—most of which are shipped to mid-latitude consuming centers as luxury commodities or industrial raw materials. Included are bananas, coconuts, cane sugar, pepper, pineapples, cloves, tobacco, tea, coffee, chocolate, rubber, cotton, and abacá, as well as many others less well known in this country. For the most part the great plantation crops have come on world markets in recent times, although tea, pepper, cloves, and a few others have been important articles of trade for centuries. Such perishable items as pineapples and bananas could not be shipped satisfactorily until canning and refrigerator shipment had been perfected. Rubber entered world trade in quantity only after the invention of the automobile. Chocolate and cane sugar, used in small quantities by the wealthy a century ago, have become household staples in lands that enjoy high purchasing power.

In the modern world, commercial output in a given region may come from both plantations and individual growers. Large plantations in the Malay Peninsula, Sumatra, and other East Indian islands are given over to rubber production, but in Java rubber is mostly grown on a lesser scale by individuals. Abacá plantations for the manila hemp used for rope are located in the southern Philippines. Hawaii grows both cane sugar and pineapples on the plantation system (Figure 18-1). Two-thirds of the world's cacao (choc-

olate) comes from West Africa and tropical America, from both large plantations and small farms. Cotton plantations are common in our subtropical southeastern states, although more is grown by independent farmers. Cotton is also grown in quantities in India, Brazil, and Egypt partly by the same system. Coconut plantations fringe the shores of South Pacific islands; and the coffee plantations of Brazil and tea plantations of Ceylon, India, and Java are famous. The tea of China and Japan comes mostly from small holdings.

Development of the plantation system in the humid tropics has resulted in widespread shifts of producing areas, as world-wide demand increased and the original producing area was found inadequate to meet the demand. Thus rubber, originally a native of the Western Hemisphere, shifted from northern Brazil to southeastern Asia, where a dependable and adequate labor supply was available. The cacao plant, source of our chocolate, cocoa, and cocoa butter, changed its principal plantation area from countries of northwest-

Figure 18-1 Pineapples under cultivation in a Hawaiian field. The rich soils formed from decomposed lavas support this fine commercial crop. Weeds are prevented from growing between rows of pineapple plants by means of paper strips fastened to the ground. (Photograph used by permission of the Hawaii Visitors Bureau.)

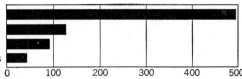

Figure 18-2   Wheat and flour exports in thousands of bushels, 1955. (From World Almanac, 1957, p. 681.)

ern South America and Brazil to Nigeria, Ghana (Gold Coast), and other West African centers. Coffee, a plant believed to have originated in Arabia, is now grown as a plantation crop in the Western Hemisphere in Central and South American highlands. Many other producing areas have been radically changed as the world has come to know and appreciate the products which tropical plantations contribute to its comfort.

Staffs of Life.   Most peoples of the world prefer a particular grain or starchy foodstuff for their "staff of life." Some of these foods are grown extensively in certain areas and shipped to distant markets; others are consumed almost entirely by the community where the crop is raised.

Wheat enters international trade to a greater extent than do other grains. Out of a total world wheat crop of about 5½ to 6 billion bushels annually more than a billion bushels are involved in foreign trade. Most export wheat comes from the United States, Canada, Argentina, and Australia; the U.S.S.R., Hungary, Romania, and North Africa usually have some surplus for sale (Figure 18-2). France, Italy, Germany, Poland, China, northern India, West Pakistan, the Balkans, and the Near East grow large amounts of wheat but can seldom spare grain for export. Even England grows some wheat, although it is the largest importer of the grain. Other countries in Southern, Western, and Northern Europe are important buyers of wheat, and some is sent to tropical countries where it cannot be raised. In Western and Southern Europe, China, India, and the eastern United States, wheat is raised on small to moderately sized farms, usually in rotation with other crops (Figure 18-3).

In the important exporting regions, wheat

is raised on large farms, often completely mechanized, and ranging from several hundred to thousands of acres in size. The areas now used for cash wheat production formerly were mainly semiarid grasslands. In North America, the wheat belt covers much of the Great Plains and extends from northern Texas northward to beyond Edmonton, Canada. The black-soil belt in the U.S.S.R. extends eastward from the southern Ukraine into Siberia and is one of the great wheat regions of the world, much of the grain coming from large communal farms.

Rice is typically grown in monsoon regions of eastern and southeastern Asia, with small amounts harvested in other tropical and warm temperate regions. Southern China, the humid lowlands of India, East Pakistan, Japan, Java, and the Philippines are large producers and consumers of rice (Figure 18-4). Burma and Thailand are the most important exporters, with the United States in third place. South Vietnam and Cambodia also export rice. In the United States, rice is grown chiefly in California, Texas, Louisiana, and Arkansas, always on large farms. Sections of Brazil, north-

Figure 18-3   World production of wheat (excluding U.S.S.R. for which data are uncertain), in millions of bushels 1955. Total world production, 7,405 million bushels. (From Encyclopedia Britannica, Book of the Year, 1957, p. 807.)

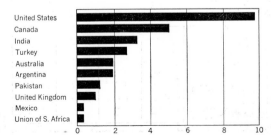

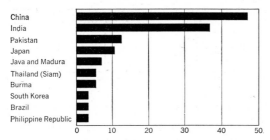

China
India
Pakistan
Japan
Java and Madura
Thailand (Siam)
Burma
South Korea
Brazil
Philippine Republic

0   10   20   30   40   50

Figure 18-4 Rice production in millions of metric tons, 1954, excluding U.S.S.R. for which data are unreliable. Total world production, 161,900 thousand metric tons. About 49 bushels of rice weigh 1 metric ton. Burma and Thailand are the largest rice exporters, and rice constituted 75 per cent of the total exports of Burma in 1955. (From The Statesman's Year Book, 1956.)

ern Argentina, Egypt, Spain, and Italy grow some rice for local consumption. Nearly half the world's people call rice their staff of life, and the quantity grown exceeds that of wheat. Most of this huge crop is raised by hand methods and is consumed by the people who plant it, as described in Chapter 6. Only in the United States are machine methods used in planting and harvesting rice.

Corn, or maize, was a native of the New World but has been carried from the Americas to Africa, Europe, and Asia, where it is becoming of increasing importance. The world crop totals approximately that of both wheat and rice. Of this total the United States grows more than half. Corn is used for food by many people, but most of the crop is fed to livestock (Figure 18-6). Some corn is processed and

Figure 18-5 Corn production in billions of bushels, 1955. Total world production, 6.28 billion bushels. (From The Statesman's Year Book, 1957.)

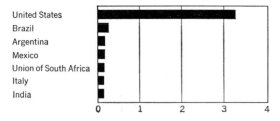

United States
Brazil
Argentina
Mexico
Union of South Africa
Italy
India

0   1   2   3   4

sold as sirup, starch, and other products. The United States is not a large exporter of corn but does export pork products after the pigs have been fattened on the grain. Although Argentina grows less corn than the United States, it ships more corn to Europe than does our country. Hungary, northern China, Africa, Mexico, and Middle and South America are among producers of corn. Corn thrives best in a humid climate with warm summers. Cold limits the northward extent of the Corn Belt in the central Mississippi Valley; dryness governs the westward limit.

Minor grains cultivated by man are numerous. Oats, used mostly for livestock, are grown in midlatitudes. Rye is so hardy that it can be planted in poor soils and on land too dry and frosty for wheat, which it will generally outyield under unfavorable conditions. Some barley is grown as a spring-planted crop in northern midlatitudes; it is also grown as a winter crop in regions with a Mediterranean climate. Barley is used as a food for both men and animals. Millet and grain sorghums supply a cheap food in regions where poor people cannot afford rice and wheat, as in Africa, northern China, and India; in the United States these grains are grown almost entirely for stock feed.

Beans and peas. Soybeans have a high protein and fat content; they serve as a valuable food, a source of oil, a stock feed, and a raw material for industry. Formerly soybeans were imported from Manchuria and other parts of China, but now they are widely grown in the central United States. Several varieties of beans are grown for human food. Similar crops include peas, pigeon peas, and lentils.

Starchy foods. Tubers and roots of many plants provide needed starch for the human diet. The white potato was native to the highlands of South America but was carried to Europe and has become a most important food on that continent where it thrives in cool rainy regions. An acre planted to potatoes will supply more food than an equal area of most other crops; hence potatoes are particularly

Figure 18-6 Corn Belt farm in Iowa, with evidence of prosperous farming. Domestic water is obtained from shallow wells operated by windmills. Barns are large enough to hold herds of cattle during the winter and to provide storage for hay and grain; silage is stored in the silo at end of barn. This farm is well provided with outbuildings for shelter of machinery, and the dwelling is large and modern. (Photograph, courtesy of the U.S. Department of Agriculture.)

useful in thickly populated areas with suitable climate. Poland, the U.S.S.R., Germany, France, and Czechoslovakia are leading producers, but most European countries grow potatoes and they have been introduced into northern China. In Europe potatoes are used to feed stock and to make beer, industrial alcohol, and starch; in the United States, their chief use is as human food.

Sweet potatoes are grown in quantity in the Southern states and throughout the tropics. They are valuable for stock feed as well as a useful food for man. Roots of the manioc, or tapioca plant, are extensively grown in rainy tropical regions. Taro, arrowroot, and the pithy trunk of the sago palm in Indonesia, and some varieties of tree ferns in the Pacific islands have been used as foods.

Fruits that contain much starch and are widely used for food include many varieties of the banana. In the Congo Basin and the Amazon Valley it is the most important food for some native tribes, and it supplements rice and other foods in many other tropical localities. Lands tributary to the Caribbean Sea raise bananas by the plantation system and export them by the shipload to the United States.

In the South Pacific islands the breadfruit has been widely used as a main source of starch in the native diet.

Livestock. When using plants he has sown, cultivated, and harvested, man goes directly to the land for his food and shelter needs. If for the sake of variety or for other reasons he uses animal products, man concentrates on their feeding and care; he eats plants indirectly, as it were.

In general, direct consumption of plant life will allow the earth to support more people than indirect consumption through livestock. In most populous parts of the world, for great masses of people, meat is a luxury food, but in more sparsely populated semiarid lands livestock can be raised on a large scale where natural conditions are unfavorable for farming. Furthermore, purchasing power and high

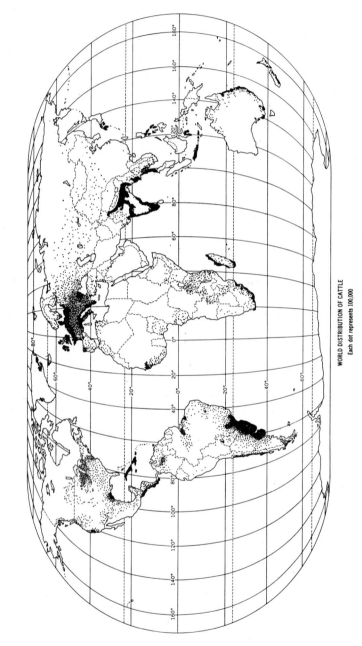

WORLD DISTRIBUTION OF CATTLE
Each dot represents 100,000

Figure 18-7 World distribution of cattle.

standards of living enable urban people in some lands to use dairy products; this creates a commercial demand for cheese and butter, and stimulates production of animals for these purposes.

In many respects herding is the same throughout the world, whether emphasis be placed upon cattle or upon sheep. In either case, it is possible to use extensive ranges or fenced small pastures. If large ranches are used, the cattleman, and to a great extent the sheepherder, tend to lead a seminomadic life, dependent upon the location of good forage for the animals. Isolation is often the stockman's lot for long periods, and he must rely on his dog and horse for companionship. Thus the cowboy, *vaquero,* or *gaucho* leads a life unfamiliar to his sedentary countrymen. Similarly, the sheepherder, whether he tends flocks on the slopes of Palestinian hills, among the Owyhee uplands of Idaho, in the Kittitas Valley of Washington, or in more remote parts of the world, follows an isolated, seminomadic pattern of life in search of water and feed for his charges.

The ancestors of the Boers or Afrikanders in South Africa came from the rainy fertile Netherlands, where intensive farming and dairying were customary. In the semiarid veld (grasslands) of their new home these people adapted themselves to quite a different environment. They became stockmen, each occupying a large tract of land and farming extensively when they farmed at all.

Arid and semiarid climatic regions may have sufficient precipitation for grasses that can be used for animal feeding but insufficient moisture to allow actual cultivation of the land with any marked success. These borderline sections occupy large parts of western North America, central Asia, and southern South America in the middle latitudes. Other similar regions include interior parts of Australia, North and South Africa, and northern South America in the lower latitudes. Generally stock-raising activities, leading to production of meat and hides, are on a very ex-

tensive scale. The same is true of sheep raising, which provides both wool and meat.

Cattle. Among the great cattle-producing countries are India and Pakistan but their cattle, largely used for draft purposes, contribute little meat or hides to the flow of world trade. The United States leads the world in beef and dairy cattle. Brazil, Argentina, and Australia also raise much cattle. In China, cattle are draft animals and are usually eaten only when they can work no longer (Figures 18-7 and 18-8). In semiarid regions there is a close relationship among numbers of cattle, quality of the forage, and expanse of land used for grazing. If grass is poor or cattle are too numerous for the "carrying capacity" of the range, the quality of the final product is bound to be inferior, the supply of good grass is destroyed or diminished, erosion sets in, and the range declines in productivity. This must be guarded against, particularly where cattle are grown extensively on a commercial basis as on the Great Plains or the Argentine Pampa. Cattle production by family or tribal units on a noncommercial basis in central Africa is less likely to bring unsatisfactory results unless abuse of the natural grazing resources prevails.

One requirement for successful livestock ranching is a large extent of range. This entails widely spaced ranch settlements, fencing or some other method of keeping cattle under control, annual gatherings for branding or slaughtering, and men specially trained in

Figure 18-8   Cattle production in thousands of head, estimated for 1955, (Soviet Union data for 1953). (From Agricultural Statistics, U.S. Department of Agriculture, Washington, 1956, pp. 306–307.)

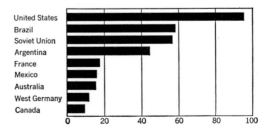

cattle ranching. Great progress in livestock ranching has been associated with improvement in cattle breeding and the elimination of insect pests. Gradually most serious cattle pests and diseases have come under control. Animal breeding can be carried on successfully with definite objectives—breeding for richer milk or larger output, heavier weight and more meat, more tender meat, and the like. The practice of artificial insemination promises to make improvement in animal stocks more widespread.

Northwestern Europe, which is unable to provide enough for its millions of people, is the chief market for meat. The United Kingdom especially is a large importer of beef products, which are also bought by Germany, Sweden, and France. Mediterranean Europe uses relatively small amounts of beef. The principal exporter of beef and beef products is Argentina, followed by Australia, New Zealand, and Brazil, but Argentina is far ahead of other nations in this trade. For its size, Ireland is an important exporter of beef cattle; these come mainly from farms smaller than those located in less rainy regions. English farms and those in our own Middle West also make significant contributions to the meat supply.

Dairying.   In contrast to the extensive activity involved in production of range cattle for beef and hides, the dairy industry illustrates intensive activity. It usually requires much smaller space in which to operate and thus is found in the more humid parts of mid-latitude regions, close to large urban centers that rely upon its milk and cheese for part of their food. The notable exception is New Zealand, whose butter and other dairy products have found a world market despite its distance from large consuming markets. This was made possible by invention of processes for preserving milk through canning, dehydrating, and rapid shipment under mechanical refrigeration. Denmark and the Netherlands both specialize on dairy products, the former on butter and the latter on cheese. Both find ready markets in neighboring nations.

Dairying as a human occupation may call for stall feeding of cows if the enterprise is located in regions of severe winter, as in the northeastern United States. This involves cutting, drying, and storing hay, silage, or other feed in amounts sufficient to carry the dairy herd through the winter, and it may add considerably to costs of production. Extreme care must be taken to ensure cleanliness of the product. Rapid transit and other considerations make dairying a highly specialized and advanced form of human economy—and a highly profitable one if geographical conditions are right. Stall feeding is also done in other places like California where alfalfa and other fodder is harvested by machines. In Western Europe many cows are stall fed because most farms are small and land, where possible, is used to grow fodder and other crops. The animal manure is carefully saved and applied to the cropland, which helps to maintain soil fertility and good yields.

Sheep, like cows, are multiple-purpose animals and of widespread distribution, though the New World did not have them before the Spanish conquest. At present sheep are raised in greatest numbers in Australia, the Soviet Union, Argentina, and New Zealand (Figure 18-9). In the Soviet Union, they are needed for food and clothing by the Russians and the many natives of central Asia. In Australia and New Zealand, sheep are grown far in excess of local needs and both mutton and wool are exported to northwestern Europe, especially to Great Britain to augment British sheep production. Other principal producing countries include Argentina, Uruguay, India, the Union of South Africa, and many Mediterranean lands. In the western United States sheep are raised mostly by the ranching method, but in the northeastern part of our country they are commonly kept in fenced pastures, as in the hills of southern Ohio. Sheep are raised successfully throughout middle latitudes, where they withstand cold winters, as well as in dry climates where they can utilize grazing too meager for larger animals. They also do well in the high altitudes of the tropics, along with

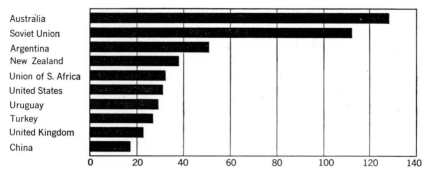

Figure 18-9   Numbers of sheep in major producing countries, in millions, 1954. (From Agricultural Statistics, U.S. Department of Agriculture, Washington, 1956, pp. 334–335.)

other wool- and hair-bearing animals such as the alpaca and llama of South America's highlands.

Goats, to a greater extent than sheep, can utilize poor forage and usually are kept in lower latitudes than either sheep or cattle. They need not range as widely as sheep or cows in search of water and thus they are well adapted to domestic production among such sedentary peoples as the oasis dwellers of Arabia or the Sahara. Goats provide a poor meat supply but produce rich and easily digested milk. They are most common in India, Pakistan, the Union of South Africa, Turkey, Spain, Greece, and other Mediterranean countries. China, the U.S.S.R., Iran, Mexico, and Argentina each has millions of goats. Their presence usually indicates low standards of living. The angora breed provides a commercial product, mohair, highly valued for cloth.

Swine are sometimes scavengers, relying on almost any form of food they can find, but in other situations may be carefully bred, fed, and cared for. Although in some parts of the world pigs are given little attention, in the Middle West they are of selected stock and are generally fattened on corn. Here pigs are not allowed to range far from the home pen and are used as little manufacturing plants to turn grain and various foods that might otherwise be wasted into excellent meat. For the amount it eats a pig puts on more weight than perhaps any other animal. The ease with which pork products is cured is an advantage in the utilization of the meat.

Swine are found in greatest numbers in China, the United States, the Soviet Union, Germany, and Brazil. In northwestern Europe and United States the pig has become the basis for a large commercial meat industry. In other parts of the world, the pig is not commercialized and merely forms one element in the subsistence economy of the peasant farmer. Among Moslems, Hindus, and Jews, religious beliefs inhibit the use of pork.

Tree Crops. Most people consider cultivation of the land, with its attendant emphasis on grains, small fruits, tubers, and the like, as its most important use. This may be true in locations where soil depth and fertility, climate, and relief of the land unite to provide a satisfactory combination of natural factors leading to agriculture. On the other hand, if soils are markedly infertile or hill slopes are too steep for successful cultivation, it may be more profitable to retain and improve native stands of trees rather than destroy the forest cover. Many trees, such as the chestnut, sugar maple, and cherry, provide food for man or animals and at the same time are valuable sources of timber. When properly handled, groves of trees may contribute more wealth to their owners than if the land were cleared or planted. Tree plantations of teak in Burma, Christmas trees in Michigan and Pennsylvania, "sugar bush" in Ohio, Pennsylvania, or Vermont, rubber in the Straits Settlements, olives in Italy, lemon groves in Sicily, or orange groves in southern California make important contributions to the world's store of products.

Trees are slow to mature; hence monetary return on investment in them is long in coming. A cork oak grove, for example, may bring no profit whatever for more than a generation of ownership. This delay in return on the investment frequently deters landowners from devoting efforts to "tree farming," and tempts them to clear and plow slopes. This can lead to the permanent detriment of the land use in their neighborhood, causing silting of streams, erosion of slopes, decrease of soil fertility, and other unfortunate accompaniments of maladjusted land use.

Farming and Self-sufficiency. Some nations from the standpoint of national defense feel that it is desirable to become as nearly self-sufficient as possible. High protective tariffs, bonuses, import quotas, and other schemes may be used to promote the production of crops that would be unprofitable without such aids. Thus several European countries produce their own sugar from beets at higher cost than they could buy cane sugar from the tropics. In time of war the nation would have its own supply; in time of peace the money that would be spent for imported sugar is retained at home. Before the Second World War, Germany and Italy endeavored to increase food crops with considerable success; lessened imports made these countries more self-sufficient. Schemes that cut down normal imports of farm crops help domestic producers at the expense of domestic consumers, who must pay higher prices for food, and of exporters in other lands where natural conditions are unusually favorable for cheap production.

Farming in the United States. Farms and ranches include about 55 per cent of the total area of the United States. The rest is mountains, forests, deserts, swamps, and parks, or is used for nonagricultural purposes like roads and towns. Only 17 per cent of the total area

of our country is in crops; this is less than one-third the acreage of farms and ranches. To every acre in crops, two acres are in pasture and wood lots. If demand for food crops increases, the acreage under cultivation could be expanded by at least one-half. The expense of farming this additional acreage would probably exceed present average costs, since the best and most easily tilled land is developed before inferior types are used. With the passing of time, changes in farm systems and increase in population alter the agricultural pattern. Thus an Ohio farm might be used first for sustenance, then for cash wheat, and now for diversified farming.

The different crops raised, whether cotton, corn, wheat, orchard fruits, tobacco, or other staples, bring decided changes in the landscape. Buildings, size of fields and farms, and number and kind of livestock are related to the money crop of a region. The buildings of a dairy farm would include a big barn for storing feed. Many windows on the ground floor indicate locations of stalls for the cows. High round silos and many sheds for pigs, poultry, and machinery are located nearby. In California with its mild winters, hay is stored in the open for the short period of feeding during the dry season, and silage is not needed. Barns are small, since cows can spend most seasons in open pastures. In tobacco country, sheds with adjustable openings for curing the leaf are characteristic features of the farm complex.

Numerous types of farm landscape are found in the United States (Figure 18-10). Thus in the northeastern region, farms are devoted to dairying or to specialty crops like potatoes in Aroostook County, Maine, or tobacco and onions in the Connecticut Valley (Figure 8-12). Dairy farms, with large barns for storing hay during the snowy winter and provision for quarters for the livestock, continue through New York, Indiana, Michigan, and Wisconsin.

In the far South the money crop consists of cotton, raised generally by tenants, both white and colored, living in poor shacks with little

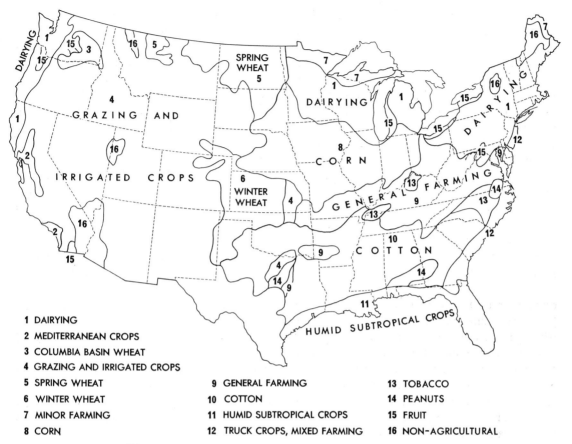

1 DAIRYING

2 MEDITERRANEAN CROPS

3 COLUMBIA BASIN WHEAT

4 GRAZING AND IRRIGATED CROPS

5 SPRING WHEAT	9 GENERAL FARMING	13 TOBACCO
6 WINTER WHEAT	10 COTTON	14 PEANUTS
7 MINOR FARMING	11 HUMID SUBTROPICAL CROPS	15 FRUIT
8 CORN	12 TRUCK CROPS, MIXED FARMING	16 NON-AGRICULTURAL

Figure 18-10   Dominant agricultural activities and crops in the United States.

livestock or equipment and handling from 10 to 20 acres of land. The amount of land planted to cotton is chiefly determined by the number of "hands" a family can muster for picking the crop. Cotton-picking machines are also used, especially on the large farms. Interspersed through the Cotton Belt are rice farms in Arkansas, Texas, and Louisiana, where conditions favor the plant, sugar cane in Louisiana and Florida, citrus orchards in central Florida, and truck gardens to supply Northern markets with vegetables and berries in winter and spring.

In areas of fertile soil, farms of the Middle Atlantic states west to the Corn Belt are generally characterized by prosperous houses, red barns, and numerous outbuildings for livestock and machinery (Figure 9-11). Farms average from 60 to more than 100 acres in size. They have pasture land, fields devoted to grain and other crops for two or three years and then planted to clover to replenish the soil, hay land, and wood lots. Milk, animals, wool, poultry, and some grain and fruit are all sold from these farms. A Corn Belt farm is generally a sort of manufacturing establishment to turn corn and other fodder into products for sale, with the animal or green manure used to maintain soil fertility.

In the Southern highlands the farming system is of a diversified type, with chickens, pigs, and a cow usually kept. Corn and other crops are raised on hilly ground that is often subject to erosion. Resulting crop yields are so poor as to permit only a low standard of living. In some sections patches of tobacco are raised as a money crop, since it is valuable enough to stand transportation costs. Although subsistence farming was once common in this region it now has almost ceased. Many rural residents farm on only a part-time basis. Coal mining or logging provide employment, as do mills in nearby towns.

On the eastern section of the Great Plains, summer rainfall and the growing season favor winter wheat in the central area and spring wheat in the northern portion. Although corn is sometimes planted, the usual light rainfall prevents average yields that equal those further east. Grain sorghum grown for stock feed is rather drought resistant and does well on the southern plains. The farms are a half-section to a section (640 acres) or more in size, and where rainfall drops below 20 inches annually, land is left in summer fallow once every third year. Sometimes this is done every other year so that the farmer has only one-half to two-thirds of his land under cultivation at one time. Some wheat farms are entirely mechanized and have no livestock whatever. Under these conditions, the house is the most prominent building. Farmers can attain a more secure existence by practicing diversification and producing livestock as a side line, rather than gambling on wheat year after year.

The drier and rougher sections of the Great Plains, Rocky Mountain, and Plateau areas are devoted to sheep and cattle ranches. Here the carrying capacity of the land is low, and 40 acres or more of land may be required to furnish fodder for one steer. Under these circumstances, ranches may average from 5,000 to 10,000 or 20,000 acres in extent, with occasional places as large as 100,000 acres or more. Many ranches have access to public range land or national forests in which grazing rights may be leased. In the grazing country not only are ranches far apart, but trading centers are also widely scattered, sometimes with intervals of 50 or 100 miles between towns, yet these centers seldom support more than a few hundred people.

Where irrigation may be practiced and a growing season of 150 days or more prevails, intensive agricultural development by irrigation has occurred. Often different sections have specialized on certain crops, although alfalfa is grown almost everywhere. Near Salt Lake City, in the Yakima and Wenatchee Valleys of Washington, and the Hood River Valley in Oregon, apples, cherries, peaches, pears, and other fruits are important (Figure 18-11). The Snake River Valley in Idaho, the Yakima and Moses Lake areas in Washington, and the delta region in California grow many potatoes. Sugar beets are a specialty of Utah and southern Idaho, as are hops in the Yakima and Willamette Valleys. The average apple orchard in the Wenatchee Valley is 15 acres in size. Owners live as near together as suburban residents and are served with running water, electricity, gas, and other facilities as though they lived in a city. Oranges, grapes, and other fruits in California are generally raised under similar conditions.

These areas are very pleasant places but when a grower produces only one crop he has no other commodity to fall back on should yield fail or prices drop. In some years many growers in the Northwest pay the railroads more for transporting their apples to market than the producers receive. Yet from that they must meet the cost of boxes, tree pruning, irrigation, spraying, picking, cultivation, and packing the crop, as well as taxes and interest on farm mortgages. Then may follow several years of bumper crops and top prices. Obviously, farm income must be averaged over a term of ten years or longer to determine whether operations are profitable.

In California some owners of fruit ranches have retired from other businesses and look upon their places rather as pleasant homes than as income producers, but the man who is dependent upon fruit for his income frequently faces a difficult situation when frost kills his crop, the price collapses, or some other misfortune occurs. Diversification for the fruitgrower so that there shall be some income or at least sustenance from an acre or two, with a cow and poultry kept as a side line, appears to be the solution to some problems of the western fruit "rancher."

Figure 18-11   Irrigation of a young apple orchard in the Columbia River Basin near Sunnyside, Washington. Note the comfortable and modern farmhouse, served by abundant and cheap electricity. (Photograph, courtesy of the U.S. Bureau of Reclamation, Department of the Interior.)

In the mild climate of Puget Sound, the Willamette lowland, and California where abundant rainfall or irrigation provides plenty of feed, there are excellent dairying and poultry sections.

Vegetables grown under irrigation in the winter and shipped to Eastern cities are a specialty of the Imperial Valley in California and the Rio Grande Valley in Texas.

Some Controls for Agriculture. Various natural factors affect the crops raised and the methods adopted by farmers. A truck gardener supplying small fruits and fresh vegetables to a nearby city market needs level land relatively free from frost, close to his market. Natural fertility of the soil may not be a controlling factor in selection of the land, since truck crops have a high value per acre, and fertilizers can well be afforded. If crops are being raised in the South during winter for sale in Northern cities, convenience to rapid transportation, labor supply, freedom from frost, and perhaps water for irrigation are factors which affect production.

Different controls limit crops in various parts of the earth. Hog raising is uncommon in Moslem lands because religious belief prevents Mohammedans from eating pork. In Australia, farming is generally limited by rainfall conditions. In the southern part of Australia, the lower limit of rainfall for wheat growing is a reliable average of 12 inches per year. Rainfall to be "effective" must not vary greatly from this average and must fall when needed by the crop. If the 12-inch average is made up of 6 inches for two years and 24 in the third year, crop failures would be so much more frequent than successful yields that wheat farming could not succeed. In northern Australia at least 20 inches of rainfall are required even for grazing as the result of excessive evaporation because of high temperatures and prolonged dry season. In Canada and Siberia temperature is the poleward limiting factor in agriculture; both short growing season and absolute lack of heat may preclude farming operations.

In some places, especially tropical countries where living is simple and cheap, a limiting factor in agriculture is the type or supply of labor available. The men may be there but are disinclined to prolonged hard labor under the tropical sun. For plantations to succeed in these places, races more accustomed to regular work may be introduced. Thus Japanese and Filipinos raise sugar cane in Hawaii. Although tobacco is typically grown by owners and sharecroppers in small fields, sometimes hired labor is used on the big places in the Bluegrass region of Kentucky (Figure 18-12), and Negroes are hired to work in the cane fields of Louisiana. Indians were brought from Asia to work in Fiji and British Guiana. Usually plantation labor is colored, but in Queensland in tropical Australia, in Peru, Argentina, Puerto Rico, and on many plantations in Brazil and Cuba, white laborers tend and cut sugar cane despite the hot sun.

Natural limiting factors may operate for or against a certain industry, such as livestock. Thus in Japan, a hilly rainy country, the livestock industry would appear to be appropriate. Native grasses are so tough and indigestible, however, that no animal can live upon them; furthermore, they tend to choke out pastures started from imported grass seed. The number of animals that can be fed from planted fodder crops is quite small for the country, since the large population needs most tilled land to raise food for people rather than for animals. Thus special handicaps limit expansion of livestock production in Japan. In contrast, New Zealand has good native grasses and extensive sown pastures of introduced grasses. Both have high carrying capacity which enables the country to keep 30 million sheep and more than 4 million cattle in an area only as large as the state of Oregon.

Insects and Diseases. Insects and insect-borne diseases of plants and animals sometimes are important environmental factors. Plagues of insects, like grasshoppers on our western plains and the locust in Mediterranean lands, sometimes occur. Nearly every plant has insect parasites that eat its fruit and leaves. They burrow under bark, gnaw roots, or injure it in some other way. Usually other insects prey on these parasites, and climatic and other natural conditions keep down their rate of increase; but occasionally controls are absent or weak, and then severe damage results.

Planting of commercial crops in plantations in the tropics, where no frost stops the natural increase in insect numbers, furnishes a vast new food supply for insect pests. They are controlled by poisons, parasites that prey on the destructive insects, and breeding of resist-

Figure 18-12 Topping tobacco plants on a Southern farm. Note the extensive plain which lends itself to mechanized cultivation when the crop will bear the costs of machinery. (Photograph, courtesy of the U.S. Department of Agriculture.)

ant species of plants. Fighting them adds to the expense and trouble of farming, but it is necessary for successful plantation operation in the tropics.

Another limiting factor for crops may be contagious diseases. Thus coffee blight has nearly wiped out coffee production in Ceylon; the witches'-broom disease has gravely injured cacao plantations in Ecuador, and the Panama disease has reduced banana output from central America. When controls for a disease are discovered, added expenses increase costs of production. Animals suffer from many diseases carried by insects. Thus the tsetse fly transmits so deadly a disease to cattle and horses that few of these creatures can survive in the damp lands of central Africa. The tick-borne Texas cattle fever, until brought under control by dipping animals in oils that killed the ticks, excluded the introduction of unaffected stock for breeding purposes. Unacclimated animals died quickly, although native-born animals had acquired an immunity to the disease. In fruit-growing sections of the United States, spraying against the codling moth, San Jose scale, and other insects, is a large item in the labor and expense of production. The cotton boll weevil (Figure 18-13), Hessian fly, corn borer, cutworm, wireworm, chinch bug, Japanese beetle, earwigs, and other crop pests are regularly fought by United States farmers, but total damage done crops in this country by insects amounts to many hundreds of millions of dollars per year.

Not all insects are harmful; some, like the bee and the silkworm, have been domesticated. Others are needed for pollination of certain plants. The fig tree, for example, produced no fruit in California until a tiny wasp that pollinated the blossoms was introduced. The spread of ordinary clover and the honeybee of necessity go together.

Government Aid to Agriculture. Many trained men, under both private and government auspices, are devoting their entire time to studying plants, soils, domestic animals, and control of pests and diseases. They ex-

Figure 18-13 Enlarged photograph of a boll weevil damaging a cotton boll. (Used by permission of the U.S. Department of Agriculture.)

periment in order to find what crops are best adapted to a region. They seek to develop new and better varieties, and to discover how to handle, improve, and conserve land. Their work helps farmers improve products, increase production, and reduce costs. Studies of the experts deal with desirable crop rotations, systems of farming that will reduce erosion, methods of marketing that prevent losses in transit, the best strains of a particular crop, and fertilizers suitable for particular soil types. Nearly every state has one or more agricultural experiment stations, and the Federal government also maintains numerous experimental farms. Plant explorers are sent out over the whole earth to find promising new plants and varieties to introduce into this country. Plant breeders have developed new types of grains and fruits that are great improvements over the original stock. Thus wheats have been bred that resist drought, rust, winterkilling, or Hessian fly, that have increased gluten content for flour, or that outyield other varieties. By crossing certain berries, the new loganberry and youngberry were developed.

Strict quarantine measures limit spread of livestock diseases like foot-and-mouth disease, Texas cattle fever, Bang's disease, and bovine tuberculosis. Plants brought into the country are carefully examined to determine if they are free of parasites and disease. When pests have been introduced or native species become damaging, the insects are studied, and poisons or other control measures recommended. Sometimes parasites can be introduced that will feed upon and largely destroy harmful plant pests. In case of a bad infestation, temporary quarantines may be enforced to prohibit shipment of infected fruit so as to prevent spread of the trouble. Thus the Mediterranean fruit fly was introduced into Florida; but by quar-

antine and destruction of infested fruit, it has apparently been exterminated.

Various modern inventions have also greatly aided the expansion and development of agriculture. Among these are laborsaving tillage and harvesting machinery, rapid transportation by railroads, trucks, and ships, refrigeration, and processing that preserves and condenses foods.

SUMMARY

The primary human economy is agriculture. Tilling the soil to improve production of crops provides food necessary as population increases. Soil conditions, slope of the fields, rainfall, sunshine, and dates of killing frost all help govern the amount and kind of food plants grown.

Much farming, especially in Asia and Africa, is done on a small scale; it is subsistence not commercial farming. In contrast, owners of commercial plantations may use mechanized equipment to farm thousands of acres of land. Any type of farm—large or small—may grow specialized or diversified crops. Grains usually provide the main food, and most people except those in very high or very low latitudes eat wheat, rice, or corn.

Products of the soil may be used as food directly or they may be fed to animals which are then used for food. The latter practice, however, requires large amounts of land for grazing or stall feeding of the animals. Parts of the world that shelter the most dense populations generally use plant foods directly; those less well populated may make meat part of their diet.

The United States has sufficient cultivable land to permit very large production of most food

staples that can be grown in a mid-latitude environment—wheat, rice, maize, oats, potatoes, fruits, beet sugar. In addition cattle, sheep, hogs, and poultry are raised extensively. Quantities of soybeans and cotton and nonedible, nonfiber crops like tobacco are grown. Nations that are able to produce foods of such wide variety and in large quantity tend to become self-sufficient and are in less need of food supplies from foreign sources.

Outline
Factors affecting agriculture
Farming types
   Subsistence
   Intensive and extensive
   Specialization
   Diversified
Staffs of life
   Grains
   Starches
Livestock and dairying
United States farming
   Types
Agricultural controls
Insects and diseases
Government aids

QUESTIONS

1. How does geography account for the principal difference between hog feeding in North America and in Europe?

2. Why did early settlers in the Middle West avoid the cultivation of grasslands?

3. Why is tobacco an undesirable crop in overpopulated lands?

4. What circumstances in the United States have led to a relative decline in the use of starchy food

staples, and a relatively large increase in our use of nonstarch foods?

5. Why is it feasible to grow sheep when it is sometimes unprofitable to grow beef cattle?

6. The commercial production of fresh vegetables is of recent origin in this country. Why did it not develop earlier? Why is it not so widely found in some other parts of the world?

7. What are the leading agricultural crops of

each of the following regions: Nigeria, Nile Valley, Iraq, northern Italy, Hungary, Uruguay, Yangtze Valley, Java, Netherlands.

8. Prepare a statement in which you explain why and how most of the surplus agricultural crops in the United States are produced by a relatively small number of farmers.

9. Several soil conservation methods appear in Figure 17-9. Can you name four of them?

10. Why are wheat and rice generally more useful for human food than corn?

11. What are the leading tree crops grown in your locality?

12. In Figure 9-11, how is the relief of the land related to the man's activities? What will happen if the slope is too great?

13. Name several insect pests that harm crops. What are some insects useful to man?

SELECTED REFERENCES

Bennett, Merrill K.: *The World's Food,* Harper & Brothers, New York, 1954.

Clark, W. H.: *Farms and Farmers: The Story of American Agriculture,* L. C. Page & Company, Boston, 1945.

Cramer, Robert E.: "Outlook for Rubber," *Focus,* 6(3):1–6, November, 1955.

Dunn, Edgar S.: *The Location of Agricultural Production,* University of Florida Press, Gainesville, 1954.

Durand, Loyal, Jr.: "American Centralizer Belt," *Economic Geography,* 31:301–320, October, 1955.

Economic Geography: Agricultural regions of the world described serially as follows: *North America* (O. E. Baker), 2–9; *Europe* (O. Jonasson), 1:207–235, 2:19–49; *South America* (C. F. Jones), 4:1–30, 159–186, 267–294; 5:109–140, 277–307, 390–421; 6:1–36; *Australia* (Griffith Taylor), 6:109–134, 213–242; *Asia* (S. Van Valkenburg, G. B. Cressey, and R. B. Hall), 7:217–237; 8:109–123; 9:1–18, 109–135; 10:14–34; 11:227–246, 325–337; 12:27–44, 231–249.

Garrison, William L., and Duane F. Marble: "The Spatial Structure of Agricultural Activities," *Annals of the Association of American Geographers,* 47:137–144, 1957.

Hewes, Leslie, and A. C. Schmiedling: "Risk in the Central Great Plains," *Geographical Review,* 46:374–387, July, 1956.

Hoselitz, Bert F.: "Agrarian Societies in Transition," *Annals of the American Academy of Political and Social Science,* 305:1–156, May, 1956.

King, F. H.: *Farmers of Forty Centuries,* Harcourt, Brace and Company, Inc., New York, 1926.

May, Jacques: "Human Starvation," *Focus,* 4:1–6, June, 1954.

Pelzer, Karl J.: *Pioneer Settlement in the Asiatic Tropics,* American Geographical Society of New York, New York, 1945.

Price, A. Grenfell: *White Settlers in the Tropics,* American Geographical Society of New York Special Publication 23, New York, 1939.

Schultz, Theodore W.: *The Economic Organization of Agriculture,* McGraw-Hill Book Company, Inc., New York, 1953.

Street, James H.: "Mechanizing the Cotton Harvest," *Agricultural History,* 31:12–22, January, 1957.

———: *The New Revolution in the Cotton Economy: Mechanization and its Consequences,* University of North Carolina Press, Chapel Hill, 1957.

U.S. Department of Agriculture: Yearbook, *Food and Life,* Washington, 1939; *Grass,* Washington, 1948; *Crops in Peace and War,* Washington, 1950–1951.

Van Royen, William: *Agricultural Resources of the World,* vol. I, *Atlas of the World's Resources,* Prentice-Hall, Inc., Englewood Cliffs, N.J., 1954.

Visher, Stephen S.: "Comparative Agricultural Potentials of the World's Regions," *Economic Geography,* 31:82–86, January, 1955.

Whittlesey, Derwent: "Shifting Cultivation," *Economic Geography,* 13:35–52, January, 1937.

———: "Fixation of Shifting Cultivation," *Economic Geography,* 13:139–154, April, 1937.

19. Mineral

Resources

MINERALS comprise one of the most valuable of the world's resources; they are so important at the present time that without them man could not maintain advanced living standards. Without minerals, health itself would suffer, for salt as well as small amounts of other minerals are essential for human growth and well being. The presence or absence of iodine and fluorine in food may mean the difference between good health and poor health, and other minerals are equally important to our existence.

Most phases of our civilization depend upon metallic minerals in various forms. Machines are made of metals and run by mineral fuels. Railroads haul more freight of mineral origin than all other commodities combined. Much of our trade with other nations, and indeed inter-

national trade in general, is made up of shipments of minerals, for Western civilization requires mineral products as much of its raw material for manufacturing. The United States and Soviet Russia are best supplied with mineral reserves, but even they must import some minerals that are not found in quantity within their vast territories; such nations as Italy and Japan must import most mineral requirements.

Each year, the United States produces minerals valued at between 15 and 16 billion dollars, about 2 billion of which represents value of the metals. Although statistics are incomplete, total annual value of all world minerals in crude form is probably three or more times this amount, with petroleum and coal the most valuable.

The primary occurrence of minerals depends

upon conditions in the geologic past that favored their deposition or accumulation. Mineral fuels (coal and petroleum), many building materials, including clay for brick, and minerals like salt, gypsum, phosphate rock, and potassium salts are associated with sedimentary rocks. Deposits of metallic minerals are usually associated with igneous rocks. Secondary deposits of minerals have been moved by some agent such as water. These resources include:

1. *Placers* of sand and gravel containing gold, platinum, tin, precious stones, or other hard insoluble materials that have been reworked by running water.

2. Salines like the nitrates or borax which have been first dissolved in water and then precipitated from solution.

3. Secondary enrichment of ores where metals were leached out by circulating ground water from the upper part of a deposit, then precipitated elsewhere, usually at lower levels. There are also instances where removal of more soluble minerals leaves concentrations of the less soluble, a process which formed the rich iron ore deposits of the Mesabi Range in Minnesota.

Development in Use of Minerals. To some degree the earth's mineral resources have been used since prehistoric times. Primitive man shaped rocks for axes, hammers, and pounders; he chipped flint and obsidian (natural glass) into arrowheads, knives, and spear points. Bits of native copper and meteoric iron were eagerly searched for and utilized. As primitive conditions changed into a civilized life, the need for minerals expanded. First to be discovered were bright metals like gold, silver, and copper that could be worked by simple methods. Men also learned to quarry stone and to make kiln-fired pottery, bricks, and other clay products. Discovery of iron opened new opportunities to improve tools, enabling the worker to accomplish vastly more in a given time than with stone, bone, and wood implements. During the last century or two, with the development of improved machinery, remarkable advances have occurred in the discovery, extraction, and utilization of mineral resources; modern industrial life would be impossible without metals, fuels, and other minerals.

Most minerals have a definite chemical composition, are composed of one or more elements, and possess characteristics by which they can be identified. Rocks usually are composed of one or more minerals; limestone rock consists of one mineral, calcite, whereas granite is a mixture of several minerals. The proportion of a certain mineral in a given rock may vary considerably. Rocks from which metals or other valuable minerals can be profitably extracted are called *ores*.

Methods of mining ores and recovering metals from them are constantly improving. With each increase in scientific management of mines, smelters, and refineries, costs can be lowered; it thus becomes possible to utilize deposits that previously could not be exploited profitably.

The search for minerals takes man to remote parts of the earth and is one of the strongest forces motivating world exploration. Some minerals like nitrates and borax come from deserts. Several minerals, especially fuels and building materials, commonly occur on plains. Mining has become a principal industry of numerous mountainous and hilly regions. In some high mountains, mining communities are the chief populated centers. Food, machinery, fuel, and other supplies must be imported to mining towns in deserts and mountains; railways and highways are therefore required. Thus mining leads to exploration and settlement of some regions that would otherwise be nearly uninhabited. Persistent search for tin ores in the time of the Phoenicians, for gold and silver after the discovery of America, and for gold in 1849 and 1898 led to peopling of distant parts of the world, establishment of permanent towns and cities, and successful utilization of lands that had hitherto been unknown or unexplored by Western man.

METALS

Metals are elements that, with some exceptions, possess a typical luster, are often hard, and can be melted, drawn into wire, or rolled into thin sheets. These properties make metals of great use in the modern world. The first metals found by primitive man were those which occur in the native state, like gold and copper. Later he learned to heat iron ore with charcoal and reduce the compound to metallic iron by smelting the ore. The ancient Greeks, Hittites, and Romans were familiar with gold, silver, iron, tin, lead, zinc, and quicksilver. They also used such nonmetallic minerals as sulfur, salt, and glass sand, and construction materials like lime, gypsum, clay, and building stone. Widespread and intensive utilization of metals was stimulated by the continued advance of the Industrial Revolution. As much iron was produced in the forty years following the Spanish-American War as in the preceding four thousand years since its first discovery. Increases nearly as great can be noted in production of copper, tin, lead, and other materials used in modern industry.

Occurrences of Metals. Most deposits of metals are associated with igneous and certain highly metamorphosed rocks. Sometimes, however, iron deposits like those at Birmingham, Alabama, are associated with sedimentary rocks, as are also a few of the lead, zinc, copper, and radium occurrences in various regions of the earth. Generally metals are concentrated in veins and other deposits thousands of feet underground and are exposed at the surface only as the result of erosion of overlying rocks. Some very young mountains seem to lack minerals, possibly because erosion has not yet cut deeply enough to disclose them. Among such ranges are the Himalayas, Alps, and Pyrenees. Mountains and plateaus formed of lava flows and volcanic ash are likewise generally poor in metals. Although most known deposits of metals are in mountainous regions, ore deposits may occur in relatively level country where former mountains have been reduced to plains, as in Canada between Lake Superior and Hudson Bay and in the interior plateau of South Africa.

In mountains, deserts, plains, or tropical jungles, ores must be mined at the place of occurrence. Unless a mineral is of high value for its weight, like gold, platinum, or precious stones, cheap transportation to world markets is essential for successful mining. Remote regions in Alaska, Siberia, and New Guinea can produce gold because its value far exceeds cost of transportation, but deposits of cheaper metals like iron, lead, or copper must be accessible to railroads or steamships in order to be worked profitably.

Iron.   Today iron is universally recognized as the metal most essential to man. Corporations engaged in mining, smelting, and manufacturing iron are among the largest establishments in industry. Some of these concerns own iron mines, railroads, and steamships to transport ore to blast furnaces, steel mills, tin-plate plants, and others that make every iron product that man uses.

Iron is smelted in blast furnaces with coke as the usual fuel; limestone is added to the charge to remove impurities in the slag. Since molten iron (pig iron) is heavy, it is drawn off near the base of the furnace; slag is drained off from a higher opening. Impure pig iron is converted into steel by burning out impurities with a hot blast of air, and adding 12 to 14 pounds of manganese and a little carbon to each ton of iron. To give steel desired characteristics such as toughness or hardness, other elements may be added. Among metals used to make such alloy steels are chromium, nickel, cobalt, titanium, tungsten, molybdenum, and vanadium. The light metals—aluminum and magnesium—are mixed with steel to produce alloys that are both light and strong.

Although iron makes up nearly 5 per cent of the weight of the earth's crust, most rocks containing iron are unsuitable sources of the metal because it would cost more to extract the iron than its value after smelting. Reserves of high-grade iron ore, where the iron content averages between 50 to 70 per cent, are not inexhaustible. Like other metals, iron should be used economically, not carelessly wasted in mining or in use. Covering iron with paint or a film of tin or zinc prevents rusting. The addition of small amounts of other elements to iron produces a much harder and more enduring steel than was formerly available; hence less iron is needed for replacement. Then, too, after machines and other articles made of iron are no longer useful they furnish scrap, an increasing and important source of iron.

Iron is manufactured at lowest cost when supplies of iron ore are close to coal for making coke. Under these circumstances, it pays to use low-grade ores that carry only 20 to 30 per cent iron. Examples of such favorable locations are found at Birmingham, Alabama; Newcas-tle, England; the Ruhr Valley in Germany; and the southern Ukraine in Soviet Russia. If the iron and coal are separated geographically, the iron ore usually is transported to the coal, because about two tons of coke (equivalent to about three tons of coal) are needed to smelt one ton of iron ore.

Iron and steel production. The greatest iron deposits of the United States are near the shores of Lake Superior in Minnesota and Michigan (Figure 19-1). Some iron ore from these regions is delivered to blast furnaces by railroads, but most is shipped by water. Ore carriers operate from ports like Duluth, Superior, and Marquette to the lower Great Lakes. There the ore is either smelted at lake ports where ore and coal meet, as at Gary, Cleveland, and Buffalo, or taken inland from discharging ports like Sandusky, Conneaut, Ashtabula, and Erie to Pittsburgh, Youngstown, and other centers in the heart of the coal fields (Figure 19-2). Some ore of the Mesabi

Figure 19-1   Coal and iron mining regions and relative production in the United States.

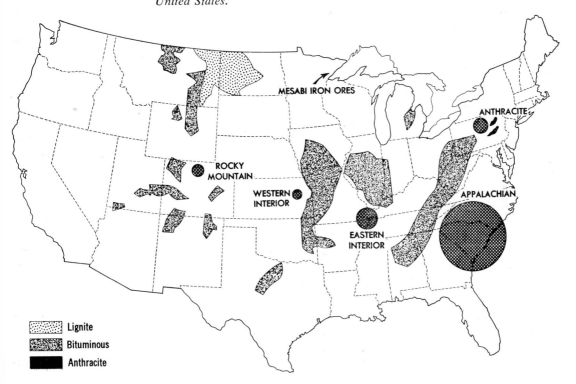

Lignite
Bituminous
Anthracite

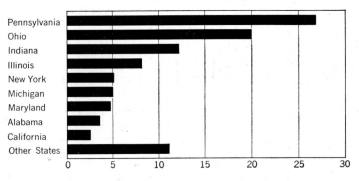

Figure 19-2 Per cent of steel production capacity in the United States, 1957, by states. (From U.S. News and World Report, June 7, 1957.)

Range in Minnesota is so soft it can be mined by mechanical shovels in open cuts, but in Michigan ore is harder and is generally produced from shafts. The ore is handled by large-scale machinery, and transportation on the Great Lakes is the cheapest per ton in the world (Figure 19-3).

Although high-grade deposits of ore in Minnesota are being rapidly exhausted, new methods of concentrating an abundant low-grade iron-bearing rock called *taconite* will greatly prolong the usefulness of the Lake Superior area as a source of much of the iron needed in the United States.

Manufacture of iron and steel in eastern Pennsylvania was based originally on charcoal and next on anthracite for smelting local supplies of ore. Now coal is imported from western Pennsylvania to make into coke, and most of the ore comes from abroad, especially from Canada, Chile, and Venezuela. North Africa, Sweden, and Liberia also ship iron ore to the United States. It is cheaper to transport iron ore thousands of miles from Chile by boat through the Panama Canal than to bring ore from Minnesota by rail to the Eastern seaboard, a much shorter distance. Some iron and steel plants are located for convenience on deepwater harbors, notably in the Baltimore and Philadelphia areas.

The most important industrial nations of the world, including the United States, Great Britain, France, Germany, and the U.S.S.R., are generally those having access to deposits of iron ore. Where nations like Italy or Japan lack important deposits of iron, they are seri-

ously handicapped both in industrial development and in promoting efforts for national defense.

Deposits of ore are widely distributed throughout the world. In the United States iron is mined in Utah, Nevada, and Wyoming, but most comes from Minnesota and Michigan, with Alabama, New York, Pennsylvania, New Jersey, Wisconsin, and Texas contributing to the approximately 115 million tons of annual output. Demand for ore is so large that 10 million tons or more are imported each year.

European countries producing iron ore include Germany, France, the U.S.S.R., Sweden, Austria, Poland, Spain, Luxembourg, and Czechoslovakia (Figure 19-4). Reserves of iron ore are smaller in Asia, but China, India, Siberia, Korea, Malaya, and the Philippines have important deposits. As pointed out, Japan has relatively small resources of iron ore. Most of the iron ore mined in Africa is exported, with the largest production coming from Algeria, Tunis, and Morocco in North Africa, and Liberia and Sierra Leone in West Africa. Australia has important deposits which are smelted at Newcastle, New South Wales. Brazil has enormous deposits in Minas Geraes and has recently established a steel plant. Chile, Venezuela, and Mexico are exporters of ore. Canada has big deposits being worked near Lake Superior and in Labrador and Newfoundland. Labrador is an especially important producer, with a railroad, company towns, and a seaport built at a cost of 300 million dollars to permit mining in a wilder-

Figure 19-3 Blast furnaces and ore carriers unloading at Lackawanna on Lake Erie near Buffalo. Note the stock piles of ore and the mechanical devices for unloading and transporting iron ore, limestone, and coke to the furnaces. (Photograph, courtesy of Bethlehem Steel Company.)

ness and shipment to distant markets, chiefly in the United States.

The United States leads the world in both mining of iron ore and production of steel. Output varies; generally over 100 million tons of ore are mined, which yield about 60 million tons of pig iron. The annual output of steel during such a year is about 80 to 100 million tons, a figure that is possible because of additions of scrap iron to the furnace charge. The United States produces nearly two-fifths that of the world's iron and steel output (Figure 19-5).

Copper. Copper, next to iron in tonnage produced and consumed, has been known and mined for thousands of years. Some American Indians made implements of native copper. Demand created by the invention and manufacture of electrical machinery led to a great spurt in modern use of the metal; more copper has been mined since 1900 than in all the preceding centuries. Each year, the United States produces about 900,000 tons of copper, approximately one-fourth of the world's supply. Ownership of foreign mines gives our corporations control of about two-thirds of the world's copper output. The foreign three-fourths of world production comes mainly from Chile, Mexico, Canada, Peru, the Belgian Congo, Northern Rhodesia, U.S.S.R., and Japan (Figure 19-6). Our domestic copper centers are mostly in the western mountain region. Arizona leads all states with mines at several centers, including Morenci, Ray, Ajo, Globe-Miami, Bisbee, Magma, and Jerome. Large mines are operated at Bingham, Utah (the second state in production and the largest mine), in Nevada, at Butte, Montana, and Chino, New Mexico. Many smaller prop-

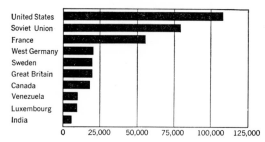

Figure 19-4   Iron ore production in thousands of short tons, 1955. Total world production, 410,200 thousand short tons. (From Encyclopedia Britannica, Book of the Year, 1957, p. 433.)

erties are also operated in these Western states.

The ore obtained from most United States mines is copper sulfide or other compound of the metal, but the Keweenaw Peninsula mines in upper Michigan are an exception, for there the ore consists of native copper. This is the largest producing area in the eastern half of the country. Until about 1900, most copper came from high-grade deposits where ore averaged from 5 to 10 per cent copper, except in Michigan where the native copper could be extracted so cheaply that ore with less than 1 per cent copper content was mined profitably.

High-grade deposits of copper proved insufficient to supply the demand of the world created by expansion of the electrical and automobile industries. Soaring prices for copper offered a great incentive to discover practical means of operating very extensive low-grade deposits. After experimentation, several methods were perfected by which deposits of copper sulfides and oxides under 1 per cent in metal content could be mined at a profit where ore bodies are large enough. The new methods include:

1. Processes of leaching ore with dilute acid and recovering copper by electrolysis or precipitation on scrap iron.

2. Concentration of ore by the oil-flotation process in which finely ground ore is mixed with water and little oil; after agitation, the metallic particles collect in a froth that forms

on top of the tank, thus separating the valuable metal from worthless sand.

Improved reverberatory furnaces have been developed for smelting copper ores. By such means, copper is produced at lower costs and increased demands from the world have been supplied. Thus scientific research has changed what was formerly worthless rock containing a small amount of metal into valuable reserves of ore. Sulfuric acid is often a by-product from smelting operations.

Lead, Zinc, and Silver. Lead and zinc ores commonly occur in closely related geographical locations, as around the Ozarks and in the Northern Rockies. Total annual United States production of lead is about 400,000 tons and of zinc about 680,000 tons, but output varies depending upon the market and prices for the metals. The United States mines more lead and zinc than any other country. Lead and zinc deposits containing silver are common in Idaho, Utah, Colorado, Montana, and other Western states. Canada, Australia, and Mexico are rich in lead and zinc; the Soviet Union, Peru, Morocco, Italy, Germany, Yugoslavia, and Spain are other producers.

Lead and zinc are used extensively in the manufacture of paints, an unfortunate practice from the standpoint of conservation, since the minerals are not recoverable. Lead used for pipe, storage batteries, conduits, and many alloys can later be recovered as scrap and used

Figure 19-5   Steel production in thousands of short tons, 1955. Total world production, 296,300 thousand short tons. (From Encyclopedia Britannica, Book of the Year, 1957, p. 434.)

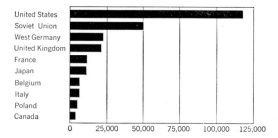

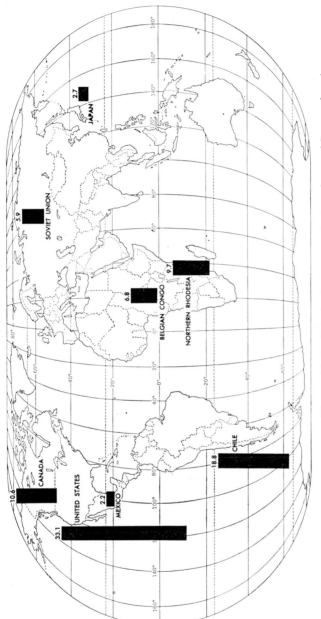

Figure 19-6 Principal areas producing the world's supply of copper ore. The figures represent the percentage of world production; minor producing areas are not indicated.

again. Substitution of mineral earths or other pigments for lead in paint would lessen the drain on the metal.

In the United States, silver is produced mainly as a by-product metal from copper mines at Butte, lead and zinc mines in Idaho, and some gold mines. Mines in Mexico and Bolivia where labor is cheap are worked primarily for silver. Canada, the U.S.S.R., and Peru are also important silver producers. United States silver production is about 40 million ounces annually—one-fifth of the world output. The largest consumers of silver are the motion picture and photography industries, where light-sensitive silver salts are used on film.

Aluminum and Magnesium.   Aluminum was a very rare and expensive metal until late in the nineteenth century when an electrolytic process was perfected to recover aluminum from a soft ore called *bauxite*. Now aluminum is a very useful metal because of its lightness, resistance to rust, and other properties. Alloyed with steel it forms duralumin which is used for frames of airships, airplane engines, and streamlined trains. Bauxite is mined near Little Rock, Arkansas, but the amount is inadequate for the needs of the United States. Much ore is imported from the Guianas in South America, Jamaica, Indonesia, West Africa and other sources. Canada, second to the United States in output of aluminum, obtains bauxite from Jamaica and British Guiana.

Aluminum is refined where cheap electricity is available, as in New York State, the Tennessee and Ohio Valleys, the Pacific Northwest, and the provinces of Quebec and British Columbia, Canada. In Europe, France is a leading producer but Hungary has the largest known reserves of bauxite. World output of aluminum exceeds 2 million tons of which the United States share is about 45 per cent and Canada's a fourth of the total. The Soviet Union stands third in world production.

A competitor of aluminum, magnesium, is also available. It is produced as a by-product from salt brines at Midland, Michigan, and from sea water in Texas. In the western United States various rocks and salts have served as ores of magnesium, the metal being extracted by electricity generated at Hoover and Grand Coulee Dams. Magnesium output greatly increased during the war years, attaining 144,-000 tons in 1944, but declined thereafter when aluminum became available again. Magnesium is frequently substituted for aluminum, however, and by experiment new uses and alloys containing magnesium have been discovered which should create a permanent demand for the metal greatly in excess of prewar demands. Present annual output is nearly 100,000 tons, mostly recovered from sea water at Freeport, Texas. Production outside the United States is small.

Tin and Other Minor Metals.   The United States has adequate supplies of most essential metals but produces less than 1 per cent of its consumption of tin, which must be imported from Malaya, Indonesia, Bolivia, the Belgian Congo, and Nigeria (Figure 19-7). Tin is used in alloys like brass and bronze, as a rust-proof covering over iron in "tin" cans, in solder and babbitt metal and in certain chemicals. After being worked for nearly four thousand years, the tin mines in Cornwall, in southwestern England, have almost ceased producing. Cornishmen, experienced hard-rock miners, have emigrated to almost every mining region in the world and have helped develop many methods used in the mines of the United States.

Other metals in which the United States is deficient include nickel, which we obtain from the province of Ontario just north of Lake Superior, platinum, produced mainly in Canada, the Soviet Union, South Africa, and Colombia, and several metals used to make steel alloys. The United States obtains its supply of molybdenum from Colorado, and considerable titanium from New York and Florida, but our supplies of tungsten, chromite, cobalt, manganese and vanadium used in the manufacture of special-purpose steels are largely imported. These metals are in great demand

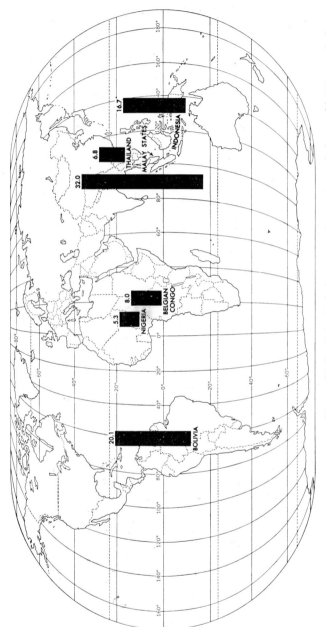

Figure 19-7   Principal tin ore mining regions of the world. Figures indicate the percentage of total world production for the leading nations.

during wartime for cannon and armor plate and during peace for tools and machine parts.

Quicksilver (mercury), the only metal that is liquid at ordinary temperatures, comes from Spain, Italy, Yugoslavia, and Mexico abroad, and some from California, Oregon, Nevada, and a few other areas in the United States. Mercury is used in electrical work, dentistry, explosive caps, medicines, disinfectants, for silvering mirrors, and in the recovery of placer gold.

Uranium, a source of atomic energy, is mined in northern Canada, Czechoslovakia, and central and southern Africa as well as in the Colorado Plateau (especially New Mexico) in the United States. The Belgian Congo leads the world in both uranium and radium production (Figure 19-8). Besides its military importance the use of atomic energy for industry is increasing. For example, submarines and other ships and several electric power plants are operated by atomic energy, yet the application of this new source of energy has barely begun.

Gold.   Gold is used widely as a standard of value and has probably been mined longer than any other metal. It forms few compounds and occurs chiefly in the native state. When a vein undergoes erosion, the heavy and insoluble gold is readily deposited along with sand and gravel to form placers. Only simple equipment is needed to recover gold from rich placers, and gold was secured from such sources even by primitive peoples. No matter how far from transportation or in what severe climatic regions gold deposits are located, men can nevertheless produce and transport it because of its high value in relation to its weight. Frozen gravels in the interior of Alaska or on the tundras of Siberia are thawed by means of

water, and the gold is then extracted by hydraulicking and dredging. When rich placers have been worked out by hand methods and simple machinery, low-grade deposits that remain may be worked by enormous and very efficient machines called gold dredges. These operate under favorable conditions on "dirt" that will produce as little as 10 cents worth of gold per cubic yard handled.

Most gold produced in the world today comes from quartz mines, although some placers are still worked. Considerable gold, especially in Utah, comes as a by-product from mines whose main values are in production of copper, lead, zinc, and silver. In the United States, California, Alaska, South Dakota, and Utah generally lead in gold mining, but gold is produced in almost every other state from the Rockies to the Pacific Coast. The Union of South Africa produces from a third to a half of all gold mined in the world. The Soviet Union is in second place, Canada third, and the United States fourth in production. Other producers include Australia, Southern Rhodesia, West Africa, the Belgian Congo, Mexico, the Philippines, Colombia, Chile, Brazil, Peru, India, Korea, and Japan. Preceding the Second World War, the value of annual production of gold in the United States was about 200 million dollars but most mines closed during the war and high costs thereafter have reduced the value of the gold mined annually to about 60 million dollars. Total world production exceeds 1.2 billion dollars yearly.

Gold mining has led to exploration and settlement of new regions. Gold has caused wars and seizure of territory and has exerted other important influences on finance and history, yet the actual value of gold produced in the United States in a single year is only a small fraction of the value of the poultry industry.

MINERAL FUELS

Mineral fuels include coal, petroleum, and natural gas. These are the greatest sources of energy, and modern industry is largely dependent on them.

Coal.   Coal is formed by chemical action on buried masses of vegetable (organic) material accumulated in swamps where oxidation was reduced to a minimum, thus preventing com-

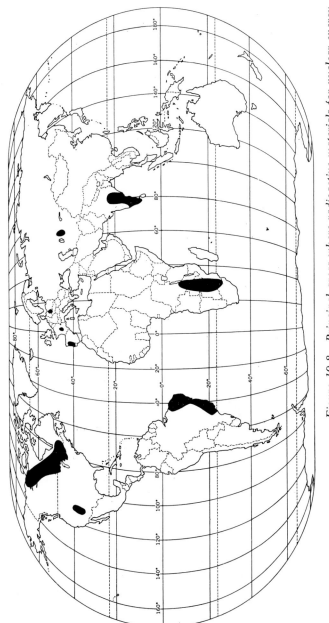

Figure 19-8 Principal areas where radioactive materials for nuclear energy occur. Brazil and India supply thorium, the others uranium ores. These are highly strategic minerals.

plete destruction of the carbonaceous matter.

World coal deposits. Coal deposits occur in all latitudes. There is coal in India and also in Svalbard. The most extensive and commercially valuable coal deposits, however, are in the midlatitudes, particularly those of the Northern Hemisphere. Of the three continents north of the equator, North America leads the world in coal resources; it has more than two-thirds of the total reserves which are estimated at over 7 trillion tons. Asia contains more than one-sixth and Europe almost one-ninth of the total. Australia, Africa, and South America combined, however, including land in those continents on both sides of the equator, contain only about 4 per cent of the world's coal resources. Western Europe, the United States, Canada, and China are favored parts of the world for coal fields.

Types of coal. Several varieties of coals are recognized, the most important of which are lignite, bituminous, and anthracite.

Lignite, a brown coal that is usually geologically recent in origin, contains more volatile matter than better coals. It is used for do-

Figure 19-9 Coal-loading machine in operation at the face of a vein in an Alabama mine. Modern machines of this type have reduced the dangers of mining and have increased production. (Photograph used by permission of the U.S. Bureau of Mines, Department of the Interior.)

mestic heating and steam production but crumbles easily and cannot be stored for any length of time. About two-fifths of the world's resources of coal are lignite. Nearly 3 trillion tons of lignite exist in North America, mostly on the Great Plains of the United States and Canada but production is small. In Germany considerable lignite is used in steam plants, and in emergencies liquid fuels were made from it as substitutes for gasoline.

Bituminous coal is a most useful type of fuel and accounts for the bulk of the world's present coal output. It is a soft coal but stores much better than lignite and has a greater heat value. Bituminous coal can be used for many purposes, including heat, power, transportation, and the manufacture of chemicals. When a special grade of bituminous coal is heated in ovens and the gas and coal tar that it contains are expelled, the residue, mostly of carbon, is called *coke.* Coking coal has greater value than noncoking grades because it can be used to supply coke for smelting and additional gas, ammonia, and coal tar for industrial and commercial uses.

Anthracite has been subjected to so much heat and pressure during its formation that it consists of nearly pure carbon and is free of volatile matter. Large deposits of anthracite exist in China, Wales, and elsewhere, but the supply of our country is almost entirely restricted to northeastern Pennsylvania, where less than 500 square miles of land is underlain with anthracite (Figure 19-1). This hard coal is well suited to domestic use, since it burns slowly without smoke or soot, has a high heating value, and is clean to handle.

Coal mining. Coal beds are often reached through shafts; but where the coal outcrops on a hillside running a drift or tunnel into the hill from the outcrop provides easy haulage and drainage. Formerly coal was mined largely by hand methods, but today in the United States mining and loading machines have nearly eliminated the heavy labor involved (Figure 19-9). Pillars of coal, supplemented by wooden props, are left to support mine roofs, for the remainder of the coal seams seldom are mined commercially. Some beds of coal have been found aggregating more than 100 feet in thickness, although this is unusual.

Strip mining is a very inexpensive method of coal production. In this process, big shovels (Figure 19-10) remove the overburden of rock and soil and dig the coal from open pits. There is no waste of coal in strip mining, and for this and other reasons the method accounts for about 30 per cent of the total United States annual output of about half a billion tons. Although strip mining completely overturns the surface of the ground, it is possible to use bulldozers to smooth away the piles of debris, then plant trees or grass, and reclaim land for use. Unfortunately this is not always done.

Uses of coal. Coal is used for heating homes, for generating steam in factories, for power plants, railroads, and steamships, for smelting and manufacture of artificial gas and various by-products like fertilizer, and for chemicals. Coal tar, a by-product from coke manufacture, formerly was thrown away; now it is used to make thousands of different commodities, including explosives, dyes, medi-cines, flavorings, perfume, and synthetic plastics (Figure 19-11). Consumption of coal for generating electrical power increases every year, although as a domestic fuel for heating and cooking, oil, natural gas, and hydroelectricity often replace it.

Coal deposits in United States and abroad. Coal is so widely distributed in the United States that its utilization depends largely upon an available market. Some thick but inaccessible seams cannot be mined profitably because of distance from consumers, or the low grade of the fuel. More than half this country's known coal resources, estimated at about 3,-500 billion tons, are in the Great Plains or the plateaus on either side of the Rocky Mountains, but this area produces little coal because it is far from large markets, and much of the fuel is the inferior lignite. The United States leads the world in coal production, 500 to 600 million tons being mined annually (Figure 19-12), about 8 per cent of which is anthracite.

The most productive coal-mining region comprises the Appalachian Plateaus in Pennsylvania, southeastern Ohio, West Virginia,

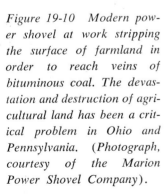

Figure 19-10 Modern power shovel at work stripping the surface of farmland in order to reach veins of bituminous coal. The devastation and destruction of agricultural land has been a critical problem in Ohio and Pennsylvania. (Photograph, courtesy of the Marion Power Shovel Company).

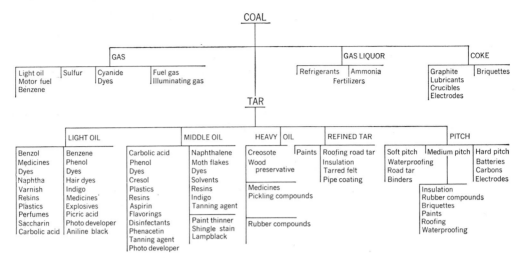

Figure 19-11   Some of the commercial products obtained from coal.

and southward to Alabama. Coal here is of high grade, and much of it can be used to manufacture coke and various chemical by-products. Appalachian coal provides the nearest source of this fuel for New York and the New England states, regions that lack a supply of their own. Appalachian coal is also exported in large volume, Appalachian coal often goes to market by cheap water routes for at least part of the way, since the coal can be conveniently shipped by boat to Canada and up the Great Lakes to regions lacking coal deposits, and by river barges down the Ohio River and other streams, west and southward. Through Atlantic coastal ports like Norfolk

Figure 19-12   Coal production, principal countries, in millions of short tons, 1955. Total world production, 2,356 million short tons. (From Encyclopedia Britannica, Book of the Year, 1957, p. 231.)

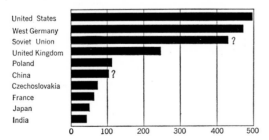

or Baltimore, Appalachian coal is also exported in large volume to Europe and other foreign lands.

In addition, part of the coal-bearing area is highly industrialized, with iron furnaces, chemical works, railroads, and factories consuming great quantities of fuel. The generation of electric power in large coal-fired steam plants requires large quantities of coal.

In Europe much of the coal of Great Britain, especially in Wales and around Newcastle, is situated conveniently for export. Ships coming to Great Britain with bulky cargoes of grain, lumber, and cotton were always sure (up to the time of the First World War) of getting cargoes of coal for shipment abroad. This helped British shipping by providing a bulky export from an industrialized country whose exports tend to be of smaller weight and volume than its imports. During the last twenty-five years fuel oil has taken markets from coal. British coal exports have declined, injuring the nation's shipping and industrial position. The most industrialized section on the mainland of Europe extends from northern France through Belgium to the Rhine and Ruhr Valleys in Germany and has abundant resources of coal (Figure 19-13). Soviet Russia has large coal deposits, and Poland and Czechoslovakia also possess much coal.

479

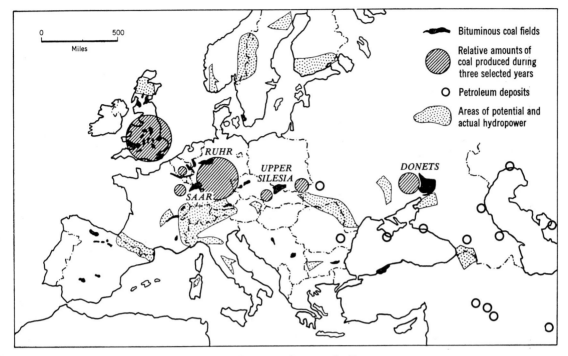

Figure 19-13   Sources of power in Europe.

In the Orient, Japan has inadequate resources of coal and therefore must import some needed by its industries. China has very large resources of coal, but output is small in relation to the large population of that country. India is an important producer of coal. Some is mined also in North Vietnam. In the Southern Hemisphere, Australia, Chile, and the Union of South Africa have deposits of coal that supply demands in those countries.

World resources of coal are estimated at between 6,300 to 8,000 billion tons. About 100 billion tons were mined to the end of 1957, and over half that amount since 1920. World production is now about 2.3 billion tons annually.

Petroleum. The development of the petroleum industry from the drilling of the first commercial oil well in western Pennsylvania in 1859 to an annual production measured by billions of barrels is the most extraordinary expansion recorded for the production of any mineral resource. Fuel oil is in increasing use for heating houses, generating steam, and operating ships. Mechanization of farms, highways, and railroads with diesel engines has also greatly increased the consumption of petroleum products.

Without petroleum, our motorcars, motorboats, and aircraft would lack cheap fuel. Furthermore there would be a great shortage of lubricants needed by all machinery in this industrial age, since plant and animal fats are much more costly than mineral oils and greases. Moreover, we should lack many everyday needs manufactured from crude oil including kerosene, petroleum jelly and many other ointments, certain cheap solvents and cleaning fluids, and the convenient compressed natural gas. Modern civilization would be greatly handicapped by a shortage of oil.

Geologic conditions favorable for petroleum deposits. Oil is associated with sedimentary rocks of many different geologic ages and is believed to have been formed by chemical action affecting organic matter. After oil has developed undergound, it may migrate or flow from its place of origin through pervious rocks like sandstones, which become soaked with it. The cause of the petroleum migration is believed to be water under pressure, which forces the lighter-weight oil ahead of and above it. Natural gas may also assist in the underground migration of petroleum. In places where suitable rock structures prevail, as in upfolds of the rocks called *anticlines,* reservoir rocks must exist in order that the oil may be held in a workable deposit under pressure. A cap rock overlies the reservoir rock to retain the oil (Figure 19-14), and the petroleum collects in the so-called "oil pools." Wells have been drilled to depths of over 3 miles (22,-559 feet in one case in Louisiana) but most of them are much shallower.

In drilling for petroleum and natural gas, prospectors search first for places of suitable geological structure; then, if a source of oil and a suitable reservoir rock and other conditions required for accumulation of petroleum are found, a new oil field may be discovered. Where exposures of bedrock fail to outcrop at the surface, geologists have learned to use special scientific instruments like seismographs,

torsion pendulums, and other inventions that can detect possible oil structures buried deeply underground. By means of such careful geologic work, new oil fields are being discovered; it is, therefore, nearly impossible accurately to estimate actual petroleum reserves.

Sources of oil. Coal occurs in beds whose extent and thickness may be gauged, but the amount of oil remaining underground is more difficult to determine. Known reserves of petroleum in the United States are estimated at nearly 30 billion barrels. Production is approximately 2.5 billion barrels per year, but that does not mean that all oil will be gone in this country within a few years. Reserves may be expected to be increased by discovery of new fields and of other productive oil sands at greater depths than those now producing. It is probable, however, that reserves of oil in this nation are much less, in proportion to those of the rest of the world, than our coal deposits.

Under present practices only about half the oil in the sands is recovered but improved methods of securing more crude oil by methods which include gas pressuring and water

Figure 19-14 Anticlinal geologic structure in which water under pressure has forced the petroleum to accumulate at the top of the fold, where it is under pressure with natural gas above it. The oil cannot escape through the cap rock until a well is drilled in a location similar to B. A well drilled at A will produce gas, but no oil.

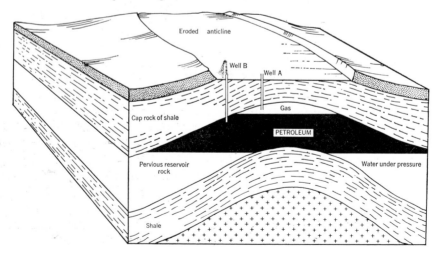

flooding are being used; recovery rates will certainly be increased in future.

Production and refining. Oil is produced from wells (Figure 19-15) which range in depth from a few hundred to many thousand feet. When water pressure or gas pressure is sufficient, oil wells flow naturally and are called "gushers," but most wells must be pumped to lift the oil to the surface. Then the oil is shipped to refineries, usually through pipelines—a cheap method compared with shipment by tank car. Special ships called *tankers* transport petroleum products by sea.

At the refinery the petroleum is successively heated to different temperatures (Figure 19-16). Liquids then boil off in succession, beginning with lightweight naphtha and followed by gasoline, kerosene, and lubricating oil. From the residue greases, paraffin, asphalt, medicines, and multitudes of other products are created. During the Second World War, synthetic rubber was manufactured in large part from petroleum. Gasoline is the refinery prod-uct in greatest demand. Its output may be increased by sudden heating of crude oil to a high temperature, which "cracks" complex compounds into the simpler gasoline, or by cooling and compressing "wet" natural gas to form casing-head gasoline.

Petroleum must be produced where oil occurs, but refineries often are located in distant centers of population and at seaports from which the refined products can be distributed easily. San Francisco, New York, and Chicago have no oil fields nearby, but large refineries are located in their suburbs. Although crude oil production in Pennsylvania has greatly declined since completion of the first well a century ago, there are still 13 refineries operated in the state, with the largest ones near Philadelphia using imported oil.

Oil fields in the United States. Thousands of individual producing areas for petroleum have been discovered in the United States, but these are especially concentrated in six areas (Figure 19-17):

Figure 19-15 Modern steel derricks and old-type wooden derricks in a California oil field. Note the barren landscape, useless for anything but the production of petroleum. (Photograph, courtesy of the Los Angeles County Chamber of Commerce.)

1. The Appalachian oil field, which extends from New York to Tennessee, is the oldest known field still producing high-quality oil, though production has declined.

2. The Lower Great Lakes field with producing areas in Ohio, Indiana, Illinois, and Michigan.

3. The Mid-Continent field, centering in Oklahoma and northern Texas and extending into Kansas, Arkansas, and Louisiana. This is the greatest producing field, and its production dominates the petroleum industry in America. Some cities, including Tulsa, Oklahoma City, and Fort Worth, have grown remarkably in population as the direct result of petroleum production in this field; hundreds of smaller communities also owe their growth to its development.

4. The Gulf Coast field which extends inland about 100 miles and includes part of the continental shelf where some production comes from beneath the sea floor. Here oil and gas occur in domes of small areal extent. Beaumont, Texas, is the most famous town in the Gulf Coast field.

5. The Rocky Mountain field, really a misnomer, because the producing areas lie within boundaries of the Great Plains east of the Rockies or within plateau regions either side of the mountain ranges. Largest production comes from Wyoming, with other known producing areas in Colorado, Montana, New Mexico, Utah, and North Dakota.

6. California, with producing areas of principal importance in the Los Angeles lowland

Figure 19-16 A modern high-octane gasoline refinery with a tank farm for oil storage in the distance. (Note extensive use of complicated structures, chiefly made of fire-resistant materials.) There is little indication of the original appearance of the landscape; this view represents a scene that is almost wholly the result of human activity. (Photograph, courtesy of the Los Angeles County Chamber of Commerce.)

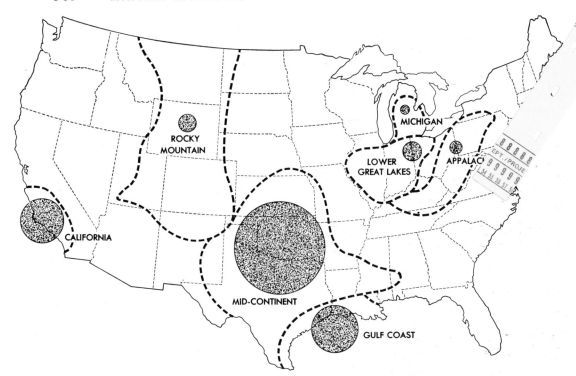

Figure 19-17   Petroleum production in the United States, by regions.

and the southern part of the San Joaquin Valley. Bakersfield, Long Beach, and Los Angeles itself have profited greatly from oil deposits in California, the only important producing area known on the Pacific coast of North America. Smaller towns and cities have sprung up whose entire economic activity stems from petroleum production.

Production of petroleum by the United States from 1859 to 1957 was about 55 billion barrels. Annual output is about 2.5 billion barrels worth nearly 6 billion dollars, the greatest value of any mineral resource of the country. In the late 1950s petroleum and natural gas together accounted for 65 per cent of the energy requirements for the United States.

New oil fields are being discovered but at a decreasing rate; although known reserves are large, they are being depleted rapidly as consumption increases. Our nation will continue to be a heavy producer of oil for many years to come but probably at a decreasing

rate after the attainment of peak production which is forecast for about 1970. Because of its very large consumption of petroleum, the United States imports much crude oil for refining, especially from the Caribbean region. Future oil imports will increase and we may begin to use substitutes for petroleum. United States exports of petroleum consist mainly of finished products from refineries.

Foreign oil fields. Oil fields in North America include those near Calgary and Edmonton in the Prairie provinces of Canada, which are large producers of petroleum and natural gas. Fields on the Gulf Coast of Mexico are near Tampico. In South America very productive fields around Lake Maracaibo account for the fact that in petroleum output Venezuela stands second to the United States among the countries of the world. Oil is produced also in Colombia, Trinidad, Peru, Ecuador, Argentina, and the lower Orinoco Basin. It is believed to exist in Bolivia and Brazil though it has not been developed there on a large scale.

In Europe, Soviet Russia leads in petroleum output with Baku on the Caspian Sea the most important field, but others are expanding production, especially near Kuibishev on the Volga River. Romania is the second largest producer in Europe, with Austria and Germany of moderate importance.

In Asia the Persian Gulf area has the largest known reserves of petroleum in the world and annual production there totals about one-half as much as the United States (Figure 19-18). Producing countries include Kuwait, Saudi Arabia, Iraq, Iran, Qatar, and Bahrein. Elsewhere in Asia, Indonesia has important fields, especially in Borneo. Brunei (British Borneo) and several fields in Siberia are other producers of petroleum.

World production of petroleum amounts to nearly 6 billion barrels annually. The United States produces about 44 per cent of this and consumes nearly one-half the entire world output. Total world production of petroleum from the start of the industry to 1957 is about 95 billion barrels.

Estimates based on inadequate information reckon that world resources of petroleum total well over 100 billion barrels. Although known petroleum reserves are probably much nearer exhaustion than those of coal, discovery of new fields and improved methods of extraction of oil from the ground may change this estimate.

Natural Gas. Natural gas may occur associated with petroleum deposits but occasionally it is found in areas where oil does not exist in commercial quantities. Industry uses large amounts of natural gas, but it serves so well as a domestic fuel that some people propose to restrict its use for manufacturing. Natural gas is especially suited to processes requiring the maintenance of even temperatures, as in the manufacture of glass. Formerly much natural gas was wasted because no markets were nearby, but the invention of spiral-steel welded pipe and ditch-digging machines has made it possible to install thousands of miles of pipeline at relatively slight cost. Today pipelines which link producing gas fields and consuming markets ensure minimum waste of natural gas. Most states now enforce laws which require that gas wells be capped when they are discovered if the gas cannot be used economically. Pipelines now deliver natural gas from Texas, Oklahoma, and Louisiana to markets in the Middle West and in the East; pipelines from Texas and New Mexico serve the Pacific Northwest and add to the supply in California. One pipeline from Alberta delivers natural gas to customers in eastern Canada and the United States, another carries natural gas to Vancouver, British Columbia, and the state of Washington. Natural gas is being imported to the United States from Mexico also. In Europe the Soviet Union has several natural gas fields in use.

The natural gas industry, with a product retailing for 12 billion dollars annually, is sixth in importance among industries of the United States, where it supplies one-quarter of the country's vast energy requirements. About 22 million homes in the United States use natural gas. Production of the fuel in 1955 amounted to 10.1 trillion cubic feet. Known reserves were estimated at 233.7 trillion cubic feet in that year, with new discoveries estimated at

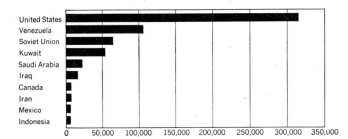

Figure 19-18 Crude petroleum production (U.S.S.R., estimated) in thousands of metric tons, 1955. Approximately 8 barrels equal a metric ton but the amount varies with the type of crude oil. (From The Statesman's Year Book, 1956.)

12 trillion cubic feet, an amount larger than the consumption that year.

The Importance and Future of Petroleum. Oil is such a convenient and clean fuel for steam production and for operation of motors that the Great Powers are competing for control of the best deposits. Where oil is not available, every effort is made to develop substitutes for motor use, even if these cost the consumer more than imported gasoline and are less efficient. Though petroleum has been used for only a short time, it is almost inconceivable how the modern world could get along without it. Perhaps substitutes for gasoline could be developed, but there is no known cheap substitute for greases and lubricants. Oil deposits should, therefore, be conserved in every way possible. Refinements in production and extraction of oil have advanced greatly in recent years, and there is less waste than formerly; but further improvements in production and utilization can still be made.

Another source of energy consists of beds of oil shale (really a soft bituminous limestone or marl) and so called "tar sands" or bituminous sandstone. Bituminous sands contain petroleum, and huge deposits which could supply hundreds of billions of barrels occur in the Athabaska River basin in northern Alberta, Canada; Iraq and Venezuela also possess bituminous sands. Oil shale does not contain petroleum but an oil called "kerogen" from which gasoline and other products can be secured by heating the shale in retorts. Reserves of oil contained in the high-grade oil shale in western Colorado and eastern Utah alone are estimated at 90 billion barrels, adequate to supply the United States for many years. In addition low-grade material when needed could supply additional hundreds of billions of tons of oil.

At present prices for crude oil, motor fuel distilled from shale costs more than when made from petroleum. In future, as the price of oil increases or when some cheaper or more efficient method is used to handle oil shale, fuel from this source may become available. Currently, petroleum products and motor fuels are made from oil shale in several places abroad including Scotland, Manchuria, Australia, and South Africa. The United States and Brazil have the largest known deposits of oil shale. Plant waste and coal are both possible substitute sources for synthetic oil products.

Petroleum production, like other forms of mining, is generally short-lived. A field is rapidly developed soon after its discovery. It reaches maximum production, and then declines steadily until finally the wells no longer produce and the field is abandoned. Discovery of deeper sands or improved methods of production may, of course, bring renewed activity. Petroleum is sometimes appropriately called "black gold," because it not only produces wealth but also leads to a rush of people to a field, wild speculation, rapid building, and other excitement that characterized the "gold rush."

NONMETALLIC RESOURCES

Construction Materials. Minerals used in construction include building stone, cement, glass, lime, and clay products like brick, tile, terra cotta, and gypsum. Sand and gravel are generally distributed over wide areas and are so cheap that they are used only to supply local demands. All these commodities are very bulky; to transport them long distances adds much to their initial cost. For this reason and because glass, building stone, brick, tile, and terra cotta are easily damaged in shipment, they are obtained from sources near where they are to be used.

Building stone. Building stone should be abundant, convenient to markets, attractive, and resistant to weathering. It should also be easily quarried. Since 1900, the use of building stone has everywhere declined relatively and actually, compared with other construction materials. This resulted from replacement of stone by concrete and other materials suitable for erection by machinery. Building stone requires much hand labor for quarrying, shaping, and laying. In the Middle Ages, when labor costs were insignificant, stone, where available, was the usual material for both public structures and houses of the better classes, but now stone is used for facing and decoration rather than for entire walls of structures.

Among common building stones are marble, granite, limestone, and sandstone, with slate serving for roofs and other special uses. Quarries near large cities lead in production of building stone because of the saving on freight from nearby quarries. Thus Vermont marble and granite quarries (Figure 19-19), Pennsylvania slate, and Bedford, Indiana, limestone, have advantages over similar deposits in the Rocky Mountains or Alaska.

Clay products. The term *ceramics* is used for any clay products that are hardened from native soft material by fire. Thus the heat of kilns changes soft clay into brick, sewer pipe, building tile, terra cotta, and pottery (Figure 21-6). Addition of special clays gives a glaze

Figure 19-19   Men and machines cutting rough blocks of marble at a quarry in Roxbury, Vermont. (Photograph used by permission of the U.S. Bureau of Mines.)

to porcelain or chinaware. Glass is made from pure sand, soda, and other materials and may be used as building material.

Clays differ greatly in properties and uses. Clay suitable for pottery or chinaware is called *kaolin,* and is usually formed from decomposition of granitic rocks that are largely composed of feldspar. Other clays are deposited in lakes, by running water, and by weathering of shale in nature. Such clays are usually used for common brick and other cheap construction materials. Except for special purposes, utilization of a clay deposit depends almost wholly upon convenience to markets, since common clays are very widely distributed.

Portland cement. In building, increasing quantities of cement and plasters have been used in modern construction. Common portland cement is manufactured from finely ground limestone and clay, mixed in the required proportions, burned in a kiln to produce a clinker, and then ground to a powder. Demand for cement created by modern dams and highways, reinforced-concrete buildings, concrete walks, foundations, and similar projects has caused an enormous development of this industry. More cement is manufactured in Pennsylvania, especially in the Lehigh Valley, than in other parts of the country. Yet because the product is heavy, it is desirable to manufacture portland cement near the point of consumption. Hence the 150 portland cement plants operated in the United States are scattered widely over the entire nation and in nearly every state of the Union. Output of portland cement in the United States is over 250 million barrels per year, which amounts to about one-fourth of world production.

Plaster and glass. When limestone is heated, carbon dioxide is driven off, and quicklime is left. In the same way, gypsum may be calcined and the resulting product makes plaster of paris. When mixed with water and sand, both lime and plaster will harden to form mortar and wall plaster respectively. The required raw materials are widely distributed in the United States, and the products are manufactured all over the country.

Glass is made from sand mixed with soda or other salts and intensely heated to fuse the materials. Formerly glass objects were made by hand, but machine methods have now been substituted for manufacture of bottles and plate glass. Opaque bricks and tile for building houses are made of glass. Modern factories need much window glass. Glass is used in camera and instrument lenses, for domestic wares, and as a decorative material.

Minor Nonmetallics.   Another nonmetallic resource is common salt, used as a food and food preservative and as a base for many chemical products, such as soda, chlorine, and bleaching powders. Michigan and New York rank first in salt output, followed by Louisiana, Kansas, Ohio, and Texas. Salt is also produced by solar evaporation in Utah and California. Sulfur is found in Texas and Louisiana in geologic structures somewhat similar to occurrences of petroleum. It is widely used for sprays, explosives, and chemical manufactures.

Other nonmetallic resources include gems and semiprecious stones, fertilizers, mica, asbestos, pigments, graphite, magnesite, talc, and abrasives.

Gems were originally formed in molten rock far below the earth's surface, but sources of gems may be exposed by erosion, which removes overlying material. Gem stones are heavy, hard, resistant to erosion, and may accumulate in placer deposits. Since precious stones are valuable in relation to their weight, they can bear the cost of transportation from very remote places. Diamonds come principally from southern and central Africa (Figure 19-20). Many gems are mined in India, Ceylon, Burma, and other places in southeastern Asia and in South America. The United States produces relatively few precious stones. Gems may be economically useful as well as valued ornaments. Industrial "black diamonds" are used widely for drills and grinding equipment in many industries; many of these diamonds come from Brazilian and Belgian Congo

Figure 19-20   Drilling holes for explosive charges in blasting blue clay in a diamond mine near Kimberley, South Africa. The machine drill is a product of American manufacture. (Photograph, courtesy of N. W. Ayer and Sons and De Beers Consolidated Mines, Ltd.)

mines. Quartz crystals suitable for radar and electronics equipment are exported mainly from Brazil and India.

Fertilizers. Some soils may lack important plant nutrients: potash, nitrates, and phosphates. Though other minerals are also required for successful plant growth, they are generally present in all soils; hence the three minerals mentioned above are the most essential fertilizers.

Potash is present in wood ashes, guano, seaweed or kelp, organic waste of different kinds, and the water of certain bitter (alkaline) lakes like the Dead Sea. The supply of mineral potash comes principally from subterranean beds of salts somewhat resembling common salt beds; they may even be associated with that mineral. In the past, the world's supply of potash came mainly from Germany. The United States once imported most of its needs but now obtains potash from domestic sources. From southeastern New Mexico and from the dried-up beds of certain salt lakes in southeastern California and in Utah, the United States now mines enough in normal times to meet its own requirements. Besides Germany, foreign producers include France, Spain, and Israel.

Nitrates needed for agriculture may come from almost any organic waste or from growing leguminous crops, but the greatest natural occurrence of mineral nitrates lies in the desert of northern Chile, where enormous deposits of this salt impregnate the soil a few feet below the surface. For fifty years or more,

Chile supplied the world with nitrates for fertilizer and explosives, but now nitrates are manufactured by electrical processes. Synthetic nitrate is produced in such quantity that it supplies nearly three-fourths of the world's needs.

Phosphates. The United States has the largest known deposits of phosphates in the world. Florida and Tennessee lead in production at present, but there are large deposits in the western Rocky Mountain region from Utah northward through Wyoming and Idaho into Montana. Changing phosphate rock into a soluble fertilizer that plants can use requires chemical treatment by sulfuric acid or some electrolytic process. Besides that made directly from sulfur itself, sulfuric acid is obtained as a by-product from smelters using sulfide ores. This by-product should be recovered to prevent excessive sulfur fumes from the smelters from destroying vegetation in their neighborhood. Although smelters in the Rocky Mountain area provide a source of sulfuric acid, a local phosphate fertilizer industry is handicapped by long distances to large consuming markets. A nearer source is in eastern Tennessee, where acid is obtained from the Ducktown copper smelter. Since phosphates usually are the most deficient soil mineral, its great deposits of this valuable fertilizer are of increasing importance to the United States as the virgin fertility of its soils becomes exhausted. United States output totals nearly 13.1 million tons a year valued at about 83 million dollars. Foreign producers include North Africa, the U.S.S.R., and several tropical islands in the Pacific.

CONSERVATION AND STRATEGY OF MINERAL SUPPLIES

Available quantities of minerals vary greatly; some (salt, clay, sand, cement rock, building stone) will last indefinitely. Large resources of others are known to exist (coal, iron, aluminum), whereas still others exist in very limited amounts (platinum, beryllium, diamonds). It is in line with conservation practices to use minerals that are abundant, sparing those in scant supply. Known resources of oil, copper,

lead, and zinc in the United States will probably be exhausted within comparatively few years; from the standpoint of conservation, they should be used economically in order to make our mineral resources last as long as possible. Some methods for conserving supplies of particular minerals have been mentioned previously, but some general methods for conserving mineral resources are:

1. Inexhaustible and abundant materials may be substituted for minerals whose quantities are more limited. Water power and hydroelectric power, for example, might replace mineral fuels. Magnesium can replace aluminum; barytes and other mineral earths rather than white lead and zinc oxide can be used in manufacture of paints.

2. Reduction of waste in mining operations is essential. Improved methods of mining reduce losses from waste; for example, open-cut mining makes it unnecessary to leave pillars to support roofs or walls. Removal and use of final residues of ore or mineral fuels from properties where cost of operations equals or exceeds the selling price is sound conservation policy and practice. Under certain circumstances, governments may be justified in providing a guaranteed price or bonus to help high-cost producers.

3. Development of improved practices leading to more complete recovery of minerals is recommended. More petroleum may be extracted from oil sands. More metal may be obtained from ores and several metals instead of only one or two may be extracted from complex ores. Price increases and better methods of extraction may change unworkable or unprofitable deposits of oil shale or low-grade ores into profitable mining enterprises.

4. Economies in use of minerals and prevention of early deterioration tend to conserve present supplies of metals. The thickness of tin coating or tin plate on cans, for example, has been reduced from the amount once thought necessary. Paint and other substances, including plastic coverings, are applied to metal surfaces, thus checking or preventing rust. Development of alloys reduces wear and hence lessens the quantity of scarce metals that may be needed. Marked improvements in utilization of fuels have taken place: automatic stokers have replaced hand firing of coal; diesel engines are used instead of the ordinary gas engine, and efficient turbines have supplanted steam engines of an older type.

5. Recovery of scrap metals is particularly important. Not all minerals can be reclaimed after they are used; this is true of coal, oil, and lead pigment. Scrap iron, copper, and tin can be recovered for further use. Even silver is recovered from discarded and used film.

6. Synthetic materials and artificial minerals can contribute greatly to the conservation of valuable metals. Substitutes for many minerals are now made by chemical processes. Carborundum is an artificial grinding material, or abrasive. Nitrates for explosives, fertilizer, and chemical uses are made by electrical processes. Certain plastic materials have replaced metals for some uses, as in manufacture of cutlery handles. Artificial graphite has replaced the natural product for many purposes. Artificial sapphires and rubies have been manufactured with such success that they have injured the market for the natural gems. Artificial soda has largely replaced the natural saline mineral, and fused quartz has partly replaced natural quartz crystal for many purposes.

7. Conservation of a nation's valuable mineral resources may be accomplished partly by importing needed materials from abroad, but this procedure would have no effect on the conservation of total world reserves.

Strategic minerals. Nations which lack important mineral sources to meet their military requirements face a special problem. Armies, navies, and air forces require great quantities of petroleum as well as metallic minerals. Occasionally a nation must conserve domestic deposits of valuable minerals for war use by importing its peacetime needs.

Necessary minerals which a nation lacks entirely or has only in quantities insufficient for its armament needs are called *strategic*. During war periods it may be difficult or even impossible to import these materials because of blockades, embargoes, ship shortages, or competitive demands of other nations. Hence nations preparing for war may import strategic materials far beyond immediate needs and to stockpile them for future emergencies. Both Japan and Germany followed this policy from 1935 to 1940.

Minerals occurring in wholly inadequate quantities within the present boundaries of the

United States include tin, nickel, chrome ore, uranium, antimony, quartz crystals for radar, and industrial diamonds. The United States imports a substantial share of its needs for critical minerals such as bauxite, mercury, tungsten, asphalt, mica, asbestos, and platinum. Other nations have different problems; England must import nearly all minerals except coal and part of her supply of iron ore and bauxite.

The location of mineral resources frequently has influenced routes followed by invading armies; it has also affected settlement of national boundaries upon the conclusion of wars. Germany, in her three wars with France since 1870 and her invasion of Russia in the Second World War, is an example of this. To a less extent, Japan also supplies an example in her temporary occupation of mineral-bearing lands in China and the Indies, from which she expected to obtain supplies of oil, tin, and other materials in which the Japanese islands are deficient.

CHARACTERISTICS OF MINING TOWNS

Mining towns are often of characteristically temporary construction. Since most mining communities are short-lived, buildings tend to be constructed of wood or some other impermanent materials. Later, if the mines or oil wells prove exceptionally productive, substantial permanent structures will be erected. This type of development occurred at Butte, Montana, in the midst of copper mines, and at Tulsa, Oklahoma, with its rich oil deposits. When mines are worked out promptly, property owners lose little if the town has been built of temporary materials. Mining regions usually have many "ghost towns" where a boom subsided or the minerals were exhausted. When residents of these towns depart, buildings burn or fall into decay (Figure 7-9), and the settlements may be almost completely abandoned.

Mining centers emphasize utility rather than appearance. At Butte, the landscape is a confused mass of intermingled shaft houses and hoists, substantial brick buildings, workers' shacks, and varied nondescript structures. Sometimes fumes from smelters destroy vegetation. Shortage of water may lead to a similar barren appearance of mining towns in deserts, as Kalgoorlie and Coolgardie, Australia. Mining towns become permanent only when other industries follow the mining development, as general manufacturing and other enterprises have developed in some of the coal-mining centers of the eastern United States

and some oil towns in the Middle West. Another example of change is found in Colorado, where some former mining centers have capitalized on scenery and climate to attract health seekers and tourists.

Because the coal-mining community often lacks capital to build houses for workmen, they may be provided by the mining company. The results have sometimes been ugly. When the coal is worked out these company towns join the metal-mining centers as ghost communities unless another source of employment develops.

The term "gold rush" has been used to describe any sudden influx of men seeking quick wealth. History records many actual gold rushes like those of California in 1849 and of Australia and the Klondike later. The modern gold prospector may travel by motorcar or airplane over remote parts of the earth looking for favorable ground, rather than use a canoe or go afoot or on burro.

In this generation a discovery of petroleum excites men more than word of gold mines; their rush is for "black gold." When a wildcat well is reported to have come in a gusher, hundreds, perhaps thousands of men hurry to the site. A new town is started, or a small nearby community begins to boom. Men scramble to buy and lease likely ground. Companies are organized and many new wells spudded in. Hastily built frame hotels, cabins, and false-fronted business blocks are thrown up. Many people live in tents; others rent cabins at prices that will return the entire cost of construction in twelve months. School facilities and often even law enforcement are absent. Gambling and liquor consumption increase the likeness to an old-time cattle town when the cowboys are paid off or a lumber town at the end of a log drive. The "boom" may last for several years or may be over in a few weeks. Sooner or later wells on the outside of the producing territory come in "dry," a term that may also refer to a water well instead of an oil well, and thus the land underlain by oil deposits is defined. The field then settles down to steady production that may last for many years, but the wild excitement and the possibilities of gamblers' profits are things of the past.

In large fields, a boom town may develop into a prosperous refining and distributing center with a permanent and substantial base for continued prosperity; more often the opposite is true. Any oil town has its special population of promoters, geologists, drillers, and other workmen who follow new discoveries from field to field and give a particular atmosphere to the community.

In the 1950s the search for uranium deposits produced boom settlements and processing plants (Figure 19-21) in New Mexico, Utah, Colorado and other localities.

SUMMARY

Our machine age requires extensive use of minerals, and the trade in these is enormous. Minerals account for over half the weight of freight carried by railroad and ocean ship. Minerals are of two general types: metallic and nonmetallic. Among the former are iron, copper, lead, zinc, silver, aluminum, tin, gold, and a long

Figure 19-21 Uranium ore-refining mill near Uravan, Colorado. This is one of the largest mills of the Colorado Plateau. (Photograph, courtesy of Union Carbide Nuclear Company.)

list of less important special-purpose metals. Before most of these metals can be used in industry, they must be extracted from ores by smelting processes. Uranium is the raw material for atomic energy which may supplement power produced from fuels or other conventional methods.

Nonmetallic minerals include the mineral fuels such as coal, petroleum and natural gas. Among nonfuels, portland cement and clay products are important because of their usefulness in building construction. Other nonmetallics include sulfur, salt, precious stones, and the mineral fertilizers, potash, nitrates, and phosphates.

Unfortunately, the formation of mineral resources is an extremely slow natural process. Some minerals like limestone, clay, and salt, or magnesium from sea water are so abundant as to be inexhaustible, but when most ores or non-metallics have been mined and used, they cannot be replaced. Careful use of most mineral resources is imperative if future generations are to have enough minerals to meet their requirements.

Outline
Minerals: importance and occurrence
Metals
Iron
Copper, aluminum, gold, etc.
Mineral fuels
Coal
Petroleum and natural gas
Nonmetallic resources
Building materials
Fertilizers, etc.
Conservation and strategy of minerals
Characteristics of mining towns

QUESTIONS

1. What raw materials of mineral origin are brought to your locality for manufacture?

2. What metals, mineral fuels, or construction materials are produced in your locality?

3. Why do the residents of mining communities fluctuate in numbers and prosperity?

4. In how many ways is crude petroleum transported?

5. Where are the principal centers of cement production in the United States?

6. What quality of copper makes it of special commercial importance?

7. What practices in the strip mining of coal have aroused public opinion and resulted in restrictive legislation?

8. Which minerals must be smelted in order to obtain commercial quantities of the product?

9. Summarize the advantages of obtaining iron ore supplies from the Mesabi district of Minnesota.

10. Each of the following areas is a producer of iron ores. Indicate the urban area toward which the ore moves for smelting, and the route by which it is shipped: northern France, Silesia, Donets Basin, India, northern Spain, Algeria, Alabama, Mesabi, Cuba, New South Wales, Labrador, Newfoundland.

11. Summarize briefly the reasons why copper has increased in importance in our modern economy.

12. Give four valid reasons why the United States, with only 7 per cent of the world's population, consumes a much larger percentage of the world's metals.

13. In Figure 19-14:
Will well *B* probably be a "gusher"?
Under what circumstances will well *B* need to be pumped?

14. Each of the following areas is well known for its production of nonmetallic minerals. Name an important earth product manufactured or produced in each section: Indiana, Florida, eastern Pennsylvania, Texas, Vermont, southeastern Ohio, Tennessee, New Jersey.

15. According to Figure 19-7 most of the world's supply of tin ore is mined in low latitudes. Most of the finished product, however, is used in middle latitudes. What is the effect of this distribution of producing and consuming areas?

16. "Of all metals used by man, gold is the least useful." Explain the significance of the statement.

17. Two gaseous products, helium and carbon dioxide, are obtained from wells. They are not fuels and are incombustible. Why are they of value?

SELECTED REFERENCES

Ayres, Eugene: *Energy Sources,* McGraw-Hill Book Company, Inc., New York, 1952.

Bateman, Alan M.: *Economic Mineral Deposits,* John Wiley & Sons, Inc., New York, 1950.

DeMille, John B.: *Strategic Minerals: A Summary of Uses, World Output, Stockpiles, Procurement,* McGraw-Hill Book Company, Inc., New York, 1947.

Doerr, Arthur, and Lee Guernsey: "Man as Geomorphical Agent: The Example of Coal Mining," *Annals of the Association of American Geographers,* 46:197–210, June, 1956.

"Energy Resources of the World," U.S. Department of State Publication 3428, Washington, 1949.

Fanning, Leonard: *Our Oil Resources,* 2d ed., McGraw-Hill Book Company, New York, 1950.

Hartley, Fred J., and C. S. Briniger: "Oil Shale and Bituminous Sand," *The Scientific Monthly,* 84:275–289, June, 1957.

Hoffman, George W.: "The Role of Nuclear Power in Europe's Future Energy Balance," *Annals of the Association of American Geographers,* 47:15–40, March, 1957.

Hubbert, M. King: Energy from Fossil Fuels, *Science,* 109:103–109, Feb. 4, 1949.

Jones, Stephen B.: "The Economic Geography of Atomic Energy, Review Article," *Economic Geography,* 27:268–274, July, 1951.

Ladoo, Raymond B.: *Nonmetallic Minerals,* 2d ed., McGraw-Hill Book Company, Inc., New York, 951.

Lamer, Mirko: *The World Fertilizer Economy,* Stanford University Press, Stanford, 1957.

Nininger, Robert D.: *Minerals for Atomic Energy,* D. Van Nostrand Company, Inc., Princeton, N.J., 1954.

Parsons, James J.: "The Geography of Natural Gas in the United States," *Economic Geography,* 26:162–178, July, 1950.

Rickard, T. A.: *Man and Metals: A History of Mining in Relation to the Development of Civilization,* 2 vols., McGraw-Hill Book Company, Inc., New York, 1932.

U.S. Bureau of Mines: *Minerals Yearbook,* Washington.

Van Royen, William: *Mineral Resources of the World,* vol. II, *Atlas of the World's Resources,* Prentice-Hall, Inc., Englewood Cliffs, N.J., 1952.

Voskuil, Walter H.: *Minerals in World Industry,* McGraw-Hill Book Company, Inc., New York, 1955.

Wilcox, Wendell G.: "Salt Production," *Scientific Monthly,* 70:157–164, March, 1950.

NOTE: The U.S. Geological Survey, Department of the Interior, Washington, publishes many pamphlets on different mining districts. A list will be supplied upon request.

20. Water

Resources

WATER is one of the most important necessities of man's life. It makes up a large part of his body weight. It is required for the support of animals and plants. It is one agency in the erosion and weathering of rocks. It is essential in many chemical and industrial processes. Water has many uses, including municipal and domestic supply, steam production, manufacturing, transportation, irrigation, and power development. A considerable quantity of fish for food comes from inland waters, which also are used extensively for recreation.

DOMESTIC AND INDUSTRIAL WATER

Domestic water should be abundant and easily secured, free from bacteria and other contamination, free from odor, taste, and color, free from suspended matter like mud or silt, and as free as possible from soluble salts like gypsum, lime, and the alkalies. Not all cities or regions have abundant water with the qualities desired. In deserts it may be difficult to find enough water for even the few inhabitants there. Industries may experience difficulty in getting soft water for their use. In regions that have been long cultivated as in northern France, and particularly where human wastes are used for fertilizer as in China and Japan, water supply from surface streams and shallow wells is almost certain to be contaminated.

Where water supplies contain lime or gypsum, the water is called "hard," and much soap is required in order to make suds. Laundries and other establishments requiring soft water find hard water undesirable. In England at the cotton-milling city of Manchester, both ground and surface water may contain chemicals derived from coal beds underlying the region; such water is entirely unsuitable for use in bleaching and dyeing. As a result, these processes are carried on in plants close to the Pennine Hills east of Manchester, where supplies of soft water are secured from a pervious sandstone.

Urban Water Supply.   Large cities may find it difficult to secure sufficient supplies of pure soft water for their residents. New York and Los Angeles have outstanding problems of water supply.

New York found its local well water and similar supplies inadequate more than a century ago. City authorities undertook to develop a source of municipal water supply at the Croton Reservoir on the eastern side of the Hudson River. Before many years elapsed, this source, too, was inadequate; additional water was then obtained from the Catskill Mountains. An aqueduct 18 miles long was built to carry the water to New York City. Finally the city went farther for water and secured it in the Delaware, Schoharie, and other watersheds. Areas that supply water are kept wooded, and watersheds are generally free of

residents. En route to New York the water is brought under the Hudson River by means of a large siphon. The problem of supplying the city with water is complicated by the location of New York on Manhattan Island, which requires tunneling through solid rock far beneath mud and water. Other tunnels are needed to supply Brooklyn and Staten Island.

Los Angeles, finding the amount of local water insufficient for the growing city, developed a supply on eastern slopes of the Sierra Nevada in Owens Valley (Figure 14-2) and brought this water by aqueduct from 240 miles away and later from Mono Lake 350 miles across the desert. As the city grew, this supply of water was not adequate. Los Angeles and nearby cities then spent large additional sums to build an aqueduct from the Colorado River (Figure 20-15). Thus river water is pumped across the desert and over mountains for 450 miles to reach the coastal cities; this is accomplished by using electrical energy produced at Hoover Dam. Water is taken from the river at Parker Dam, some miles south of Hoover Dam, where it is comparatively free from silt. In fact, most of the mud that gave the Colorado its name is now deposited upstream from Hoover Dam in the large reservoir known as Lake Mead (Figure 20-1). Eventually the dam will impound so

Figure 20-1 Hoover Dam on the Colorado River, impounding a lake known as Lake Mead in the heart of the Colorado desert. This dam has two principal purposes: prevention of floods on the lower Colorado River, and production of hydroelectric power for use in southern California cities. The landscape is desert in type. (Photograph, courtesy of the U.S. Bureau of Reclamation.)

much silt that it will no longer function for storage; estimates suggest that this will occur in about 200 years. Until then water passing through the power plants will produce a wealth of energy for the use of cities as well as for pumping water across the desert. Lake Mead also provides a desert recreation center with boating and resorts; the dam itself is an important tourist attraction. Water for irrigating the Imperial Valley is obtained from dams located downstream from Hoover Dam. Most water reaching Los Angeles from the Colorado is too expensive for irrigation, and is reserved principally for industrial and domestic use.

Cities on rivers and lakes have large quantities of water available; but as population increases the supply becomes contaminated from towns upstream or settlements along lake shores because bodies of water are convenient for sewer outlets as well as for water intakes. Sooner or later contamination causes disease. Filtering lake and river water through layers of sand and charcoal removes suspended silt and lessens danger of contamination. To make water entirely safe, however, a chemical such as chlorine may be added to destroy bacteria.

Chicago's water problem. Chicago is located near the southern end of Lake Michigan, on the land divide separating drainage into Lake Michigan from water tributary to the Mississippi River. When Chicago was smaller it obtained good water by pumping from Lake Michigan; as population increased, this supply became seriously polluted with surface and sewage drainage. To overcome the difficulty a sanitary district was organized in 1889, and under its direction a drainage canal was built, using the Chicago River as a channel. Normally this stream emptied into Lake Michigan but an excavation of only 10 feet reversed its flow and sent its waters into tributaries of the Mississippi. Then, by pumping water from Lake Michigan into the drainage canal, the city's wastes could be flushed away from the lake instead of toward it.

As long as Chicago remained relatively small no great amount of water was needed, but as the city grew it required more water. By 1907, the large amounts of water taken from Lake Michigan by the city were beginning to affect navigation on the Great Lakes. Withdrawal of nearly 10,000 cubic feet of water per second (a volume greater than the flow of the American Falls at Niagara), in combination with several years of reduced rainfall, lowered levels of Lakes Huron, Erie, and Ontario from 5 to 7 inches, and the harbor at Montreal from 9 to 10 inches. This greatly hampered shipping, made canals less navigable, threatened the water supplies of many industries, and generally created serious hazards throughout the Great Lakes region.

The Canadian government and states fronting on the lakes protested. The entire situation was reviewed by the courts and became a matter of some international consequence before Chicago was required to reduce the daily consumption of Lake Michigan water and establish a system for disposal of sewage and industrial wastes without impairing levels of four of the Great Lakes as well as the St. Lawrence. During the early 1950s a series of rainy years caused the level of the Great Lakes to rise. The rising water was helpful for shipping but damaged homes and docks along the shore. Then some would have welcomed a lowering of lake levels by increasing flow through the drainage canal. Incidentally, the canal carries considerable traffic, especially barges loaded with coal and petroleum products.

Recreation, Health, and Inland Fisheries.
Many health or pleasure resorts depend on mineral or hot springs (often both), like those at Baden, Germany; Lourdes, France; and Hot Springs, Arkansas.

Development of the automobile has made it possible for many people to use inland lakes and rivers for fishing, camping, boating, swimming, and other recreation. The modern accessibility of resorts on inland waters has led to the utilization of many lakes and streams formerly ignored.

Much fish for food is caught in the Great

Lakes and the larger streams. In addition to commercial fresh-water fisheries, quantities of game fish are taken. Usually both catching and sale of game fish are restricted in order to protect the species from extermination (Figure 20-2). Most men regard fresh-water fishing as a sport rather than a source of food and gladly spend large sums of money for the pleasure. Catering to fishermen has become a big business in areas such as Maine, Minnesota, northern Wisconsin and Michigan, Colorado, and Ontario.

In some countries, notably China, quantities of fish are raised for food in artificial ponds. It is reported that more weight of food —fish, edible bulbs, ducks—can come from a pond than from an equal area of fertile cropped soil.

Stream and Ground-water Pollution. Many rivers in the United States are seriously polluted. Too often the stream bed has been a dumping ground for all kinds of refuse, and former beauty spots have become eyesores and nuisances. Industrial wastes from steel and paper mills, oil from refineries, and sewerage of cities contaminate streams. This pollution frequently is so great that it kills fish and makes water from these streams impossible for human beings to use. In industrial parts of the United States action is required to prevent pollution, most of which could be avoided.

Cities are sometimes founded where large springs are available. In limestone regions solution caverns exist and much drainage is underground. The only reliable domestic water supply may be found at points where subsurface flow breaks out to form springs. Numerous towns in Greece and Syria were founded at "fountainheads." In limestone regions, great care must be used to avoid contaminated water since pollution may occur underground.

WATER POWER

Water power has served man as a source of energy for many centuries. Swift-flowing water was used as a source of power along streams in China; it operated water wheels in the Near East and lifted water for irrigation in Egypt. Power for grinding grain and operating

Figure 20-2 Celilo Falls on the Columbia River. This was a traditional spot for fishing before the construction of new dams; here some northwestern Indians were accustomed to fish from wooden platforms, catching salmon as the fish made their way to spawning grounds farther up the Columbia River. This falls is now drowned by the Dalles Dam. (Photograph, courtesy of the U.S. Fish and Wildlife Service.)

other small manufacturing plants came from old-fashioned water wheels in many parts of Europe and colonial America, especially in New England. Many important industrial centers of today received their early impetus from harnessing of energy of a waterfall.

Factors Affecting Water-power Use. Since flowing water can be used indefinitely as a source of energy, the development of hydroelectric power is one of the best ways to conserve coal and petroleum. Electricity produced by water power is not always cheaper than that generated by large efficient steam plants whose fuel is coal, petroleum, or natural gas; hence hundreds of small water-power sites have been abandoned in favor of power purchased from large generating plants. Favorable sites for development of water power are common along swift-flowing streams. Often these have waterfalls and rapids in narrow gorges or canyons which make desirable locations for dam sites.

Waterfalls along the Fall Line (Figure 13-6) and within the Appalachian Piedmont and New England regions are frequently caused by resistant rock strata. Occasionally this type of bedrock forces rivers to change courses, thus providing excellent power sites. Many power sites of this type occur in the northern United States and Northern Europe as the result of glacial erosion and deposition.

A good power site should have a large amount of water falling a considerable distance, and flow should be steady. To be profitably developed for electrical energy, a market should be at hand. An ideal situation is that at Niagara Falls, where the river drains the Great Lakes and therefore has very steady flow and large volume, falling 150 feet. Manufacturing plants along the river above the falls make effective use of the available power. This is an important factor in the growth of Buffalo and other industrial centers. Lakes are an advantage in maintaining regular flow of streams thus helping to produce a steady current of hydroelectric power. The Great Lakes and other glacial lakes provide many examples, as well as the artificial lakes impounded by dams, as at Lake Mead.

Geographical conditions sometimes can make it impossible or impractical to develop power. The fall of the Mississippi River is only a fraction of an inch per mile below Cairo, Illinois, so it naturally has no good power sites along its lower course. African rivers

Figure 20-3 Bonneville Dam, a principal power plant in the Pacific Northwest, in its Columbia Gorge setting. Note the "fish ladders" at left of the dam. A large lock at this dam can lift ocean-going vessels 70 feet into slack water that now covers formerly dangerous rapids. (Photograph, courtesy of Bonneville Power Administration.)

are large in volume as they plunge over the edge of the central plateau not far from their mouths, but these rivers have no nearby markets for hydroelectric power. Africa has more potential water power than any other continent, but the amount developed is small. The same is true of vast power resources of eastern South America and southern and eastern Asia.

Water Power in the United States. Potential water power available in the United States for 90 per cent of the time is estimated at 35 million horsepower, and that available for 50 per cent of the time at 55 million horsepower. Nearly two-fifths of the potential water power of the United States is located in the three Pacific Coast states, and more than half is in the five states of California, Oregon, Washington, Idaho, and Montana. Power has been developed rapidly in the Pacific Northwest, partly at government hydroelectric plants at Bonneville (Figure 20-3) and Grand Coulee (Figure 20-14) on the Columbia River. Together they produce nearly 2½ million horsepower. Other large federally built dams on the Columbia include Chief Joseph Dam near Grand Coulee, and McNary Dam on the Washington-Oregon boundary. Hoover Dam on the Colorado River, with a capacity of 1,660 million horsepower, and Shasta Dam in California are other Federal projects. Nevertheless as compared with potential power, development in the Western states leaves them behind the eastern part of the nation, with its large market for electrical energy.

Many accessible power sites in New England, the Middle Atlantic, and the North Central states have been developed, in contrast with the relatively small part of available power in the four northwestern states now utilized. In New England three-fourths of all water-power sites are in use. The United States has an installed capacity of nearly 22 million horsepower of hydroelectric energy (Table 20-1), which is about one-half the amount of electricity generated by steam. Leading states in water-power development

are Washington, California, New York, Tennessee, Alabama, Oregon, North Carolina, South Carolina, Nevada, Arizona, Idaho, and Montana. Hydroelectric plants built by the Tennessee Valley Authority have a capacity of nearly 3 million horsepower. Considerable water power has been developed also in Michigan, Wisconsin, and Pennsylvania. One of the greatest undeveloped power projects in the East is that of the St. Lawrence River, scheduled for completion in 1960. Only a fraction of the potential power at Niagara Falls has yet been developed.

Water Power Abroad. Developed water power of the world, according to the U.S. Geological Survey, amounts to 86 million horsepower. After the United States, which leads in capacity of installed hydroelectric plants, the leading countries are Canada, Norway, Sweden, Italy, the U.S.S.R., Japan, France, Germany, Austria, and Switzerland (Figure 20-4). A statement of the relative power production of the different nations, however, fails to give a complete picture. In such countries as Canada and Norway, which have abundant water-power resources, electrical output of generators is greater per unit installed than in other countries such as France and Germany, whose resources are not so great. In Canada and Norway only the best sites are utilized, and at these sites only as much machinery is installed as can be operated throughout a

Figure 20-4 Water power plant capacity, selected countries, in millions of horsepower, 1954. (From Economic Almanac, 1956, p. 30.)

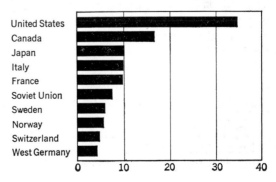

TABLE 20-1. HYDROELECTRIC POWER, UNITED STATES, 1954

Region	Number of plants Federal and private	Capacity in kilowatts*
Pacific Northwest	229	6,842,389
South Pacific (Calif.)	105	2,250,000
Colorado River basin	45	1,773,665
Missouri River basin	81	783,111
Mississippi River basin	362	5,659,275
North Atlantic	490	2,267,243
Great Lakes–St. Lawrence	380	1,545,285
South Atlantic	149	1,455,576
Total	**1,841**	**22,576,544**
United States installed Federal and private		22,576,544
Federal projects completed		8,393,520
Federal projects under construction		6,340,450

* 1 kw = 1.34 HP

large part of the year with the water available; in countries where demand for power is great and potential water-power resources comparatively small, machinery is installed to use water power that is available for only part of each year, with steam supplying power for the remaining period.

In Europe, Italy, Switzerland, Austria, and France, nations with large resources of water power in the Alps and insufficient coal for industrial energy, are leading producers of hydroelectricity (Figure 20-4). Other countries important for water-power production include Spain and Finland. Without water power, large-scale manufacturing would be greatly handicapped in Switzerland and Norway, where even railroads are electrified. The low-lying British Isles have little available power, and England's abundant coal supply discourages its development. Eire, on the other hand, has only peat as a source of fuel, hence Eire has encouraged water-power development. Japan, a rainy and mountainous land with numerous swift rivers, needs power since it has rather small coal resources; hence this industrialized country leads in development of water power in Asia. Korea has several large hydroelectric plants, but the great potential resources of China are hardly touched.

Potential water power of the world is esti-mated at 664 million horsepower for minimum flow and about 2,000 million horsepower for mean flow. North America and Europe lead the continents in installed capacity of plants. Asia is third and South America a poor fourth. Africa leads all continents in potential water power but is last in production of hydroelectricity, although plants under construction or planned will soon make Africa exceed the combined developed hydroelectric production of Australia and New Zealand.

Use of Water Power. In the past, factories were located directly at waterfalls with machinery being turned by a water wheel. Factories and homes of workmen were often in narrow valleys in order to be near the power source. Today waterfalls are no longer important sites for cities. Only the power plant itself need be at the falls, and from there the energy is transmitted to mills, cities, and other consumers.

Water power may produce energy no more cheaply than mineral fuels, since large efficient plants using cheap coal or fuel oil produce power very economically. From the standpoint of conservation, however, it would be desirable to develop all economical water power in order to husband exhaustible coal and oil reserves.

To avoid the possibility that consumers of hydroelectricity will lack energy in case of accident to a single source of supply, power producers commonly have auxiliary steam plants to provide energy in emergencies. Moreover, different power plants are tied together by interlocking distribution systems; if service from one plant is interrupted, energy can be secured quickly through other connections.

Hydroelectric power is particularly suited to plants such as paper mills and pulp mills, which operate twenty-four hours a day, since energy of falling water can be continuously applied to these manufacturing processes. As a result, many paper and pulp mills in New England, New York, Michigan, Wisconsin, Quebec, and Ontario are located on rivers down which pulpwood comes to sites furnishing power for operation of the mills. If the site is convenient for lake or ocean transportation, that is an additional advantage. Most pulp and paper mills in the Pacific Northwest have tidewater locations, convenient for receipt of rafts of pulpwood and shipment of paper by ocean vessel to markets along the Eastern seaboard.

WATER TRANSPORTATION

River Transportation in the United States. Inland waterways were one of the earliest methods man used for transportation. American Indians utilized the extensive system of rivers and glacial lakes for hunting and trading expeditions in the northeastern United States and eastern Canada. Similar routes were followed by French fur traders and explorers. The first outlet for the produce of the agricultural settlements in Ohio and Kentucky was by way of the rivers to New Orleans, using flatboats and rafts to carry goods downstream. The wealth of lumber from forests of northern Pennsylvania was rafted down the Susquehanna River to markets in Harrisburg, Baltimore, and other cities. To carry goods upstream, however, was very laborious, whether by rowing, poling, sail, or towrope. Invention of the steamboat made it possible for vessels to move upstream on the Mississippi, Ohio, Missouri, and other rivers.

For about sixty years during the middle of the last century, river traffic went from Pittsburgh down the Ohio and up the Missouri to Fort Benton, Montana, then at the head of navigation to St. Paul on the Mississippi, and to New Orleans down the "Father of Waters." Then competition with railroads and poor landing facilities brought decline in river transportation; by 1900, traffic had dropped to only a fraction of its former amount. Since then the Federal government has sought to revive the use of inland waterways. The government established barge lines on the Mississippi and other streams to provide regular service. Some progress has been made in increasing the use of our rivers, but only in transport of bulk goods has traffic attained anything approaching its former importance.

The Monongahela River carries more tonnage than the Mississippi because it is convenient for coal mines, steel mills, limestone quarries, and cement works. As a result the stream has been canalized and carries an enormous traffic, which furnishes evidence that America does not neglect waterways when it is highly advantageous to use them. Passing from the Monongahela into the Ohio River at Pittsburgh (Figure 24-10), it is possible to utilize a controlled stream, marked by a series of more than fifty dams and lock systems, in making the trip downstream to the confluence with the Mississippi. It has taken the better part of the last century to complete the original plan for the improvement, and the success of the plan is attested by the flourishing cities that now line its course—Pittsburgh, Wheeling, Huntington, Cincinnati, Covington, Louisville, Evansville, and Cairo. Without the advantage of a navigable channel, these and many other towns would have been unable to market their bulky commodities efficiently and cheaply. Improvements in navigation of the Ohio River have made that stream one of the prime transport units in the world. Further improvements are in progress.

The Great Lakes. For all commodities that can be handled in bulk with a minimum of human labor, the cheapest transport per ton-mile anywhere lies between the head of Lake Superior and the foot of Lake Erie. Cargoes of iron ore, lumber, and grain coming down the lakes, and coal going up to markets which have no nearby supplies of mineral fuels, provide a constantly changing stream of shipments during those months when the lakes are ice-free. The Federal government has improved navigation on the lakes by building canals and dams, and dredging, surveying, and marking channels. No other nations have the marked advantages of a coordinated system of water transport similar to that enjoyed by Canada and the United States (Figure 20-5).

Disadvantages and Advantages of River Transport. Rivers possess both advantages and disadvantages as routes of travel. A river is irrevocably related to its geographical setting—its latitude, extent of basin, direction of flow, volume, and other physical aspects. Hence its usefulness to man must be understood and interpreted in relation to that setting, and the direction in which it trends will determine the flow of river-borne trade within its basin. Demand for trade routes in the United States is in an east-west direction so that goods from the interior can be shipped readily to Europe and products returned. Our largest river system, the Mississippi, trends north and south, at right angles to the needed direction.

Other disadvantages of rivers include widely meandering courses that may greatly increase the distance between towns as contrasted with

Figure 20-5   St. Lawrence Seaway—one of the world's most important inland waterway routes.

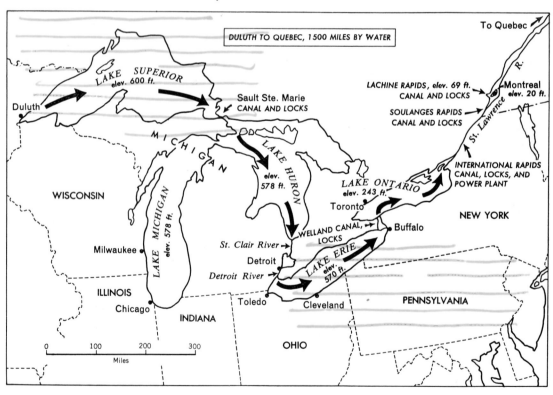

the direct line of a railroad. Extreme fluctuation of flow may cause trouble from floods. Rivers present a variety of other hindrances: lack of navigable depth or breadth of water, obstructions to navigation, such as sand bars, snags, and rocks, shifting channels, dangerously swift currents, rapids or waterfalls requiring that cargoes be portaged or canals constructed, navigable lengths of water too short to use economically, ice, fogs, and other troublesome climatic conditions, and lack of suitable landing places.

Two great advantages of rivers are (1) rights of way are provided without cost although improvements must be made on many river beds to fit them for transportation, and (2) for bulky goods water transportation is cheaper than rail if the waterway connects the source with the market. Thus the Rhine River is the most used stream in Europe though not the largest. The iron ore of northern France is brought by canal to the Rhine and then up the Ruhr Valley to the coal regions. Coal and imported grain are transported upstream and lumber cargoes downstream. Potash, cement rock, and all kinds of construction materials are shipped on barges. The Rhine is a useful stream because it lies in a highly industrialized and densely populated part of the world.

The Volga River has large volume, slight current, and a fairly fertile hinterland, but it would be more advantageous if it flowed into the open sea rather than into the enclosed Caspian. The Danube River is much larger than the Rhine, and from its source in the Black Forest of Germany to its mouth at the Black Sea it flows through or touches many countries; yet it is not used nearly so much as the lesser Rhine because the Danube Basin is less populous and industrialized. Political considerations also affect use of the Danube, since the river serves seven countries.

In Asia the Yangtze Kiang connects the interior with the coast and is widely used in spite of need to navigate through deep gorges where rapids are a hazard. The Amazon has the most extensive system, but the small population limits its use. The Ganges, Paraná, Magdalena, Nile, and Tigris are among other useful rivers.

Canals. Canals are built to connect systems of natural inland waterways and provide uninterrupted navigation where unfavorable natural conditions of terrain would otherwise require portages. The Grand Canal in China was built more than a thousand years ago and extends for 1,200 miles from Peking southward to Hangchow (Figure 20-6). Some canals in Europe are centuries old.

The first important canal in the United States was the Erie Canal, connecting the Hudson River near Albany with Lake Erie near Buffalo. This canal lowered transportation costs from farmlands tributary to the southern Great Lakes and greatly assisted regional development. In New York State, nine cities with populations in excess of 75,000 lie along the Erie Canal or the Hudson River system. When railroads to the West took most of the traffic from the Erie Canal, the State of New York deepened and widened it into the New York State Barge Canal in the hope of making this waterway regain its former importance. No significant increase in traffic has resulted, however, and bulky commodities like grain, gravel, and iron products are almost the only freight carried on the canal today.

Canals were built during the middle of the

Figure 20-6   Grand Canal and the Great Wall of China.

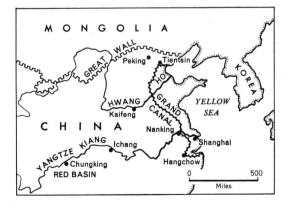

last century to connect Lake Erie and Lake Michigan with the Ohio River, across Ohio, Indiana, and Illinois. They utilized several tributaries of the Mississippi and Ohio Rivers. Most of these canals have been abandoned because of competition from railways and highways.

In the Eastern states a canal across Cape Cod is used by steamers traveling between Boston and New York. Another crosses the Delmarva Peninsula between Delaware and Chesapeake Bays. A very popular waterway for pleasure craft connects New York Harbor with the resorts of the Florida coast. Most of its course is in coastal sounds and other waters where offshore bars and islands afford protection. Only short stretches on this Intercoastal Canal require a motorboat to venture into the open sea. An extension of the coastal canal system connects the Mississippi River with Houston, Texas, and is much used by barges to carry petroleum, cotton, and other bulky cargoes. Houston is also connected by a ship canal to the Gulf of Mexico. On the West Coast, a large canal at Seattle connects Puget Sound and Lake Washington by way of Lake Union. Locks at Bonneville and McNary Dams on the Columbia River permit ocean vessels to ascend the stream to a point over 200 miles inland. Stockton, California, has been made into a seaport by dredging the San Joaquin River.

The most used canal is that at Sault Ste. Marie connecting Lake Superior and Lake Huron (Figure 20-7). In the summer season, when shipping is at its peak, four locks on the American side and one on the Canadian side are constantly operating to keep the great freighters moving around the rapids of the St. Marys River. The "Soo Canal" is open only about eight months of the year, but during this time it may carry double the tonnage of that passing through the Panama Canal, which operates twelve months each year.

The St. Lawrence Seaway. The St. Lawrence River, between its head at Lake Ontario and its estuary below Quebec, is a large stream by which small vessels have been able to penetrate the interior of the continent of North America for many years, owing to construction of canals around the river's rapids near Montreal and the Welland Canal around

Figure 20-7 Soo Canal, looking eastward down the St. Marys River and locks. A powerhouse, using power from St. Marys Falls, is at left. Part of the town of Sault Ste. Marie is at right. Note ore vessels in the canal locks; those headed for Lake Superior ride high in the water because they are empty, those headed for Lake Huron in the distance are filled with iron ore. (Photograph, courtesy of the U.S. War Department, Corps of Engineers.)

Niagara Falls (Figure 20-5). The canals, however, cannot accommodate large ocean vessels, and a deepening of the river and its canals has been planned, along with a large increase of hydroelectric power to be generated along the river at new power plants. This project—the St. Lawrence Seaway—built jointly by the Dominion of Canada and the United States, is worthwhile in spite of the fact that the river flow is interrupted by ice during winter. The completed seaway, deepened to 27 feet, makes it possible for ocean vessels to enter Lake Ontario in some numbers. When further improvements of the Welland Canal and connections between Lakes Huron and Erie are undertaken, the Great Lakes cities will have some of the advantages of seaports. Construction of the seaway has been particularly urgent in view of our declining resources of high-grade iron ore in the Great Lakes area, since it makes possible transport of ore from Labrador up the St. Lawrence River to steel mills at Hamilton, Buffalo, Cleveland, Lorain, and Gary, or for transshipment to Pittsburgh and Youngstown.

Canals in Europe connect navigable rivers and form a fairly complete transportation network in countries of moderate relief like the Soviet Union, Germany, France, and England. The Low Countries of the Netherlands and Belgium have a complete system of canals, used for transportation and drainage. Cheapness of water transport is a factor in location of the steel industry in the Ruhr Valley, where iron ore is brought to coal supplies by canal and river routes. In Russia canals connect the Volga with the Dnieper, Don, Dvina, and other streams; though closed in winter, the waterways are nevertheless much used. By using the ship canal across the peninsula of Jutland from the port of Kiel, boats can avoid the long journey through two straits and the North Sea. The Manchester Ship Canal in England has made a port of a former inland city. The ports of Amsterdam, Rotterdam, and Antwerp are served by numerous canals. In Germany canals connect the Rhine, Elbe, Oder, and Danube Rivers.

Rivers as Barriers. Rivers are useful for transportation, but they also form barriers. Broad swampy floodplains and deltas like those of the lower Mississippi, Danube, and Volga are very difficult to cross. Even small streams, if their channels are incised, may hinder transportation. Location of fords, ferries, and bridges affects the selection of sites and growth of river towns. Names of many English and American cities suggest this—Oxford, Cambridge, and Harpers Ferry. Great numbers of streams in a humid climate may compel frequent departures from a straight route to seek a way across water barriers. Because cities cannot afford bridges over a wide river on every street heading streamward, bridges tend to become traffic bottlenecks. Even animals sometimes find wide rivers effective barriers to movement. Thus the chimpanzee and okapi are said to live only on the north side of the Congo River and have been unable to cross that stream.

Rivers as Boundaries. "Barrier" rivers like the Mississippi, Rio Grande, St. Lawrence, and Columbia may serve as state or national boundaries. A river valley, however, is an economic unit that should be included in a single political unit, for many rivers occupy shifting channels, and these make delimitation of a boundary difficult and subject to controversy. Most rivers produce unstable boundaries and cause disputes, as the Rio Grande has between Mexico and the United States, or the Red River between Texas and Oklahoma. The latter case gave rise to litigation between the two states regarding ownership of oil deposits beneath the channel of the stream.

The usual rule applied to river boundaries is that, if a change results from slow cutting on one bank and deposit on the other shore, the new deposit belongs to the owner of the adjacent land. In very rapid or catastrophic change such as the formation of an oxbow cutoff across the neck on an inner meander, the detached area remains the property of the former owner. Under this rule, in the Mississippi floodplain, some Iowa land lies east of the present main channel of the river, and Illinois has land on the west side. On the Mississippi floodplain near Vicksburg in 1876, a large looped meander was suddenly cut off, leaving the town without river transportation and putting the Louisiana land within the meander east of the river (Figure 13-2). The boundary between Mississippi and Louisiana at this point was in dispute for many years. From time to time, a river commission must try to effect exchange of land between Mexican and Texan owners along the Rio Grande, where the channel has changed abruptly and transferred land from one side of the river to the other.

Lakes.   Lakes are often useful and pleasurable features of a community. They are very irregular in distribution. Minnesota, for example, has thousands of lakes in contrast to their rarity in Oklahoma and Kansas. Regions that have been recently glaciated usually have numerous lakes. These result from glacial scour, dams of debris dropped by melting ice, and irregularity of deposits in which depressions called *kettle holes* were left. Glaciers may act as dams themselves, and some large temporary lakes resulted from this cause, for example, glacial Lake Maumee in northern Ohio. Some lakes are located in natural basins as the result of earth movements. Examples include the Caspian Sea, Lake Baikal, and Lake Okeechobee. Solution of limestone by ground water

has formed many ponds in the resulting sinkholes; these are found in northern Florida, central Indiana, and near the head of the Adriatic Sea. River changes on floodplains sometimes form oxbow lakes; there are also delta lakes and others resulting from vagaries of deposition. Bars along a coast may cut off part of a bay or shore line, thus forming a lagoon.

A lake is a temporary geographic feature, for forces begin to destroy it as soon as it has been formed. These may be listed among the principal destructive forces: erosion of the outlet, filling of the bottom with sediment and vegetation, and loss of tributary water by evaporation, use, or removal elsewhere. Salt lakes have no outlet and those in deserts are caused by concentration of salt from inflowing water that contains the mineral in small amounts. Other lakes may have been salt originally and may have resulted from the separation of a portion of the ocean by land. Temporary wet-weather lakes in deserts of the United States are called *playas*. Existence of former lakes can be proved by the presence of lake terraces, old beach lines, and deposits once made in water but now located on the land.

Lakes may store water for irrigation and power as well as supply water for domestic and commercial use. Fish in lakes add to local food supply. Large lakes may be navigable and so serve trade. Health and pleasure resorts are often built near lakes.

FLOODS

Floods may constitute one of the greatest disasters of nature. Partly as a result of human activities, floods seem to be increasing in frequency and severity. They are especially destructive in broad floodplains and level deltas; because of their natural fertility these are densely populated, sometimes supporting more than a thousand people per square mile. Floods from the Yellow River in northern China and on the Yangtze Kiang in central China have made tens of millions of people homeless and caused hundreds of thousands

—perhaps millions—to die from starvation because of the drowning out of crops.

The U.S. Weather Bureau estimates that the average flood damage in the United States totals 35 million dollars per year (Figure 20-8). Great floods may exceed the average destruction; the Mississippi Valley flood of 1927 did more than 280 million dollars in damage. In 1937, the flooding Ohio River rose 87 feet at Louisville and ruined scores of millions of dollars' worth of property. In the spring of 1938, floods in the neighborhood of Los An-

Figure 20-8   Flood damage in Waterbury, Connecticut, resulting from heavy rainfall associated with a hurricane in September, 1955, causing severe damage throughout New England. (Photograph, courtesy of the American Brass Company.)

geles (where there are no large permanent rivers) destroyed property estimated at 65 million dollars and caused the deaths of more than a hundred people. In December, 1955, floods in Oregon and California cost over 50 lives and at least 150 million dollars in property damage.

Causes of Floods.   Many factors affect runoff and contribute to the formation of floods. Sometimes a single cause is the obvious explanation, but more frequently numerous causes unite to make a flood. Among physical conditions affecting runoff are amount and character of precipitation, rate of melting snow, natural vegetation, topography, including the shape of the drainage basin, and character of soils and bedrock. Total rainfall is less important than the amount in a given time. Local floods result from intense storms that may produce several inches of rain in a few hours. These cloudbursts are common features of rainfall in western mountains and plateaus of America. Even deserts may experience local thunderstorms that lead to floods.

Great floods, like those in the northeastern United States in 1936, the Mississippi flood in 1927, and the California disaster of 1938, all resulted from prolonged heavy rains, following a previous wet season that had already thoroughly soaked the ground. When more rain fell, it could not sink in and be absorbed by the earth; instead it was forced to run off the surface, however well forested the region. From 1 to 2 feet of rain have been known to fall in less than a week, as a result of a series of cyclonic storms closely following each other along the same path or of a storm's becoming localized in a particular watershed and remaining there for several consecutive days instead of moving in its usual easterly direction.

Although great floods may come in forested regions when litter under the trees and the soil itself become thoroughly soaked, runoff from bare mountain slopes is much more rapid than where a natural vegetation cover exists. In southern California adjacent watersheds that had similar rainfall and relief, but only one of which was covered by vegetation, the others having been burned over, showed marked differences in the amount of runoff. Heavy rainfall on the barren burned-over watershed produced floods that brought extensive damage and dumped enormous quantities of coarse gravel and boulders over fertile alluvial soil. The same rainfall on the watershed that was undamaged by fire did no harm, since more water sank into the ground and the runoff was slower.

In Utah and the Colorado Plateau country, damaging floods have resulted from destruction of natural vegetation by overgrazing. If large areas of ground are underlain by highly pervious material, like recent lava flows or very coarse gravel deposits, floods seldom occur because the water sinks into the ground almost as soon as it falls. Even pervious soil, if frozen, however, may allow rapidly melting snow to run off and cause local flood conditions. The great Columbia River flood in 1948 was partly caused by this factor.

Human activities may help to produce floods. In addition to destruction of natural vegetation by fires, overgrazing, and cultivation of the ground, men may encroach upon stream channels with bridges, buildings, walls, or levees until the stream in high water has insufficient channel to carry the flow. Drainage of swamps and lakes, which formerly served as regulators of flow, will tend to make runoff more rapid. Most large rivers, at least in their lower courses, flow across floodplains that are covered by water when the great floods occur, usually at intervals of many years.

Fertile floodplains are frequently reclaimed for agriculture by building embankments or levees to keep areas from being covered by water at flood stages. As long as only a few men reclaimed farms in this way, little harm resulted; but when a whole floodplain was thus protected by high levees, trouble began. Levees restrained the flow of water during ordi-

nary floods, but the great floods that come a few times each century are often too high for the limited water channel remaining; the rivers therefore overtopped or broke through the levees and did vast damage. The Yellow River of China, Po River of northern Italy, San Joaquin and Sacramento delta region in California, and parts of the lower Mississippi floodplain have such high natural or artificial levees that the rivers literally flow above the surrounding land, and enormous areas are subject to flooding when a break occurs.

Control of Floods.   How can flood damage be lessened? Factors like the amount and intensity of rainfall are obviously beyond man's control; but where human activities help produce floods, such errors may be corrected. Control of great floods like those on the Mississippi is a national problem because the damaging floodwater may come from distant states. Reforestation, building reservoirs to retard and store floodwaters, moving levees back from the riverbank so as to allow more temporary floodwater basins, and removal of encroachments on the stream are all helpful. After the great floods of 1913, control dams and other installations checked floodwaters of the Miami and Scioto, tributaries of the Ohio River. More recently, flood-control measures have been instituted in the Muskingum watershed and on other streams for the purpose of preventing flood damage within the river basins themselves as well as reducing the flood danger within the Ohio River valley (Figure 20-9).

One control measure that seems at least partly successful is the construction of spillways or floodways on the lower courses of rivers; these serve as bypasses to allow some floodwater to reach the sea by routes other than the main river channel (Figure 20-10).

Figure 20-9 Dover Dam, near New Philadelphia, Ohio, built for flood control in 1938 to keep the Tuscarawas River from damaging farmland and other property in its lower reaches. The Muskingum Valley and its tributary valleys have 14 dams constructed for purposes of retarding floodwaters. (Photograph, courtesy of the U.S. Soil Conservation Service.)

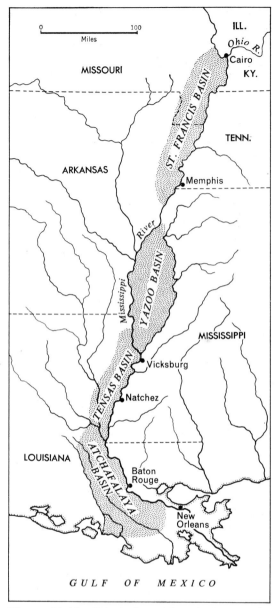

Figure 20-10 Principal overflow basins on the lower Mississippi River.

sippi, the Federal government spent much money on flood prevention along the river and its tributaries. The new levees and spillways to the Gulf of Mexico showed their worth in 1937 when serious floods in the Ohio Valley were handled by the lower Mississippi without important damage to the latter area.

Swamp Drainage. Some land is covered with water in time of flood; it may also be far too wet most of the time to allow profitable farming until it has been drained. Much farmland of the Netherlands lies below sea level and has been reclaimed from coastal swamps bordering the North Sea or the bed of the Ijselmeer, a shallow salt-water lake or bay. Low wet meadows in England and in Germany have likewise been reclaimed for farming.

In the United States, Florida and Louisiana have the largest areas of swampland, but swamps are common all along the Gulf and South Atlantic Coasts; Virginia has the large Dismal Swamp, and Georgia has its Okefenokee Swamp. Many swamps are found in glaciated sections of the northern United States, especially in the states bordering the Great Lakes. Delta lands of the San Joaquin and Sacramento Rivers in California required extensive drainage and diking to protect them against floods. Some floodplains along the Mississippi and other rivers require drainage.

Some drained swampland is highly fertile and is now in productive farms (Figure 13-5), but not all swamps are underlain by good soil. Before drainage, the soil of swamps should be investigated, because some swamps are worth more for hunting ducks, trapping muskrats, and cutting timber than for farms. Some are underlain by peat, which is combustible after the land has been drained. In such cases, great care should be used to prevent starting peat fires, which in some places have done damage, as in the Everglades of Florida.

Most of the lower Sacramento Valley is covered with flood-control devices of this type. After the great flood of 1927 on the Missis-

IRRIGATION

In deserts the supply of water is the most important factor affecting distribution of population and land utilization. Without water, no desert can be reclaimed. After satisfying the demands of desert dwellers for water for personal use and for their livestock, irrigation forms the next most important use of water, ranking ahead of power or transportation. In the Murray River region of Australia, for example, irrigation has so reduced the depth and flow of the river that its use by boats has declined. Since practically all water of the Colorado River is now used for irrigation or municipal supply, that stream no longer contributes an appreciable flow into the Gulf of California, and its former mouth has been replaced by a mud flat.

Development of Irrigation.   Some of the earliest civilizations were founded on irrigated farming, developed in river plains and deserts. Success in raising crops by irrigation required cooperation, peace, and recognition of individual property rights. The protection afforded by organized government permitted men to utilize their leisure time for cultural advances that led to the development, improvement, and application of knowledge and other attributes of civilization. Great centers of civilization that evolved in this type of geographical setting include those of the Tigris-Euphrates floodplain of Iraq and the Nile civilization of Egypt. In irrigated areas today as in the past, there is great density of population and the exchange of ideas and knowledge is rapid and easy compared with the situation in mountains and other thinly peopled places. Unless very isolated from the world, like some oases in the interior of the Sahara, irrigated regions are among the most progressive farming areas. Applied intelligence is required to carry on successful farming with irrigation.

Irrigation in Asia.   More land is irrigated in Asia than in all the rest of the world (Figure 20-11). India, with over 50 million acres, has more irrigated land than any country in the world. Pakistan is in second place, and China fourth. Although canals, mostly built by the government, have reclaimed over half the land, over 10 million acres are irrigated from wells and 7 million acres from "tanks," as small homemade reservoirs are called. The

largest areas requiring irrigation in Pakistan are along the Indus River. In India irrigation is practiced in the upper Ganges Valley, and in the central part of the Deccan Peninsula. Water from tanks and wells in the interior of India may permit farmers to raise two staple crops per year, one supplied by normal summer monsoon rains and a second by irrigation. The province of Madras claims nearly 70,000 tanks, most of which furnish water to only a few acres. In China the deltas and floodplains of the Yellow, Yangtze, and Si-kiang are a maze of canals and ditches used for transportation and irrigation of rice fields.

Tilled land in Iraq is irrigated from the Tigris and to a less extent from the Euphrates River. Without this water, the land would be a hopeless desert populated by a few nomadic herdsmen.

Irrigation in Egypt.   Without the Nile, there would be no Egypt as we know it, where for over six thousand years man has raised crops by irrigation. In early summer, torrential rains in the highlands of Ethiopia cause floods to descend on the Blue Nile and the Atbara. These waters reach Egypt by July and last through September. Egypt was early in developing a basin system of irrigation. Water is allowed to enter basins enclosed by dikes, where it is retained until the ground is thoroughly soaked. Then the residue is drained away, and crops are planted in the mud, which contains enough moisture to mature the crop. Since ancient times a little land for a second crop could be irrigated by pumping water from the river, often by hand methods. More land has been reclaimed by building a large dam at Aswan, the first cataract, to store wa-

Figure 20-11   Irrigated land, selected countries, in millions of acres, 1956. (From Americana Yearbooks, 1952–1956.)

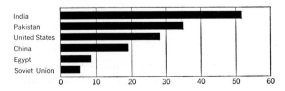

Figure 20-12   Aswan Dam on the Nile, in Egypt. The first control of the river was the construction of a barrage on the delta. This permitted the irrigation of the land through canals and its subsequent drainage. Thus Lower Egypt began to produce two or three crops each year instead of one. The great dam was made available to farm five-sixths of Egypt's arable acres throughout the year. It is hoped to increase the height of the dam, thus making more water available for irrigation. (Photograph used by permission of the British Information Service.)

ter (Figure 20-12). Heightening this structure to increase storage capacity is projected when Egypt can secure funds. Four other dams downstream divert water into ditches for irrigation. Other works have been built in the delta, by which the area under crops has been materially increased and a million more people can be supported by farming.

Irrigation in the United States. In the United States more than 20 million acres of crops are raised by irrigation methods, and over a billion dollars has been invested to put water on this land. The leading state is California, with nearly 5 million acres, followed by Colorado, Idaho, Montana, Utah, and Wyoming, each of which has over a million acres

under irrigation. Other important states for irrigation are Arizona, Nebraska, Nevada, New Mexico, Oregon, Texas, and Washington. Completion of the irrigation project in connection with Grand Coulee Dam in Washington will add over a million irrigated acres to that state's agricultural lands. Humid Arkansas and Louisiana have large areas under irrigation for growing rice, although land there requires drainage more often than irrigation.

Irrigation in America was begun on a small scale by Indians in Peru and Mexico and in a few parts of what is now the southwestern United States. The first large-scale application of irrigation by the whites was that of the Mormons, who began to reclaim desert land in Utah during the 1840s. Later other immigrants began irrigation in Colorado and California, and soon men were experimenting with the practice wherever arid land and supplies of water could be brought together.

Advantages of Irrigation.   There are several obvious advantages of irrigation:

1. Desert soil is unleached because of light rains and therefore contains abundant plant food, generally lacking only humus which is readily supplied by legumes.

2. Water can be supplied as needed to the growing plants, and there is no dependence upon the vagaries of rainfall, which may come at the wrong time or in too great or too little amounts.

3. Abundance of sunshine in deserts favors production of quality fruits and other crops, and during harvest there is no danger of damage to the product from rain, as is often the case in humid lands.

4. Drying of fruit is simplified.

5. Conditions are nearly ideal for farm work.

6. Irrigation water sometimes carries silt in suspension, furnishing fertilizer to the soil.

7. There is comparatively little damage from weeds and insects. Yield per acre under irrigation is high, resulting in dense populations and generally advanced levels of culture (Figure 18-11).

Irrigation Problems. Irrigation has problems and disadvantages as well as favorable aspects. Among geographic handicaps of irrigated regions are:

1. A tendency for alkali to accumulate in low or poorly drained ground and ruin the soil for crop production; this situation is sometimes relieved by flooding the ground to dissolve salts and draining the water by tiling and ditches built for the purpose.

2. Heavy clay soils may become water-logged and sour, especially if they are located at the center of a basin in which the flow of ground water is increased from excessive application of water on higher lands. Problems of this particular type have been faced by ranchers who attempt to farm low ground along the western sides of the Sacramento and San Joaquin River valleys; a similar problem has developed in the basin in which Mexico City is located. The remedy seems to lie in better drainage, and this may be expensive to install.

3. The very productivity of irrigated lands may injure farmers by glutting available markets with an oversupply of products, resulting in decreased prices as disastrous as crop failures to farmers.

4. Sometimes the supply of water is insufficient for the needs of crops, especially if its chief source is from storage of floodwater.

On the whole, advantages of irrigation much exceed its disadvantages; but experience is needed to succeed at irrigated farming. Some failures in this country have resulted from poor handling of land and water, poor judgment in crop selection, excessive cost of water, labor, and transportation, lack of capital, and speculatively high land prices. Several years are needed to develop an irrigated tract to the point of making money for its owner. After many settlers on certain irrigation projects in the intermountain country had failed and abandoned their farms, a government survey showed that most failures had little capital and no experience with irrigated farming. Some had never farmed before, yet they undertook the task of developing raw land.

Irrigation Practices. Sources of irrigation water include the natural flow of rivers and creeks, reservoirs built for storing water from winter snows and spring rains, and water pumped from underground sources. Occasionally natural lakes provide water for irrigation, or the flow from a spring will furnish a rancher with water.

In the Western states, water rights are recognized as a form of property to be bought and sold. Men who wish to irrigate land file a claim on the natural flow of some stream, and water is then supplied to the farmers in the amount of the right and in the order in which filings were made. The usual way of calculating water flow in the West is by the miner's inch, an amount that varies according to laws of the different states, or by the second-foot (1 cubic foot of water flowing each second). The acre-foot (1 acre of water 1 foot in depth) is used to describe the storage capacity of a reservoir.

Irrigation methods vary with conditions and crops. Pastures and meadows may be irrigated by flooding; row crops are watered by rills between the rows. Artificial basins may be built and then flooded. Sprinkling is employed in some regions and for special types of crops. Water usually is carried to the irrigable land in open ditches, which are often lined with concrete and sometimes covered to prevent excessive loss of water by evaporation. In some orchard districts and truck-farming areas water may be distributed by pipes of wood, metal, or tile.

The amount of water that will be available for the irrigation season within a farming district is very important to the landowners. Careful studies are made of the amount of snowfall and its water content early each spring in the mountains that furnish the water to the district. These studies determine the amount of potential runoff of water so that plans can be made to use the flow to the best advantage.

Federal Reclamation Projects. Where conditions for reclamation of arid land were such

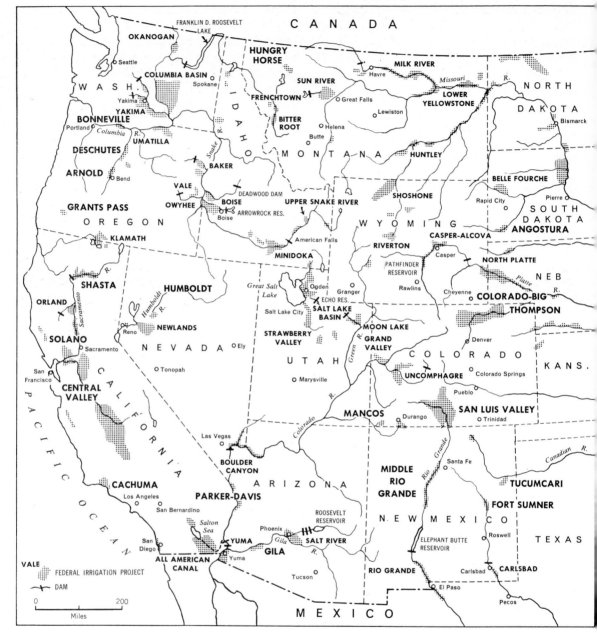

Figure 20-13   Federal irrigation and power projects in the western United States. Compare this with Figure 11-2 and note the relationship with the national forests as sources of water.

that costs were beyond the ability of individual property owners to bear, the United States government has built about 30 irrigation projects in 15 Western states since 1902 (Figure 20-13). On these projects, thousands of families are supported on land that would be nothing but desert or a few scattered cattle ranches. Some storage reservoirs are held by dams that are among the largest on earth. The Grand Coulee Dam on the Columbia

Figure 20-14   Grand Coulee Dam on the Columbia River in Washington is a multiple-purpose structure. It is the largest power development in the world, consisting of 18 generators, capable of producing 144,000 horsepower each. Water is lifted from Lake Franklin D. Roosevelt above the dam and will ultimately irrigate about a million acres in the Columbia Basin. (Photograph, courtesy of the U.S. Bureau of Reclamation.)

River is 4,300 feet long, rising 550 feet from bedrock, and contains 11,250,000 cubic yards of concrete. It impounds a lake or reservoir 150 miles in length (Figures 20-14 and 20-13).

Hoover Dam on the Colorado River is the highest in the world, 727 feet above bedrock and capable of raising the level of the river 584 feet to create the world's largest artificial lake, Lake Mead. This reservoir is long and contains 30.5 million acre-feet of water (Figure 20-1). Hoover Dam regulates the flow and prevents floods on the lower Colorado and makes possible the irrigation of parts of the Imperial Valley and land in Arizona. The power plant generates 1.8 million horsepower of electrical energy, some of which is used to pump water from the Colorado River to supply the city of Los Angeles, as previously described (Figure 20-15).

Another large multiple-purpose dam has been built on the upper Sacramento River. Shasta Dam is more than 500 feet high, and the reservoir behind it impounds water in amount exceeded only by the reservoirs of Hoover and Grand Coulee Dams. When this water is released during the dry summer, a 6-foot navigation channel is maintained in the Sacramento River for 90 miles upstream from the delta. Encroachment of salt water from San Francisco Bay is prevented, valuable delta farmlands have been reclaimed, and floods of dangerous proportions no longer threaten the levee system of the lower river. Shasta Dam generates sufficient power to pay for half the cost of the project; much of this power is used to pump surplus water from the Sacramento Valley onto the higher parts of the San Joaquin Valley (Figure 20-16), thus expanding the irrigated area in central California. Shasta Dam is only a part of a large plan whereby the Central Valley Project serves as

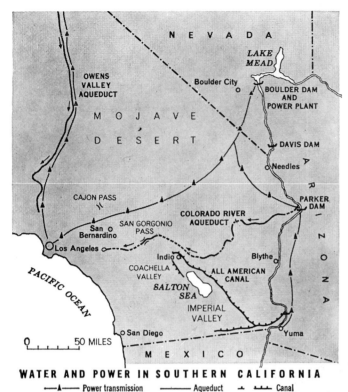

WATER AND POWER IN SOUTHERN CALIFORNIA

—▲— Power transmission   ———— Aqueduct   ⊥ ᴸᴸᴸ Canal

Figure 20-15 Reclamation in the lower Colorado River basin: 1, flood control and generation of hydroelectric power at Hoover (Boulder) Dam, 2, urban water supply for coastal cities via Metropolitan Aqueduct, 3, flood control, urban and rural water supply by the All-American Canal.

a major reclamation scheme to improve farming conditions around Fresno and in other parts of the Great Valley (Figure 20-17).

Under construction by the state of California is a huge dam on the Feather River near Oroville. The dam, 730 feet high will be 3 feet higher than Hoover Dam and 2,500 feet longer than Grand Coulee Dam, making it the largest concrete structure on earth. The reservoir will cover about 5,400 square miles and water will be delivered to the west side of the San Joaquin Valley and nearly to San Diego

Figure 20-16 Contra Costa Canal, a part of the system of water redistribution in the Central Valley Project, California.

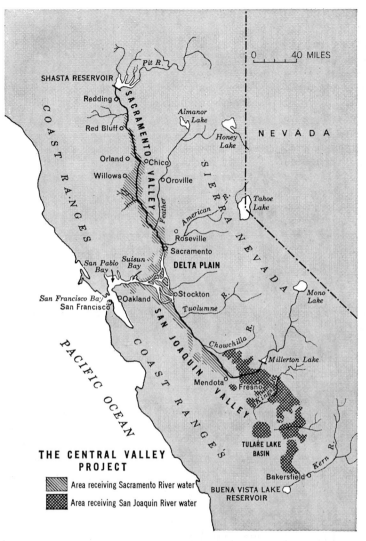

Figure 20-17 Central Valley Project, California.

in southern California. The project will cost 1.5 billion dollars and is planned for completion in 1970.

The Bureau of Reclamation has completed over 100 storage dams in 17 Western states since 1902. The first of its dams for reclamation to be completed was the Shoshone Dam in Wyoming in 1910, which is 328 feet high; its height exceeds its length of only 200 feet at the top. The Roosevelt Dam on the Salt River Project in Arizona, the Elephant Butte Dam across the Rio Grande, and the Arrowrock Dam near Boise are among the important structures built by the United States government to store water for irrigation. Hungry Horse Dam, in Montana near Glacier National Park, serves the dual purpose of supplying water for irrigation and electricity for power. Several dams built for irrigation have been paid for largely from sale of power; this is true of the Roosevelt Dam in Arizona.

SUMMARY

Pure and adequate supplies of water are essential for human health. Many industries require large amounts of water to process certain commodities. With increasing population and industrialization, protecting municipal water supplies from pollution by bacteria, filth, and chemicals has become a great problem. Potential water power depends upon the amount of the water and the distance it falls. Hence rainy and elevated regions generally possess water power. For development, hydropower must have a market within about 200 miles and the stream should preferably have a steady flow. In dry regions water for irrigation is secured from rivers, wells, and supplies stored in lakes which often are artificial. By irrigation the productivity of land in dry regions is greatly increased. Inland waterways—rivers, canals, and large lakes—are much used for navigation, especially for carrying bulky, nonperishable goods. Floods are usually the result of too much rain for the streams to carry, although deforestation,

swamp drainage, and encroachment on river beds are contributory factors.

Outline
Domestic and industrial water
Recreation and inland fishing
Stream pollution
Water power
    Location and development
Transportation
    Rivers, canals, Great Lakes
Rivers as barriers and boundaries
Floods
    Cause and control
Irrigation
    Location, practices, and problems
    Federal Reclamation Projects

QUESTIONS

1. Does stream pollution occur in your locality? If so, what measures have been taken to correct it?

2. The use of a river for commerce is influenced by depth, length, course, current, seasonal variation of flow. With these items in mind, account for the importance of the Danube, Congo, Mississippi, Nile, and the St. Lawrence.

3. What is the distinction between water power and hydroelectric power?

4. Does your locality suffer from either a shortage or an excess of water?
    If so, why?

5. What geographical conditions, aside from abundant annual rainfall and differences in relief of the land, combine to give the Pacific North-

west states the greatest potential development of water power in the nation?

6. For what reasons are floods more destructive than they were a century ago?

7. In what specific ways is water used in your locality?

8. Referring to Table 20-1, what per cent of total electricity capacity in the United States is produced by water? By coal or another source of energy?

9. Why has canal and river transport declined relatively in the United States but not in eastern Asia or Western Europe?

10. If large-scale irrigation is attempted, why does it usually require government financing and government supervision?

SELECTED REFERENCES

Behre, Charles H.: "Our Most Important Mineral —Water," *Focus,* 5(5):1–6 January, 1957.

Blake, Nelson M.: *Water for the Cities,* Maxwell Graduate School of Citizenship and Public Affairs, Syracuse, N.Y., 1956.

Cressey, George B.: "Water in the Desert," *Annals of the Association of American Geographers,* 47:105–124, June, 1957.

Fox, Cyril S.: *Water: A Study of its Properties, its Constitution, its Circulation on the Earth, and its Utilization by Man,* Philosophical Library, Inc., New York, 1952.

Freeman, O. W., and others: "The Columbia Basin Project," *School Science and Mathematics,* 48:3–20, January, 1948.

Graham, Jack B., and Meredith Burrill: *Water for Industry,* American Association for the Advancement of Science, Washington, 1956.

Huffman, Roy E.: *Irrigation Development and Public Water Policy,* The Ronald Press Company, New York, 1953.

King, Thomson: *Water, Miracle of Nature,* The Macmillan Company, New York, 1950.

Kuenen, P. H.: *Realms of Water,* John Wiley & Sons, Inc., New York, 1956.

Mead, Daniel W.: *Hydrology,* McGraw-Hill Book Company, Inc., New York, 1950.

Netboy, Anthony: *Water, Land, and People,* Alfred A. Knopf, Inc., New York, 1950.

U.S. Department of Agriculture: Yearbook, *Water,* Washington, 1955.

U.S. Geological Survey: "Developed and Potential Water Power of the World," Information Circular, Washington, 1948.

NOTE: The Federal Power Commission, Washington, publishes a number of items dealing with power resources. U.S. Soil Conservation Service, Washington, publishes various books and pamphlets on its subject. U.S. Bureau of Reclamation, Washington, issues many publications dealing with aspects of reclamation in this country. U.S. Geological Survey, Washington, publishes a series of Water Supply Papers dealing with aspects of water power, floods, ground water, and other water resources. The U.S. Department of the Army, Annual Report of the Chief of Engineers, Washington, deals in part with the development of waterways, power sites, etc.

21. Manufacturing

THE manufacture or processing of raw materials seeks to increase their usefulness to man. Foodstuffs must be preserved. Most chemicals must be altered in form before they can be used, as borax is combined with other substances in the manufacture of soap. Much material is processed in order to reduce weight or bulk, thereby effecting economies in shipping costs. Devices are manufactured to improve transportation methods—street signals to direct traffic flow, for example. Many manufactured products are equipment designed to save labor, such as harvesting machinery, power saws, power shovels, and the like.

Manufacturing processes, fabricates, and combines materials to produce goods with desired qualities, such as less weight, greater permanence, or increased usefulness. Among primitive peoples many things were collected and used without processing. Originally individuals made the entire article and there was little division of labor. Indians manufactured articles of clothing from skins and hides, canoes from logs and bark, arrowheads, knives, and hatchets from stone, and pottery from clay. During the Middle Ages, most goods were made in the household or by craftsmen.

In colonial and pioneer America, small sawmills and gristmills were established because they saved much hand labor and their output was in demand locally. Articles of clothing, tools, furniture, and simple household appliances were made at home by the family that needed them.

The pioneers preferred small streams for power with which to operate early mills, since the energy required was not great, and development was relatively inexpensive and easily accomplished compared with that needed on large rivers. Under pioneer conditions, the first manufactures in great demand were necessities like sawed lumber, iron nails and tools, flour and meal, leather, knit goods of wool, and firearms.

Invention of laborsaving machinery and the use of steam engines for power led to the Industrial Revolution and development of the factory system and modern capitalism. Hand methods of manufacture could not compete with machinery, and the numerous and diverse types of household industry have, for the most part, disappeared from present-day economy. Today civilized man specializes, and large manufacturing establishments have been built to turn out quantities of a single product. Modern life, especially in cities, is directly dependent upon manufacturing and the transportation and exchange of commodities. Food, fuel, shelter, clothing, and conveniences of life depend upon industrial plants.

Integrated industries. Some large corporations are integrated, from the production of raw material down to the wholesaling and even retailing of finished articles. A copper company, for example, mines and smelts ore, refines copper and recovers other metals as by-products, operates the railroad between mines and reduction works, manufactures sulfuric acid from smelter fumes, uses the acid to make explosives and superphosphate fertilizer, produces its own coal, saws its own mine props and timber, and manufactures brass, copper wire, pipe, and sheet metals for the market. Petroleum companies operate their own oil wells, pipelines, and refineries. They make synthetic rubber and other chemicals, distribute the oil and gasoline in their own tank cars and trucks, and even control many retail outlets. A steel company may own mines, ships, and railroads and operate blast furnaces, steel mills, rolling mills, wire plants, sheet and tube mills, and plants making nails, rails, bridges, ship plates, and construction steel. Chemical companies may manufacture thousands of different products from many sorts of raw materials.

Although the modern tendency is in the direction of large corporations which manufacture a variety of products and have branch plants throughout the country and abroad, our economy also has a place for the small plant, efficiently managed by its owner. A majority of the manufacturing establishments in the United States are of this kind.

Development of the assembly line (Figure 21-1) and of machines that replace hand meth-

Figure 21-1 Six-cylinder engines on a conveyor assembly line. These devices have reduced the amount of human effort required in many factories. (Photograph, courtesy of the News Department, Ford Motor Company.)

ods temporarily lessens the demand for labor. Yet because of reduced costs that result, sales of articles sometimes increase to such a degree that the final effect may be to employ as many laborers as ever.

LOCATION FACTORS

Location of manufacturing activities depends upon various factors: accessible raw materials, power, markets, transportation, capital, labor, experience, inventions, and legislation. Though mills often seem to have been located by chance, it is probable that at least two or more of the above factors must be favorable; otherwise the concern will fail financially or cease to operate.

Raw Materials. Materials used in manufacturing may be of mineral, animal, or plant origin. Raw materials of large volume compared with the finished product are processed near the sources of supply in order to reduce transportation costs. Examples include the concentration, reduction, and smelting of ores, extraction of sugar from beets and cane, sawing of lumber, and preparation of extracts like tannin from wood. Some of these materials may be refined near markets. For example, raw sugar is refined at Philadelphia and near San Francisco, and nickel at Perth Amboy, New Jersey. Portland cement, plaster, and clay products are made near sources of material, but the use of these sources depends on convenient markets because the products themselves are bulky and heavy.

Perishable materials like soft fruits, vegetables, milk, and fish must be processed near their points of production. Slaughter of livestock (40 per cent of a steer is nonedible) and grinding of flour often occur between large producing and consuming areas, as at Kansas City, Chicago, Minneapolis, and Buffalo, the last two being chiefly important for flour. By-products from these plants may be an additional source of income and may lead to the establishment of satellite factories that utilize them. Examples of factories depending upon surplus and waste products include glue and fertilizer plants in slaughtering centers and fish-meal plants near fish canneries. Manufacture of soap is often incidental to the meat-packing industry. Originally waste fat from animals was used in soap plants at Kansas City, Milwaukee, and Chicago, although Cincinnati and other places now depend principally on cottonseed and other plant oils.

Processing of raw materials accounts for the location and growth of many cities. Anaconda, Montana (Figure 21-2), and Trail, British Columbia, are smelter towns. Hull near Ottawa, Canada; New Brunswick, Georgia; Tacoma, and Longview, Washington; Klamath Falls, and Coos Bay, Oregon; and Eureka, California, are among the many sawmill centers of North America. Numerous cities were once leaders in the lumber industry, but after the best timber was cut they turned to the manufacture of other products; examples include Bangor, Maine; Williamsport, Pennsylvania; and Saginaw and Muskegan, Michigan. Fish or shellfish processing helps to account for the location and growth of Astoria, Oregon; Gloucester, Massachusetts; Baltimore, Maryland; and Ketchikan, Alaska. Los Angeles and San Diego are important for canning tuna. Processing fruits and vegetables is a specialty of California and the Middle Atlantic states, but Indiana leads in tomato canning, and Walla Walla, Washington, and towns nearby are important for the canning of peas. Florida leads in the production of citrus juices.

Sometimes conditions and factors that affect manufacturing change: sources of material are exhausted, new materials both raw and partly processed may become available, or market demands vary. These changes are reflected in the closing and opening of plants, modification of products manufactured, and increase or decrease in population of the affected communities.

Power. There are many sources of power, as described in a previous chapter. Sometimes their use for manufacturing purposes is comparatively simple; in Egypt and China human beings and animals operate devices for lifting water, but in the United States windmills or engines are used. In the Netherlands, windmills still grind some grain and pump water from low ground (Figure 13-3), though they have been largely replaced by more efficient engines. Water power operated the first mills in New England and determined the sites of many manufacturing centers, as Holyoke, Lawrence, and Manchester. The presence of waterfalls nearby helps account for the growth of Passaic, Minneapolis, Spokane, and the cities along the Fall Line.

Toward the end of the nineteenth century, hydroelectrical development and the long-distance transmission of power accelerated the growth of cities favorably located with regard to falls. Power sites are usually found in narrow gorges where there is insufficient land for the construction of factories or homes for workmen. Now, with transmission of the power to points some distance from its origin, factories and towns may be built away from the falls, on sites that are convenient and suitable for urban centers. While Grand Coulee Dam was under construction, thousands of laborers lived in adjacent towns, but now only a fraction of the original number remains nearby. Upon completion of the dam, however, tens of thousands of people in distant places benefit from its hydroelectric power. Abundant power attracts plants requiring vast blocks of energy; both aluminum and atomic energy plants were located in relation to Grand Coulee and Tennessee Valley hydroelectric power sources.

Principal fuels used for power are coal, petroleum, and natural gas. Wood is used in small installations usually remote from supplies of mineral fuels. In some places, sawdust and refuse from sugar mills are important for boiler fuel.

Leading manufacturing regions of the world in Western Europe and the northeastern United States are located near large coal resources. Manufacturing on the Pacific Coast is operated principally by petroleum and water power. Soviet Russia has several industrial districts close to coal, oil, and water power. India and Japan have supplies of coal but not in quantities sufficient for their manufacturing needs. Coal alone will not produce mechanized manufacturing; China, for example, has never made great use of its large coal deposits for industrial purposes.

Figure 21-2 Copper reduction works, Anaconda, Montana. (Photograph, courtesy of Anaconda Copper Mining Company.)

Figure 21-3   A modern power station in the vicinity of Chicago, planned for the peacetime production of power through the use of nuclear energy. (Drawing used by permission of Commonwealth Edison Company.)

Operations like the manufacture of iron and steel, consuming much coal for fuel as well as for power, usually are located near the coal mines or at points, like the shores of the Great Lakes, where coal and iron ore can conveniently meet, even if the iron ore must be shipped longer distances than the coal (Figure 19-3). Industries using little power or bulky raw materials compared with the value of their finished product, such as clothing, shoes, clocks, and other small articles, prefer locations near markets and labor supply or at sites with established reputations for their product.

Atomic energy is being rapidly developed as a commercial source of power (Figure 21-3). Of several installations under construction in the United States, the first to supply electric power for commercial sale was that at Shippingport, Pennsylvania, in December, 1957. In countries where fuel is scarce or expensive as in parts of Europe, atomic power plants seemingly are a practical substitute. Submarines powered by atomic energy have operated very successfully, and other types of vessels and airborne transport are under construction equipped with atomic power plants.

Markets. Until transportation to large markets is available, the output of little mills is limited to small local sales. Where processing plants depend upon distant markets, a location near or on the seacoast is an advantage because ocean transport is cheap. It is economical, for example, to refine petroleum from Venezuela on nearby islands, Curaçao and Aruba, which have good harbors to which oil from the mainland is shipped in small shallow-draft tankers. A further reason for the location of these refineries is that these possessions of the Netherlands enjoy political stability. Again, western Washington logs are usually sawed into lumber at deep-water ports on Puget Sound rather than at interior points that are served only by rail and truck. Seaports have advantages in using raw materials from distant sources to manufacture goods for reexport and distribution inland. Marseille manufactures soap and oleomargarine from tropical plant oils, and this industry is important in Los Angeles, San Francisco, New York, and other ports. New Orleans and San Francisco process and ship coffee, tea, and spices, as well as cane sugar. In the metal industry seaboard locations are often chosen for extractive plants because of the convenience of receiving bulky raw materials and shipping the metallic products. For example, steel is manufactured near Baltimore and Philadelphia, copper is smelted at Tacoma, bauxite is processed at Mobile, and extraction of tin from its ore is important at Singapore.

Manufacture of heavy goods is done to greatest advantage near consuming markets. Agricultural machinery factories are concentrated in the Middle West, among America's best farming lands. Pumps, dynamos, engines, tractors, railroad cars, hoists, mining machinery, cranes, and machines to make steel parts are made in Pennsylvania and near the lower Great Lakes (Figure 21-4), where steel is available and many customers are found. Automobile parts are produced in scores of cities in Michigan, Ohio, Indiana, and Illinois, located conveniently with reference to assembly plants at Detroit, Flint, Toledo, South Bend, and other centers. Tire manufacture at Akron

Figure 21-4 Continuous hot-roll steel mill. Sheets of finished steel are manufactured without interruption as they roll from the mill. Relatively few laborers are needed here. (Photograph, courtesy of the Youngstown Sheet and Tube Corporation.)

presents another example, although other factors—particularly an early start—are important in this case.

Bulky building materials like brick, tile, sewer pipe, windows, doors, and cabinets are preferably manufactured near large cities or other densely populated regions. Mills shaping building stone, and cement and plaster plants turning out bulky and heavy products that are expensive to ship long distances succeed near centers of population or other markets for construction material.

Perishable goods, like bakery products, usually are sold locally. Newspapers likewise have limited areas of circulation, and the trading area of a metropolis often is calculated from newspaper distribution. Cities are style centers, and the manufacture of clothing, jewelry, and the like is concentrated there.

Transportation. Like markets, transportation helps determine plant location. Heavy industries, along with cereal mills, meat-packing plants, paper mills, and woodworking factories often seek out railroads, though navigable

rivers, canals, lakes, and seacoasts are also desirable. Light industries, such as textile, printing, and shoe manufacture are less dependent on rail transport, since their products are valuable rather than heavy and can bear the expense of trucking to freight depots. Commodities which are perishable or on which fast delivery is needed are usually manufactured in railroad centers from which lines diverge in all directions. Meat packing, bakeries, publishing houses, and mail-order concerns are advantageously located in Chicago.

Seaports may process imported materials and also materials from the hinterlands for export. At Seattle, flour is made from Columbia Basin wheat, and lumber from the Cascade Ranges is made into furniture and other goods. Petroleum products from inland oil fields are refined at Richmond, California, and at Philadelphia. Cost of freight is an important factor to consider in manufacturing at seaboard locations. Formerly freight rates were higher in the Southern states than in the Northeastern states, but a reduction in rates in the South has been achieved and may encourage additional manufacturing there. In general all manufacturing regions of the world—in the United States, Western and Central Europe, and Japan—are provided with adequate transportation. Without this, the receipt of fuel, raw materials, food for the workmen, and shipment of finished goods would be impossible.

The Need for Capital. Some manufacturing requires only a small investment. Individuals and cooperative associations of small means can provide the essential buildings and machinery. Portable sawmills, neighborhood bakeries, community creameries and cheese factories, local printing plants, tailoring shops, and laundries are of this type, although large corporations also engage in some of these businesses on a large scale. Cooperatives also sometimes operate fertilizer works, flour mills, and small oil refineries. In contrast, industries which require large investments, such as heavy machinery, textiles, petroleum refineries, metal processing, sugar refining, chemicals, and shipbuilding, are carried on by large corporations or wealthy individuals.

Long-settled regions and well-established cities usually have capital available for investment and can finance new industries and plant expansion. Of course, the mills and factories are not always located in the area furnishing the capital, but that is probable unless nearness to raw materials and special markets is especially desired.

In some countries industrial plants are located with regard to military and political factors. When governments control plant location, they may stress remoteness from attack, available labor supply, power, and materials. To an increasing extent, corporations make intensive surveys before they decide on new plant sites, and their chances for financial success rise with attention to sound economic and geographic principles. Some rapidly growing communities like southern California have capital available from newcomers, part of which may go into new industries like airplane manufacture at Los Angeles and San Diego. Sometimes a town gives a bonus or some other inducement to attract a manufacturing plant in hope of increased employment that would benefit the community. A few thousand dollars induced a rubber company to move to Akron, thus beginning a concentration of rubber manufactures which made that city the tire capital of the world.

Labor. A supply of labor may attract industry; for example, silk and rayon mills are common in the coal and iron centers of eastern Pennsylvania partly because these light industries employ many women, and the wives and daughters of the men who mine coal and work in the steel plants are available for factory employment. Labor is less important today than formerly, however, because the use of laborsaving machinery in many mills has eliminated the need for many workers. Some manufacturers need seasonal labor; and if this is not available locally, it must be imported at increased expense. This situation is prevalent in canning of fish, in harvesting and canning fruit and vegetables, and in similar industries. Most clothing is made in the larger cities because the factories use many employees in a small space; furthermore, the industry is near metropolitan markets and style centers.

Mass production requires less skill than the hand methods used in the past. Years of apprenticeship are not required of workmen on an assembly line; farm hands, city housewives, and recent immigrants can be trained in a short time to feed a machine, pull a lever, or perform a required task. Textile mills that moved from New England to the southern Piedmont brought in only a skeleton force, key men, who soon trained local laborers to operate the machines. Nevertheless skilled labor is an advantage, and newcomers to the manufacturing field may locate in a city important for the article to be manufactured; thus the laborers employed are already experienced. The making of accurate machines, typewriters, rifles, locks, watches, and other small metal articles is a specialty of Bridgeport, Hartford, Springfield, and other New England towns. A famous inventor of machine guns lived in Utah, but the weapons were manufactured in the Connecticut Valley.

Invention, Early Start, and Reputation. Many manufacturing establishments are in their present-day locations because an inventor whose ideas were expanded into a large industry lived there, or because an immigrant having special skills and salesmanship set up a manufacturing establishment. Among industries which grew near the homes of inventors are the manufacture of automobiles or motor parts in Detroit, Indianapolis, and Cleveland, breakfast foods in Battle Creek, Michigan, adding machines in Dayton, Ohio, cameras and film in Rochester, New York, and household games in Salem, Massachusetts. Many large mills and factories began in a small way and after long years in their original location have accumulated valuable good will and reputation. This is true of optical goods made in Southbridge, Massachusetts, lodge emblems in Attleboro, Massachusetts, flour and cereals in Minneapolis, tires in Akron, hats in Danbury, Connecticut, and watches in Waltham, Massachusetts, and Elgin, Illinois.

When corporations have large investments in a certain location, an industry tends to remain there, though some other site might be preferred if the company were beginning operations. Pittsburgh with its iron and steel industry is a good example of this type of industrial inertia. Of course, if the original site is a real handicap, even large concerns may move, as did the Lackawanna Steel Company from eastern Pennsylvania to Buffalo, and textile mills from the Merrimac Valley to the Piedmont. An owner may sometimes keep plants in the home town for personal reasons.

Reputation for design in a city may attract persons who are interested in a particular line of goods; they may be buyers or manufacturers. This is the case with clothes designing in Paris, New York, and London; but the Hollywood stylist is also important, particularly in women's sport clothes. Furniture styles that evolve in Grand Rapids, Michigan, are popular in this country. New York, Paris, and Amsterdam are centers of jewelry design. Precision machines are manufactured in Switzerland, Germany, and the Connecticut Valley. These places often govern the styles in their respective lines.

Government and Manufacturing. Governments may exert marked influences upon manufacturing by their use of protective tariffs, import quotas, currency controls, exchange of finished goods for raw materials, loans, bonuses for export, and other practices. In order to favor the employment of American laborers, the tariff on raw materials generally is less than on the finished goods. This encourages the refining of sugar and metals in this country and the manufacture of cigars from imported leaf tobacco.

With the aid of their government, Japanese industrialists can sometimes "dump" cottons, toys, electric light globes, and many other articles below the cost of production in other countries. Japanese shipments of cheap ceramic wares, for example, nearly put some American potteries out of business because of the difference in production costs in the two nations.

Prewar Nazi Germany followed the policy of buying quantities of foodstuffs and raw materials but requiring the purchase of unwanted manufactured goods in return. Germany also paid for her imports with currency that could be spent only within Germany. To protect their own industries, nations suffering from dumping of goods may place a quota on imports from those nations which pursue such policies. The U.S.S.R. has made barter arrangements with a number of countries; but the goods shipped by Russia have not always been what the recipient wanted or at the price expected. Economists contend that free trade and the law of supply and demand in theory will promote the production of goods where it can be done most efficiently and economically, but in practice nations continually interfere with the natural flow of goods.

For strategic reasons of self-sufficiency in case of war, some countries build and operate plants at a loss in order to have key industries available when they are needed. Armament, chemicals, aircraft, synthetic gasoline and rub-

ber, and other commodities are among these essential manufactures.

DISTRIBUTION OF MANUFACTURING

Many densely populated areas of the world result from the concentration of manufacturing. For many years it has been apparent that increase of manufacturing has been accompanied by the growth of cities. The principal causes that contribute to the geographical location of manufacturing districts have been discussed; obviously these factors must be exceptionally favorable where our most important industrialized regions are found.

United States and Canada.   The most important manufacturing region in North America extends westward in a broad belt from the Atlantic Coast between southern Maine and Chesapeake Bay as far as St. Louis and the twin cities of Minneapolis and St. Paul. It includes southern Michigan, peninsular Ontario, and the St. Lawrence Valley as far downriver as Montreal, but excludes some rural regions like the Adirondacks. Within this American manufacturing belt (Figure 21-5), there is a considerable degree of specialization.

New England is favored by abundant water power and raw materials obtainable from her

forests but lacks supplies of iron ore, coal, and petroleum. Coal is brought from the Appalachian fields, and the import of petroleum products and raw materials for manufacture (cotton, wool, hides, and the like) is favored by New England's seaboard location. Traditionally New England is important for its textile mills and metal-fabricating establishments. Textile manufactures were concentrated at water-power sites like Lowell and Lawrence, Massachusetts and Concord, New Hampshire, in the Merrimac Valley of Massachusetts and New Hampshire, and the Blackstone Valley, between Worcester and Providence. Still other centers were around Narragansett Bay at New Bedford and Fall River. Since the 1920s so many cotton mills have ceased operations in New England that the region in the 1950s had only 14 per cent of the nation's active spindles as compared with 40 per cent in the mid-twenties. Competition from other areas, particularly the southern Piedmont, is the chief cause for the decrease in cotton manufacturing in New England, but production of woolens has been little affected.

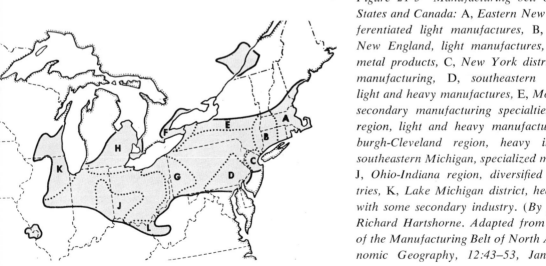

Figure 21-5 Manufacturing belt of the United States and Canada: A, Eastern New England, differentiated light manufactures, B, southwestern New England, light manufactures, emphasis on metal products, C, New York district, secondary manufacturing, D, southeastern Pennsylvania, light and heavy manufactures, E, Mohawk Valley, secondary manufacturing specialties, F, Ontario region, light and heavy manufactures, G, Pittsburgh-Cleveland region, heavy industries, H, southeastern Michigan, specialized manufacturing, J, Ohio-Indiana region, diversified metal industries, K, Lake Michigan district, heavy industries with some secondary industry. (By permission of Richard Hartshorne. Adapted from A New Map of the Manufacturing Belt of North America, Economic Geography, 12:43–53, January, 1936.)

Fabrication of metal products requiring skill rather than weight of material, such as hardware, tools, firearms, and electrical supplies, is a manufacturing specialty of the Connecticut Valley, particularly in the cities of New Haven, Hartford, and Springfield. Paper manufacture at Holyoke, Massachusetts and in some towns in Maine, machinery of many types, clothing, and publishing are typical industrial activities of New England. The manufacture of shoes and other leather goods is important in eastern Massachusetts at Haverhill, Lynn, and Brockton. Optical goods, watches, clocks, and hundreds of small items are products of New England's mills and factories.

The *Middle Atlantic* manufacturing centers are divided into two main groups: those located near or on the coast, and those occupying inland sites. The important coastal nuclei include the large cities of New York, Philadelphia, and Baltimore, with their affiliated satellite cities and metropolitan areas. These three large port cities process many imported raw materials for local use and for shipment both inland and abroad. New York, for example, imports both cotton and woolen yard goods from New England and Southern mills and fabricates the material into clothing, and this city is the center of the American clothing trades. The city also serves as a center for many publishing houses of national scope. Washington, D.C., has little manufacturing compared with other cities of equal population in this country, although its printing and publishing business is well developed.

An advantage of this seaboard area is the ease with which coal is secured from the Appalachian fields by rail and petroleum by pipeline and ocean tanker. Much iron and steel is manufactured in eastern Pennsylvania and near Baltimore. Ships, locomotives, electrical equipment, chemicals, and small metalwares are made near Philadelphia. Baltimore is famous for its airplane plants; Wilmington, Delaware, is an important center for the manufacture of ships, chemicals, and explosives. The cities of eastern New Jersey that are tributary to New York carry on the refining of oil and processing of metals and foodstuffs.

Leather goods is an important industry in southeastern Pennsylvania and southern New York, with towns in the vicinity of Binghamton, New York, making quantities of shoes. The seaboard manufactures a variety of other products too numerous to itemize.

A well-industrialized zone extends across upper New York State from Albany to Rochester along the line of the New York Barge Canal and several main railroad lines that traverse this low corridor connecting the Hudson River and Lake Erie. Schenectady, Syracuse, and Utica are manufacturing centers within this zone. Textiles, clothing, chemicals, photographic supplies (at Rochester particularly), metalwares, electrical and other types of machinery, paper, and scientific instruments are among the goods produced in this part of the manufacturing belt.

In western Pennsylvania and West Virginia, the cities and mills are located in stream valley bottoms; they obtain such raw materials as coal, oil, limestone, and other needs from the adjoining hills of the plateau. The making of iron and steel, and its use for the manufacture of all types of machinery, pipe, structural steel, and other products, is the leading industry. Chemicals, cement, clay products, petroleum refining, and glass-making occupy many people. Pittsburgh is the leading city, although there are many other centers of heavy industry, including Charleston, Wheeling, and Huntington, West Virginia. Scores of industrial towns and cities lie within the Pittsburgh district, with Youngstown (Figure 21-6), Massillon, and Canton, Ohio, on its periphery, where the influence of Cleveland's activities is felt to a degree.

The *southern Great Lakes* district is among the nation's most important manufacturing areas. Here coal brought by rail from the interior meets iron ore, lumber, and grain brought by ship down the lakes. The zone continues along both shores of Lake Ontario and for some distance down the St. Lawrence; it includes some inland areas that are tributary to the lakes. Some of its industrial centers, like Gary, Cleveland, and Buffalo, specialize in production of iron and steel goods. These

Figure 21-6   Part of the Campbell works of the Youngstown Sheet and Tube Company, Youngstown, Ohio. Two blast furnaces and part of the stock pile for iron ore appear at upper left; open-hearth mill is in center. Note sharp division between use of industrial land in foreground and residential property in distance. Note also the intensification of rail lines in foreground; these bring coal and iron ore to Youngstown. (Photograph, courtesy of the Youngstown Vindicator.)

cities, with others like Chicago, Milwaukee, Racine, Detroit, Toledo, and Toronto, manufacture machinery and a wide assortment of iron articles. Detroit and other southern Michigan cities, notably Flint, Lansing and Pontiac, lead in the manufacture of motor vehicles, an industry that is also important in Toledo, South

Bend, and many other centers. Akron, Ohio, specializes in rubber manufactures.

Shipbuilding, tractors, railroad cars, paint, furniture, paper, clothing, chemicals, agricultural implements, clay products (Figure 21-7), and publishing are important activities within this part of the industrial zone; many of these goods are specialties of Chicago factories. The manufacture of flour, and processing of meat, fruits and vegetables, corn and soybean products, and many other types of economic enterprise in this region depend upon the abundance of farm products, some of local origin, others shipped in from Western states. Buffalo, for example, leads the nation in flour milling.

The *Ohio and upper Mississippi Valleys* include the river towns, and inland centers like Indianapolis, Columbus, and Dayton. Cincinnati, Evansville, and Louisville are important on the Ohio, and St. Louis, Rock Island, Moline, Davenport, and the Twin Cities, Minneapolis and St. Paul, on the Mississippi. Fuel is at hand, except for the Twin Cities, and many materials are available for manufacture, including farm products, timber, iron, lead and zinc, and clay and stone. Since the region is near the nation's center of population, customers are within easy reach, and more distant markets are brought close by rail transportation. Metalworking, chemicals, shoes, meat

Figure 21-7 The upper Ohio Valley is a center of manufacture for low- and medium-grade dinnerware. In this view the men are inspecting the finished product for defective pieces. (Photograph, courtesy of the Ohio Development and Publicity Commission.)

packing, clothing, furniture, automobile parts, and the fabrication of many types of machines are among important industries of this region. Processing of foodstuffs is particularly important.

The westernmost part of this industrial zone extends to Kansas City and Omaha, Nebraska, and Wichita, Kansas, where meat packing, flour milling (Figure 24-2), oil refining, and car shops are among the important economic activities. Wichita is also a center for the manufacture of airplanes.

The *South* has made great advances in manufacturing during the present century. The Piedmont area, extending from Virginia through the Carolinas into Georgia, has become the leading center of cotton and rayon textile manufacture; Greenville, South Carolina, asserts that its output of cotton cloth is greater than any other city in the United States. Cheap and plentiful hydroelectric power and relatively low-cost labor are two advantages of the Piedmont. Cigarette manufacture is a specialty of Durham and Winston-Salem, North Carolina. Farther south, Birmingham, Alabama, with its coal and iron ore supplies close together, manufactures much iron and steel. Atlanta, Georgia, and the Tennessee cities of Nashville, Memphis, Chattanooga, and Knoxville are gaining in importance. Electric power from the dams installed on the Tennessee Valley Authority project has been a factor attracting aluminum smelters and various chemical industries. Timber and raw cotton, with supplies of water power or coal near at hand, are industrial advantages here. Savannah, Georgia; Jacksonville, Florida; and other coastal cities of the South depend on forests for their output of lumber, paper, and ship's stores.

New Orleans and Baton Rouge in Louisiana; Houston, Texas; and the cities along the coast of that state are important in the refining of petroleum and in the manufacture of chemicals; they are also increasing their processing of food products and their general manufactures. Inland, Fort Worth, Dallas, and Oklahoma City are among the growing cities that process the products of farms and ranches and

have profited from the wealth of the Mid-Continent petroleum field.

The *West Coast,* too, is growing industrially, although it lacks some of the essentials which have contributed to the success of industry in other parts of the country. Aircraft manufacture is especially important at San Diego, Los Angeles and its surrounding communities, and Seattle. In the Los Angeles and San Francisco areas, petroleum refining, shipbuilding, clothing manufacture, home furnishings, publishing, and food processing are important activities. Hollywood is still world famous for its motion pictures. The Northwest cities of Portland, Oregon; Seattle and Tacoma, Washington; and Vancouver, British Columbia, are traditionally important in the lumber, paper, and fishing industries of that section; but they have begun to expand in many other lines. Cheap hydroelectric power is encouraging the growth of the aluminum industry, steel making, and manufacture of chemicals.

European Industrial Areas. A combination of circumstances—an early start, accumulated capital, skilled labor, available power and raw materials, especially coal and iron—has made Europe the most highly industrialized continent. Furthermore the Continent is accessible for trade, produces many raw materials, and has a large local market in its population. Inventions and factory methods used during the Industrial Revolution were first applied in European industry.

The heavy industries of Europe depend on coal and iron, and the location of these essentials described in the preceding chapter accounts for the concentration of coal mines, blast furnaces, steel mills, and machinery manufacture in Great Britain, the Ruhr Valley of western Germany, northern France, Belgium, southwestern Poland, Czechoslovakia, and Saxony, the Donets Basin, Moscow, and the southern Ural regions of the U.S.S.R. Chemical manufacture often accompanies heavy industry. Many light industries, such as clothing, publishing, food processing, and drugs, are located in the cities.

Among *United Kingdom* centers of industry are the Midlands region near Birmingham and Sheffield which is important for machinery, vehicles, hardware, munitions, chemicals, glass, and numerous small articles. London must import coal but is a great manufacturing center nevertheless; its industries include clothing, publishing, soap, food processing, and chemicals. Northeast England at Newcastle and other towns manufactures iron and steel into machinery, ships, and cars, and makes chemicals from salt and coal. Western England leads in weaving of cotton textiles at cities like Manchester, Preston, Bolton, Blackburn, and Oldham. In these centers, coal for fuel was readily available. Here machine spinning and weaving received an early start, as did manufacture of machinery needed for such enterprises.

The port of Liverpool on the west coast maintains much ocean traffic with America, whence come raw cotton, grain, and meat, all needed in this industrial area. Woolen manufactures are a specialty of the Yorkshire district, which obtains some of its supply of raw material from the nearby Pennine Hills but imports more from Australia and other regions. Leeds, Bradford, and Halifax also man-

ufacture woolen goods. The principal manufacturing area in Scotland includes the city of Glasgow, famed for its shipbuilding, machinery, and cotton, wool, linen, and jute textiles. Belfast in Northern Ireland also is a center of shipbuilding and linen manufactures.

Manufacturing industries of *France* are located principally in the northern and northeastern part of the country, where coal and iron ore are at hand. This industrial district extends into Belgium and the Saar Basin on the north and east and connects with the Ruhr Valley in Germany. In France, the cities of Valenciennes, Lille, and Nancy are large centers of textile manufacture. The Belgian cities devoted to this industry include Namur, Liége, Brussels, and the port of Antwerp. These centers also are engaged in heavy and light industry, including iron manufactures, chemicals, and food processing. Paris is world famous for designing and manufacturing clothing, millinery, and other luxury goods. Lyon in the Rhone Valley makes silk fabrics, automotive equipment, and fine soaps.

The Ruhr Valley (Figure 21-8) is *Germany's* leading industrial area, largely because of its rich coal deposits. Essen, Dortmund, and Bochum lead in heavy industry and formerly

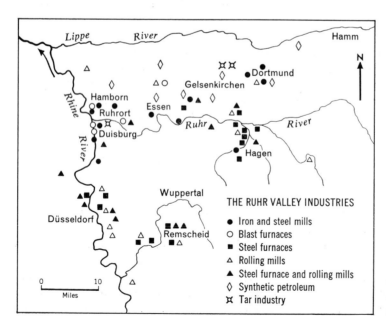

Figure 21-8 Ruhr Valley industries. (Data used by permission of Chauncy Harris.)

led in munitions manufacture. In Duisburg, Cologne, and a dozen other large cities of the area, light metalwares are made, including hardware and firearms; other activities are directed toward weaving of textiles and manufacture of chemicals, cement, among other products. Berlin, Munich, and Hamburg are important for their general industries. In Saxony, a part of East Germany, textiles are extensively manufactured. Its cities include Leipzig famous as a publishing center, and Dresden important for its porcelain. Silesia, which is now incorporated within Poland, has deposits of coal, iron, and zinc; Breslau is the largest manufacturing center.

Czechoslovakia is fortunate in having a variety of resources, including coal, and this nation is important for manufactures of both heavy and light metal goods. Vienna, Austria, and Budapest, Hungary, are large cities with some light industry, but they are still handicapped by loss of some political position and trade territory in consequence of World War II.

Southern Europe has scattered industrial centers, the most important of which is in northern Italy with its cities of Milan, Turin, and Genoa. Switzerland tends to manufacture articles small in bulk but large in value and demanding much skill in their assembly, such as watches and clocks. The nation has no nearby coal supplies but profits from a considerable development of hydroelectric power. Barcelona, Spain, and Marseille in southern France are important manufacturing cities of the western Mediterranean, with the former noted for its cotton textiles, which supply Spain's needs.

The *U.S.S.R.* has made great efforts to industrialize and to establish new manufacturing centers. Coal deposits in the Donets Basin and near Moscow supply fuel for Russian factories. Water power has been developed on the Dnieper River. Kharkov, Rostov, and Stalingrad are important centers of heavy industry. Moscow, like most large cities, has numerous manufactures, including textiles, publishing, machinery, clothing, and food processing. Len-

ingrad is a leader for sawmills and other woodworking establishments. The southern Urals, with some coal and much iron ore, in company with other minerals, have important plants for steel, machinery, and munitions at Magnitogorsk, Sverdlovsk, and other centers. Farther east in Siberia, steel and chemical plants are located at Stalinsk, Novosibirsk, and other cities in the Kuznetsk Basin.

Eastern and Southeastern Asia. *Japan* has only limited coal fields, and even less iron ore, but its minerals are readily accessible for manufacturing. Japan leads Asia in the development of heavy industry and hydroelectric power. Domestic supplies are supplemented by imports of coal and iron ore. Most of Japan's petroleum is also imported. The country must buy almost all its supply of raw cotton abroad, along with rubber and many other materials essential for a modern manufacturing economy. Its industrial base is therefore insufficient to maintain Japan as a great power, although the nation is a large exporter of cotton cloth, rayon, silk, cement, and many small manufactured articles. The future of manufacturing in Japan is not clear, but the country is progressing in both light industry and heavy goods. Shipbuilding has regained its former importance, and many mills making metalwares operate at capacity.

The coastwise location of most of Japan's industries and their concentration in relatively few cities made them highly vulnerable during the Second World War. Japan's manufacturing belt extends east-west and is concentrated along or near the coast between Tokyo and the northern part of Kyushu Island. Other coastal industrial centers include Yokohama, Nagoya, Osaka, Kobe, Yamada, and Nagasaki. Of large cities only Kyoto is inland.

China has lagged in modern industrial development and much of its manufacturing is in the handicraft stage. Currently, China is striving to increase its manufactures, especially in the field of heavy industry. China has large coal deposits and an abundant labor supply. Shanghai is a leading city for textiles, flour milling, and a variety of light industries, with Hankow and Tientsin of some importance. The iron and steel industry is most important in Manchuria, with some production near Hankow.

India has made some progress toward industrialization, particularly in the manufacture of jute at Calcutta, cottons at Bombay and in western India, and iron and steel in the northeast. India has coal, some iron ore, and a little petroleum upon which to base her industries, as well as a large supply of labor. Capital, however, is scarce, and the separation of India from Pakistan has increased problems of industrialization. For example, agricultural West Pakistan has few factories whereas India raises insufficient foodstuffs.

The Southern Hemisphere. This part of the world has made slow progress in the direction of industrial development but cannot supply its own needs for manufactured goods. Coal is generally scarce, although iron ore and other minerals are abundant in places. Petroleum has been found in South America but, although much exploration for oil fields is under way in parts of Africa and Australia, commercial production is not significant. Water power is available for development regionally.

Australia has a small population within a large area and has devoted itself principally to farming and ranching, though much industrial growth has recently occurred. Food processing, meat packing, and smelting of ores are under way to a limited extent, and woolen goods are being manufactured. Steel is made at Newcastle, New South Wales; some tools, vehicles, and other manufactures of iron are fabricated. New Zealand's plants are chiefly concerned with such foods as butter, cheese, and meat, though some woolen textiles are made, and sawmills are busy.

In *South America,* in addition to the refining of petroleum and the reduction of minerals, there is manufacture of textiles and many other articles for local consumption. These activities are expanding in many countries, but only Brazil and Argentina have large-scale manufacturing establishments. In these nations textiles, clothing, shoes, furniture, and many other necessities are made. Meat packing is very important at Buenos Aires and Montevideo in Uruguay. Agricultural implements and other machines are also made in Buenos Aires. São Paulo, Brazil, has many cotton textile mills, and a modern steel plant is operated at Volta Redonda, Brazil.

SUMMARY

Manufacturing is related to such geographic conditions as availability of raw materials, development of transportation, and power to operate machines. Other factors include capital for processing raw materials, finishing articles, and marketing them when made, a large supply of dependable and able labor, and a market for goods. Not all aspects of the location of manufactures are readily explained in terms of geography, because of the great complexity of present-day industry. Nongeographic factors, such as financial ingenuity, local interest in inventions, or governmental encouragement may bring about industrial growth in areas where geographical conditions are not highly favorable.

The leading centers of manufacture are located in the northeastern United States and southeastern Canada, and in northwestern European nations, especially the United Kingdom, France, Belgium, and Germany. Rapidly growing newer centers in Asia are being developed, especially in Japan, parts of China, India, and the Soviet Union.

Outline
Manufacturing: from hand methods to integrated industries
Location factors affecting manufacturing
  Raw materials
  Power
  Markets
  Transportation
  Capital
  Labor

Inventions
Governmental
World distribution
United States and Canada

Europe
Eastern and Southern Asia
Africa and Australia
South America

QUESTIONS

1. What geographical conditions have favored the development of manufacturing in your city or near your home?

2. Why does the Pittsburgh district lead in the manufacture of iron and steel?

3. Explain the recent development of manufacturing along the Gulf Coast of Texas.

4. What geographical conditions account for the concentration of each of these industries and where is the principal center of production: paper, sugar refining, silk, naval stores, fertilizer, flour, cotton textiles, clothing?

5. Account for the presence of a great iron and steel industry in the vicinity of Chicago, although this area has no supplies of coking coal or iron ore in the immediate vicinity.

6. If you live within the American manufacturing belt as it appears in Figure 21-5, prepare a brief statement in which you analyze the industries of your neighborhood or community in relation to other industries within the limits of the belt.

If you live outside the American manufacturing belt, prepare a statement in which you show the relationships between factories of your community and those within the belt.

7. In densely populated regions like Western Europe, why is industrial development more profitable than stress upon agricultural land and skills?

8. Why do many nations encourage home manufacturing even though they might import products more cheaply than their own factories can make them?

SELECTED REFERENCES

Alexander, John W.: "Geography of Manufacturing: What Is It?," *Journal of Geography,* 49:284–288, October, 1950.

Bengtson, Nels A., and William Van Royen: *Fundamentals of Economic Geography,* 4th ed., Prentice-Hall, Inc., Englewood Cliffs, N.J.

Carlson, Albert S. (ed.): *Economic Geography of Industrial Materials,* Reinhold Publishing Corporation, New York, 1956.

Cressey, George B.: *Asia's Lands and Peoples,* McGraw-Hill Book Company, Inc., New York, 1951.

———: *How Strong Is Russia? A Geographic Appraisal,* Syracuse University Press, Syracuse, 1954.

Dicken, S. N.: *A Regional Economic Geography,* D. C. Heath and Company, Boston, 1949.

Elliott, Francis E.: "Locational Factors Affecting Industrial Plants," *Economic Geography,* 24:283–285, October, 1948.

Harris, Chauncy D.: "The Ruhr Coal-mining District," *Geographical Review,* 36:194–221, April, 1946.

Hartshorne, Richard: "A New Map of the Manufacturing Belt of North America," *Economic Geography,* 12:45–53, January, 1936.

Hubbard, George D.: *The Geography of Europe,* Appleton-Century-Crofts, Inc., New York, 1952.

Jones, C. F., and G. G. Darkenwald: *Economic Geography,* The Macmillan Company, New York, 1954.

Klimm, Lester F., Otis P. Starkey, Joseph A. Russell, and Van H. English: *Introductory Economic Geography,* Harcourt, Brace and Company, Inc. New York, 1956.

Miller, George J., Almon E. Parkins, and Bert Hudgins: *Geography of North America,* John Wiley & Sons, Inc., New York, 1954, chaps. 4, 13, 18.

Osborn, David G.: *Geographical Features of the Automation of Industry,* University of Chicago Press, Chicago, 1953.

Shaw, Earl B.: *World Economic Geography,* John Wiley & Sons, Inc., New York, 1955.

Smith, J. Russell, M. Ogden Phillips, and Thomas R. Smith: *Industrial and Commercial Geography,* 4th ed., Henry Holt and Company, Inc., New York, 1955.

Stewart, W. B.: "Shifts in the Geographical and Industrial Pattern of Economic Activity," *American Economic Review,* 36:36–51, May, 1946.

Wright, A. J.: *The United States and Canada,* Appleton-Century-Crofts, Inc., New York, 1956, chaps. 4, 7, 12, 14.

White, C. Langdon, and Edwin J. Foscue: *Regional Geography of Anglo-America,* Prentice-Hall, Inc., Englewood Cliffs, N.J., 1954, chap. 3.

———, and Donald J. Alderson: "Industrialization: Panacea for Latin America," *Journal of Geography,* 56:325–332, October, 1957.

Zimmermann, E. W.: *World Resources and Industries,* rev. ed., Harper & Brothers, New York, 1951.

NOTE: U.S. Bureau of the Census, Washington, publishes many pamphlets dealing with manufactures.

22. Trade, Transportation, and Communication

COMMUNICATION of ideas and information, transportation of man and his possessions, and development of routes and carriers for exchange of goods between people all facilitate economic and cultural progress. Modern rapid communication reaches most parts of the earth and supplies the information needed by governments, businessmen, and individuals in order to reach decisions of all kinds—political, economic, military. Ease of communication is a strong unifying factor within a nation; it tends to provide bonds of interest between different nations, and generally is of great importance to human society.

Value of Communication and Transportation.*
Primitive peoples can communicate for short distances by means of smoke signals or drums; early empires used runners or messengers who

* Aspects of navigation on inland waterways were discussed in Chap. 20.

went by ship or rode animals. Today man has the railroad, ocean vessel, automobile, telegraph, telephone, cable, newspaper, radio, and television. Those qualities which tend to develop among peoples as the result of isolation tend to disappear when modern radio, television, and highway reach them; in this country, for example, "Americans" differ so little it is hard to tell from what part of the nation an individual comes. This tendency toward uniformity has been one result of excellent systems of communication, by which ideas, knowledge, and education have spread among most of our citizens.

People who live in areas lacking efficient transportation must practice subsistence farming and construct for themselves most articles they desire, or go without. Only a few wealthy individuals can afford imported goods since transport costs are high; under these circumstances only a few items can be exported, and the volume of trade remains small. Improved transportation and lower costs make possible greater exchange of commodities. Producer and consumer both gain as a result and the volume of world trade tends to increase.

Man's conquest of space through modern communication, transportation, and transmission of electrical energy ranks among his greatest achievements. The whole economy of the modern world depends upon its pattern of transport, transmission, and communication facilities. Development of transportation and trade is fundamental to the extension of knowledge and advance in standards of living. Natural factors affect transportation routes on each continent and on the ocean. The location and growth of cities for trade and industry, discussed in a later chapter, depend to a great degree upon transportation.

TRADE

Primitive Transportation and Development of Trade. Even primitive people need some transportation and trade. The Eskimo requires a dog sled to bring home his captured seal; the northern forest Indian uses the birchbark canoe to carry his catch of furs to market and bring back a steel trap or some other necessity that his environment does not provide. Caravan routes over desert wastes show the need for crossing the broad barrier separating two productive regions as well as for supplying needs of the few inhabitants.

The Norsemen fearlessly sailed the stormy North Atlantic and settled in Iceland and Greenland nearly a thousand years ago. From Greenland at least two trips were made to the mainland of America centuries before the first voyage of Columbus. The Polynesians, aptly called the "Vikings of the Pacific," early in the Christian era left southeastern Asia and explored the previously unknown Pacific; they discovered and populated all the island groups from Hawaii to New Zealand and eastward to the Marquesas Islands, Tuamotou Archipelago, and Easter Island.

Thousands of years ago traders brought amber from the Baltic regions to the Mediterranean on backs of men and animals through the same passes and routes later followed by railroads. Seashells were brought far inland by North American Indians, who also exchanged turquoise, copper, pipestone, jadeite, and obsidian over distances up to 1,000 miles or more.

Growth of Trade. Trade tends to develop between regions having more products on hand than they can use conveniently; the growth of trade is particularly noticeable when surplus commodities are of different kinds. The growth of trade is encouraged by these factors:

1. Differences in stage of economic development, for example, Great Britain sends manufactures to Canada and receives foodstuffs and raw materials in exchange.

2. Differences in climatic condition, such as those between the humid midlatitudes and tropical lands, subpolar regions, deserts, and steppes; thus Europe and the United States buy rubber, palm oil, cane sugar, and spices from the tropics, which take flour, fish products, and machinery.

3. Differences in the type or quantity of natural resources: minerals, timber, and fish, for example. Thus the United States requires tin, whereas France, the United Kingdom, Sweden, and Japan need petroleum.

4. Regions may specialize in different commodities which are shipped as market demands require; this accounts for part of the trade in the most-used route in the world, the North Atlantic between North America and Europe.

Trade of the United States. A large part of the imports reaching the United States are tropical commodities: rubber, coffee, tea, cane sugar, jute, hemp, coconut and palm oil, bananas, cacao, and spices. From colder regions come paper pulp, fish, furs, and some animal fats, though their value is much less than that of products from the tropics. Mineral imports include tin and several metals used in alloy steels. From Europe come certain manufactured goods like watches, bicycles, clothing, jewelry, and art objects, which differ from our manufactured specialties or are preferred to the home product.

Formerly Europe exchanged its manufactures for the material and foodstuffs of the United States and other countries less advanced industrially, but increasing industrialization outside Europe has made it difficult for some European nations to sell enough manufactures and thus buy needed food and raw materials. In Latin America and southeastern Asia the trade with the United States may depend upon differences in climate or—as in the instance of Argentina—upon degree of industrialization. Our trade with other nations may be linked to their possession of needed minerals, as Chile with its nitrates and copper.

Importance of Foreign Trade. The value of a country's foreign trade depends largely upon its self-sufficiency. Large countries usually can supply more of their own needs than small countries. Some small nations, like Switzerland, have more foreign trade per person than a country the size of France, where diversity of resources is great. In total value, Europe's foreign trade exceeds that of all the rest of the world, but in part this reflects the small size of nations on that continent and its numerous international boundary lines. What might be regarded as domestic trade on continents where countries are larger becomes foreign trade in Europe. Domestic trade of the United States is about eight times our foreign trade, a proportion that indicates the degree of self-sufficiency. This is based upon the large size of the country and the great diversity of raw materials and labor available within its boundaries, as well as its high living standards.

It is difficult or impossible to secure statistics on foreign trade from all countries. Hence the value of this trade is uncertain, but it considerably exceeds 100 billion dollars annually. The value of foreign trade of the United States is between 25 and 30 billion dollars a year.

The amount of trade is greatly affected by the economic level attained by different peoples. Asia contains over one-half the population of the earth; but because its millions of people live in relatively undeveloped economies, their purchasing power per capita is lower than that of other parts of the world. In contrast, volume of trade per inhabitant of Western European nations is large because that area is highly industrialized and its standards of living are high. This results in large imports of foodstuffs, raw materials, and fuels, as well as export of valuable manufactured articles.

Factors Correcting Unfavorable Balance of Trade. Most European countries have an unfavorable balance of trade; i.e., the value of their imports exceeds that of their exports. Sometimes this represents purchases made from proceeds of international or private loans and other forms of credit, but certain "invisible" factors operate to correct the unfavorable balance of trade. The more important of these are (1) interest on foreign investments, (2) profits from ocean shipping, (3) insurance, (4) royalties and commissions, (5) money spent by tourists, which amounts to over a billion dollars a year by the United States in Europe alone, (6) money sent back to the homeland by emigrants and temporary wage earners abroad. Generally in peacetime income from these and other sources has provided the means with which nations like the United Kingdom paid for imports and accumulated capital.

TRANSPORTATION METHODS AND ROUTES

Many methods of transportation have been utilized during the course of economic development. Man, pack animals, canoes and rowboats, sleds, carts, wagons, sailing vessels, steamships, railroads, motorboats, automobiles and trucks, and aircraft have been used successively for transport. All are still used in some parts of the world. Modern means of transportation have enormously speeded the exchange of commodities and broadly extended the field of trade. Power machinery has multiplied many times the work that can be done in a given period.

In the past transportation routes have been either across the earth's surface or oceans and other waterways traversing both land and sea; transportation, in other words, was "land-bound" or "water-bound" or both (Figure 22-3). Now airways follow indifferently routes over land or water bodies; except for weather conditions and the highest mountain ranges, they are largely independent of the facts of terrestrial geography.

Water Transportation. Any body of water, and especially the sea, exerts an attraction for man, who early developed some means of water transport. Boats have been built of dugout logs, birchbark, hides stretched on framework, bits of board sewed together, bundles of reeds, inflated skins of animals, and other ma-

terials. Some primitive men attained great skill in boat construction and built seaworthy craft in which they completed voyages of thousands of miles. Modern boats are commonly built of metal plates, riveted or welded together. Barges have been made of such unlikely materials as reinforced concrete.

In the Pacific Ocean the Polynesians, who inhabited islands from Hawaii to New Zealand, attached outriggers to canoes or fastened two canoes together to make craft propelled by sails of matting. They sailed their craft on long voyages, such as from Tahiti to Hawaii, 2,400 miles (Figure 22-1).

In the Mediterranean navigation developed early, but sailors rarely tried voyages in winter when storms might be violent. Indeed many ships carrying goods between Egypt Greece would creep along the coast from headland to headland rather than venture out of sight of land and take short routes directly across the sea. Oars, as well as sails hung from a single mast, were used for power. Early

Figure 22-1   Outrigger canoe, a relatively primitive type of water transportation, in heavy surf off the coast of Hawaii. The extinct volcano known as Diamond Head appears in the distance. (Photograph used by permission of the Hawaii Visitors Bureau.)

boats lacked a keel and could not beat against contrary winds. Navigators also lacked the compass.

Routes for sailing ships. Increased knowledge of navigation and improvement in sailing ships made possible the voyages of discovery of Columbus, Vasco da Gama, Magellan, Cook, and other navigators. Merchants following the explorers soon found the routes on which favorable winds would carry them to their destination. Indeed, sailing routes were largely determined by winds. Ships from Europe bound for India followed the northeast trades well westward toward Brazil, then beat southward across the equator, and continued south with the southeast trades abeam. The westerlies then were picked up, taking the boat around Africa into the Indian Ocean, where their arrival was timed to coincide with the summer monsoon, which would blow northeastward to India. The return was made after the northerly winter monsoon was established, and after reaching South Africa, the southeast trades were used to the equator. Then because of difficulty in tacking against northeast trades, the boats usually steered north into the mid-Atlantic to the westerlies, which blew them to the home port. By following favorable winds a ship traveled a longer distance but sailed to its destination more quickly than by attempting to beat against contrary winds.

Steamship routes. After steam replaced sail, it became possible to follow the shortest distance between ports without regard to favorable or unfavorable winds. Although ocean steamship routes depend primarily on the shortest path between terminals, it is necessary to consider other factors: currents, tides, winds, floating ice, fog, prevalence of storms, character of coast lines, distribution of population, and available products for shipment. Other things being equal, a steamship follows a great-circle route between ports (Figure 1-2).

The ocean joins all countries having seacoasts and forms a free highway open to everyone. Seaports need some improvements, such as wharves, fuel docks, warehouses, breakwaters, dredging, lighthouses, and other facilities, but their cost is small compared with that of building a highway or railroad equal in length to an ocean route. The Great Lakes, a superb inland water route, are like enclosed seas in their numerous advantages for shipping. Operating cost of ships per ton-mile for freight shipments is much lower than for any type of land transport—a prime advantage to those who can use water transportation. For bulky commodities, rivers (Figure 22-2) and canals are excellent means of transport, but service is slow; hence railroads or motor trucks are preferred for shipments requiring speedy delivery.

Ocean trade routes. Various factors determine locations of ocean routes, which are not fixed like railroads; steamship routes may be changed from time to time with little difficulty if there is need for a different route. The general conditions that govern the routing of ocean trade include:

1. Distance that must be traversed in order to reach the desired destination.

2. Amount of freight available for cargo.

3. Location of fueling and supply stations on the route.

4. In the case of sailing vessels, prevailing winds that must be taken into account. Now, with steam and motorship, the most direct practical route is followed, though ocean currents and the prevalence of floating ice may cause some divergence from the shortest route.

The *North Atlantic* is the most used route for ocean traffic; it connects the central portion of the eastern North American seaboard with Western Europe (Figure 22-3). These populous regions are highly productive of freight; some of the world's greatest seaports are terminals of this route. The North Atlantic sea lane branches on its eastern end into the Mediterranean, and it also has a branch leading to the Baltic Sea. A few ships go to the Far North past North Cape, heading for the Arctic ports of Europe. An important branch operates between eastern North America and Mediterranean ports.

Figure 22-2   A string of barges ("tow") transporting bulky industrial raw materials on the Ohio River. The Allegheny Plateau upland appears beyond the river. (Photograph, courtesy of the Ohio Development and Publicity Commission.)

The *Mediterranean–Indian Ocean* route to Asia is an important traffic lane; in England it has been called the "highway of empire," since at one time it was a principal link connecting Britain and its colonial possessions. The route leads from Western Europe through the Mediterranean Sea, Suez Canal, Red Sea, and Indian Ocean to southeastern Asia and Australia.

The building of the Suez Canal shortened the journey from England to India by about 4,500 miles. In 1955 about 118 million tons of shipping were carried through the Suez Canal. About two-thirds of this total was petroleum and its products from the Persian Gulf region for Western Europe.

The *South African* route from Europe serves ports of western and southern Africa and continues on to Australia and New Zealand. Formerly this was also the main route to Asia, and it is still followed by some few remaining sailing ships and freighters if their owners wish to avoid payment of canal tolls at Suez.

The route from Europe to *South America* is important for shipments of freight; it serves ports on the east coast of South America, although a few ships continue to use the Strait of Magellan to reach the west coast or continue on their way to Australia. Sailing vessels find it easier to round Cape Horn than to use the strait, where there is little sea room; furthermore, they can maneuver better in the open sea because they must sail into the "roaring forties" in these latitudes.

The *Panama Canal* route connects the Eastern and Gulf Coast ports of the United States with the west coast of both North and South America. Ships also use this route between Europe and western American ports. Some ships moving from Europe and from the eastern United States traverse the canal route on their way to the Orient and Australia. The Panama Canal is of highest strategic importance to the United States, but its commercial usefulness in shortening the route between our eastern and western coasts should not be overlooked. Construction of the Suez and the Panama Canals was responsible for shortening and realigning older ocean trade routes.

The *North Pacific* route connects western North America with eastern Asia. The shortest way is to follow the great-circle route, which lies toward the north near the Aleutian Islands. Passenger liners to the Orient normally take a route that diverges from a direct

TRADE ROUTES OF THE SEAS
AND INLAND WATERWAYS

Volume of trade is proportional to width of lines

- - - - - Navigable streams

Figure 22-3   Trade routes of the seas.

course between terminals to break their voyage at Honolulu, a natural mid-ocean crossroads.

Another route in the Pacific extends from the western coast of the United States and Canada to Australia and New Zealand. Ships following this route also may go by way of Honolulu and may stop at Suva in Fiji and at Pago Pago in Samoa. A few ships use a route from eastern Asia bound either southward to Australia or eastward to South America, but trade in this part of the world is small and passengers are few. In general, Pacific Ocean routes are much less important than Atlantic routes. Some of the shores of the Pacific are thinly populated. Further, Asiatic peoples though numerous do not have the high purchasing power which increases trade and shipping.

Fueling, repair, and supply stations for ships are sometimes established at strategic locations on islands or on the mainland when coastal

Figure 22-4 Where rail and water transport meet, large facilities are required to handle the shipments speedily. In this view, the loading yard can accommodate 6,200 railway cars at tidewater. (Photograph, courtesy of the Norfolk and Western Railroad.)

sites are placed approximately on courses of ocean trade routes (Figure 22-4). Sometimes these installations serve a dual purpose as naval and air bases. Aden, Gibraltar, Malta, Port Said, Mauritius, the Falkland, Azores, Virgin Islands, and Punta Arenas (Magallanes) are important service points for ocean shipping, and some of these are fortified.

Figure 22-5 Tanker fleets, in thousands of hundredweight tons, 1956. Total world tanker tonnage, 40,179,000 tons. (From World Almanac, 1957, p. 694.)

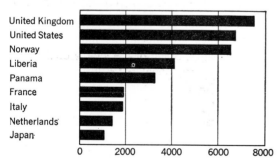

Merchant Marines.   Ships are economical carriers. The ocean right of way is free. Since ocean shipments cost less per ton-mile of freight, rates are lower than railroad freight, hence large quantities of goods are carried by coastwise vessels. Legally in the United States, coastwise shipping includes traffic between all ports under our flag; traffic to and from Hawaii, Alaska, Puerto Rico, and the mainland is called *coastwise*. By law only United States ships can engage in this trade. Many other countries have similar legislation.

Three principal types of ocean carriers are in use, liners, tramp steamers, and specialty ships like tankers, ore carriers, or refrigerator vessels.

Liners follow recognized routes, move on regular schedules between designated ports, and frequently combine freight with passenger traffic and mail shipments. Their freight usually consists of shipments of relatively valuable products of small bulk and "clean" to handle. Liners would not usually take on cargo made up of strong-smelling substances like copra, dirty materials like coal, or bulk shipments like wheat. Some luxury liners carry little freight and specialize on speed and passenger service; this type of vessel generally is found on the Europe–North America run. Some liners, on the other hand, are essentially freighters sailing on schedule and carrying passengers as a side issue. On the whole, however, it is the small, dirty, and unspectacular freighter that handles the major part of the world's freight shipments.

Tramp steamers follow any ocean route and move at any speed, since they are not bound by shipping schedules. They arrange to go from port to port, picking up cargo and discharging goods according to the freight that may be available at the time. They carry much (possibly one-sixth) of the world's ocean freight. Some tramp vessels rarely visit their home ports; some may return to home port on the average about every three to five years.

Among *specialty* boats, the tanker has a strategic position (Figure 22-5). Tankers spe-

Figure 22-6 Modern method of loading crude petroleum from storage tanks on shore into the hold of an oil tanker for shipment by sea. (Photograph, courtesy of the Los Angeles County Chamber of Commerce.)

cialize in transportation of petroleum (Figure 22-6) and its products. These probably supply the most tonnage of any of the world's commodities. Sometimes tankers are used to carry vegetable oils; this can be done successfully if the holds are steam-cleaned properly. Large tankers are being built to transport up to 100,000 barrels of oil. Two-thirds of the freight through the Suez Canal consists of petroleum and its products.

The *ore carrier* is especially important on the Great Lakes but it is also significant in ocean shipping. Ore carriers operate on regular routes, transporting iron ore from Chile, northern Spain, northern Sweden, or Algeria to consuming markets. They also carry coal, phosphate rock, and other heavy, bulky commodities. Combination ore and bulk oil carriers are being built. For example, such a vessel might transport iron ore from Labrador to Philadelphia in summer, and petroleum from Venezuela to Europe in winter. Such continuous use distributes the overhead expense of operations over an entire year instead of the summer season only.

Refrigerator ships are used principally to carry meat and bananas. They often carry passengers as well and may run on regular schedules as liners. Other specialty vessels include cattle boats, cable layers, whaling ships, and icebreakers.

Although the Second World War caused great destruction of ocean shipping, by the middle of the 1950s these losses had been largely replaced. The world's gross tonnage is about 90 million, of which the United States owns 30 per cent. The British Commonwealth, despite wartime losses, is second with 19 million, about 90 per cent being registered in Great Britain and the remainder distributed among other members of the Commonwealth.

Figure 22-7 Merchant shipping fleets in millions of gross tons, 1956. Total world tonnage 92,944,000 tons. (From World Almanac, 1957, p. 694.)

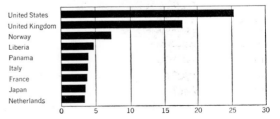

The leading nations of the world in ocean shipping, besides Great Britain and the United States, are Japan, Norway, Germany, Italy, France, the Netherlands, Greece, Sweden, Spain, the Soviet Union, Denmark, Liberia, and Panama; each operates over one million gross tons of shipping (Figure 22-7). The total number of vessels owned larger than 1,000 tons burden is nearly 15,000. The ships operated under Liberian and Panamanian flags are mainly tankers (Figure 22-5) which use this registry to reduce taxes and operating costs.

LAND TRANSPORTATION

Land routes seek the shortest and easiest path connecting two points, although political considerations, subdivisions of land, certain relief features, and unusual sources of freight may cause divergence from the most direct course. Mountains or hills, swamps, lakes, wide rivers, and inlets of the sea are physical barriers that often deflect land routes. Deserts and other unpeopled regions are avoided when possible, since little or no freight is anticipated in those areas. Generally there is close correlation between dense networks of railways or highways and the density of populations.

Man himself was the first burden bearer, and he is still used for this purpose in tropical Africa, New Guinea, and a few other remote places. Pack animals, the dog, horse, camel, yak, llama, and others, were domesticated relatively early in man's history; they are still in use in some mountains, deserts, and other little-developed regions. Canoes, rafts, and

Figure 22-8 Vehicles, drawn by animals, still move people and goods long distances in remote parts of the world. This modern version of the covered wagon may be seen in parts of New Mexico and Arizona today.

other boats were built for use on streams. Invention of the wheel and the comparative ease with which goods can be transported by wheeled vehicles was a significant advance in transportation (Figure 22-8). Use of the wind for propelling boats on both the ocean and inland waters also helped greatly. The invention of the internal-combustion engine and its application to transport has been of tremendous importance to trade and travel in our time.

Explorers and early settlers in a region usually plan foot and horse trails; later these are followed by the construction of roads to accommodate wheeled vehicles. If commercial development of the region proceeds and population increases accordingly, the highways are improved for use by automotive equipment, or railroads are built. The degree of improvement and surfacing of the roads will depend upon such factors as physical features of the landscape, stage of human progress in the area, amount of traffic, and available funds.

The United States, Canada, most European nations, and some regions on other continents are well supplied with railroads and highways (Figure 22-13). Complete systems of transportation permit wide distribution of goods, rapid exchange of ideas, and consequent high standards of living—at least during periods of peace and noninterference with trade by governments.

Highways. Until man began to use roads, exchange of commodities and ideas was very slow. Highways are important factors in the advance of civilization and in the spread of culture throughout the world.

Most roads were built to serve local needs for transportation, although some roads today may be hundreds or even thousands of miles in length. Early roads generally joined farm and market, connecting seaports with their hinterlands, or serving as portages between navigable waterways. Longer roads were built between great cities, like the Tokyo to Kyoto highway in old Japan or early highways connecting ancient capital cities of medieval Europe. The old "silk road" from China to the Mediterranean was a caravan route on which only luxury goods could bear the costs of transport. Some roads were developed to aid the growth of pioneer settlements, including the Cumberland Road across the Appalachian barrier to the Ohio River country, and the Wilderness Road down the Great Valley of Virginia through the Cumberland Gap to the Blue Grass region of Kentucky and the Ohio River. These and other routes were followed

by thousands of settlers during early days of expanding settlement in the United States.

Other famous American highway routes include the Santa Fe Trail, Overland Trail to California, and Oregon Trail; these were used by settlers and traders long before transcontinental railroads were built (Figure 22-9). The famous Natchez Trace was an overland route by which traders who had taken their goods down the Mississippi on flatboats could return to Ohio by a route northward and eastward from Natchez through Nashville to Cincinnati and Pittsburgh. Zane's Trace connected important early settlements in southeastern Ohio. The Chisholm Trail, extending from the Gulf Coast of Texas through Oklahoma, Kansas, and Nebraska, was an important cattle trail during middle years of the nineteenth century. On the West Coast, El Camino Real (the

Figure 22-9   Railway network of the United States, with early routes of land transportation: 1, Boston Post Road, 2, Mohawk-Hudson route, 3, Susquehanna Corridor, 4, Braddock Road, 5, Forbes Road, 6, Wilderness Road, 7, Cumberland Road–National Road, 8, Natchez Trace, 9, Chisholm Trail, 10, Oregon Trail, 11, California Trail, 12, Spanish Trail, 13, Santa Fe Trail, 14, Jornada del Muerto, 15, El Camino Real.

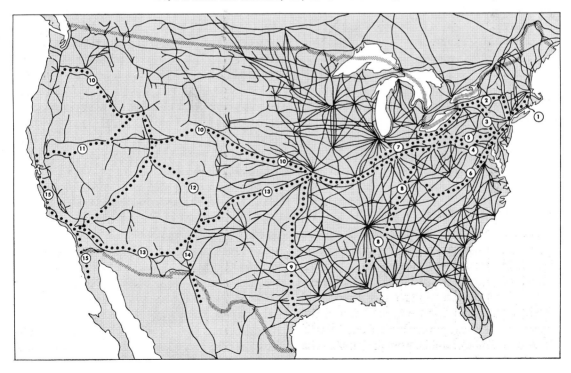

Figure 22-10 A maze of superhighways in the heart of downtown Los Angeles, built to improve traffic conditions in a densely settled urban area. (Photograph, courtesy of the Los Angeles County Chamber of Commerce.)

king's highway) was a trail connecting the 21 California missions.

The pattern of roads as it appears on maps is often related to physical features of the terrain. In plains regions, roads normally follow straight lines, especially in those parts of the United States and Canada where land was subdivided on a checkerboard system based on meridians and parallels. In steep hilly regions, roads wind to adapt themselves to the hills. In swampy land, highways seek higher ground and the divides that separate water bodies. Desert roads may connect watering places, settlements, and ranches. Mountain highways often converge at either end of a pass, and they tend to follow valleys if possible.

Some highways are built primarily for military or other strategic purposes, to reach frontier boundaries or unite outlying parts of a nation. Such a road extended from Leningrad and Moscow across Siberia to the Pacific and was used by sleds in winter and wheeled vehicles in summer. During the Second World War the Alaska Highway was built from Dawson Creek, British Columbia, to Alaska. Another strategic highway was the "Burma Road" from Burma into China; this deteriorated rapidly after the war.

Paving roads helps speed travel, lowers costs of carriage, and decreases danger of interference by bad weather conditions. The Romans built paved military roads that bound their empire together, but these roads also served to promote exchange of merchandise between outlying parts of the realm and the capital city. Indians in the mountains of Peru built paved roads upon which foot travelers and llama caravans were able to reach distant parts of the Incan empire; these roads, like those of Rome, contributed greatly to unite the political divisions of the nation.

Highway Transport in the United States. The development of highways is generally related to the degree of industrialization and density of population of a nation. The United States has more paved highways than any other country (Figure 22-10), more than 750,000 miles. Roads in the United States total over 3 million miles in length—about a mile of road for each square mile of area—but three-fourths of this mileage consists of unpaved rural roads, used for local traffic.

Trunk line highways, all paved and controlled by the Federal government, total over 90,000 miles; highways controlled by state governments total about 600,000 miles.

Highway Transport Abroad. Western Europe has a close and intricate network of roads, many of which are paved. The U.S.S.R. is second to the United States in its total road mileage. Japan has a dense network of roads, but most parts of Asia are not well served by highways, and extension of the paved roads is desirable. There are few roads in the tropical parts of Africa or South America; there, river transportation may take the place of land routes (Figure 22-11). In a few places in the tropics, however, short rail lines and highways are vital transportation; this is true at many points near the coast of Africa where rivers from the interior are interrupted by falls or rapids as they plunge over the edge of the central African plateau before reaching the sea.

Highways are being extended in Mexico and several South American countries, where they help attract tourists as well as serve the needs of local residents. The Pan-American Highway, when completed, together with its connections, will permit automobile travel from the United States to all the Latin-American countries. The populated parts of Canada, Australia, and New Zealand are generally well supplied with roads.

Motor Transportation. Vast expansion in the use of automotive equipment since 1900 stimulated the paving of roads and invention of machines by which paving can be done more quickly and cheaply than by hand methods once widely used. Motorcars, trucks, and busses represent a modern development of transportation, but their efficient use is not possible unless the principal routes of travel have been paved. There are over 56 million automotive vehicles licensed to operate in the United States. Our country owns nearly 74 per cent of the world's automobiles, 60 per cent of the trucks, and about the same percentage of

Figure 22-11   Transportation of hardwood logs in the tropics is difficult and expensive. Here mahogany logs have been assembled and made into a raft for shipment downstream. Compare this view with similar operations in midlatitudes as shown in Figures 11-7 and 11-9. (Photograph, courtesy of the Mahogany Association, Inc.)

busses. Of nearly 80 million motor vehicles in the world over two-thirds are in the United States.

Much traffic that was formerly handled by railways now is transported by motor vehicles. Motorcars, trucks, and busses are flexible in their movements and routes compared with rail traffic, which is restricted to tracks. In addition, motor vehicles on highways can travel on steeper grades than railway trains, and for short distances they about equal the speed of rail travel. Throughout the entire United States, Canada, Western Europe, and wherever highways have been built for them, trucks and busses have become important common carriers. They are especially well adapted to quick transport of passengers, package freight, and perishable goods if shipping distances are not too great. Trucks do not have the advantage in transporting very bulky commodities or those perishables which can best be transported by air. Nevertheless, the advantages of highway transportation are evident, and the volume of motor transport tends to increase. About 1.5 million miles of bus lines operate in the United States, a figure greatly exceeding the total mileage of railroads in our country (222,000 miles).

Railway Transport.   Railroad construction requires a great amount of capital to build a level roadbed, bridges, and tunnels and to install railway stations, lay track, and produce many other types of construction. It also calls for a high degree of skill in engineering. Rail lines tend to be built in the most highly industrialized and fertile farming regions, because in those parts of the earth there will be sufficient need for their services to make the investment in them seem likely to return a profit. Occasionally railroads have been built for military or other strategic purposes, in order to reach a productive region or coastal outlets beyond desert and mountain barriers, or to open scenic areas for pleasure resorts. The main trunk railroads have terminals at the chief seaports or leading inland cities (Figure 22-12). From these main railroads, branches lead into tributary territory as dictated by trade conditions and the productive capacity of the region. Government controls over rates, tariffs, and labor costs also affect railroad construction and operation.

The first railroad began operations in 1825; from this small beginning in England, rail lines spread over many parts of the earth in little more than a century. The railroad is particularly important in those sections of the world which engage widely in manufacturing and world trade, as in Europe, the United States, Canada, and Japan. Railroads transport heavy loads rapidly. The support of large modern cities, marketing of staple and perishable farm produce, and swift exploitation of many forest and mineral resources are possible largely because of railroads.

Rail mileage of the world is nearly 803,000 miles, of which nearly 30 per cent is in the United States. The U.S.S.R. is second, with Canada, India, Germany, Australia, France, Argentina, Brazil, and Great Britain following. Japan has about the same density of railroads per square mile as the United States, and several European countries exceed our

Figure 22-12   Lakeside facilities for unloading iron ore at a steel plant. Note the close connections between railroads and ships, the ore stock pile, the ore-handling machines, and the large deck hatch openings to speed unloading. (Photograph, courtesy of the Bethlehem Steel Company.)

density, including small but thickly populated countries like Belgium, Denmark, and the Netherlands.

The distribution of railroads, as is illustrated by the railroad map of the different continents (Figure 22-13), shows several densities. The eastern half of the United States, the Ontario Peninsula in Canada, and most of Western Europe have such a close network of railroads that only small areas are located more than 10 miles from rail service. The U.S.S.R., India, Japan, southeastern Australia, South Africa, and part of Argentina and Brazil have less rail service. In much of Africa, South America, Australia, and Asia railroads are short feeders extending into the interior from principal seaports.

United States railroads lead all countries of the world in length of mileage; they have helped greatly in the rapid development of the country and were even responsible in some states for settlement of farming land and for establishment of towns and cities. Some of the earliest railroads were built to connect existing cities, or ports and rivers, but soon rail lines were extended beyond the frontiers of settlement and in defiance of the river systems. The importance of railroads in the development of the United States is indicated by general familiarity with railroad names; these are as well known to most Americans as are the great rivers of the nation.

From such Atlantic seaports as New York, Philadelphia, and Baltimore (Figure 22-14), railroads of the northeastern United States pushed inland to reach fertile farms and industrial centers of the Mississippi Valley and the Great Lakes regions. Among these railroads are the New York Central, Pennsylvania, Erie, Chesapeake and Ohio, and Baltimore and Ohio, the last being the first railroad to be started on this continent. These lines cross the Appalachian barrier by various routes, usually following rivers and using water gaps. The lowest "water-level" grade is that of the Mohawk–Genesee Valley route, which is utilized by the New York Central.

The Southern Railroad, with other lines, serves the Atlantic Coastal Plain southward to the Gulf states.

In the interior, Chicago is the preeminent focal center for railroads, but St. Louis, Indianapolis, Cleveland, Detroit, St. Paul, and Kansas City are among other urban centers toward which our rail lines tend to converge. From the Middle West, railroads extend south to the Gulf ports, westward to the Pacific, and north into Canada. Among the railroads from Chicago to the South are the Illinois Central, whose route tends to parallel the Mississippi River, and the Louisville and Nashville.

So-called "transcontinental" railroads do not cross the continent but begin at Chicago, St. Louis, or New Orleans. Chicago is the principal starting point for these lines. Railroads using the northern route are the Chicago, Milwaukee, St. Paul and Pacific, and in combination with the "Burlington" Railroad, the Northern Pacific and Great Northern lines. The Union Pacific occupies the strategic central route. Its main line extends from Omaha to Ogden, with connections to Chicago and other Middle Western points. From Utah, the oasis lines run southwest to Los Angeles, west to San Francisco, and northwest to Portland, Seattle, and Spokane, with a connection north to Butte and Yellowstone Park. On the southern route, the Santa Fe operates from Chicago to Los Angeles and San Francisco, and trains run on other lines from Chicago to El Paso and thence by way of the Southern Pacific to California.

From St. Louis a combination of the Missouri Pacific to Pueblo, Colorado, the Denver and Rio Grande Western to Salt Lake City, and the Western Pacific to San Francisco offers a route through the scenic Colorado Rockies—a difficult route avoided by other rail lines.

The Southern Pacific offers through service from New Orleans to California on its Sunset Route, and from there the Shasta Route of the same line connects with rail facilities at Portland, Oregon.

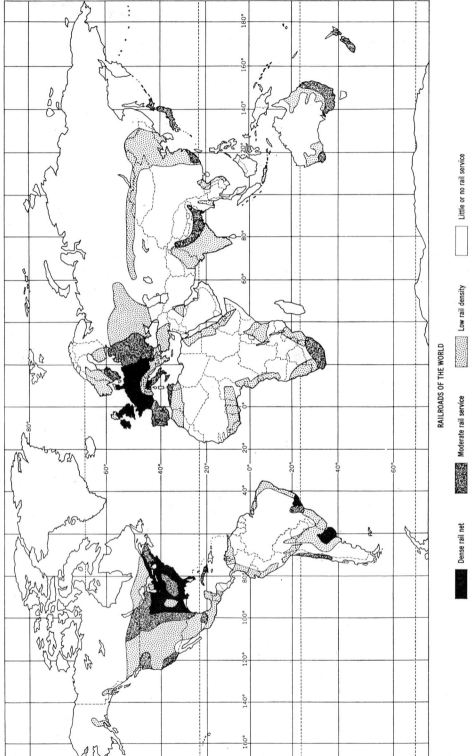

RAILROADS OF THE WORLD

■ Dense rail net ▨ Moderate rail service ▨ Low rail density ☐ Little or no rail service

Figure 22-13   The world's railroads.

Canada's railroads consist of the privately operated Canadian Pacific and the government-operated Canadian National Railways. Both lines have eastern terminals at Montreal or Quebec, and connections with Halifax, Nova Scotia. Their Pacific terminals are located at Vancouver, British Columbia. The Canadian National Railways also reaches the Pacific at Prince Rupert, British Columbia. Canadian lines are truly transcontinental in that they operate through trains from Atlantic to Pacific seaports.

The principal interior railroad center of Canada is at Winnipeg, near the southern end of Lake Winnipeg. Railroads from the western Canadian prairies converge at Winnipeg, just as the railroads crossing the Great Plains meet at Chicago. From the plains west of Winnipeg, a rail line has been built to Port Churchill on Hudson Bay; this was constructed to help export wheat to United Kingdom, but it is handicapped because its terminal on Hudson Bay is frozen a large part of the year. Numerous railroads connect Canadian cities with railroads in the United States, and one loop of the New York Central operates through Canada between Buffalo and Detroit. Most Canadian railroads are located in Ontario, the Prairie provinces, and just north of the United States–Canada boundary.

Mexico is moderately well supplied with railroads, considering the somewhat difficult climatic conditions and terrain of that land. Mexico City is the great focus of rail routes in the interior. Mexican railroads connect at several points with lines in the United States.

Railroads in *Central America* are short and of only local significance. Some are little more than private lines built by corporations to serve the needs of their plantations.

Europe's railroad map indicates that railroads of that continent tend to converge like spokes of a wheel toward the capital cities, with local convergence in the directions of major seaports and certain industrial centers. London, Paris, Berlin, Vienna, Warsaw, and Moscow represent the principal concentrations of railways. Birmingham, Essen, Cologne,

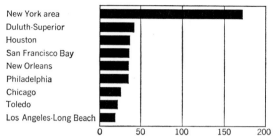

Figure 22-14 Tonnage shipments of United States ports, in millions of short tons, 1954. (From World Almanac, 1957, p. 688.)

Leipzig, Dresden, Munich, Hamburg, Frankfurt, Antwerp, Rome, Kiev, Kharkov, and Leningrad represent smaller foci of railroads. Most large cities of Europe were founded before railroads were invented, and lines were largely built to connect existing cities. This accounts for the prevalence of railroad centers from which lines radiate in all directions. Some countries, too, have built strategic railroads to their borders from interior bases; these roads were constructed for military use rather than promotion of trade with neighboring nations. The longest railroad in the world is the Trans-Siberian line, which starts at Leningrad and Moscow and continues to the Pacific at Vladivostok. To some extent this is a strategic rail line that serves to link the far eastern portions of the Soviet Union with the better developed European part. Numerous international boundaries, with their customs regulations and restrictions, are a serious handicap to development of long-distance train service in Europe.

In contrast to the close network of railroads in most of Western Europe is the more open net in Russia, Spain, and the Balkans—nations that are less developed from the industrial standpoint than those of Western Europe. In Russia waterways are used considerably for transport. Only a few rail lines reach the Arctic ports of Russia, Finland, Sweden, and Norway.

Asia, with its great size and population, is inadequately supplied with railroads. Japan, which has a close network of lines, and India are moderately well served. China has some railroads but needs much more mileage than it now has before the remote interior parts of that nation can be developed for trade. Railroads of southeastern Asia and Java are of only local importance. The Trans-Siberian line is the only railroad crossing the continent; with its connections branching southward into Turkestan, it serves an enormous territory within the U.S.S.R. Railroads also connect with lines to Mongolia, Manchuria, and into China. There are only a few railroads in Turkey and other parts of the Near East, and only one line in Iran. The high mountains and plateaus of central Asia are not readily penetrated by railroads, nor are there people or goods to justify the cost of construction.

South American railroads are located principally in Argentina, Uruguay, southeastern Brazil, and Chile. Elsewhere the lines run inland from seaports and do not form a connected network. There are few railroads in tropical parts of the continent. It is possible to cross South America along three routes, two of which pass through Bolivia, by using connecting railroads from Chile and Peruvian seaports to Buenos Aires. Much freight traffic of South America is carried by coastal steamships; mail and passengers move by air.

Africa is poorly supplied with railroads except in South Africa and in parts of North Africa, where an open network of lines exists. Most railroads run from coastal ports into the interior, usually without connections with other lines. Africa can be crossed by using a combination of several different railroads between the Portuguese colony of Angola on the Atlantic and ports in Southeast Africa on the Indian Ocean, but travel by this route is slow and unsatisfactory and involves many practical difficulties. One famous African rail line, the Benguela railway, was built from that port on the west coast into the interior of the Belgian Congo in order to deliver supplies of valuable copper to coastal steamers. It would not have been necessary to build this line had the Congo River been more easily navigable.

Australia's railroads are mainly concentrated along the eastern and southern margins of that continent. One transcontinental railroad was built by the Commonwealth and extends inland some distance from the southern coast to connect the populated southeastern and southwestern parts of the continent. One rail line from the south penetrates to the community of Alice Springs near the desert center of the continent. Several lines have been built at right angles to the coast, running short distances inland to gather freight for export. Much of Australia is too desert or too tropical in character to attract settlers or furnish valuable goods for shipment; hence it is meagerly equipped with modern transportation facilities.

Air Transportation. The air is used for transportation mainly by peoples who are well advanced in industry and commerce, but airfields are being developed all over the world, with the result that increasing numbers of people and amounts of freight are being moved daily by means of the airplane. Aircraft are affected little by those natural barriers which deflect roads and rails from their direct routes (Figure 22-15). At sea the air lanes may follow great-circle routes without interruption, but often flights will be planned to take advantage of stops on different island or shore bases. Some oceanic islands, formerly of little use, have great strategic value as bases for air travel; among hundreds of others, Canton and Wake Islands in the Pacific and Fernando Noronha in the Atlantic have assumed importance in recent years.

Commercial air transportation began shortly after the First World War; its services were greatly enlarged and expanded after the Second World War. Today a network of air lines covers the United States and extends into Canada, Alaska, Mexico, Hawaii, and the Caribbean islands. Planes fly on frequent schedules to South America. Transoceanic planes cross the Atlantic to the United Kingdom and the Continent, from which air connections extend into Asia and Africa. Transocean air lines with scores of daily flights transport about three-fourths of the passengers—ships about one-fourth. Over the Pacific Ocean, two flying lanes

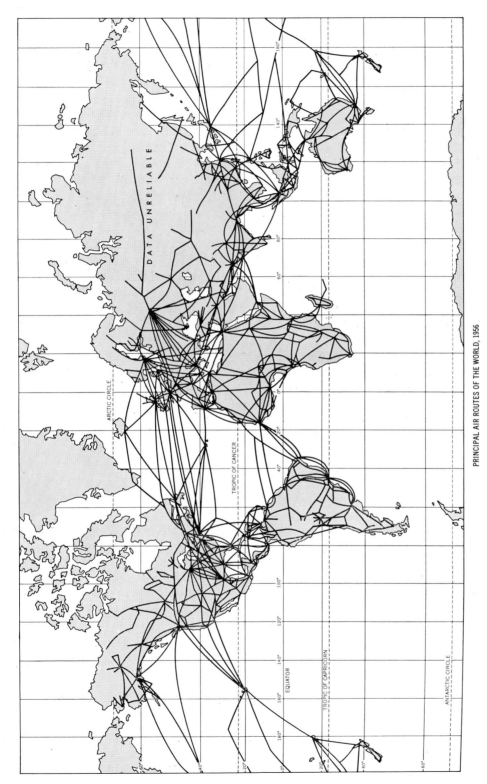

PRINCIPAL AIR ROUTES OF THE WORLD, 1956

Figure 22-15 Principal air routes of the world, 1956. (Data through courtesy of G. Etzel Pearcy and the Journal of Geography.)

connect with Asia; one follows the North Pacific great-circle route, and the second uses several islands on its route by way of Hawaii, Midway, Wake, Guam, and Manila. Plane service is also available to Australia and New Zealand, with stops selected from Canton Island, Suva in Fiji, Nouméa in New Caledonia, or Samoa, depending upon the route followed. Air lanes now encircle the world.

In 1957, air lines served 544 United States cities. Twelve trunk lines and 13 local service lines enabled passengers to reach any city from another within a few hours. The domestic lines connect with fast international flights that link all nations together more closely each year. Air lines make important contributions to business, pleasure, and better relations between nations. Air travel is an essential in modern living. In addition to the regular air lines there are many unscheduled flights, and thousands of planes are owned and flown by individuals. Corporations often maintain planes for the convenience of key personnel. The U.S. government spends billions of dollars on its air force annually and employs hundreds of thousands of men including civilians.

Air transport has the advantage of speed and is used for carrying passengers, mail, and freight items which can bear rates higher than those charged by land or sea. Airplanes are particularly adapted for rapid long-distance travel. The greatest concentration of air lanes today is in the United States and Western Europe, but aircraft carry passengers and make freight deliveries to out-of-the-way locations where land routes are poor and slow. This is particularly true in northern Canada in the taiga and tundra zones, in Alaska, in the interior of both humid and dry tropical Africa, in New Guinea, with its dense forest cover, and in the interior of South America, where railroads and highways are not available. In these and many other remote parts of the world the airplane has preceded railroads and helps bring comforts and necessities to the residents. Weeks of travel can be saved in such regions by the use of planes.

Growth of the airplane industry has been extraordinary, especially since World War I. Although the industry is only a few decades old, yet in the United States many billions of dollars have been invested in it. More than 1,100,000 persons are employed in manufacturing plants, subcontracting facilities, and commercial air lines in the nation. It is estimated that these employees receive 6 billion dollars annually for wages and salaries.

COMMUNICATION

Communication devices, telegraph, telephone, cable, radio, and television, transmit messages with startling speed. All the world can receive news at almost the same moment. The different means of communication are useful geographically in many ways: in forecasting weather, obtaining information on supply, demand, and prices of commodities, transmitting knowledge of international tensions, and conducting business affairs. Besides sending news and transocean messages, radio and television offer entertainment combined with advertising and publicity.

The first ocean cable was successfully laid across the Atlantic in 1866, and several now operate in this part of the world. Cables cross the Pacific and have been laid from Europe to South America, Africa, and Australia. The United Kingdom's cable system extends around the world, and that country controls about half the world's cables.

For carrying transocean messages the cable has been supplemented by the radio and telephone. These have proved useful for business and the dissemination of news as well as entertainment. Communication by telephone between Europe and the United States is available at relatively low rates. About half the world's telephones are in operation in the United States and one-third are in Europe. This country has about a third of the telegraph mileage, and much of the rest is in Europe.

Nearly half the world's receiving radio sets are in the United States, where over 52 million homes have one or more sets, with an additional 36 million sets in automobiles. Radio sets abroad (Figure 22-16) total 135 million, 80 million of these in Europe. Radio is useful not only for sending messages but also for guiding planes through storms and fog and in instrument landings, and for communication with ships at sea. It has been a valuable advertising medium and disseminator of news.

Television is an outstanding news, advertising, and amusement medium, with about 42 million sets operating in the United States alone

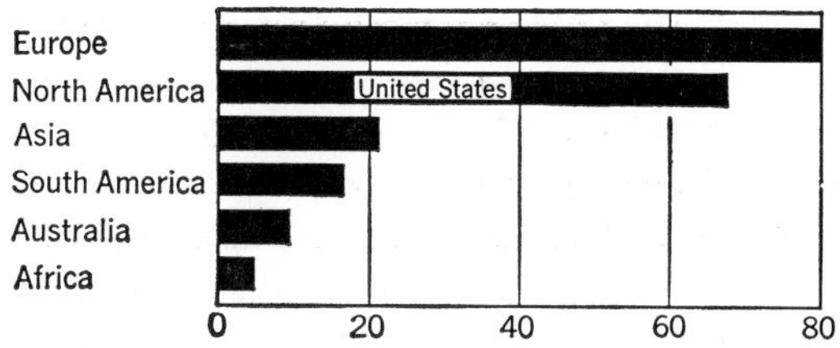

Figure 22-16 Radio sets in use as of December, 1956, in millions. (From World Almanac, 1957, p. 774.)

at this time. Its usefulness is limited to continental areas as yet, though transoceanic telecasts are planned in the future.

SUMMARY

Since goods used by man are unevenly distributed throughout the world, some method of transferring desirable or surplus materials from one place to another is essential.

Trade routes by water naturally tend to unite those parts of the world where production is great, and those parts where the needs are equally great. The importance of different water routes varies widely. The present most used route traverses the North Atlantic between Europe and North America; other leading routes connect Europe and the eastern coast of South America, and Europe and southeastern Asia via the Mediterranean Sea and the Suez Canal.

Highways and railroads develop on substantially the same basis, as connecting links between important places and sources of freight, with due regard to location of surface features. The automobile, bus, and truck have taken over much of the traffic formerly carried by rail, especially on short hauls.

For long-distance travel, air transport has ended the monopoly which ships and railroads had on passenger traffic. Air lines commonly use great-circle routes to attain shortness of distance.

As yet, however, commercial air transport is directed mainly at the handling of high-value, low-bulk freight.

Commerce and dissemination of news and knowledge is advanced further by such media of communication as the cable, telephone, telegraph, radio, and television; each plays a significant part in the modern geographic picture.

Outline
Value of communication and transportation
Origin and growth of trade
  United States trade
  Foreign trade
Transportation: ocean and land
  Early development
  Sailing ships
  Steamship routes
  Types of ocean carriers
United States highways
Railroads
  United States railroads
  Foreign railroads
Airlines
Communication

QUESTIONS

1. Why are the following regions inadequately served by rail lines: southern Nevada, northern Maine, eastern Oregon, Finland, Paraguay, Madagascar?

2. What traffic obstruction prevails on the route that connects each of the following places?

Lake Superior and Lake Huron
Montreal and Toronto
San Francisco and Oakland
Montreal and Toronto
San Francisco and Oakland
Denver and Salt Lake City

Red Sea and Mediterranean Sea
Lake Erie and Lake Ontario
How has the problem been solved, if that has been done?

3. Name the principal transportation corridor that connects each of the following: Albany and Buffalo, Detroit and Toledo, Montreal and Quebec, Cincinnati and St. Louis, Houston and Galveston, Belgrade and Budapest, Mainz and Cologne, Vienna and Budapest, Paris and Le Havre, Delhi and Calcutta, Baghdad and Aleppo, Hankow and Nanking.

4. Summarize the advantages and disadvantages of the relative locations of the Baltimore and Ohio and the Pennsylvania railway lines; the Union Pacific and the Santa Fe.

5. What principal points do the following routes connect: the Iron Gate, Gibraltar Strait, Khyber Pass, Malacca Strait, Fertile Crescent, the "silk road," Suez Canal, Strait of Messina, Dover Channel.
What principal points do they separate?

6. In Figure 22-9 the railway net of the United States is noticeably dense east of the 100th meridian. West of this meridian the net is incomplete and the rail lines are spaced widely. Organize a satisfactory explanation of this situation, using every geographical argument at your command.

7. Figure 22-9 indicates that our principal railway lines are oriented in an east-west direction. What geographical explanation do you propose to account for this emphasis?

8. Investigate the transportation and communication services that are available in your home community, analyze the type of service that each renders, and justify the operation of that service in your community.

9. In air transport, each of the following places has become important although it had never functioned widely as a center of transportation before the development of aircraft. In each case, account for the importance of the place: Dakar, Karachi, Azores, Eire, Newfoundland, Greenland, Iceland, Nova Scotia, Midway.

10. Under the heading, The Growth of Trade, three reasons appear for the exchange of goods between different parts of the world, giving rise to international trade. After you have studied the paragraph, classify each of the following commercial contacts as (1), (2), or (3), depending upon the circumstances described in the paragraph.

	Origin	*Destination*	*Commodity*
1.	Brazil	United States	coffee
2.	Venezuela	United States	iron ore
3.	Hawaii	United States	cane sugar
4.	West Africa	United States	chocolate
5.	Indonesia	United States	rubber
6.	Ceylon	Great Britain	tea
7.	French West Africa	France	palm nut oil
8.	Cuba	United States	cane sugar
9.	United States	Pakistan	electrical goods
10.	Cuba	United States	tobacco
11.	Egypt	Great Britain	cotton
12.	Great Britain	United States	chinaware

SELECTED REFERENCES

Ballert, Albert G.: "The Soo versus the Suez," *Canadian Geographical Journal,* 53:160–167, November, 1956.

Cunningham, William G.: *The Aircraft Industry: A Study in Industrial Location,* L. L. Morrison, Los Angeles, Calif., 1951.

Huntington, Ellsworth: *Geography in the Twentieth Century,* Thomas Y. Crowell Company, New York, 1951, chap. 22.

Jefferson, Mark: "The Civilizing Rails," *Economic Geography,* 4:217–231, 1928.

Lyon, Thorburn C.: *Air Geography: A Global View,* D. Van Nostrand Company, Inc., Princeton, N.J., 1951.

Petterson, Donald R.: "Great Lakes Traffic: An Aspect of Commercial Geography," *Journal of Geography,* 56:212–222, May, 1957.

Pearcy, G. E., and Lewis M. Alexander: "Pattern of Commercial Air Service Availability in the Western Hemisphere," *Economic Geography,* 27:316–320, October, 1951.

———: "Pattern of Air Service Availability in the Eastern Hemisphere," *Economic Geography,* 29:74–78, January, 1953.

Smith, Henry L.: *Airways Abroad: The Story of American World Air Routes,* University of Wisconsin Press, Madison, 1950.

Taafe, Edward J.: "Air Transportation and United States Urban Distribution," *Geographical Review,* 46:219–238, April, 1956.

Thomas, Benjamin E.: "Modern Trans-Saharan Routes," *Geographical Review,* 42:267–282, April, 1952.

Ullman, Edward: *American Commodity Flow,* University of Washington Press, Seattle, 1957.

Van Cleef, Eugene: *Trade Centers and Trade Routes,* Appleton-Century-Crofts, Inc., New York, 1937.

Wilson, Charles M.: *Oil Across the World: The American Saga of Pipelines,* Longmans, Green & Co., Inc., New York, 1946.

NOTE: The Bureau of Foreign and Domestic Commerce, Washington, publishes many pamphlets on trade and transportation.

23. Occupations
and Distribution
of
People

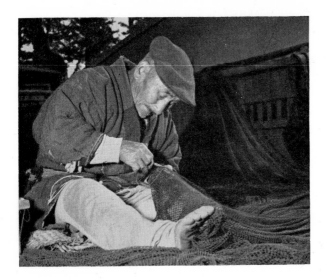

MORE than 2½ billion people live in the world. Estimates reckon about 170,000 babies are born each day, at a rate of two each second. Deaths occur at a rate of about 114,000 every day, leaving a net daily gain in human population of over 50,000 people. Although no exact statistics are available, the annual birth rate is believed to be about 30 per 1,000, which gives the world a yearly increase of nearly 36 million people. Not all the world's people are as favored as those who live in the United States and Western Europe. Two-thirds of the world population live in poverty. They work hard for a bare existence, usually earned by subsistence farming.

The geographer is concerned with where the people of the world live and why they live where they do. His study of geography soon makes it clear that density of population is closely related to the ways by which man gets his living. Some occupations require the use of large areas of land; others lead to close settlement and intensive use of small areas. Some economies develop into the complex organization of an industrial civilization, which is accompanied by large growth of cities.

OCCUPATIONS OF MAN

People have many different ways of earning a living, but most economies may be grouped according to the classification of human occupations which appears in Figure 23-1. Some of these occupations may be pursued with small investment since they involve no great amount of equipment or complex machinery, though they may, nevertheless, often demand a high degree of skill and the application of intelligent thought.

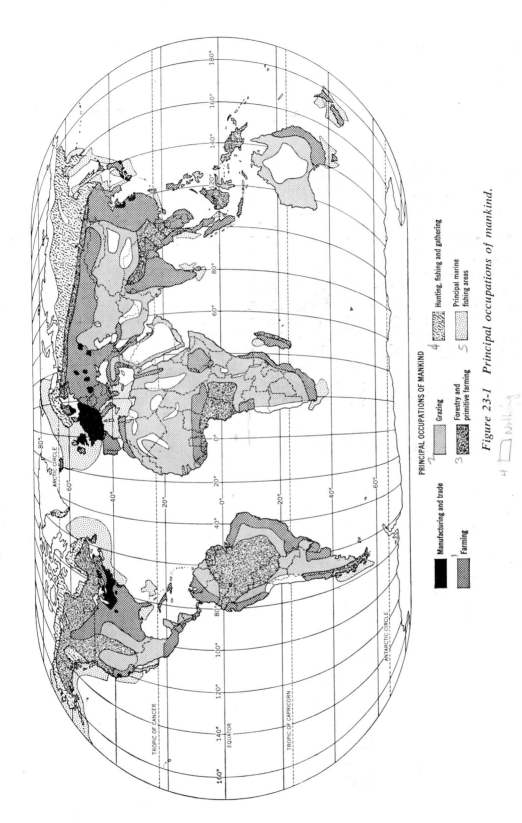

PRINCIPAL OCCUPATIONS OF MANKIND

1 Manufacturing and trade
2 Grazing
3 Farming
4 Forestry and primitive farming
4 Hunting, fishing and gathering
5 Principal marine fishing areas

4 ☐ Nothing

Figure 23-1 Principal occupations of mankind.

Hunting and Gathering. Primitive hunting, collecting, and fishing call for skill in the manufacture (Figure 23-2) of weapons and boats —harpoons, slings, arrows, traps, nets, and baskets, as well as canoes, kayaks, paddles, and sails. Often the pursuit of these occupations leads to extensive migrations and travel. Since the products of the chase and the fishery are highly perishable, primitive people must consume them soon after the catch has been taken. This leads to alternate periods of feast and famine, which the more capable attempt to avoid by providing a more steady supply of food, either by inventing methods of storage or by attempts to make the earth produce their needs by agriculture.

Some parts of the world are still occupied by people who live at low economic levels and provide most of their needs without recourse to processing raw materials or exchanging commodities with their neighbors. The map (Figure 23-1) indicates that parts of Borneo and New Guinea, the Arctic shores, and most of Labrador and the northern interior of Canada are populated by natives who rely on primitive hunting, fishing, and food collecting.

Needs of primitive men include protection and shelter; these may be obtained by taking refuge in trees or caverns. Shortly the search for shelter leads to construction of houses, which can be built with relative ease from nature's supplies of grass (Figure 6-6), timber, mud, or the skins of animals. Pursuit of these requirements, in addition to the need for fuel, led men to penetrate the dark forests. Tall grasslands with their wildlife were searched for animal skins to provide shelter and clothing for human beings. Forest dwellers and wood users eventually came to rely on the trees for their principal needs and upon forestry as an occupation.

Agriculture. Primitive or subsistence farming began early along man's road to more advanced civilization. Probably grains were first domesticated on grasslands and the practice of raising such crops spread into the irrigated floodplains of desert rivers. Forest dwellers also early learned to plant crops in clearings to supplement the meat from hunting and natural products gathered in the woods. Today primitive farmers are found in many parts of Mexico, Scandinavia, north central and Southeast Asia, the Amazon and Congo Basins, and New Guinea.

Factors that influence farming include

Figure 23-2 Sawing a board by primitive methods in Rota in the Marianas Islands. (Official photograph, U.S. Navy.)

quality of soil, slope and drainage of the land, amount and distribution of rainfall, temperature and length of the growing season, available seeds and plants, domestic animals, presence of insect pests and plant diseases, and sometimes water for irrigation. Skill, energy, and ability to reason and learn from experience are important human factors. If farming is to succeed commercially, costs, prices, freight rates, and transportation to markets should be favorable.

If climatic conditions are satisfactory, yields of crops are in proportion to the soil fertility and care used by the farmer. Agriculture supports dense populations of 800 to more than 1,000 persons per square mile in India, China, and Japan on fertile plains in humid regions having a long growing season. Irrigated valleys in deserts may also support great density of population, as in the Nile floodplain and delta in Egypt. Tropical lowlands seldom support large numbers of people; but the mountainous island of Java, almost under the equator, has singularly fertile soil and feeds 50 million persons besides exporting large quantities of plant products. Farms of the Orient are small, hand methods are used, and most food crops are of necessity consumed locally by farm families.

In contrast to this subsistence agriculture are the large farms operated by machine methods in the Middle Western Corn Belt and the wheat farms on the Great Plains of the United States. Here one farmer may produce enough grain or meat to feed thousands of people; in a good year a farmer with 1,000 acres in wheat may sell 30,000 bushels— the annual consumption of a town of 5,000 inhabitants. Some orchardists grow enough apples or other fruit to supply the demand of an entire city. In general, regions with fertile soil have higher living standards and have made greater contributions to progress than areas handicapped by poor land. People living in tropical rain forests, as in central Africa, those farming in remote places, and those who struggle for a living from tiny farms in countries like India and China are subsistence farmers. The largest occupational group on earth, which includes nearly half of the world's population, is made up of these relatively self-sufficient farmers.

Herding. The change from the hunting of wild animals to the domestication of sheep, goats, cows, horses, and other adaptable creatures led to the establishment of grazing as an occupation. Herding may be an occupation for primitive peoples who wander with their animals over vast grazing grounds remote from civilization, or it may be a highly organized and specialized industry such as sheep raising in Australia or cattle ranches on the Argentine Pampa.

In general the herdsman utilizes lands unfit for farming. Mountain meadows, undrained swamps, desert browse, and the grass of semiarid hills and plains can all supply feed for domestic animals. Even arctic tundras furnish food required by reindeer. Usually only sparse grazing is available to herds on the types of land mentioned. The herds must roam widely for feed, and the human population is very limited in numbers. Much grazing land of the world supports fewer than one human inhabitant per square mile. Transportation is less important to the herder than to the farmer, because animals can carry themselves long distances to market. Furthermore some animal products such as wool, hides, and tallow are valuable enough to stand costs for transport that are prohibitive for cheap grains like wheat or rice. The culture of tribes that make a living by herding is generally simpler than that of neighboring agricultural peoples.

Forestry. Exploitation of forest resources is today largely associated with complex modern civilization. Only in remote forested regions are found widely scattered natives who eke out a living by hunting, trapping furs, fishing, gathering wild products, and sometimes doing a little gardening. Examples of peoples living in this way include the Chippewa Indians of Canada, some Indians in tropical South America, and some natives in Siberian forests.

The lumberman uses machines to cut, saw, and carry wood to markets that are sometimes on the opposite side of the earth. Too often, after cutting down trees, he abandons an area, and moves to other forests where he repeats the process. Parts of northern Michigan and Wisconsin have been devastated by such methods. Lumbermen might better organize operations that would ensure permanent settlements. In Europe woodsmen more often use selective logging and other methods to perpetuate forests and keep steady employment in their local areas. Forests in Finland, Sweden, Switzerland, and Germany are managed in this way.

Commercial lumbering is a principal occupation in Quebec, British Columbia, and the northwestern United States, as well as in Finland. Forested areas of the Southern Hemisphere are small compared with those of the Northern Hemisphere and are too distant from world markets for commercial exploitation of large quantities of timber from those regions at present.

Population density is low in forested regions so long as a growing forest occupies the land. Whether agricultural settlement follows cutting of the trees depends on the soil, climate, and demand for land. Most good farmland in Western Europe and the eastern United States was once forested. Wooded areas in populous countries are usually restricted to mountains and hills or areas on which the soil is poor.

Mining. The development of mining on a large scale is associated with the needs of our machine age. In ancient times man's requirements for minerals were small and consisted of stone, clay, salt, and a few metals. Minerals are distributed very unevenly in nature and mining operations must be carried on where ores, fuels, or rocks occur. All mineral deposits occur where the geology has favored their formation. Since the geographical location of such metals as iron, lead, tin, and copper is principally a result of geologic structure and deposition, and since the most favorable conditions are related to mountain-forming processes, men who depend upon the extraction of metals usually live in hilly or mountainous areas. Hence we commonly find mining and quarrying in the highlands of the United States and Mexico, the central Andes, eastern Brazil, southeastern Africa, and in widely separated parts of Europe, Asia, and Australia where past geological conditions favored ore deposition.

Metal mines located in mountains are sometimes at such high elevations or so isolated that no one would live there if veins of ore had not been discovered. Many mines are short-lived, and mining towns are abandoned after deposits are exhausted. Some deposits are so extensive, however, that they are productive for centuries.

Very valuable minerals like gold and precious stones can be brought from a remote wilderness, desert, or jungle to which transportation is difficult and charges high, because their value is so great that expense for freight can be disregarded.

Useful mineral occurrences situated near centers of population are particularly profitable because costs of shipment are reduced; this circumstance allows exploitation of low-grade ores that would be impossible otherwise. Ore containing only 20 to 30 per cent iron is used at nearby furnaces in Birmingham, Alabama, and in England, whereas only ore carrying twice this iron content is mined profitably in Labrador, which is distant from the furnaces and mills.

Not all minerals occur in mountains. Some iron and many of the nonmetallic minerals like coal, petroleum, clay, sulfur, and salt are among those frequently found in lowlands. Deposits of coal and oil have many times proved a major factor in the growth of cities and the establishing of factories that need cheap power. Manufacturing in the "Black Country" of England, the Ruhr Valley in Germany, and the industrial cities in the Donets Basin and in western Siberia of the U.S.S.R. is based primarily on coal. Pennsylvania and West Virginia coal beds are a major factor leading to industrial expansion. Petroleum deposits account for the growth of scores of cities in the United States, including Oklahoma City and

Tulsa, Oklahoma; Bakersfield, California; Casper, Wyoming; and Beaumont, Texas.

Fishing.   Fishing is done both by natives for their major support or to supplement other food sources and by commercial fishermen who sell their catch as a means of livelihood. Where coastal soils near fishing grounds are sandy, swampy, rocky or otherwise unfavorable for agriculture, men tend to turn to the sea for a living. Early man investigated the lakes for a supply of fresh fish; indeed his settlements were often located with reference to this food supply, near shallow parts of the Swiss lakes and along the shores of many shallow bays. Extensive prehistoric shell mounds line the shores of lagoons and swamps around the edges of bays like those at San Francisco and Los Angeles. Nearness to fishing grounds is a requirement for natives using canoes and small boats, but commercial fishermen in large sea-worthy vessels may journey many hundreds of miles from the home port to the fishing areas. Breton fishermen have long made regular summer voyages between their French homes and the fishing grounds off Iceland and Newfoundland.

The great commercial fishing grounds are on the banks or shoal water near the continents in midlatitudes. Here conditions for fish food are especially good (Figure 23-3). The home ports for commercial fishermen are preferably near large cities if the fish are to be sold fresh. Fish are also marketed quick-frozen, dried, salted, and canned. These methods permit a wider distribution without spoilage.

Good fishing areas are especially exploited in the Northern Hemisphere. Important fishing ports include Gloucester and Boston, Massachusetts; Bergen and Trondheim, Norway; Grimsby and Yarmouth, England; Ketchikan, Alaska; and Monterey, Los Angeles, and San Francisco, California. Except for whaling near Antarctica, the fishing grounds of the Southern Hemisphere are relatively unimportant and contribute little food fish to the world's supply.

Intensification and Expansion of Industry. In their early stages, the primary human activities described in the preceding paragraphs are relatively simple in operation and call for varying amounts of skill and exertion in their performance. Greater need can stimulate advances beyond this point. Such need arises when man's existence is threatened by loss or failure of easily produced food and fuel supplies. Then man is forced to make adequate provision against famine and hardship if he and his family are to survive; he begins to accumulate surplus commodities. With this development comes trade with his neighbors and commercial development and processing of raw materials of all types (Figure 23-5). Agriculture becomes more intensive and specialized, as in the eastern and central United States, plantations of Indonesia, Hawaii, Cuba, Central America, and southeastern Brazil, the La Plata region, most of Europe, and southeastern Asia. Fisheries are established on a commercial basis, and methods of food preservation are advanced.

Manufacturing, treated in Chapter 21, is of great and increasing importance. Each year millions of people, many of whom were formerly employed in agriculture or other primary occupations, join the labor force in mills and factories. Distributing concerns and other associated enterprises occupy others.

The complexities of modern living give employment to millions of people in trade, finance, the professions, and all sorts of services. These sources of livelihood are too numerous to list, but account for an increasing portion of the nearly 65 million persons employed or in business for themselves in the United States.

POPULATION DISTRIBUTION

The population of the earth is very unevenly distributed (Figure 23-4). Any explanation of the distribution of people on the earth must take account of both natural and human factors but great variations in population density can be explained to a large degree by geography. Comparison of world maps of population density (Figure 23-4) with those of rainfall (Figure 5-1), temperature (Figure 3-6), and natural vegetation (Figure 5-2) will suggest these factors which help determine the areas favorable to settlement and development, compared with other regions in which natural conditions are unfavorable for human activities. Other factors affecting the distribution of population include relief features of the earth, proximity of the sea, water supplies, occurrence of mineral resources, soil conditions, and location with regard to trade routes and world markets. In addition to the combined effect of various natural factors, such factors as religion, habits, standards of living, and general cultural level of a people are very important in affecting the birth rate and density of population in a given part of the earth. Certainly the factors affecting population increase and density are exceedingly complex, although some broad generalizations seem reasonable.

In general, regions in which hunting, herding, logging, forest agriculture, and other primitive occupations are widespread have low densities of population. On the other hand, regions where the combination of soil and climatic conditions foster agriculture and where industrialization has occurred can support relatively high densities of population.

Regions of Dense Population.　The regions of the world having extensive land areas and dense population include southeastern Asia, Western and Central Europe, and the northeastern United States. Small regions of dense population include Java, the lower Nile Valley, southeastern Brazil, and the vicinity of certain cities like Buenos Aires and Los Angeles. Large populations in India, Pakistan, China, and Japan are the result of favorable geographic conditions, particularly of seasonal rainfall and adequate growing season of the monsoon climate, together with fertility of the soil. These conditions permit growing two food crops annually and particularly the production of large amounts of rice. Java has exceptionally fertile soils and other conditions of benefit to crops. Irrigated lands having a long growing season, like the Nile Valley and southern

California, can support dense populations by means of agriculture. In the midlatitudes of Europe and the United States where dense populations are found, regions have advanced because of the combination of favorable climate, access to the sea, and industrialization; other factors, including the ability and energy of the people, have contributed to rapid increase of population in the last two centuries. This in turn has led to the spectacular growth of cities.

In a big country of large population, people are as a rule unevenly distributed. Only countries or regions that are small enough to have uniform conditions of farming and have no major city display even distributions of population. In China, India, Pakistan, and Japan, fertile lowlands may support more than 1,000 people per square mile by means of intensive agriculture. The Indus Valley, Ganges Delta, North China Plain, and Kwanto Plain near Toyko represent this condition. Land adjacent to these densely populated rural regions may be less favorable for farming and unable to support large numbers of people per square

mile, partly because of antiquated methods of farming by hand. In the Orient, farmers use hand methods of tillage and harvesting and can care for only small farms. In order to get maximum production per acre, they must cultivate very fertile land, since there is just as much work involved in cultivating good land as in cultivating poor land. By means of mechanized farming, inferior land could be used if large units were available, but this method has not been introduced into the Orient.

The most complex phases of human activity are related to advances in the use of the products of mining, for large-scale manufacturing is associated with the invention and fabrication of elaborate and costly machines made of metal. Only a few parts of the world have attained a manufacturing economy. The two outstanding areas are the American manufacturing belt in the northeastern United States and southeastern Canada, and parts of northwestern Europe: the British Isles, France, Belgium, the Netherlands, and West Germany. Outlying centers are located in the Soviet Union, Japan, India, and China. There are

Figure 23-3 Fishing for salmon near the mouth of the Columbia River, in the Pacific Northwest. (Photograph, courtesy of the U.S. Fish and Wildlife Service.)

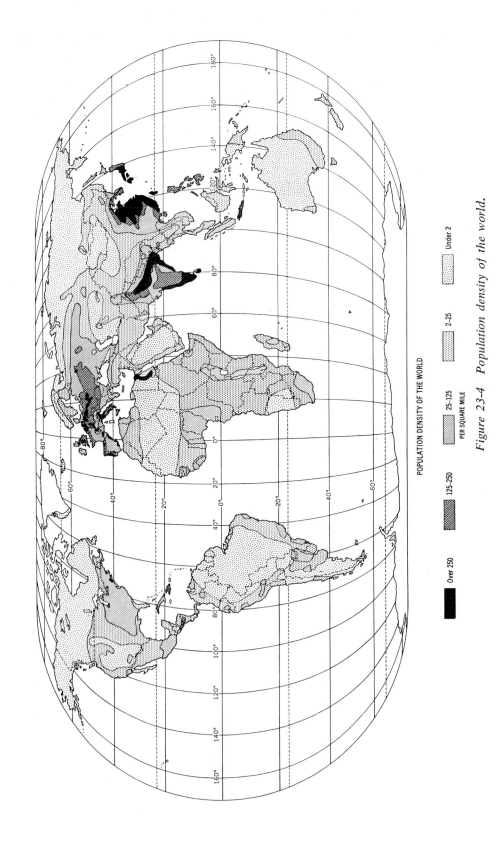

POPULATION DENSITY OF THE WORLD

Over 250   125-250   25-125   125-250   2-25   Under 2

PER SQUARE MILE

Figure 23-4   Population density of the world.

numerous manufacturing centers in the Southern Hemisphere; but they are mostly small, partly because of the relatively small population and the distance from consuming markets.

Regions of Sparse Population. The world contains numerous unpopulated and thinly populated regions. Among the causes for small population density are climate (cold, lack of rainfall or other water, extremes of temperature, and high humidity together with heat), roughness of surface, and sterile soil.

The least populated parts of the earth are those with such low average temperatures that sources of human food are almost entirely lacking, namely, the Antarctic continent and the interior of Greenland. Altitude as well as latitude may preclude dense population. Tibet, lying higher than 10,000 feet above sea level, has such a rigorous climate that only a few people can live on the meager resources provided by the elevated plateau environment. Because of their climatic conditions, the glacier-covered regions, high rugged mountains, and very elevated plateaus are parts of the earth most inimical to human residence.

Another poor environment is represented by the vast oceanic expanses, which are also notably deficient in human food, with the exception of fish. Nevertheless, at any given time, thousands of people live on the oceans for varying periods, while engaged in marine activities or travel. Too much water is detrimental to human existence, but so is too little.

Dry deserts of the world are very sparsely populated, except in those fortunate oases where water from some steady source (often outside the desert) may be obtained. It has been truly said, "The deserts are the gaps in the world's civilization." Those dry deserts which are least habitable include the largest—the Sahara—as well as Arabia and central Australia. Slightly more useful and somewhat more populated is the Thar of northwestern India, which has been reclaimed in part by irrigation and thus supports a moderately dense population. Other dry areas which support some population are the coastal desert of northern Chile and southern Peru, which locally can obtain water from Andean streams, the Kalahari of southern Africa, which receives slightly more rainfall than the other regions, and the Colorado or Sonoran desert of southwestern North America. In general the mid-latitude deserts of the Great Basin, Caspian Basin, Gobi, and Takla Makan are relatively unused by man, since they fail to provide adequate water or food.

Some parts of the earth experience the opposite extreme of deserts, namely, an excess of water and woody vegetation, which combine to make life difficult. Much of the Amazon Basin, the Congo and Niger Basins, and most of the lowland areas of the East Indian Archipelago are so difficult to penetrate that they remain unpopulated and only partly explored. On the other hand, some parts of southeastern Asia that receive annual rainfall greater than that of the Amazon and Congo are densely peopled. Here rainfall occurs seasonally, leaving a time each year when grain crops like rice may ripen and providing conditions more favorable to man than where rains continue throughout the year.

World Population. In terms of the continents, population distribution is extremely uneven. Approximate figures for each continent are given in Table 23-1, although the figure for Asia may be unreliable because of lack of adequate data on the population of China and several other countries.

Reasons for this unequal distribution are partly geographical and partly historical. Obviously Antarctica is unpopulated because of its adverse climatic conditions, whereas Australia is relatively unpopulated because nearly half of it is desert and also because it has been opened to white settlement but a short time. Another factor enters here, less easy to evaluate; man sometimes cannot compete with newcomers better equipped to make use of the environment. Hence, the Bushmen of South Africa, Pygmies of the Congo region, and some of the American Indian tribes have failed to reproduce in sufficient numbers to maintain their identity in much of their original homelands.

It would be a mistake to assume that the present world population map is stable. Rather it changes constantly, though some parts are more stable than others. People move from place to place, thus redistributing human residence and activity to new and possibly unpopulated parts. Following closely upon the period of great explorations by sea in the sixteenth century, Europeans moved by thousands and millions to the New World to form permanent settlements, thereby adding greatly to the total population of North and South America. A similar move took place in Australia in the eighteenth and nineteenth centuries. Another example was the migration of 30 million Chinese into Manchuria during a 40-year period earlier in this century. The Industrial Revolution contributed to the great increase in population of many regions, for example, northeastern United States, west central Europe, and many urbanized areas in Japan and other parts of the world.

Obviously these movements revised the world map of population distribution. More violent redistribution occurs during wars or as the result of crop failures, inadequate water supply, or failure of forage supplies for animals. Abnormally low periods of rainfall may result in major population movements or in serious

TABLE 23-1. ESTIMATED POPULATION OF THE WORLD*

Area	Population
Asia, excluding the U.S.S.R.	1,514,000,000
Europe, excluding the U.S.S.R.	412,000,000
North America	246,000,000
Africa	220,000,000
U.S.S.R.	200,000,000
South America	129,000,000
Australia and Oceania	15,100,000
Antarctica	
Approximate Total	**2,737,000,000**

* SOURCE: *United Nations Demographic Yearbook,* 1957, New York, 1957.

decline in total population. This was the apparent cause of many changes among native Indian tribes of the southwestern United States, and in part it accounts for loss of population on the northern Great Plains between 1920 and 1950.

Migrations. Migration of peoples has occurred from the dawn of tribal man to the present. Methods of transportation play an important part in redistribution of the world's people through migration. The migrations of tribesmen of the central Asian steppes are of necessity slow if they must move on foot, and the territory they occupy is limited in extent by the mode of transport. The situation is eased if people are able to make use of simple carts and draft animals, but only if the mass movement takes place on terrain of low relief or if well-marked roadways and passes can be utilized. Migrations over larger areas may be carried out if swift animals like the horse or the camel are available. Migrations, with the accompanying redistribution of population, may be of several types. Whole agglomerations, such as villages or religious groups, may move en masse. On the other hand, the move may be accomplished by slow infiltration of individuals or families, without any group movement. The first type of population movement is represented by the settlements of Mormons in Utah, of Dukhobors in the plains provinces of Canada, or of Germans at Llanquihue in southern Chile. Occasionally these movements may be fostered by government action, especially if it is desirable to obtain settlers for a newly opened frontier. This was the case in Chile.

Infiltration of individuals and families brings about redistribution of populations when prospects for better living conditions or increased wealth lead to migrations. Boston's population was considerably increased during the nineteenth century by infiltration of Irish, partly because of serious crop failures and food shortages in Ireland. California's population increased greatly through a 5-year infiltration of miners following the gold rush discoveries of 1848 and 1849. Either mass movements or infiltration may establish populations thinly on the world's frontier areas and so change a frontier of low economic level to more intensive human use, making it a productive region with generally improved standards of living.

Notable changes in population occur when frontiers are opened to settlement. Among examples are the Boer treks in South Africa, opening of the Caspian Steppe lands, swarming of Chinese into Manchuria, and settling of the Argentine Pampa and the Great Plains of the United States and Canada. For a time in the fifteenth and sixteenth centuries all of North and South America were frontiers, open to exploitation and settlement. Gradually the best outlying lands were occupied, and today there are relatively few frontiers that will provide adequate support for many people. Among those lands still available are the Peace River section of Canada, which remains relatively unpopulated, parts of the Orinoco plains in Venezuela and Colombia, some of interior Brazil, some highland country in Kenya and Tanganyika in East Africa, and portions of interior Asia.

Population Distribution in North America.
In the *United States,* most people live in the humid eastern half of the country. The population, along with the rainfall, declines noticeably westward from about the 98th meridian. It then becomes dense again in the lowlands of southern California, the Great Valley of California, and the Willamette-Puget lowland of western Oregon and Washington as far north as Vancouver, British Columbia, across the Canadian boundary. Between the West Coast valleys and the eastern humid regions in the United States are extensive areas of population concentration in irrigated lands, as in eastern Utah and southern Idaho or on the wheat lands made cultivable by increased rainfall, as in eastern Washington and northern Oregon. Clusters or concentrations of people in much of the eastern part of the nation are

largely the result of city growth and development of centers of manufacturing. Rural population is spread rather evenly over the plains and rolling hills, though population tends to be sparse in mountain areas, like the Adirondacks or the coniferous forest regions of northwest Maine and upper Michigan. It also tends to be sparse in undrained swamplands like those of the extreme eastern seaboard or the Florida Everglades.

In *Canada* the brief growing season limits agricultural settlement in the northern direction, and most Canadians live in the Ontario Peninsula, the St. Lawrence Valley, and maritime regions near the international boundary and on fertile plains of the Prairie provinces in the interior. Most of the Pacific coast of Canada is too mountainous to attract many settlers, but a small area near Vancouver and Victoria, B.C., has a mild climate, good soil, great forests, and excellent harbors, and most of the people of the province live in these cities or nearby. North of Lake Huron and Lake Superior on the Laurentian Upland, a thinly populated wilderness separates the wheat lands of the prairies from the general farming and industrial sections of eastern Canada. In both the United States and Canada cities are located principally in the eastern parts of the countries, especially in those sections which are engaged in manufacturing. Factors affecting urban location and growth will be treated in the next chapter.

About two-thirds of *Mexico's* population and that of Central America live in the cooler healthier uplands in preference to the lowlands, a condition directly opposite to that of the mid-latitude lowlands.

Population in Other Continents. The zone of dense population in *Europe* extends from England through northern France, Belgium, the Netherlands, central Germany, western Czechoslovakia, Poland, and into the Ukraine of southern U.S.S.R. Within this zone is a combination of geographical factors suitable for the advance of industry, including coal de-

posits, access to consuming markets, presence of raw materials for manufacture, fertile soil, and an early start in manufactures. All these led to a great increase of population and urbanization, especially during the past century. In Southern Europe dense populations are local rather than arranged in a long zone; these clusters of settlement are usually found in deltas, river valleys, and coastal zones. The Po Valley, outstanding among them, combines agriculture and industry within its limits. The coast of eastern Spain near Barcelona, the Naples area, the district around Salonika in Greece, the Lyon-Marseille cluster in France, and the vicinity of Istanbul are among the important minor concentrations of population.

Asia, except in Japan and parts of Siberia and India, has been only slightly affected by industrial development. On this continent most areas of dense population coincide with locations of intensive agriculture, with the large thinly peopled areas devoted more directly to herding, forestry, and a little subsistence farming. The introduction of mechanized farming methods would make possible some extensions of farming into grasslands of Asia. In all probability this would lead to a corresponding increase of population in that part of the world, provided that satisfactory methods of transportation were installed by which export crops of wheat could be marketed.

In tropical *South America* the densely populated areas are in the highlands, as in Central America and Mexico, but in the southern part of the continent, in midlatitudes, the inhabitants are concentrated on the lowlands, which are favorable for agriculture. Moun-

Figure 23-5 The interior of a Greek tobacco grower's home. The owner's daughters string fresh tobacco leaves, which are then dried in the sun and later are hung from the ceiling of the room. Much of the world's work consists of this simple type of hand labor. (Photograph, courtesy MSA.)

tains, forests, and dry grasslands toward the southern tip of South America are able to support few people compared with the Pampa near Buenos Aires, rolling plains of Uruguay, or the central valley of Chile.

In *Africa* population concentration occurs principally near the Mediterranean Sea, in Nigeria and West Africa, the highlands of East Africa, and southern and eastern parts of the continent. Among very dense populations existing by means of agriculture are those of the delta and floodplain of the Nile River, with 1,500 people per square mile in its lower part; this density contrasts sharply with the adjacent deserts, which are almost uninhabited.

A large part of *Australia* is almost empty of people, but there are some concentrations in the southeastern part around Melbourne and Sydney and moderate population along the Queensland coast and in the southwest.

SUMMARY

The occupations of gathering, herding, and subsistence farming are carried on today chiefly in poorly developed regions.

Subsistence farming is practiced also in densely populated lands, for example, in Southeast Asia. Commercial agriculture, mining, forestry, and fishing are characteristic of the Industrial Revolution along with workmen in manufacturing enterprises and hosts of people engaged in trade, services, and professions.

The 2½ billion inhabitants of the world are unevenly distributed. Dense populations occur in manufacturing and urbanized regions and on intensively cultivated fertile farmland in humid climates with long or frostless growing seasons. Oases also support dense populations for the area of tilled land. Sparse populations are characteristic of unirrigated deserts, high, cold, and rocky mountains and plateaus, tundras, the colder parts of the taiga, and tropical rain forests.

Outline
Primary occupations
  Gathering
  Agriculture
  Herding
  Forestry
  Mining
  Fishing
  Other occupations
Distribution of world population
  Areas of dense population
  Areas of sparse population
  In the different continents

QUESTIONS

1. List some of the advances that have made possible the utilization of lands in:
  a. The hot humid regions
  b. The cold humid regions
  c. The hot dry regions
  d. The cold dry regions

2. What is the physical pattern of the population distribution in the vicinity of your home community? How is this pattern related to the local physical geography?

3. Refer to the map of population densities (Figure 23-4), then answer the following questions:

Why are the greatest population densities in the United States east of the 100th meridian west longitude?

What part of the equatorial tropics is most densely populated? Why?

What desert area supports the greatest population?

What climatic realm has the widest area having over 250 people per square mile?

4. Not all parts of Australia lie in the desert, but why is the continent underpopulated?

5. New Zealand's climate is not unlike that of parts of northwestern Europe but it is sparsely populated by comparison. Why?

6. What two parts of Africa are least populated? Why?

TOPICS FOR DISCUSSION

1. In each case, a major redistribution of population occurred in the year indicated, or soon thereafter. What parts of the world became more completely settled as a result? 1492, 1519, 1787, 1607, 1849, 1620, 1530.

SELECTED REFERENCES

Arbos, Philippe: "The Geography of Pastoral Life, Illustrated with European Examples," *Geographical Review,* 13:559–575, October, 1923.

Bogue, Donald J.: "The Geography of Recent Population Trends in the United States," *Annals of the Association of American Geographers,* 44:124–134, June, 1954. (See also articles by other authors in this issue.)

———: "Changes in Population Distribution since 1940," *American Journal of Sociology,* 56:43–57, July, 1950.

Brunhes, Jean: *Human Geography,* Rand McNally & Company, Chicago, 1902, pp. 74–110.

Chandrasekhar, Sripate: *Hungry People and Empty Lands,* The Macmillan Company, New York, 1955.

Cressey, George B.: "Land for 2.4 Billion Neighbors," *Economic Geography,* 20:1–9, January, 1953.

Dice, Lee R.: "Ecology and Overpopulation," *Scientific Monthly,* 84:165–170, April, 1957.

Finch, V. C., G. T. Trewartha, Arthur H. Robinson, and Edwin H. Hammond: *Elements of Geography,* 4th ed., McGraw-Hill Book Company, Inc., New York, 1957, pp. 501–537.

Geddes, Arthur: "Variability in Change of Population in the United States and Canada, 1900–1951," *Geographical Review,* 44:88–100, January, 1954.

Hertzler, Joyce: *Crisis in World Population,* University of Nebraska Press, Lincoln, 1956.

Huxley, Julian: "World Population," *Scientific American,* 194:64–76, March, 1956.

Osborn, Fairfield: *Limits of the Earth,* Little, Brown & Company, Boston, 1953.

Princeton University, Office of Population Research: *The Economic Demography of Eastern and Northern Europe,* Columbia University Press, New York, 1947.

Russell, John: *World Population and World Food Supplies,* The Macmillan Company, New York, 1955.

Stilgenbauer, Floyd: *A New Population Map of the United States,* Rand McNally & Company, Chicago, 1952.

Trewartha, Glenn T.: "A Case for Population Geography," *Annals of the Association of American Geographers,* 43:71–97, June, 1953.

24. Rural and Urban Life

Most human beings are gregarious; the very nature of man himself calls for contacts with fellow beings and development of mutual trusts that eventually help both individuals and groups. The simplest form of contact is that of the family, in which individuals are related not only by blood but by feeling of kinship. This is the principal reason why a small group of people unite their efforts for mutual benefit. Working together, they can produce more and better food than if they worked singly. Joint action to protect themselves against enemies may mean their long-run survival.

It is but a step from the family with few members to the larger group that takes the form of the tribe or clan. Family and tribe together constitute the principal social units of primitive man. Within the tribe, there are blood relationships and recognition of the family group. Emergence of such a tribe as a social unit provides better economic conditions and military defense than a smaller group might achieve. Later, as human groups begin to have fixed dwelling places, settlements appear.

Under conditions of widely dispersed settlement, the farmstead of the family becomes a community in miniature. It is not found in all parts of the world since family groups have not always been able to risk living in open country, lest they be attacked by marauders. This was true in northwestern Europe, but in the United States single farmsteads are widespread in many sections. The density of these farm settlements depends upon ability of the land to produce crops; farmsteads in unproductive areas such as northern Michigan are few and widely separated, but dispersed farms in the fertile Shenandoah Valley of Virginia are numerous.

No matter where the farm may be, certain

basic structures are essential to its successful operation. These usually include a dwelling for the farmer and his family, and a barn to house livestock or poultry or to serve as storage for hay and grain. These two structures (sometimes combined in a single building in Switzerland) may be regarded as the basic needs of any farm. Other structures within the farmstead may include pig and poultry houses, a barnyard, springhouse, structures for shelter of farm machinery, silo, milkhouse, and several other functional units. Buildings may vary from place to place; in southern California, for example, there is little need for large silos for storing cattle feed because the mild climate allows pasturage out-of-doors. On the marine windward coast of western Washington, the corncrib is absent because the Pacific Northwest climate is too cool for quantity production of corn. In other parts of the world, farm structures reflect local needs of the farm operator; and even the buildings themselves appear in widely different forms such as the highly useful "bank barn" of the Swiss valleys. This is a hillside structure with cattle stalls on the lowest level and ramp approach to the haying floor on the upper level.

A second type of single-family settlement is represented by the *ranch,* a word introduced into this country by early Spanish settlers of the Southwest. This type of settlement is associated mainly with those parts of the world where cattle raising is the leading economic operation. Appearance of the ranch may differ greatly from that of the farm, because needs of the cattle rancher call for dwelling, corrals, shelter for horses, well house, and other outbuildings. The large barn of the dairy regions, the corncrib, silo, and milkhouse are foreign to the ranch settlement. Contrasts are sharp in the physical appearance of these economic units. Furthermore, the inability of cattle country to support large numbers of people implies that ranch settlements are very widely dispersed. The actual site of the ranch may reflect the presence of water in sufficient amount to meet needs of the ranch owner and his livestock.

Beginnings of Settlement.   As soon as human beings abandon a nomadic existence and turn to some selected location to live for part or all of each year, then beginnings of settlement can be readily observed. The community may consist of only a few dwellings or even, in some cases, a single dwelling of large size. Settlements may have no high degree of permanence, but once occupied their owners call them home. Settlements utilize a wide variety of sites, including large and airy caves, small islands in a stream, small hilltops, or offshore islands. Settlement sites can be analyzed with reference to advantages they offer those who occupy them. Islands, for example, may be so situated that they provide excellent natural protection against attack. Hilltop locations may be fortified with relatively little difficulty against intruders. The cave entrance may be so unapproachable that it can be defended by a handful of people. In remote parts of the world these primitive settlements still exist in mountainous interiors of southwestern China, dry lands of Arabia, and along arctic shores. As civilization advances, however, the primitive settlements tend to disappear entirely or grow in size to become communities of a more advanced culture.

After several families have joined together and are living in a small settlement, the village nucleus appears. Villages may take the form of clusters of dwellings belonging to a half-dozen families of fishermen, as along the coast of Japan, or may be very compact communities like the vineyard towns of the central Rhine Valley. They develop when several ranch owners establish holdings near each other in the Great Plains of central Canada, or when loggers live near together for companionship. Such a community is commonly called a *hamlet.* In its simplest form it is little more than a few families living near each other. It supports few community activities though its location may be dignified by a name. The settlement will be recognized by travelers and the name may appear on maps. Many settlements never advance beyond this initial stage. They may, on the other hand, attract enough residents to become communities of size and importance. They may disappear entirely, leaving behind nothing more than a name on the map.

Settlement sites. Before the development of rail transportation, important settlements and cities were either seaports or located on navigable *rivers*. Most large European cities and towns are seaports or river ports. Every capital city of the 18 original provinces of China is said to have been built on a navigable stream. Even with some decline in traffic on streams in the United States, many settlements owe their start, if not their continued growth, to a river location.

Among useful settlement and city sites are locations at or near the confluence of streams. People who live near the junction of two streams can command traffic and trade through three river valleys—upriver on two streams and downriver on one. A location of this sort is highly advantageous; generally communities that develop at confluence sites are busily engaged in commerce, as at Pittsburgh, St. Louis, and Cairo, Illinois. The ground at the junction of rivers should be high enough to provide a site above flood waters. Some streams join in low swampy land that is entirely unsuited for building; at these places no cities or settlements of importance can develop without major changes in the site condition. The junction of the Red River and the Mississippi, or the Arkansas and Mississippi, for example, is unsatisfactory for building; and neither confluence is occupied by an important community. Rivers may erode the ground at their confluence; the site of the old trading post of Fort Union, located at the junction of the Yellowstone and Missouri a century ago, has entirely disappeared; and the mouth of the Yellowstone is nearly 5 miles away from its former location. These conditions thwart the continued existence of city or village.

A second important settlement site is located where land and water routes join, diverge, or cross. This type of site is often found near the mouth of a river as it enters the sea (Figure 24-1). The land route emerges from the river valley; the river mouth may be sufficiently large to admit shipping. These settlements are commonly located at the head of ocean navigation in the stream valley, whether it be a short distance upstream at the innermost point reached by ocean vessels, or a greater distance upstream at the head of all river navigation. The first type of city is represented by the position of New Orleans; the second by the location of St. Paul.

Still another type of settlement is found in mountainous regions where land travel is funneled through passes, taking advantage of the lowest and easiest transportation routes at right angles to the trend of mountain ranges. *Pass settlements* of this type may be found at either end of a pass, where routes fan out or concentrate as travelers leave or enter the pass itself.

One settlement site is commonly located in a central position in the heart of a large and productive plain within which traffic and

Figure 24-1   Riga, Latvia, an unpatterned town within a pattern fortification: 1, nunnery, 2, guildhall, 3, cathedral, 4, town hall and market place, 5, cathedral, 6, Rigebach, a tributary of the Duna, 7, the Duna, 8, fortifications. (Used by courtesy of J. B. Leighly.)

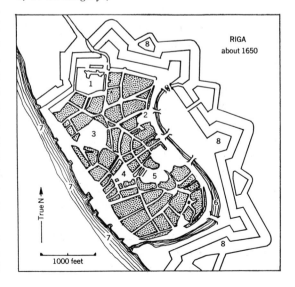

goods move toward the center where important *market centers* are located. Settlements of this type engage in trade and commerce and perhaps in manufacturing activities on a large scale.

Any marked *transportation* break is likely to foster the establishment of a settlement, especially along streams where traffic is interrupted by large waterfalls or rapids. An additional reason for settling here is the steady supply of *power* available for manufacturing processes. In fact, any important source of power, whether it be falling water, coal supplies, or petroleum deposits, may provide a base for founding settlements of size and importance. In more arid parts of the world where *water* is at a premium, the presence of a flowing stream or perennial spring accounts for the establishment and growth of many communities.

It is apparent that selection of settlement sites is strongly affected by (1) presence of transportation routes, (2) resources, including available food supply, power, and water, and (3) local conditions that favor defense. Other factors may be significant, but these seem to be principal reasons why particular living sites are selected. In addition, natural factors such as hilltops or mountain passes may be important considerations, but the mere presence of desirable landscape features does not necessarily imply that a settlement will be located there. There are excellent harbors that should serve as important sites for ports along the coasts of southern Chile, but other geographical advantages are absent; hence the population in that remote part of the world remains small and settlements are few.

Many other reasons account for the presence of settlements. Human beings can make a wide range of choices, and they may select a location without regard for conditions that nature provided. This type of settlement is occasionally found in highly industrialized regions, but if the choice of site has been too poor, the settlement may exist for only a short period.

Community services. The real life of the community begins when the hamlet becomes so large that its residents require greater protection for property than their own efforts can give. Community services then develop and come to include fire protection, schools, and even sanitation and water supply. These represent the principal aspects of local government, and the number of services usually is closely related to size of the community and its ability to pay for them. Nongovernmental community services include provision for religious worship, a burial place, and a building to accommodate social gatherings. Very small communities sometimes maintain parks for recreational purposes.

As the community grows and prospers, its residents may find it desirable to provide a plan whereby the best qualities of the settlement will be perpetuated; that is, community planning is placed in operation, though as a general rule people do not realize the need for it until the village or town is of some size. The particular services available in any community will vary with time and place; but among very primitive people there is often a surprising amount of joint action accomplished on behalf of the entire settlement.

Settlement patterns. The pattern of a community as it appears upon a map may take any of several different forms, such as a circular cluster of huts, houses arranged at a crossing, or streets planned on latticework (grid) patterns or in the form of a Y. Often the pattern of the community reflects local transportation conditions. A settlement located at a river confluence, for example, may develop with a distinct Y pattern; a settlement at a transportation crossroads may appear on the map as an X. One common type of hamlet pattern is extremely simple and consists of two rows of structures facing each other along a single street. This is sometimes referred to as a "string" settlement or "string town." It is probable that settlement patterns are more frequently tied to local transportation routes than to features of natural relief such as hills or streams.

Most community maps show a focal point

or node where greatest community activity takes place. This may be at a highway intersection, in the vicinity of retail stores, or around a small park. In arid lands, the focal point may be the well from which people must obtain domestic water supplies. In many communities the leading activity is related to the church or an ancient castle. In southeastern United States, the plantation type of settlement was established at an early date; in hamlets of this type the focal point of activity was the large mansion of the owner, often facing a navigable stream. Around this structure much community activity revolved.

THE CITY

The city as it exists in most countries today is a relatively modern phenomenon. In ancient times and under primitive conditions of travel, the distribution of population tended to be widespread. There were only a few large cities in antiquity such as Athens, Alexandria, or Rome; most people lived in a rural environment—either on dispersed farmsteads, or more commonly, in small settlement agglomerations, hamlets, or villages. As transport improves, people tend to live together in larger numbers. The settlement beginning as a small wilderness fort, crossroads center, or forest camp grows to large size, might even become a city of several millions. Generally the larger the city, the greater the degree of complexity of living conditions among its residents.

Left to themselves, very large cities are incapable of providing sufficient food or fuel for their inhabitants. Although those who live in cities may be engaged in manufacturing and in production of goods that they themselves use or trade, they are not in a position to obtain raw materials from which those goods must be made. They depend upon transportation facilities to bring them most materials needed for the support and comfort of the people in the city itself. The modern city represents a somewhat artificial way of living; as suggested earlier in this book, the study of urban geography is much more complex than the study of rural geography; hence the study of city activities is more involved than study of farm activities, where human beings live in comparatively close relationship to conditions that nature provides.

The city site. There is little difference between site conditions characteristic of small settlements and those of large urban centers. Common types of city sites include those located at stream confluences, crossroads junctions, and at points where it is customary to change the method by which shipments are made. Cities may attain large size if located near desirable harbors in a productive area. Even frontier settlements with their fortifications find it possible to abandon aspects of military life and become major urban agglomerations. Fortified city locations related to a military frontier are usually termed *march sites*. Some of the world's largest cities began in this fashion, including Berlin, Chicago, Detroit, and Pittsburgh. The hilltop that can be fortified represents one type of location well adapted for small settlements; such a site, however, does not lend itself to development of a large city.

Cities as well as hamlets grow at any site where transportation is interrupted. Buffalo, for example, prospers from the fact that water transport between Lake Erie and Lake Ontario is interrupted at Niagara Falls. As a result of the interruption, the Erie Canal was completed in 1825 along a route through central New York State that made it possible to circumvent Niagara Falls. Not even construction of the Welland Canal connecting Lakes Erie and Ontario has given rise to growth of a city of the size or importance of Buffalo.

Another important location lies at any break in transportation that may result from falls or rapids around which goods must be portaged, as at Louisville on the "Falls of the Ohio," and The Dalles, Oregon, on the Columbia River. Other towns are located at convenient junctions of canals and rivers, as at Albany and Troy, New York, or of land routes and water routes, as at Cincinnati and Kansas City. Manufacturing towns, as mentioned previously, developed quickly at sources of water power, as at Minneapolis (Figure 24-2), Spokane, and Holyoke. Early trading towns along the Ohio River include Marietta and Portsmouth, Ohio; Madison, Indiana; and Paducah, Kentucky.

Sometimes "twin cities" develop, one at the head of navigation and the other at the rapids, as St. Paul and Minneapolis. Twin cities may also grow on opposite sides of rivers or bays. As a city expands, those who wish to practice gardening or poultry raising may live on the other shore where land is cheap. Factories may also be located opposite the large city on cheaper building sites. Twin cities having these characteristics are numerous: St. Louis and East St. Louis; Kansas City, Kansas, North Kansas City and Kansas City, Missouri; Cincinnati and Covington; Detroit and Windsor; New York and the Jersey shore cities; San Francisco and Oakland.

Local geographic conditions at the site may favor city growth. Kansas City, Missouri, for example, is situated at sufficient height above the Missouri River so that it has excellent drainage and is free from flood. The land surface is so nearly level that it is comparatively simple for this city to grow in any direction away from the river. Its location is central within the United States with many railways and highways intersecting there, providing first-class transportation. Kansas City is also an important center of air transport. The highly productive hinterland is in the heart of one of the best agricultural sections of the entire nation. Transportation of limited type is possible on the river.

In contrast, the city of Seattle is not centrally located with respect to any part of the United States. It occupies a relatively narrow and hilly neck of land between a deep salt-water inlet on its western side and a long and narrow fresh-water lake to the east. Until a floating bridge was built across the lake, it was necessary for land traffic moving in or out of Seattle to go entirely around one end of the lake. Not only is the neck of land thickly congested, but its surface is extremely hilly, thereby reducing the desirable land that might otherwise be available for growth of the city and making costs of city services very high. Furthermore, not far east of Seattle the Cascade Range forms a traffic barrier and limits Seattle's productive hinterland.

It is apparent from the preceding discussion that cities sometimes become large in spite of

Figure 24-2 Modern flour mills and grain elevators at Minneapolis, Minnesota. Storage bins for grain appear at the right and flour mills in the center. (Photograph, courtesy of Minneapolis Grain Exchange, from George Miles Ryan Studio.)

unfavorable geographic factors. To return to Seattle as an example, local conditions seemingly do not encourage progress, but Seattle does enjoy the advantage of favorable location on a great-circle route to eastern Asia. It also has extensive nearby forests and what might be regarded as a marine hinterland to the west, from which quantities of commercial fish are obtained. Further, it enjoys a favored position with respect to Alaskan trade. Other favorable geographic factors tend to offset disadvantages previously described.

Because of wide variation in local geographic conditions, it is obvious that no two cities can be identical in development or characteristics. Each urban center has its own personality; and though it is possible to generalize to a certain extent, contrasting geographical conditions always distinguish it from its neighbor.

City Patterns. The map of a city is easily recognizable because of the network of intersecting lines representing transportation routes within the city. Such a map presents a pattern of streets—a pattern that may reflect any one of several widely different geographic circumstances. In very hilly terrain, for example, it is difficult to impose a system of mathematical lines upon the map with success. If for any reason the site occupies discontinuous swamplands or lakes are numerous within the city limits, the grid or latticework pattern is unsuitable because that produces many dead-end streets or other interruptions. In hill cities, it is more logical to arrange the pattern so that streets mount steep slopes with gradual rise. This brings about a pattern that has little uniformity. Unfortunately, cities like San Francisco and Seattle have used the grid pattern in spite of very steep hills.

Figure 24-3   William Penn's plan for the city of Philadelphia. One of the earliest examples of city planning on the grid, or lattice, pattern transferred to North American settlements. The center of the city was occupied by an open space, where the present city hall stands. Four other open areas, to be used as parks, were located symmetrically. Note that this plan takes account of the natural conformation of the site at only one place, in the southeastern corner of the city. Shaded areas indicate the actual settled urban community of Philadelphia in 1776.

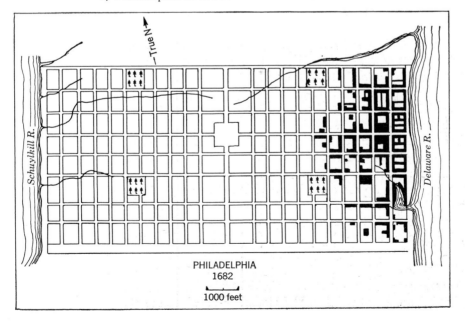

Some city patterns are arranged so that streets are parallel to or at right angles to some geographic feature such as a coast or river shore (Figure 24-3). Others may be closely related to direction of rail lines or major highways. Still others appear on maps as circles or other mathematical figures, though those are rare. At first glance, some city maps seem to display no pattern whatever; but closer inspection usually indicates some reason behind the street layout and often that reason is geographic. Many Oriental and European cities founded before the days of wheeled vehicles are almost unpatterned, with narrow twisting alleys instead of streets.

As suggested earlier, city patterns occasionally show plainly the city's history, as in the case of the Paris boulevards which were originally locations of city walls. In the United States, travelers are so accustomed to the usual grid pattern (which is well designed for level ground) that they cannot understand why older cities such as Boston have confused street patterns. Therein lies the difference between a city laid out in advance of settlement, and the unplanned city which began as a small community and developed slowly without consideration of the relation between streets and site conditions.

THE FUNCTIONS OF CITIES

Cities may be classified not only as to site and location, but also by principal services that they provide. In general, the more services the broader will be the base of the urban economy and the more stable the city's trade and commerce. Cities whose function is highly specialized may experience great difficulty

if for any reason the single source of wealth is impaired. To select a particular example, economic activities of the city of Gary, Indiana, are directed almost wholly at production of one basic commodity—steel. If the steel mills close down for any reason the people of Gary have no other major source of income

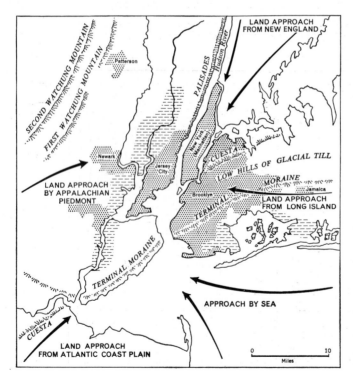

Figure 24-4 New York as a focal center for transportation routes. (After Carl O. Sauer.)

to support them for any length of time. In contrast, a city like Fort Wayne, Indiana, which has a varied list of industries, is in a more secure economic position and is less likely to experience difficulty if one of its industries is out of operation, since other local manufacturing plants will take up the slack.

Changes in functions of cities. Sometimes cities outlive the original reason for their location; for example, Bruges and Ghent in Belgium were important ports during the Middle Ages, but their harbors silted up and could no longer be used by large ships. Venice has too shallow a harbor for modern shipping and this former great seaport now earns much of its living from the tourist trade. Cities dependent on minerals and forest products are

often short-lived because of exhaustion of raw materials, unless some other industry replaces the original one; thus Saginaw and Bay City, Michigan, once famous for lumber mills, now make automobile parts and other machinery.

Commercial cities and trade centers. Leading functions of cities at the present time are those of the manufacturing center and commercial or trading center. Upon these two types, or a combination of the two, rests the greater part of the world's urban economic activity. A commercial city above all else must have convenience of transportation. An ideal location is on a good harbor with easy access by river or rail to a rich hinterland or tributary territory. Great commercial cities like New York (Figure 24-4) and London (Figure 24-5) are favored by locations on

Figure 24-5 Aerial view of the heart of London, showing the Houses of Parliament and Westminster Abbey in the foreground and St. Paul's Cathedral in the upper right. Many bridges are needed to maintain traffic between the right and left banks of the Thames. (Photograph used by courtesy of British Information Services.)

main world trade routes. Human activities further the growth of commercial centers; thus Hong Kong and Singapore, developed by the British from mere villages to large cities in a single century, are free ports and have become great entrepôts where goods are assembled from all parts of the world to be redistributed to other markets. If islands on which Hong Kong and Singapore are located had remained under control of the Chinese and Malays respectively, their development would have been greatly retarded. Some inland cities like Chicago and St. Louis are also of great commercial importance, although less favored than ocean ports, which profit from both domestic and foreign trade. Commercial cities employ many people in the transportation and wholesaling of goods. An example is Spokane, Washington, at the junction of rail, highway, and air transportation, where cheap hydropower is available for industry (Figure 24-6).

Transportation. The city whose major activity is related to transportation is of importance no matter where it has been located. When a transport center has several

Figure 24-6 Spokane, Washington, as a center of rail, highway, and air transportation routes.

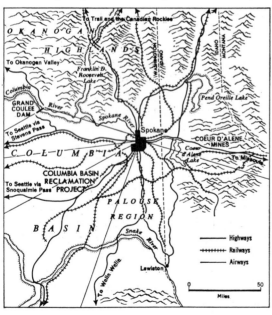

different types of carriers, its economic position is more secure than if it must rely upon river or highway alone. A growing city should be well provided with rail lines, first-class highways, river, ocean, or canal transport, and facilities for air transportation. Lack of any one of these might not necessarily handicap city growth; for example, many thriving centers have no water transportation.

Without adequate transportation, no populous center can exist. Many cities began as mere crossroads trading centers. Transfer of commodities from one form of transportation to another is a common necessity; thus there are the market towns to which farm products are hauled by wagon or truck and shipped by rail or boat to distant places. The junction of railroads, division points, and location of car-shops all provide employment and add to population of cities.

Cities develop where there is a change from one form of transportation to another, especially when bulk commodities are handled. This is known as "breaking of bulk." Thus Duluth receives wheat, flax, lumber, and iron ore by rail and then ships these products down the Great Lakes by steamer. In return, coal, automobiles, and some other manufactures are brought to Duluth for distribution inland by rail.

Intersections of railroads, highways, or waterways with similar or different forms of transportation always favor growth of cities. Natural relief features may control transportation routes and hence town locations. In Europe intersection of trade routes accounts largely for the economic importance of Berlin, Moscow, Vienna, Paris, and London, though military activities were also an important factor in the establishment and growth of all these centers. In North America, Chicago, St. Louis, Kansas City, and Montreal, Canada, offer good examples of transport centers.

Railroad cities. Railroads have accounted for the location and growth of cities in the United States and in other new countries like Canada, since railroads often preceded settlement in the central and western parts of these nations. Among natural factors involved are the ends of barriers like lakes, mountains, deserts, or arms of the sea, the ends of passes, natural crossings or junctions of routes, or any natural break in transportation en route and at terminal points (Figure 24-7). Selection of one of several possible routes for the railroad or location of a station may have determined which of several centers would develop into important cities and which would languish for want of trade. In railroad-building days, the construction town at the constantly extending end of the line enjoyed a temporary boom. Similar construction towns develop during building of dams like Hoover and Grand Coulee, of tunnels like the Metropolitan Aqueduct in southern California, and sometimes of highways and war-training centers.

Railroads themselves were built first from city to city, often to connect two waterways, and were located along previous routes of travel. Thus they helped the growth of cities already established and extended markets for factories and other producers in the area. Usually railroads were built on the easiest route available where population and freight were at hand. Sometimes a rail line must cross unproductive territory like Nevada in order to connect developed regions like the Middle West and the Pacific Coast, but no important city in this country is without railroad freight service.

Resource cities. Mining, fishing, and lumbering centers resemble each other in that they collect natural products and distribute them to distant markets; only small amounts of the products are used in the immediate vicinity. Obviously a town that exploits a natural product must have a location near a supply of it. Examples of mining towns include Butte, Johannesburg, the mining centers of Pennsylvania, and Hibbing, Minnesota. Though a mine must be near ores, a smelter or refinery may be built where conditions are more favorable than those near the mines (Figure 21-2). Fishing centers, as mentioned elsewhere, must be conveniently located with regard both to the supply of fish and to sale of the product. Lumber cen-

Figure 24-7   The core of a modern American city, Toledo, Ohio, with the Maumee River and its bridges. Note the power plant near the river, where fuel can be shipped easily by water. (Photograph, courtesy of the Ohio Development and Publicity Commission.)

ters are preferably on navigable waterways by which sawed lumber may be shipped and logs received.

Fairs and exhibits. City growth is often helped by regular market days or annual fairs and exhibitions to promote sale of goods. In many towns in Europe and Latin America, the open square usually located in front of cathedral or town hall is used as a market place. Sometimes fairs that began as a convenience for exchange of goods led to building of warehouses and factories and resulted in founding of permanent trade centers. Around the Central Plateau in France lies a peripheral row of cities where crops of the nearby lowlands were traded for livestock products of the uplands; locations of these and other ancient fairs have sometimes developed into important urban centers.

In the highlands of South America, Peruvian Indians still hold primitive markets at designated spots on certain days of the week or month. Usually a church is located there along with other buildings, but except on market days the place is nearly deserted. As the country develops industrially, these accepted places for exchange of commodities may develop into urban centers.

Educational centers. Institutions of higher education sometimes form the principal support of the community where they are located, for example, Gainesville, Florida; Urbana, Illinois; Oxford and Cambridge, England; Palo Alto, California. On the other hand, most cities of more than 100,000 people in the United States have one or more colleges and universities because the number of persons seeking education encourages establishment of institutions of higher learning.

Religious centers. Cathedrals and other religious centers attract people in numbers and sometimes form nuclei of urban centers. Occasionally cities grow or survive because they are selected as headquarters of a religious faith, which was the case at Rome, Salt Lake City, Mecca, and Benares. Some towns have grown around monasteries, like Lhasa. Certain settlements have been started by groups who wished to live together communally or who assembled because of peculiarities of religious beliefs. Summer chautauquas, camp meetings, or institutes at some lake or other pleasant location may attract visitors who affect growth of nearby towns. Religious centers, however, usually remain small, though Salt Lake City and the important Roman Catholic shrine center of Lourdes in southern France are exceptions.

Military and government centers. Military installations, as noted earlier, usually are small, but if geographic conditions favor city growth, they may lose the military aspect and become very large cities. Examples of military and naval cities include Toulon, San Diego, Norfolk, and Bremerton, Washington.

Washington, D.C., represents a city whose activities are devoted almost entirely to maintenance of government functions; to a certain extent Madrid, Rome, New Delhi, and Ottawa fall in the same category. They may have other aspects, for Rome is also a tourist, trading, and religious center. Washington was placed at the head of navigation on the Potomac River, from which George Washington anticipated canals would be built over the mountains to tributaries of the Ohio. Its site was nearly at the center of the 13 original colonies and was then close to the center of population in America. Cities selected as provincial or national capitals enjoy an advantage over towns that lack this designation since clerical and administrative work requires many employees. Usually a capital is also a social center and may be a religious center.

Generally capitals are located at convenient points near centers of population more often than in the middle of an area. The capital of the United States, if a new site were to be selected today, would no doubt lie west of the Appalachian barrier in a location less exposed to attack and more accessible to citizens of the nation. It is interesting that when a site was chosen for building storage vaults for gold, the place selected was in the state of Kentucky.

Sometimes a city like London or Paris is of such overwhelming importance to a nation that it seems inevitable for it to be the capital. On the other hand, Madrid has no advantages over other towns in interior Spain. In fact it is cold, dry, and dusty compared with Toledo, the former capital; yet after the rulers chose Madrid as the new capital, its importance was greatly enhanced. Leningrad (St. Petersburg) was the largest city as well as the capital of imperial Russia. The marshy site was selected by Peter the Great along the Neva River. It had few natural advantages. Under the Soviet regime the capital was moved to Moscow, nearer the population center in the European part of the nation, and less exposed to attack from a foreign power; Leningrad has declined in population and importance since the change was made.

In China, when the central government

was strong and vigorous, the capital was usually located at Peking (northern capital), from which nomads of Manchuria and Mongolia could be best controlled; but when the government became weak and unorganized, the capital was withdrawn to Nanking (southern capital), which was less exposed to attack. Much of the northern part of the country might be abandoned to vigorous and warlike Mongols upon occasion. The site of the Australian capital at Canberra was chosen in a healthful and picturesque basin in the interior, about midway between Sydney and Melbourne. Before Canberra was built, the location had no settlement of importance but was occupied only by a sheep ranch.

Just as Washington, D.C., is now on the eastern margin of the United States instead of near the population center, so some state capitals are in corners of their respective governments. Usually this occurs because sites were selected before the states became well settled. Thus Helena in Montana was chosen before settlement of the agricultural eastern part of that state and at a time when mining was the only important industry in the territory. Tallahassee in northern Florida was chosen when the southern part of that state was populated only by a few Indians. Salem in the northern Willamette Valley of western Oregon was decided upon when only that fertile lowland was occupied. On the other hand, cities like Indianapolis, Columbus, Springfield, and Des Moines have the advantage of location near centers of their respective states—a factor that was certainly taken into consideration in selection of their sites. Even the choice of a town as a county seat brings employment, visitors, and growth of business and population to the community.

Recreational and health centers. Recreational and health resorts normally do not attain large size and in most cases cannot be regarded as cities. To succeed as a resort, location must be attractive or become fashionable; it must be readily accessible to people who can afford the recreation they desire. Atlantic City, New Jersey, has a fine sandy beach and pleasant summer weather; of equal importance, it can be reached with ease by rail and highway from New York, Philadelphia, and scores of other large cities. Ostend, Belgium; Brighton, England; and Nice and Biarritz in France represent examples of beach resorts in Europe, easily reached from nearby great cities. In hot countries "summer capitals" are often established in cooler highlands, like Darjeeling for Calcutta and Simla for Delhi.

Although resorts like those of southern Florida (Figure 24-8) and southern California have special climatic attractions, they had to become accessible in order to be used extensively. The Hawaiian Islands and Bermuda are reached readily by steamship and air and are good examples of oceanic resorts. In Hawaii, the "third" industry, or tourist trade, has greatly helped growth of the city of Honolulu (Figure 24-9).

Some centers, like Rome, Venice, and Naples in Italy and Athens, Greece, have capitalized on their history; thousands of visitors and tourists come to see old buildings and monuments of past greatness.

In recent years, winter sports have become popular; St. Moritz in Switzerland; Lake Placid, New York; Sun Valley, Idaho; and other places have flourished as a result. Pleasure resorts vary in population with the season of the year, since both pleasure seekers and those who serve them are mostly seasonal residents.

Reputations as health resorts may be the principal support of a town. It may have sunshine and clear air, as at Colorado Springs, Albuquerque, Tucson, or Phoenix. In other cases, hot mineral springs are the attraction for people who bathe in or drink the water. Familiar examples include Hot Springs, Arkansas; French Lick, Indiana; and Saratoga Springs, New York; these resorts cater to pleasure seekers as well as health seekers.

Residential centers. Some communities serve almost entirely as places of residence and lack commerce or manufactures. These sometimes have the character of recreation centers. In this country, Pasadena, California, and suburban areas surrounding New York represent the type. Often there is close relationship between the residential community and recreational facilities, for it is difficult to say whether Miami, Florida, is a recreational center or a residential city. A community may be so completely devoted to use as a residential center that the people who live there regard it as a "dormitory town" in which they live, in some cases commuting great distance to their work. Almost every large American city has numbers of these suburban dormitory towns on its outskirts; this is also true of many European and some Asiatic cities.

Industrial cities. A combination of natural and human factors makes cities important for manufactures. When a well-managed factory located near markets and sources of raw materials succeeds it provides employment and thereby aids growth of the city. In con-

trast, a factory established in defiance of geographic principles, at some distance from markets and using materials from distant regions is handicapped from the start and will probably fail. Competition is tremendously keen in industry, and the human factor of management is very important. Efficient concerns tend to eliminate or absorb many rivals. Of hundreds of concerns that once made automobiles, a half-dozen now manufacture the great majority used in this country. Once there were dozens of breakfast-food factories at Battle Creek but now only two large firms handle the business.

Some factory towns were deliberately selected because they offer natural advantages for certain industries. Thus Birmingham in Alabama has self-fluxing iron ore and nearby coal; it was chosen for the location of blast furnaces and steel mills. A steel mill requires a

large space for the plant and water. A preferred location is a site near a large city but on cheap ground outside the city limits. Thus Pittsburgh (Figure 24-10) is surrounded by many minor iron-smelting and manufacturing centers: McKees Rocks, Carnegie, McKeesport, Braddock, Homestead, and Duquesne. When a new steel plant was needed near Chicago, a site at Gary among the Indiana sand dunes was selected, where ore brought down the Great Lakes met coal at the lakeside.

As mentioned before, many manufacturing centers became large cities without much geographic reason: by accident an inventor happened to live in a town and he began a small industry which flourished; luck and good management, in other cases, developed small enterprises into an industry. Among examples of this type are manufacture of automobiles at Detroit, tires and other rubber goods at Ak-ron, optical goods at Southbridge, Massachusetts, cameras at Rochester, washing machines at Newton, Iowa, and cash registers at Dayton.

The presence of coal, oil, gas, or water power to furnish energy for industries is always an attraction to manufacturers and therefore greatly helps city growth. Without a source of power at a reasonable price, large-scale competitive manufacturing is obviously impossible. Only in industries where skill is more important than raw material and power, like optical goods, watches, or scientific instruments made in Switzerland, is this factor unimportant.

Forces affecting City Growth. Small settlements, towns, and villages often thrive for a time and then, if conditions for further growth become unfavorable, they stagnate,

Figure 24-8 Miami, Florida, with the Miami River in the foreground, the downtown business and hotel section in the middle distance, and Biscayne Bay in the background. This city owes its existence largely to the demand for tourist accommodations and capitalizes on its fine winter weather. Popular resort hotels of Miami Beach appear near the sky line on an offshore sand bar that is reached from the mainland by causeways. (Photograph, courtesy of the City of Miami News Bureau.)

Figure 24-9 The harbor of Honolulu developed largely because of its central location in the Pacific, where it serves as exporting point for Hawaiian agricultural products and as a stopping place for transpacific vessels. Note assemblage of warehouses and wharves. Note also that this port, unlike most others, has no large space devoted to rail lines. (Photograph used by permission of the Hawaii Visitors Bureau.)

decline, and even disappear. One may think of these communities as passing through a life cycle: infancy, youth, maturity, and old age. Usually when a city attains maturity, it remains in existence for a long time if it is free from internal stress and external pressures. Many large cities of the past, such as Carthage, have disappeared; cities may dwindle as the result of bitter wars, decline in food supplies, or decrease in trade.

Many factors affect the growth of cities. Some (centrifugal forces) originate within the city itself. A city may grow or decline depending upon its management or mismanagement by residents and officials. A city that lacks adequate space to meet the needs of large industries finds it difficult to attract new enter-

prises. Unless its officials take steps to correct this undesirable condition the city may suffer seriously from ill effects of poor government or lack of foresight. Sudden political disturbances within a city sometimes lead to decline. Transportation bottlenecks, inadequate dock space, insufficient water supply, obsolete factory structures, or inability to attract skilled labor are among the long list of misfortunes that may lead to collapse of the urban economy. These and other shortcomings must be corrected by city and business planners if the city continues to progress.

In recreation centers, destruction of recreation facilities, decay or change of transportation services, or the intrusion of unwanted industries may bring sharp decline in popularity of the resort. This type of deterioration occurred at Venice, California, when a petrolem field was tapped beneath the shore. In a very short time, land use within the community changed from that of a popular recreational center to an oil-well town. Once such changes occur, it is difficult to restore those aspects of recreation that led to establishment of the original settlement.

The modern city is subject to many influences originating outside the city itself, in its immediate surroundings or from neighboring cities. These forces operating from outside the metropolitan area (centripetal forces) include the amount and type of trade carried on with distant places, impact of military and political forces, and development of transportation facilities connecting the city with distant points. For example, a city whose site is on low ground near a large river may experience great flood damage. The city must seek to protect itself against such disaster. Over a long period, external forces may have greater effect on residents of a city than conditions operating entirely within its limits. In war, very large areas of cities may be entirely destroyed as a result of hostilities, as in Cologne and Hamburg. Yet in general, conditions within the city are more likely to have a direct effect upon urban residents than those which originate at a distance.

Figure 24-10 *Confluence of the Allegheny (at left) and Monongahela (at right) Rivers, forming the Ohio River (at bottom of picture). Set in the small space between the rivers is the downtown section of the city of Pittsburgh, connected with its suburbs by many bridges. (Photograph by Newman-Schmidt Studios, courtesy of the Pittsburgh Convention Bureau.)*

Central Business District. The presence in any community of a node that serves as the principal center of activity has already been noted. Almost without exception communities, whether small or large, have well-defined central business districts which serve as the main retail shopping centers. Here, land values tend to be higher than in other sections, traffic is more congested, and the principal use of land is for commercial purposes. As the city grows, the central business district may become multistoried; and the retail core becomes conspicuously marked by the presence of these higher buildings. In certain large cities, buildings of the central core are sometimes so distinctive in form that the skyline or profile of the city is easily identified in silhouette. The Eiffel Tower of Paris, St. Paul's Cathedral in London, the Empire State Building in New York, the Terminal Tower in Cleveland, and the Los Angeles City Hall all represent distinctive landmarks in their respective cities, though the largest and tallest structures are not always found in the heart of the business center.

In some cities the central business district remains essentially in the same location in which it originally developed, but in most cities business tends to migrate to new locations as older structures become obsolete. The central business district of New York, for exam-

ple, started at a point far south on lower Manhattan Island; in the course of decades, it has moved northward to its present location just south of Central Park. The older core has been converted to a financial center and to manufacturing and wholesaling activities, among others. In general, the older the city, the greater the distance the central business district migrates from its original location.

Other Functional Zones. Most cities when mapped show a general tendency toward zoning of functions. Not far from the central business district in American cities there is usually an unattractive, run-down· section devoted to wholesale trade, or perhaps to automobile sales and service. Other neighboring districts may engage in light manufacturing or may have most activities concerned with transportation. Part of a city may have developed as a cultural center within which are located leading educational institutions, churches, art galleries, and museums. Generally property values are lower in these sections than in the central business district. It should also be noted that all these parts of the city usually lack permanent residents. Housing is generally in the form of centrally located hotels and apartment houses, but the central business district and the wholesale and manufacturing areas of the modern city tend to be almost deserted at night or on holidays and Sundays.

Residential Areas.   Beyond the limits of the "downtown" or "uptown" section of a city lie those areas occupied by apartments or private dwellings. Not far from the commercial district there is often a zone of large houses undergoing conversion for uses other than residence. Once those were first-class high-priced residence sections, but since taste in houses changes quickly, mansions may be outdated within a short time. Today they are often converted to multiple dwellings, showrooms, medical offices, or similar uses. If land values are increasing in the neighborhood and houses are totally unsuited for present use, buildings may be razed and sites turned into automobile parking space if the area is within reach of the retail core. It should be noted that this is a typical American pattern and is not found in foreign cities to the same degree.

At greater distances from the central business district are lower-class and middle-class residence zones, often compactly arranged and with the land area utilized to the greatest possible extent. In large cities, this condition results in multiple-storied structures or large blocks of flats and apartments. In this part of the city the greatest numbers of people live; to reach their work, they need rapid, low-priced transportation. This may involve construction of widened highways or establishment of numerous bus or rail lines or similar transportation facilities.

At some distance from the central business district, most cities have broad zones of expensive residential property, landscaped with parks and trees, and displaying large houses set in broad lawns. Crowding is not common in these sections; in order to live here, considerable income is needed to meet added costs of transportation and other expenses attendant upon residence in a wealthy community. These residence districts are usually located on outer fringes of the city, distant from noise, smoke, odors, and congestion. Automobiles made possible the extensions of such residential areas.

Suburban Development.   Near the outermost city limits, population density is less than in the congested central areas. Here are the city suburbs; they may range from streets lined by small cheaply constructed houses to the expensive and attractive residences of the wealthy. Once outside city limits, usually minimum legal regulations govern house construction. When this is the case, city suburbs often start as outlying slum districts, particularly noticeable if unfavorable conditions prevail in the immediate neighborhood, such as the presence of railway lines or river bottomlands that are subject to flood.

At first glance it would seem that living might be cheaper in outlying suburbs, since those are not subjected to city taxes. Added costs of transportation to work in the city center may offset other economies. The suburban dweller, if he does not live too near a factory or railway area, does have one marked advantage: he is in a location to enjoy more space, cleaner air, and more sunlight than those who live near the central business district.

Rapid growth of suburbs near large cities stems from modern methods of transportation at the disposal of all classes of people, from those who use the bus daily to those to operate their own three-car garages.

City Zoning.   In modern times, the functional use to which different zones in a city have been put has led to increased demand for regulation of urban growth and for restricting land use within certain sections. It is generally recognized that it is undesirable to establish certain industries too near residential districts. Some industries, such as tanneries, paper manufacture, metalworking, chemical plants, are so objectionable that they are banned in city areas. Some residence sections are restricted in regard to size of house, portion of lot that may be built upon, and even style of architecture.

The need to control growth and development of urban centers has thus led to legislation establishing city zoning and zoning commissions, whose rulings may be supported by the courts. Regulation is the objective of city planning, which attempts to improve local living conditions, maintain property values, and keep the appearance of parts of the city as attractive as possible. It seeks to eliminate some of the decay that affects older parts of the city and to retard the rate of obsolescence of structures. Those who undertake city planning should thoroughly understand local conditions; a satisfactory city plan must necessarily take account of important phases of local geography.

Urban decentralization. Improvements of city transportation, as already noted, account for expansion of modern cities, in many cases far beyond the actual city limits. This dispersal of city population appears in the form of distant suburbs; sometimes settlements thus established are in no way different from the nucleus of the original settlement. That is, the central node, residence sections of varying quality, and the like, repeat the general pattern of the original city, but on smaller scale. If suburbs are primarily residential, then manufacturing districts will be absent. On the other hand, if suburbs are industrial in character, then the residence function will be subordinated to industry. In either case, decentralization is marked. Sometimes it occurs in an orderly and well-planned fashion, with autonomous suburbs, or these may merge with the original city. At other times decentralization is unplanned and haphazard, with many small real estate developments and communities springing up without adequate attention to their relations with the main urban center. This often results in complicated tax structures, confused zoning regulations, and inadequate transportation facilities, among other undesirable conditions. Outlying suburbs may have inadequate fire and police protection and may be unable to support schools as good as those of the larger and more wealthy city.

When decentralization has advanced so that many people live on the outskirts of the city, local business districts—often the "shopping center"—grow to meet demands for retail trade, making it unnecessary for suburban dwellers to make the long trip into the central business district. These centers frequently include branch department stores and branch banks as well as numerous specialty shops and members of nationwide chain stores. Again, it should be emphasized that this type of growth has occurred in recent years with the aid of mass transportation. Although these conditions have been characteristic of American life for the last two decades, they are only beginning to become apparent in foreign cities. The trend, nevertheless, is strongly marked.

Urban hinterlands. Well distant from the outer city limits and beyond the last of the suburbs live many people who look to the city as the principal supplier of needs and for other contacts. This large surrounding zone, tributary to the city, is called the *hinterland;* the prosperity of the city depends largely upon the geographic characteristics of its hinterland. Some hinterlands extend for several hundred miles in all directions, joined to the city by networks of rail, highway, and air lines which take goods into the city for sale, processing, and shipment, and in turn distribute the products of the city. A highly productive hinterland implies the presence of supplies of raw material, an excellent system of transport, and food in quantity to meet the principal needs of the city. The hinterland should also have a population needing manufactured goods that city factories produce. These conditions cannot be met unless the hinterland is located in a climate suitable for food production, with soils of good quality and relief of the land that encourages rather than impedes human contacts. Interaction of the city and its hinterland is constant; neither will move toward full development without support from the other.

Hinterlands of cities vary greatly in extent, and sometimes overlap. New Orleans, for example, commands trade and traffic as far north as Cairo, at the confluence of the Ohio and Mississippi Rivers; north of that point, freight and passengers look to Chicago as their principal urban center. Los Angeles and San Francisco compete for the rich hinterland area of the San Joaquin Valley. Ports of northwestern Europe—especially Amsterdam and

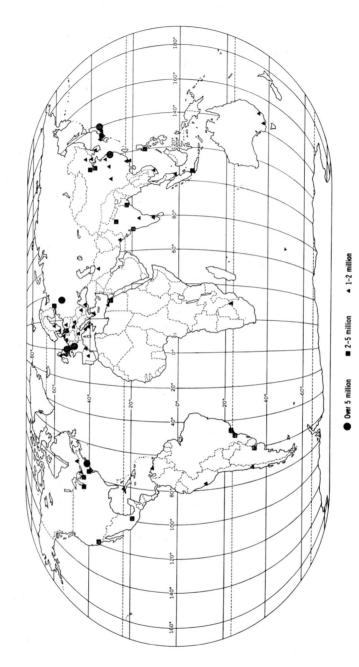

● Over 5 million   ■ 2–5 million   ▲ 1–2 million

Figure 24-11 Distribution of cities of more than one million population, 1950–1960.

Hamburg—compete for trade and traffic moving toward the North Sea. Toledo and Cleveland, Ohio, compete for their hinterlands along the southern shore of Lake Erie, whereas Chicago and Toledo compete for shipments of goods from northern Indiana and northwestern Ohio.

The "Million" Cities. As the world's population increases, people live together in larger numbers, a tendency reflected in the growing numbers of cities with 1 million or more inhabitants. Twenty-five years ago cities of this population were relatively few. Today the world has 24 cities of more than 2 million people; of these, 6 have more than 5 million residents (Figure 24-11).

Analysis of the distribution of these "million cities" shows that largest numbers are on the continent of Asia: Peking, Shanghai, Tientsin, Bombay, Calcutta, New Delhi, Jakarta, Osaka, Tokyo, and Manila each has more than 2 million people. At this level, North America and Europe have five each; the former with New York, Chicago, Los Angeles, Philadelphia, and Mexico City, the latter with London, Moscow, Paris, Berlin, and Leningrad. South America has 3 cities of over 2 million: Buenos Aires, Rio de Janeiro, and São Paulo. Africa has a single city, Cairo, of over 2 million, and Australia has none. The map of the world (Figure 24-11) shows wide expanses of territory within which there are no cities with a million inhabitants. These spaces include all of central Asia, most of the East Indies and Australia, all of Africa, the interior of South America, and western and northern North America.

Of cities numbering between 1 and 2 million, Asia and Europe each has seventeen; North America has four, South America three, and Africa and Australia two of this size. All

but nine of the "million cities" are located in the Northern Hemisphere, a fact which stresses urban growth in relation to increase of population and trade in this part of the world. Smaller numbers of large cities south of the equator reflect the smaller extent of continental masses in that hemisphere as well as the late date of population expansion compared with that on continents like Asia and Europe.

Of the world's large cities, thirty-two, or not quite half the total, are capitals of their respective countries; certainly their leading position as government centers has been a most important factor contributing to their size. The sites of thirty-one of the "million cities" are in locations where ocean transportation is available, either in the form of a natural harbor, or as in the case of Los Angeles, by means of the construction of an artificial port. Three of the cities are lake ports, and in eight a certain amount of river-borne traffic is possible. Twenty-seven cities occupy interior locations where there is little or no transportation by water. Only three of the largest cities in tropical latitudes—Mexico City, Caracas, and Lima—are situated at altitudes sufficiently high to lift them above the tropical surroundings that their latitude would otherwise provide. Another, New Delhi, has a long dry season to make life more bearable. Eleven tropical cities, however, are seaports, an indication of increasing commerce between tropical and middle latitudes. Some of the world's largest cities occupy positions that would seem at first glance to preclude growth of over a million. These include Johannesburg, Madrid, Lima, Chungking, Leningrad, Tehran, and Karachi. In some cases, the presence of valuable minerals (Johannesburg), newly established capitals (Karachi), ancient capitals (Lima and Leningrad), and central location (Madrid) help to explain the great increase in urban population.

SUMMARY

With increase of the world population, people began to dwell in compact units. Settlement gathered, among other reasons, to serve as trading centers, transport centers, and for protection. From these early nuclei came beginnings of modern town and city life. In spite of the current importance of cities more than half the world's people live in rural environments or small villages. Millions never visit a city at any time during their lives, although their existence may be closely tied to towns. This is particularly true outside the United States.

Cities occupy many different kinds of sites: on rivers, seacoasts, lake shores, or in mountains. Some sites are related to such natural features as mountain passes, stream confluences, or heads of deltas. City functions may number one or a combination of the following: residential, industrial, military, recreational, educational, governmental, and commercial. Functions tend to change as cities grow; Pittsburgh, originally a military and fur-trading establishment at a river confluence, is now an industrial city. Its site, however, remains unchanged. Most cities, when mapped, may be classified according to their characteristic street patterns.

Within each city, one generally finds such functional zones as the wholesale, retail, residential, and recreational districts, among others. Older sections may have deteriorated or changed character until they no longer serve in their original capacity; residents then seek newer sections that are more desirable for their purposes. Thus one sees two changes: a "blighted zone" in the old section, and decentralization of activities leading to suburban development. When carried to excess, either or both of these changes are detrimental to the city organism. It is evident that the city as a place of human residence and activity is undergoing constant change in appearance, function, and growth; it is dynamic to a high degree.

Outline
Rural settlement
    Dispersed, hamlets
Settlement sites
    Transportation: river, land
    Services
    Markets
    Power
    Patterns
The city
    Site: advantages, handicaps
    Pattern
    Functions and types of centers
    Forces affecting growth
    Central business district
    Other zones and suburbs
    City zoning and hinterlands
The "million" cities

QUESTIONS

1. Select one of the following commercial cities, and analyze its advantages and disadvantages as a trading center, with special reference to its most important exports and imports: San Francisco, Houston, Amsterdam, Philadelphia, Marseille, Buenos Aires, Melbourne, Hong Kong, Montreal, Chicago.

2. Name a city that is noted for each of the following:
A resort
A city important for mining
A city having a favorable climate
A city handicapped by an unfavorable climate
A city commanding the entrance to a pass
A city that serves as a transportation center
A port city
A river port
A canal city
A city that handles and mills wheat products
A city noted for fruit marketing

A city on a coastal plain
A city on an alluvial piedmont
A city on a glaciated plain
A delta city
A plateau city
A city situated in a tropical highland environment
A city located at a roadstead anchorage
A city whose trade is handicapped by a shallow harbor
A city handicapped by a frozen harbor
A city having an artificial harbor
A city located on a fiord
A city on an estuary
A city at the head of ocean navigation
A city important for power
A naval base
A city at a waterfall

3. What is the metropolitan area nearest your community? What type of goods do you buy there? Why? What services does that city provide for you?

4. Select several communities near your home and determine what local geographical conditions gave rise to the formation of settlements at those particular places.

5. What is the street pattern of the town or city in which you live, or one nearest your home? Is it related to conditions of local land relief? How? How might street patterns be improved?

6. Does your community show evidences of town planning in advance of actual settlement? In what way?

7. Is there legal provision for zoning of activities in your community? How does this affect the growth of the community?

8. What resource of importance has led to the growth of each of these cities: Dallas, Winnipeg, Grand Rapids, Hankow, Joplin, Minneapolis, Duluth, Baku, Düsseldorf.

SELECTED REFERENCES

Ahlmann, Hans W.: "The Geographical Study of Settlements: Examples from Italy, Germany, Denmark, and Norway," *Geographical Review,* 18:93–128, January, 1928.

Beals, Ralph L.: "The Village in an Industrial World," *Scientific Monthly,* 77(2), August, 1953.

Brush, John E., and Howard E. Bracey: "Rural Service Centers in Southwestern Wisconsin and Southern England," *Geographical Review,* 45:559–569, October, 1955.

Colby, C. C.: "Centrifugal and Centripetal Forces in Urban Geography," *Annals of the Association of American Geographers,* 23:1–20, 1933.

Dickinson, Robert E.: *City Region and Regionalism,* Oxford University Press, New York, 1947.

Hallenbeck, Wilbur C.: *American Urban Communities,* Harper & Brothers, New York, 1951.

Harris, Chauncy D.: "A Functional Classification of Cities in the United States," *Geographical Review,* 33:86–99, January, 1943.

———, and Edward L. Ullman: "The Nature of Cities," *Annals of the American Academy of Political and Social Science,* 242:7–17, November, 1945.

Hart, John F.: "Functions and Occupational Structures of Cities of the American South," *Annals of the Association of American Geographers,* 45:269–286, September, 1955.

Hartman, George W.: "The Central Business District: A Study in Urban Geography," *Eco-*nomic Geography, 26:237–244, October, 1950.

Morton, W. L.: "The Significance of Site in the Settlement of the American and Canadian West," *Agricultural History,* 25:97–104, July, 1951.

Mumford, Lewis: *The Culture of Cities,* Harcourt, Brace and Company, Inc., New York, 1938.

Murphey, Rhoads: "The City as Center of Change: Western Europe and China," *Annals of the Association of American Geographers,* 44:349–362, December, 1954.

Murphy, Raymond E., and J. E. Vance: "A Comparative Study of Nine Central Business Districts," *Economic Geography,* 30:301–336, October, 1954.

———, ———, and Bart J. Epstein: "Internal Structure of the CBD (Central Business District)," *Economic Geography,* 31:21–46, January, 1955.

Nelson, Howard J.: "A Service Classification of American Cities," *Economic Geography,* 31:189–210, July, 1955.

Nelson, Lowry: *The Mormon Village,* University of Utah Press, Salt Lake City, 1952.

Rostlund, Erhard: "Geographic Setting of San Francisco," *Journal of Geography,* 54:441–448, December, 1955.

Smailes, Arthur F.: *The Geography of Towns,* Longmans, Green & Co., Inc., New York, 1954.

Taylor, Griffith: *Urban Geography: A Study of Site, Evolution, Patterns, and Classification in Villages, Towns, and Cities,* E. P. Dutton & Co., Inc. New York, 1949.

Vance, Rupert B.: *The Urban South,* University of North Carolina, Chapel Hill, 1955.

National Research Council—Rural Settlement Patterns in the United States as Illustrated on One Hundred Topographic Quadrangle maps. National Research Council, Division of Earth Sciences, Committee to Select Topographic Quadrangles Illustrating Cultural Geography, Washington, D.C., 1956.

25. Geography and Nations

TODAY no nation can be isolated from contacts with others: for this reason citizens should become thoroughly familiar with those aspects of political geography that affect their daily activities. Boundary disputes between neighboring nations may provoke each to tax itself heavily to support a large standing army. A country whose natural resources do not include vital materials such as petroleum may seek to get those materials by trade or by aggression and war. In either case, political geography is an important factor, for out of these clashes and needs come international alliances, tariffs and customs regulations, or treaties concerning territorial rights in the waters of the sea.

Most students learn the basic facts of political geography by study of the political map, upon which locations, boundaries, and principal cities of states and nations are shown. Political maps, however, should portray political changes that constantly take place in most parts of the inhabited world. Many people regard the world political map with which they are familiar as inviolable. In this notion they are supported by national interest which seeks to keep traditional boundaries intact as against the aspirations of foreigners outside.

BOUNDARIES

Political boundaries of all kinds—national, state, province, county, or city as the case may be—represent the confines within which people recognize certain bonds and within which they have a community of interest. The limits of a nation, for example, might well enclose a group of people who speak the same language, observe the same laws and customs, approve the same form of government, and prefer the same religious beliefs. People may join together for mutual defense against warlike neighbors and finally evolve into a nation. Any number of bonds might serve to unite people into a group sufficiently strong to form a nation. The land thus occupied may then be defined by boundaries that show the area under sovereignty. Even primitive people whose government is entirely local and whose territory is small recognize boundaries that may never appear on maps. Thus, nomadic herders recognize tribal grazing grounds and even hunting or primitive farming peoples like the American Indians called certain fairly well-defined areas theirs. Boundaries, therefore, must be regarded as significant in the field of geographic studies.

There are many types of boundaries. Some national boundaries are located along seacoasts or in the center of lakes or streams. Others appear on the map as mathematical lines or follow devious turnings of mountain divides. Some boundaries are ascertained with surveyors' instruments and marked by monuments; others may be wide swaths cut through dense forests. Still others are established and defended by means of fortifications, of which the Great Wall of China is a notable example. And some national boundaries are so poorly marked that it is possible to cross them without being aware of it.

Some geographers contend that political boundaries are not lines but zones of transition separating major differences among people—race, language, culture, ideology, and the like. A "racial" or, better, a cultural boundary is suggested by the line that separates Burma from India, whose cultures are quite different. A "language" boundary is indicated by the French-Spanish border. These boundaries are seldom clear-cut, however. A "cultural" boundary follows the Mexican–United States border, yet the zone of change is greatly blurred, with strong Mexican cultural elements located far north of the border in Arizona, New Mexico, and Texas.

Many political boundaries represent conditions of great stability; they have not changed in position for long periods of time. But rare indeed is the nation whose boundaries are so well fixed that no neighbor can challenge them. Stable boundaries represent peaceful relations between nations. Unstable boundaries represent hostile clashes of ambition; effort to change or to preserve them may threaten or endanger world peace.

Some types of boundaries reflect the course of history, as the eastern boundary of Alaska represents the penetration of Russians in that direction on the North American continent. In South America, the limits of Brazil mark roughly that part of the continent occupied by the Portuguese. Many national boundaries represent cultural or language differences; others are fixed by frontiers of military conquest. In Africa, economic invasion by and political rivalries among European nations in the closing years of the nineteenth century divided the continent into a patchwork of political units with a distinctive boundary pattern of straight lines that disregarded river drainage basins, climatic regions, natural relief features, tribal land claims, areas occupied by different races and similarities of land usage.

Types of Boundaries. Customarily, boundaries are called *natural* when special conditions of relief, such as mountain ranges, coincide with political boundaries, and this practice has been followed in this volume. In contrast, a mathematical boundary like that between the United States and Canada west of the Great Lakes is referred to as *artificial*. Natural boundaries are of many types other than those associated with mountains. Some useful landforms that demarcate boundaries include the ocean shore or an arbitrary boundary at a stated distance offshore, straits, the river or lake shore boundary, the navigable channel (distinct from the river shore), tidal markings, and water divides or drainage basins. Less well-defined boundaries may be expressed in terms of deserts, valley floors or bottoms, or swamps.

Determining locations of boundaries often is troublesome even when the natural feature involved seems well marked and conspicuous. The feature in question must first be defined and then surveyed in accordance with the legal definition of the boundary. Sometimes it is almost impossible to obtain a satisfactory legal definition; for example, a boundary located in relation to tides might be defined as mean high tide, mean low tide, mean tide, the highest points reached by tidal action, or other interpretations of the phrase.

As examples two main types of *natural* boundaries—ocean shores and mountains—will be considered in some detail, and the *artificial,* or mathematical, boundary will also be discussed.

Ocean boundaries.   Up to the present time, one of the most satisfactory types of national boundaries is represented by use of ocean shores. As long as principal contacts between nations are maintained by sea, the shore provides a degree of isolation that strengthens national defense, particularly along rugged coasts. The type of shore sometimes affects the development of a nation. The irregular ria coast of Dalmatia provides Yugoslavia with excellent anchorages, but poor access to the interior of the country inhibits invasion from the sea. Denmark's coast line is extensive, but good anchorages are few. Shores of the Soviet Union are often icebound; Alaska's seacoast is distant from world trade routes. Peru's desert coast discourages approach by sea. These and other aspects of political boundaries based upon the shore play a large part in the way in which "maritime" nations participate in world affairs.

Access to the sea, however, is not necessarily essential to successful development of a nation. An isolated position in the heart of a continent may lead to a degree of political unity in nations like Switzerland, Bolivia, Austria, and Hungary. Nevertheless for strength and stability, a major political power should have adequate shores from which its people can maintain contacts with other nations. Some political units have no boundaries other than seacoasts; these include New Zealand, Australia, and Japan. These boundaries affect the national characteristics and activities of the nations and their people. Isolation by sea, experienced by Hawaii, Corsica, Sicily, Jamaica, or Newfoundland, provides smaller political units with a distinctive character of their own even though they are dependencies of larger governments.

Mountain boundaries.   In a few parts of the world, political boundaries follow mountain crests, as in the case of Chile and Argentina or Norway and Sweden, but boundaries of this type are relatively rare. Generally, they tend to be stable; and since they traverse no densely populated areas, seldom contain great mineral wealth, and can be defended with comparative ease, they are not often disturbed. Furthermore, any differences that may arise over such boundaries are usually compromised. Chile and Argentina seem to have reconciled their claims along their mountain boundary. France and Spain have a joint working agreement for Andorra, and Italy and Switzerland have no serious boundary arguments. That is not to say that knotty problems do not exist, for the South Tirol question and several others remain unsettled after years of dispute. Certainly it should not be inferred that mountain boundaries are necessarily the most satisfactory—on the contrary, they prevent easy intercourse and understanding between nations, for mountains are barriers to land travel. Furthermore, mountain boundaries are difficult to patrol, hence smuggling, and consequent ill-feeling, may develop along these borders.

Mathematical boundaries.   Mathematical boundaries may be straight lines that follow meridians or parallels of latitude, like the greater part of the United States–Canada boundary. They may follow curved lines, similar to the southeastern boundary of Pennsylvania, which is plotted on the arc of a circle. Even when these boundaries are defined legally, they are not always surveyed at once; for many years the southern boundary of Canada remained unsurveyed. Unfortunately, a mathematical boundary too often separates interdependent geographical units or violates geographical conditions in other ways. Not far south of San Diego, the United States–Mexican boundary along the straight line eastward to the Colorado River neatly separates San Diego from Lower California and parts of Sonora—territory that would contribute raw materials and commerce to the port did it not lie within foreign territory.

Boundary Difficulties.   Many political boundaries follow courses of rivers, but river channels or shores may change suddenly during flood time. One of the most difficult river boundaries divides the United States and Mexico along the course of the lower Rio Grande. The meandering condition of this stream and rapid deposition of silt in the river channel prevent a satisfactory physical basis for determination of the boundary. In the last two decades the channel has been straightened and the river's course shortened by cutting through the necks of meanders. Most of the cost of the operations has been borne by the United States, since this country profits most by the river improvements. A boundary of this type often causes trouble, separating valuable mineral deposits like an oil field or dividing regions of dense population. The problems become more acute when such a boundary line divides a city, although in many countries this phenomenon rarely occurs. More frequently, boundary cities at the national borders develop as twin cities on either side of the demarcation, providing urban accommodations for tourists, customs employees, importers, or transportation workers. "Pairs" of boundary cities include El Paso and Juárez, Detroit and Windsor, Calexico and Mexicali, and Niagara Falls in New York and in Ontario.

In many parts of the world, international boundaries traverse open plains upon which there are no marked physical features by which location of the boundary line may be readily established. Then it may be necessary to survey the boundary with care, and possibly provide fortifications if the boundary location

is in dispute. On the other hand some plains, like those in Belgium where marked language differences separate the Walloons and Flemings, lack important political boundaries.

Local Boundaries.   Although international boundaries attract most attention, from the standpoint of total effect on human activity local governmental boundaries are more important. The city, county, parish, state, or province boundary largely determines whether city governments will provide conveniences or whether a given area will remain essentially rural. In this country, local boundaries tend to follow mathematical patterns, particularly in the Middle West and the Far West; but in Japan, Norway, Switzerland, and other parts of the world there is a greater tendency to rely on natural features, property lines, or historical boundaries in determining limits of secondary political units.

Boundaries are often insufficiently flexible to permit change as population increases; thus growth of urban centers can eclipse the original county in which they were located, as at San Francisco and New York. In these instances county boundaries have become meaningless, and city and county governments have been merged. Both primary and secondary boundaries should be so planned that they will be adaptable to changes in the geography, population, sociology, and economics of a given region. Otherwise they tend to become restrictive features of the cultural environment and thus create unending dispute.

State boundaries in this nation have been the cause of numerous legal arguments which have been taken to the Supreme Court from time to time. Texas and Oklahoma have had difficulty determining the position of their boundary along the Red River, important because of finding of oil deposits on the floodplain. Pennsylvania and Maryland have had a boundary dispute. Louisiana and Mississippi have disagreed over De Soto Island near Vicksburg (Figure 13-2). Wisconsin and Michigan have brought a boundary case to court, and North Carolina's southern boundary has been challenged.

Boundary Disputes. It would be expected that bitter boundary disputes might develop between nations of very dense population, but even in South America, with its relatively small numbers of people, political arguments over boundary lines have been numerous. Argentina and Bolivia have argued over possession of the Puna de Atacama; Argentina and Uruguay have disagreed over ownership of a small island near the mouth of the Rio Uruguay. Bolivia and Paraguay went to war over the Chaco. Chile struggled with Peru and Bolivia over desert lands of Antofagasta, Tacna, and Arica, provinces taken in the War of the Pacific in 1871. Ecuador, Colombia, and Peru disagreed over control of the Leticia district. If this list seems formidable, it should be recalled that arbitration has settled about twenty other South American boundary problems of major importance with some degree of satisfaction.

European political boundary disputes are extremely involved and frequently are stated as important precipitating causes of war. Among significant problems is the insistence of Eire that she control Northern Ireland (Ulster) and erase the boundary that now separates the northern counties from southern Ireland. Italy tried to acquire Corsica, Nice, and Dalmatia. Denmark has a claim on Schleswig. Bulgaria would like to annex the upper Vardar Valley. German claims to Alsace and Lorraine, Yugoslavia's desire for Trieste, and Bulgaria's demand for western Thrace and southern Dobruja have been upheld by some because of language, history, or trade relations. Boundaries of Poland, Romania, Finland, Czechoslovakia, Greece, and other European states have been in a highly fluid—almost volatile—condition for decades or centuries. In fact most of Central Europe's "shatter belt" boundaries from Finland southward to Greece have been persistently unstable, partly because misfortunes of war have forced people of different languages and clashing cultures into political units they consider alien.

The United States–Canadian Boundary. At first glance it would seem that this international boundary must be extremely unsatisfactory, interfering with transportation routes, movements of people, and normal flow of trade. In practice it has been eminently successful in function, though not without some disturbances and recriminations on both sides. As time goes on, the boundary seems to lose its few barrier functions and characteristics; it has become a monument to the mutual understanding and common interests of the two nations that border it. Many historians have called it the *unguarded* boundary.

The eastern portion between Maine and New Brunswick and the western part between British Columbia and the "Oregon country" represent compromises brought about by lengthy negotiations. Disputes of some consequence raged at various times over those portions of the boundary along the St. Croix River, the Maine–New Brunswick boundary, the Oregon boundary, the San Juan Islands, and the Alaska-Canada boundary. Many sections of the Canadian boundary run counter to relief of the land; the Okanogan-Okanagan Valley and uplands, Columbia River Basin, Rocky Mountains, Red River Valley, the Great Plains, and Lake Champlain lowland are crossed nearly at right angles by the boundary. Lines passing through such major natural features as the Great Lakes, upper St. Lawrence River, and Juan de Fuca Strait divide them respectively between the two nations.

Buffer States. One political device, the "buffer state," has been used as a method of separating two major powers. In a sense, the buffer state represents a widened boundary zone within which a small and relatively weak nation has been established in order to prevent direct contact between two powerful states. Therefore the existence of the buffer state depends upon the continued good will of those nations bordering it, since the weaker nation seldom is able to maintain a strong military organization with which to defend itself against aggression. It may even lack a common national language, as do Belgium and Switzerland. Other nations that have functioned as buffer states include the Netherlands,

Afghanistan, Burma, Poland, Romania, and Finland. At times, small boundary states, such as Luxembourg and Andorra, that occupy boundary locations may function as buffers, but often like Liechtenstein, they represent political relics, which have never been absorbed by more powerful neighbors. As a device to prevent surprise attack, the buffer state established along a critical national boundary zone seems outmoded by the speed with which modern warfare can attack.

Fortified Boundaries.   For centuries past, fortified boundaries have succeeded in preventing complete freedom of movement of military forces. Hadrian's Wall, the Roman limes, the Great Wall of China, the Maginot line, and the Siegfried line—these represent attempts to fortify boundaries, and for varying lengths of time, they have succeeded in blocking military maneuvers by land. During World War II, however, the collapse of very strongly fortified boundaries showed that they cannot be successfully defended by land forces; indeed, they have only limited value as devices used for delaying action. The concept of a national boundary serving as a fortress behind which a nation can retire and enjoy undisturbed seclusion is becoming obsolete as modern military devices and methods, combined with aerial warfare, guided missiles, and the speed of aircraft, make fortified boundaries ineffectual as military barriers.

FACTORS OF NATIONAL STRENGTH AND WEAKNESS

The Core of a Nation.   The economic heart of a nation often occupies an interior central location; sometimes, however, this "heartland" lies nearer the national boundaries. In the Soviet Union, for example, the most important activities of the nation are centered in the midst of the enormous land mass of Eurasia. In contrast, the most populated and most developed section of Brazil lies on a highland not far from the sea, and in France the heart may be said to exist near Paris and Lyon rather than on the outskirts of the country at Bordeaux, Marseille, or Nantes. Whether central or peripheral in location, these "core areas" are the real centers of any political unit, and from these cores the nations derive their greatest economic and military strength. In those countries whose economic activities are mainly related to the sea, the principal source of national wealth and strength may come from marine locations rather than an internal core. This is the case in Norway, Iceland, and to a certain extent, England. Until recently, a centrally located "heartland" provided a measure of protection against destruction of a nation's resources and people as a result of invasion from abroad, but the high speed of modern aircraft has removed most of the advantages of central location as a factor of protection in wartime.

The geography of the core of a nation, whether located far inland or near its borders, is of the utmost importance to the state. If the land is too humid, too cold, or too warm or dry for developing successful trade and manufacturing, the outlook is unfavorable for growth of a powerful nation. Such a state would be constantly hampered by insufficient fuel, food supplies, and necessary raw materials for manufactured goods, including munitions. Other relatively unfavorable conditions that deter national growth include poor harbors, areas of poor soil, inadequate amounts of farmland, and similar geographical shortcomings. To cite one example, Argentina's physical environment favors agriculture and grazing, but supplies of coal, iron, and other minerals are wholly inadequate to support her as an industrial and military power in competition with other states better endowed with geographical advantages.

The size of the "heartland" is a factor of great consequence in national development. Size alone may be a disadvantage, leading to internal transportation and communication difficulties and eventually to misunderstanding and disunity among the people. From 1850 to 1869 the United States occupied a core area of such wide extent that conflicting economies and sectional interests developed to a point which made civil war possible. Canada almost lost the province of British Columbia because of inability of the national government to maintain satisfactory contacts with west-coast citizens. Both Canada and the United States still recognize strong sectional differences and feelings, but these need no longer be considered as serious threats to national unity because both nations now have excellent facilities for communication and transportation.

Geographic features under multiple sovereignty. Conflict of national interest sometimes occurs over international control of large water or land areas, shared among many nations. A body of water like the Mediterranean Sea, joining the borders of three continents, serves large numbers of people whose interests, abilities, languages, and races are widely diversified. The Mediterranean provides a nucleus for the maritime activities of Italians, Spaniards, French, Yugoslavs, Greeks, Turks, Syrians, Egyptians, and other European, African, and Asiatic peoples. Similarly, the Caribbean Sea, Sea of Japan, and other landlocked water bodies have been shared politically by diverse peoples and nations. A large river basin such as the Danube is divided politically among Austrians, Germans, Czechoslovaks, Hungarians, Yugoslavs, Bulgarians, and Romanians as well as a multitude of minority peoples. About the Rhine may be found another river-centered group of nationalities, including the Swiss, French, Alsatians, Germans, Dutch, and Belgians. In these cases the common interest in the use of the river and its basin is less unifying in its effect than that of the inland seas.

The Soviet Union. The Union of Soviet Socialist Republics is the outstanding example of an oversize nation whose core area is almost too large to achieve national unity. Whether Russian efforts to unify the widely different languages and peoples within the borders of the state will be successful remains to be seen.

Development of a national sense of unity is accelerated by telegraph, railway, airplane, and radio. But Russia's core area, with valuable minerals, electrical power, labor supply, and other resources, is not necessarily ideal for the growth of an exceptionally strong state, for there are undeniable serious disadvantages. The country has a very long coast line, but its usefulness is handicapped by harbors that are icebound much of the year. Those facing the Pacific are far distant from the nation's heart. Those on the Baltic are not only icebound in winter but are located long distances from the open sea. Ports on the Black Sea also face the latter problem. Siberian rivers are not well adapted for transport, since they do not flow in the direction of normal east-west trade routes, become icebound each year, and are mostly tributary to remote Arctic seas. One of Russia's largest rivers, the Volga, is important in internal transport but suffers from the handicap of flowing into an enclosed sea, the Caspian.

Some geographic handicaps. Not only is large size sometimes a handicap to a nation, but occasionally internal geography is not wholly advantageous. In the United States, the Mississippi River would be more important if it flowed in the direction of our principal routes, toward either Europe or Asia. On the other hand, mere presence of an excellent waterway open to the sea—the Amazon, for example—is no guarantee that the nation using it will be greatly enriched thereby if other geographical conditions are unfavorable.

Military and Economic Strength. If, besides a well-established cultural unity, a large population and a good supply of natural resources are combined within the core area, the political strength of a nation is greatly enhanced by seemingly passive geographical conditions. This combination of circumstances leads directly to "strong" states. Though the combination is uncommon, it accounts in large part for the military and economic stability of the United States. Recent years have witnessed other nations beginning to capitalize on great wealth of core areas. Cases in point include the Soviet Union, Brazil, and probably to a greater degree in future, China. On the other hand, a political unit that lacks the necessary combination of geographical factors in sufficient force will be unable to maintain integrity of its borders. Australia, Arabia, Finland, and Norway would seem, on this basis, to be deficient in those elements upon which strong national states are built.

Applying the concept on a continental scale, the idea of a "heartland," rich in natural resources, serving as an inexhaustible storehouse upon which a nation or group of nations may draw for support, has been proposed to account for development of economically and militarily "strong" nations. Carried to an extreme, however, this policy would make a country almost wholly dependent upon its own resources. Such self-sufficiency implies a withdrawal from world affairs and a sharp decline in trade and cultural relations with other nations. In the modern world, effort to attain complete isolation would eventually bring national ruin.

Earlier in this chapter it was suggested that a nation of very great size formerly enjoyed an immunity from outside attack. For many years it was believed that an economic and military retreat to a "heartland" would provide adequate protection against enemies. A movement of this type was termed a "defense in depth," in which constant retreat toward the core drew an enemy force so far from its base of operations that problems of logistics tended to weaken the invading armies. The bitter defense of Stalingrad marked the climax of such a "defense in depth" on the part of the Russian defenders during World War II. Somewhat similar developments occurred when the seat of the Chinese government was moved to Chungking, inland from gorges on the Yangtze River, effectively if not entirely removing it from threat of capture by Japanese forces.

The Strategy of Materials. It is impractical to regard the ownership of any single resource as guarantee of a strong state, for in the constantly changing modern world the emphasis shifts rapidly from one commodity to another. Once, plenty of good timber, supplies of naval stores, and skilled labor were adequate material to build a naval defense force. In more recent times, armor plate, munitions, fuel oil, and medical supplies were essentials of warfare. In time to come, supplies of rare minerals such as uranium and extremely advanced technological processes may contribute more to success of military operations than any other national resources.

Available supply of fuels and other minerals is a highly important consideration in determining the strength or weakness of a modern nation, whether the material can be obtained from sources inside the national boundaries or whether it is obtainable from other nations. Iron ore, coal, petroleum, uranium, copper, lead, zinc, aluminum, and nitrates are among essential mineral resources for manufacturing goods at the present time, whether the completed products are to be used in peace or in war. These resources, combined with human ingenuity and human labor, represent the foundations of strong military, economic, and political organizations today. To use raw materials effectively, supplies of labor and power as well as some animal and vegetable products such as cotton, rubber, and wool should be available in sufficient quantity.

Metals and fuels. Besides the mineral resources just mentioned, important metals used in smaller quantities include tungsten, nickel, magnesium, molybdenum, tin, vanadium, manganese, chromite, and titanium. Important sources of power at the present time include coal, petroleum, natural gas, and hydroelectricity, with uranium likely to be added. Even wood is used in appreciable amounts for power. Without a reasonable supply of these resources or access to them, no nation is in a favorable position to maintain first-rank production of manufactured goods or to provide itself with material for the successful accomplishment of modern warfare.

A quick glance at our own resources indicates that the United States has adequate sup-

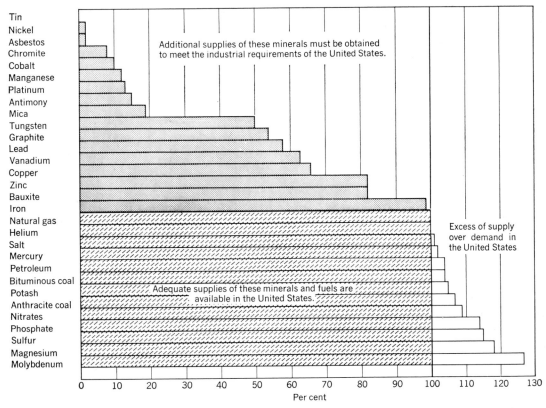

Tin
Nickel
Asbestos
Chromite
Cobalt
Manganese
Platinum
Antimony
Mica
Tungsten
Graphite
Lead
Vanadium
Copper
Zinc
Bauxite
Iron
Natural gas
Helium
Salt
Mercury
Petroleum
Bituminous coal
Potash
Anthracite coal
Nitrates
Phosphate
Sulfur
Magnesium
Molybdenum

Additional supplies of these minerals must be obtained to meet the industrial requirements of the United States.

Excess of supply over demand in the United States

Adequate supplies of these minerals and fuels are available in the United States.

0   10   20   30   40   50   60   70   80   90   100   110   120   130
Per cent

Figure 25-1   Supplies of mineral raw materials available in the United States in relation to shortages.

plies (or access thereto from its neighbors) of the above materials with the exception of manganese, chromite, and tin (Figure 25-1). Our relative strength in mineral resources is one reason we have been able to maintain a highly complex industrial organization and an effective military establishment, in contrast with nations whose resources do not include such quantities of mineral wealth.

Significant nonmineral resources. Minerals alone are not enough to form the basis of a strong military and economic structure; other resources must be at hand in order that the minerals and fuels can be utilized to the fullest extent. Foodstuffs, for example, are essential in quantity if the health of the nation is to be maintained at a high level. In part because of the climatic pattern of the world, not all nations are equally well endowed with food supplies. The United States is fortunate in that

it can provide its people with foods essential to sustain them and at a high level of health. We lead in commercial production of wheat, corn, oats, and hogs and we have moderate to adequate amounts of beet sugar, rice, cattle, sheep, and fish. Important as they seem to Americans, such foods as chocolate, coffee, bananas, and cane sugar are not essential to a well-balanced diet.

Other commodities that are essential in building a nation of great economic strength include cotton, wool, soybeans, hemp and flax, jute, rubber, and lumber. We are leaders in cotton production and soybeans. Our supplies of lumber and wool need to be augmented by imports from abroad. Handicapped by a lack of natural rubber, we have turned to the synthetic product as a reasonably satisfactory substitute. We must import all our jute from Pakistan or India.

To occupy a position of world power, a nation must have a population sufficiently large to provide a labor force capable of processing the raw materials discussed above. Further, the labor supply must be used in the most economically productive way. More than a quarter of the total numbers of employees in the United States are engaged in manufacturing; 18 per cent are employed in trade and commerce, and 16 per cent in agriculture. Compare these figures with the occupations of the Chinese people, of whom three-fourths are engaged in agriculture and only 5 per cent in trade and commerce. The numbers of Chinese in manufacturing enterprises are almost negligible. Obviously large numbers of people alone will not necessarily develop a strong economic or military nation; to attain this objective there must be the right combination of minerals and fuels, food supplies, and other resources, and all these must be utilized by a properly distributed labor force.

Efforts toward Economic and Political Self-sufficiency. Though mineral resources are basic in modern economics, they are not enough to establish strong states, as we have indicated in preceding paragraphs. The Soviet Union and China, both well endowed by nature with a wealth of minerals, have been extremely backward in economic and political development. Their large labor reserve and other resources, however, are now operating to further their industrialization at a rapid pace.

Control of raw materials should lead to economic strength; hence the scramble for colonial possessions and the sorry attempts to create empires based primarily on conquest. Almost the entire political map of the continent of Africa bears witness to the late nineteenth-century scramble for control of raw materials, including supplies of cheap labor. A nation that lacks essential raw materials can maintain a stable economy without possession of a colonial empire, as Sweden has successfully shown for many years; but it is almost impossible for that nation to have an aggressive military organization. Political integrity can be maintained for centuries, even if both raw materials and internal unity of culture are lacking, as Switzerland effectively demonstrates.

Deficiency of essential raw materials may be overcome to a certain extent by successful trade supplemented by profitable conquests; the wealth of the city of Venice in the fifteenth century was based on such extensions of commercial power. Later, particularly during the seventeenth and eighteenth centuries, the world witnessed the great expansion of the British people and development of Britain's colonial empire. In the nineteenth century the British "Highway of Empire" to India and the Orient by way of the Mediterranean was established after the opening of the Suez Canal. Britain possessed coal in quantity, a labor supply, and the human wit to invent machinery to turn out large amounts of goods at small cost. Britain's island location encouraged her people to undertake a seafaring life; ships and shipping they knew well. The ingenious combination of labor, fuel, and transport led to the creation of "a vaster empire than has been." In the case of England, certainly, a strong naval power was created in spite of a serious deficiency of many raw materials within the confines of the home islands.

Shortages of essential raw materials may lead to military aggression if people believe that their national existence depends upon the acquisition of more sources of economic products—hence more land. This was the "have-not" argument that military leaders of Germany used on two occasions to persuade their subjects to undertake wars of aggression. Japan also embarked upon similar expansion and aggressive war on the continent of Asia and in Pacific waters. Certainly inadequate space for living as well as raw-material deficiencies are highly important in any list of the causes of war.

On the other hand, deficiency of raw materials and inadequate supplies of food may lead to weakening of a nation through emigration; this occurred in Ireland during early years of the eighteenth century and again in the nineteenth century, when famine struck the land and many families were forced to leave for America and other parts of the world. Other migrations of major importance have stemmed from similar causes in east central Asia.

Generally, however, it is becoming more difficult for nations to use exploration, migration, or outright conquest as a means of political advancement. So much of the world is held in strong ownership that some nations argue over claims to seemingly worthless land such as that in Antarctica.

Distribution of land. One of the important political and social problems related to relief of land and distribution of resources is the size of landholdings. Under circumstances that allow concentration of large landholdings and wealth in the hands of a few people, political structure tends to become strongly undemocratic. Where the actual extent of cultivable land is limited, as in Japan, India, or even Hawaii, a feudal state may develop if most of the wealth is held by the few. On the other hand, with wide fertile lands available for distribution to many people, as in Canada or the United States, there is a tendency toward a democratic state. Some nations have attempted to correct maldistribution of land and to change economic life and political structure by law, as in Denmark, Poland, and Mexico. Sometimes this can be arranged peacefully; occasionally it leads to bitter internal conflict.

Importance of Geographic Location. (Figure 25-2). A large number of places, by reason of peculiar geographical location, assume political importance out of all proportion to size or resources. These special sites include certain mountain passes, straits, corridors (longer and wider than passes), channels, and the like. Some, like the mountain passes discussed earlier—Khyber Pass and Brenner Pass—or the defile at Marathon—are famous, and their history is long and varied. Others are less important in political history but loom large in directing the course of events. Biskra's gateway to the Sahara, the Jade Gate near the western end of the Chinese Wall, the Cumberland Gap, or the Mohawk or Susquehanna corridors

have all attained special geographical significance. To them should be added strategic straits, such as Malacca, Gibraltar, and Dover, which in reality are water passes.

Other important strategic locations may involve peninsulas, like Florida guarding the Strait of Florida, Korea, or Cornwall. Occasionally an isthmus location becomes highly significant, as at Suez or Panama, but passes, straits, and the like vary in importance according to the course of world events; each may be extremely useful for a brief time and then lose its significant position. Once the Cumberland Gap and Magellan Strait commanded important routes, the first into rich lands of Kentucky and Ohio, and the other from the Atlantic into the fabulous "South Sea," or Pacific; today they are relatively unused, for the Cumberland Gap has been replaced by more useful routes, and construction of the Panama Canal made a trip around South America unnecessary for most shipping. It is difficult indeed to predict which particular location may assume importance in future; who can guess where another Korean peninsula will provide the rallying point for military action.

One highly strategic European location is controlled by a second- or third-rate power—Austria, with its capital at Vienna (Figure 14-7). The Danube, flowing eastward from Bavaria, traverses a narrow lowland between the Bohemian Forest, the Alpine ranges, and the Carpathians. Northward there is easy access to the plains of Bohemia, the Moravian Gate, Upper Silesia, and the Baltic. Southeastward the Danube enters the Hungarian plains, then the Iron Gate, and eventually the Black Sea. Southward the mountain routes of Styria lead over Alpine passes into Yugoslavia, Italy, and the Adriatic. At this commanding site, a weak Austrian state is in position to control much European rail and river traffic and to stand, when necessary, as a focal point for movement of land troops. Today Austria is a buffer, taking the brunt of attack by any power that moves eastward toward the Danubian Basin or westward toward the plains of southern Germany.

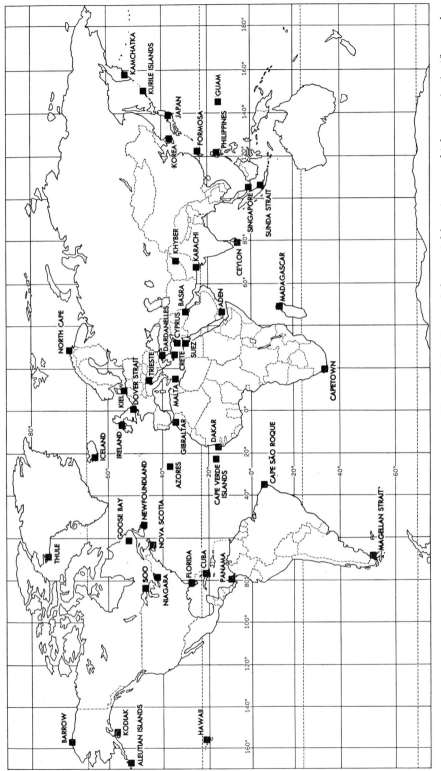

Figure 25-2   Some of the special locations to which strategic significance has become attached.

DYNAMIC ASPECTS OF POLITICAL GEOGRAPHY

The foregoing material on national boundaries, the strength and weakness of nations, and strategic location has been viewed largely from the standpoint of sea and land transportation. The introduction of air transport during the last quarter-century has materially altered some earlier concepts of political geography. Boundaries that at one time seemed well defended and almost impregnable can now be breached with comparatively little difficulty and very rapidly by means of air transport, which in theory is free from the necessity of observing national boundaries as they appear on the map. In fact, however, such boundaries are watched scrupulously in order to avoid international incidents. Core areas and heartlands no longer enjoy the impenetrability they experienced before present air speeds were attained.

Not even such strategic locations as Gibraltar, Malta, Panama, or Singapore can command movements by land and sea as they once did; today these strong bastions can be by-passed at altitudes so high that it is almost impossible to provide complete protection against air attack. Furthermore, it is almost certain that invention and use of thermonuclear weapons would imply complete destruction of fortifications and immobilization of former strongly fortified points. In other words, the speed and height at which aircraft can now perform is so great, and the weapons they can carry so deadly, that traditional aspects of political geography—and especially the matter of strategic location—have been altered. When the Netherlands can be crossed by air in less than fifteen minutes, as is now the case, it is apparent that Dutch national boundaries, surface fortifications, communications, and cities are almost entirely dominated by this new factor in international relations. Inevitably a reevaluation of the importance of boundaries, heartlands, and location must be undertaken in the light of modern transportation development. Today a single airfield may easily acquire the importance of a Gibraltar. A mountain range such as the Pyrenees that formerly served as an adequate barrier between two nations can be crossed rapidly and easily by air, and its military usefulness is almost completely destroyed though it may continue to function in preventing free movement by land. The core of any nation can be penetrated, in the absence of antiaircraft defenses, thus destroying advantages of the defense in depth theory of military action.

Students of international affairs should not, however, conclude that modern aircraft and weapons have eliminated need to know such geographic facts as national boundaries and strategic location. On the contrary, we must be thoroughly familiar not only with the traditional considerations, but with the manner in which those have been affected by modern communication and transport methods. Even the casual reader must be aware that it is almost impossible to avoid frequent contact with foreign nations, whether that contact be for peaceful purposes or whether it be national military activity in war. As speed and altitude of travel increase, relationships with other peoples inevitably will become more frequent and probably more complex. The implications are plain; we need to know all we possibly can about other peoples and countries if we are to maintain our present strong position among the nations.

SUMMARY

Similarities in race, language, religion, and other conditions of human existence lead men to band together in groups with common interests. Recognition of the bonds sometimes leads to organization of small groupings of families, or tribes. These, with their leaders, dwelling places, defenses, and similar characteristics, tend to emerge as nuclei of political states, recognizing land and sea limits within which each state is to operate. The limits thus established then become political boundaries of that nation which they enclose. Geographic features often are instrumental in locating national boundaries, especially when people are willing to make the boundary coincide with a natural feature, such as a mountain range or a river. Some national boundaries, when fairly planned and acknowledged by nations bordering them, remain stable for long periods of time. Others are disputed frequently and become significant causes of war.

The ability of a nation to grow and prosper also depends in large part upon its geographic characteristics. Some states are well centered near supplies of natural resources upon which they draw to sustain themselves and upon which they depend for raw materials in time of war. Those nations whose boundaries enclose occurrences of metallic ores and fuels are especially fortunate in time of national emergency. Lacking industrial raw materials, it may be necessary for a nation to develop trade to a high degree.

Certain strategic locations confer, in themselves, an element of political importance. Turkey, for example, occupies a commanding position with respect to the water link between the Black and Aegean Seas, and the land link between Southern Europe and western Asia. These locations, however, have become less significant with the development of military aviation and thermonuclear weapons.

The real power of any nation, then, in peace or in war, is related closely to the geographic characteristics of the land it occupies. A nation is favored indeed when its boundaries can be defended successfully against aggressors, and when its territory supplies abundant raw materials, foodstuffs, and a large working population. If in addition it enjoys a strategic and commanding location on well-traveled routes with access to the open sea and has wise and farseeing men as leaders of its government it may take its place among the leading nations of the world.

Outline
Boundaries
 Types: ocean, mountain, mathematical
 Difficulties and disputes
 Buffer states
Factors of national strength and weakness
 Core of a nation
 Handicaps of some nations
 Economic and military strength
 Strategic materials
 Economic and political self-sufficiency
 Geographic location
Dynamic aspects of political geography

QUESTIONS

1. Analyze each of the following with respect to its functions as an international boundary: the Andes, the 49th parallel in North America, the Rhine, Dover Strait.

2. Do rivers normally make good international boundaries? Defend your answer, using specific illustrations.

3. Revise the boundaries of Africa to conform more closely with the geographical regions of that continent.

4. What part of the Canadian-American boundary do you consider most satisfactory? Why? Which part is least satisfactory? Why?

5. To what degree is the possession of unexploited mineral resources a liability to a nation whose military defenses are weak?

6. On a map of the world, indicate in red those international boundaries which are currently in dispute.

7. Under conditions of aerial warfare, where have the principal strategic locations shifted? Why?

8. Using material presented in this and in earlier chapters, present your opinion concerning the ability of the peoples of India to wage modern warfare, if forced to fight with no resources other than their own. Support your statement with valid arguments.

SELECTED REFERENCES

Alexander, Lewis M.: *World Political Patterns,* Rand McNally and Company, Chicago, 1957.

Beck, James R.: "The Global Distribution of Primary Governmental Types," *Journal of Geography,* 50:114–123, March, 1951.

Boggs, S. Whittemore: *International Boundaries: A Study of Boundary Functions and Problems,* Columbia University Press, New York, 1940.

———: "National Claims in Adjacent Seas," *Geographical Review,* 41:185–209, April, 1951.

Bowman, Isaiah: *The New World,* World Book Company, Yonkers, N.Y., 1928.

East, W. Gordon, and A. E. Moodie: *The Changing World: Studies in Political Geography,* World Book Company, Yonkers, N.Y., 1956.

Fairgrieve, James: *Geography and World Power,* 8th ed., E. P. Dutton & Co., Inc., New York, 1941.

Hall, Arthur R.: "Mackinder and the Course of Events," *Annals of the Association of American Geographers,* 45:109–126, June, 1955.

Hartshorne, Richard: "The Functional Approach in Political Geography," *Annals of the Association of American Geographers,* 40:95–130, June, 1950.

Hoffman, George: "Toward Greater Integration in Europe," *Journal of Geography,* 55:165–176, April, 1956.

Jones, Stephen B.: "Global Strategic Views," *Geographical Review,* 45:492–508, October, 1955.

———: "Views of the Political World," *Geographical Review,* 45:492–508, October, 1955.

Mackinder, H. J.: *Democratic Ideals and Reality,* Henry Holt and Company, Inc., New York, 1950.

Miller, E. Willard, George T. Renner, and associates: *Global Geography,* Thomas Y. Crowell Company, New York, 1957.

Pearcy, G. Etzel, and Russell H. Fifield: *World Political Geography,* 2d ed., Thomas Y. Crowell Company, New York, 1957.

Pounds, Norman J. G.: "The Political Geography of the Straits of Gibraltar," *Journal of Geography,* 51:165–170, April, 1952.

President's Materials Policy Commission: *Resources for Freedom,* vol. II, *The Outlook for Key Commodities,* Washington, June, 1952.

Randal, Richard R.: "Political Geography of the Klagenfurt Basin," *Geographical Review,* 47:406–419, 1957.

Raup, H. F.: *Fundamentals of Global Geography,* Air University, Montgomery, Ala., 1955.

Sprout, Harold: *Foundations of National Power,* D. Van Nostrand Company, Inc., Princeton, N.J., 1951.

Strausz-Hupé, Robert, and Stefan T. Possony (eds.): "Air Power and National Security," *Annals of the American Academy of Political and Social Science,* vol. 299, May, 1955.

Van Valkenburg, Samuel: *Elements of Political Geography,* Prentice-Hall, Inc., Englewood Cliffs, N.J., 1954.

Van Royen, William, and Oliver Bowles: *The Mineral Resources of the World,* vol. II, *Atlas of the World's Resources,* Prentice-Hall, Inc., Englewood Cliffs, N.J., 1952.

———: *The Agricultural Resources of the World,* vol. I, *Atlas of the World's Resources,* Prentice-Hall, Inc., Englewood Cliffs, N.J., 1954.

Whittlesey, Derwent: *The Earth and the State,* Henry Holt and Company, Inc., New York, 1944.

Weigert, Hans W., and others: *Principles of Political Geography,* Appleton-Century-Crofts, Inc., New York, 1957.

26. A Survey of
the Continents

THE seven continents are divided, as a rule, into those of the Old World—Asia, Europe, and Africa—and those of the New World—North America and South America—with isolated Australia and uninhabited Antarctica the only ones lying wholly within the Southern Hemisphere. Most land area of the world lies in the Northern Hemisphere, as indicated in Table 26-1; hence we commonly refer to the Southern Hemisphere as the *water hemisphere*.

THE WORLD ISLAND OR OLD WORLD

The Old World, or world island of some geographers, consists of three closely contiguous continents—Europe, Asia, and Africa. From a physiographic standpoint, Europe is essentially a peninsula of Asia or of the continent which might better be called Eurasia. Only a portion of the Ural Mountains is now used as a Europe-Asia boundary, and the Caucasus Range is included with Europe along with the trans-Caucasian region south of the mountains. Delimitations of the Europe-Asia boundary are based more on cultural, racial, and historical grounds than on natural earth features. The boundary between Europe and Africa is all water, and that between Asia and Africa is mostly along the water. The Sinai Peninsula is a part of Egypt, an African country; hence the Africa-Asia boundary line runs from the Gulf of Aqaba to the Mediterranean and not across the Isthmus of Suez, which is the narrowest land connection between the continents.

Europe is wholly outside the tropics, and most of the continent is in the northern midlatitudes. Asia is wholly north of the equator, but extends over so many degrees of latitude that most types of climate—from wet equatorial to the polar tundras—are found on the continent. The principal exception is the west-coast marine climate which occurs in Europe but not in Asia. Africa is crossed by the equator at about the middle distance from the northern and southern limits of the continent; thus Africa essentially is a tropical and subtropical land mass. Until less than a century ago interior tropical Africa was unknown to Europeans; for the extensive desert toward the north, swamps on the upper Nile, rapids on other rivers, and swampy forested coasts backed by steep cliffs combined to discourage exploration and penetration for trade and settlement.

Each of the three continents has a core or "shield" of ancient rock, to which more recent geologic formations have been added. The highest mountain ranges are geologically young. They trend generally east and west and are located between areas of hard old rock, which probably were resistant blocks of the earth's surface; between these, weaker rocks were folded and heaved up to form such mountain systems as the Pyrenees, Atlas, Alps, Carpathians, Caucasus, Hindu Kush, Altai, Himalayas, among others. In Europe the chief remnant of very old land is in Scandinavia. Asia has two centers of hard ancient rocks, one in Siberia and the other in India. The area of old rocks in Africa makes up most of that continent south of the Sahara.

Europe.   Europe's area is approximately 3,-750,000 square miles—only a little larger than the United States including Alaska—yet in this territory live over a half a billion people. Europe, exclusive of the U.S.S.R., has 400 million people in an area of about 2 million square miles. From these figures, it is apparent that Europe offers great advantages as a home for man.

Europe's Favorable Geography.   Environmental factors prevailing in Europe, including

TABLE 26-1. AREA OF THE CONTINENTS

Continent	Millions of square miles to nearest thousand
Africa	11,710,000
Asia	17,000,000
Europe	3,750,000
North America	8,665,000
South America	6,938,000
Australia	2,975,000
Antarctica	5,250,000 (estimated)

climates, relief features, shore lines, and natural resources, are generally favorable for man. Climatic conditions are stimulating, and in most areas there is adequate rainfall and favorable temperature for plant growth. Only a small part of the Continent north of the Caspian Sea is too dry, and the arctic shore line and higher mountains are too cold for crops. The mountains trend generally east-west, protecting Mediterranean shores from excessive winter cold and permitting mild moist air from the Atlantic to moderate the climate of west central Europe.

Europe has many plains; and though some are of small extent, they support large numbers of people. Hills and mountains are smaller in area than the plains, and many upland regions are not too rugged to support numbers of people. There are many navigable rivers; water transportation is furthered by the generally low elevation of the land, which makes canal construction feasible. Extensive plains are an aid to land transportation because construction of railroads and highways is easier and cheaper than would be possible were Europe a more mountainous continent. Relief features often vary widely within limited areas.

Ocean transportation is generally easier around Europe's shores and in her harbors than on any other continent. Good harbors are fairly numerous as the result of an irregular shore line, which is marked by ports at mouths of numerous navigable rivers. The continent is deeply penetrated by seas—the North Sea, Baltic, Mediterranean, Black Sea, and Adriatic

—and these provide ocean ports located within a few hundred miles of any part of Western and Southern Europe. The interior of no other continent has the degree of accessibility that Europe enjoys in its ocean transport and its coasts and harbors.

Natural resources of Europe are many, though they are not always adequate for the needs of her people. Coal, petroleum, and water power provide energy, and agriculture is highly productive on large areas of fertile soil. Forests are important in some parts and contribute wealth to human activities. Iron ore is abundant, and many other metals and nonmetallic minerals occur. Local differences in relief features, soils, and resources result in much differentation and variety of industry; this in turn encourages exchange of products between adjoining areas of the continent.

Physical Regions. The three great physical relief regions in Europe are (1) the northwestern highlands, (2) the central plain, and (3) Southern Europe. The last consists principally of peninsula, mountains, and small basins.

Northwestern highlands. The foundation of the Continent consists of old crystalline rock, which outcrops chiefly in the northern highlands across Ireland, Scotland, Scandinavia, and Finland. In this northern portion, highlands are hilly uplands and rolling plateaus cut by deep valleys except for parts of the Norway coast. In Finland and adjacent areas, erosion has reduced former high mountains to a gently rolling plain. All the northern area has been strongly glaciated, with the result that lakes abound, though much of the scoured bedrock lacks good soil. Tillable land is limited to valleys, and soil is often poor. This, combined with a short growing season, limits crops to hay, roots, and hardy grains. Forest products, grazing, dairying, and fishing are typical industries. The meager population is concentrated in the lowlands. Coasts are much indented with deep fiords, of which those of Norway are noteworthy. In Norway and other rugged areas much water power is available, and some chemical and other manufactures are based on cheap hydroelectricity. Building stone occurs widely and there are some metals, of which the iron of Sweden is best known. Stockholm, Oslo, and Helsinki are both seaports and capital cities and are the largest population centers in their respective countries. Bergen, Norway, and Göteborg, Sweden, are other seaports. No large cities are located in interior regions.

The central plain. The central lowland or great European plain, leads the Continent in agriculture, manufactures, commerce, and population. The region extends from southern Ireland and England over western France, Denmark, northern Germany, Poland, and most of Russia from the Black Sea to the Arctic. Most rocks that outcrop on these plains are sedimentary, and coal beds are common in some parts. Sometimes the surface is broken by occurrence of small hill areas of older rock and, toward the north, of glacial moraines and other deposits. Many lakes and abandoned glacial spillways that once carried meltwater from the ice front are indicators of the extent of continental glaciation.

The climate of the plain is dominated by frequent cyclonic storms, which bring rainfall and changeable weather. Exposure to winds from the Atlantic Ocean moderates temperatures far inland because no high mountain ranges stand across the path of the westerlies. Winters are long, cold, and snowy in Russia but become progressively less severe westward. The central plains are the most favored parts of Europe for human activity. They grow wheat and other grains, sugar beets, potatoes, and flax and support the majority of the livestock on the Continent. Toward the north where coniferous forests are dominant, soils tend to be infertile, but in most areas where natural vegetation consisted of hardwood trees and grass the soils are rich and productive. Black soil of the level grasslands in Romania and the Ukraine is ideal for growing wheat.

These plains are drained by navigable rivers, the Thames, Rhine, Elbe, Oder, Vistula, Dnieper, Volga, and others. Building canals, railroads, and highways is easy, and manufacturing is based largely on supplies of local iron ore, coal, and other materials as well as on imported products.

Nearly three-fourths of the entire population of the Continent dwells on the plain. Most large cities of Europe, including many main seaports, are located here. A railroad map indicates that in most European countries many lines diverge like spokes of a wheel from the capitals and some other centers. London, Paris, Berlin, Warsaw, and Moscow are major foci for rail routes. Other inland centers devoted to industry include Birmingham, Essen, Cologne, Leipzig, Dresden, Frankfurt, Kiev, and Kharkov.

Many leading seaports of Northern Europe are near mouths of rivers whose valleys provide natural routes to the hinterland. Liverpool, London, Bristol, and Newcastle are English cities of this type. In France, Bordeaux, Nantes, and Le Havre are ports near river mouths. Antwerp in Belgium, Hamburg, Bremen, Emden, and Lübeck in Germany, Riga and Leningrad in the U.S.S.R., and Danzig in Poland are among other ports of the central plains. Odessa in the Soviet Union, and Constanța, Romania, are leading ports on the Black Sea. From these and others are sent manufactured goods from the Continent; and in return minerals, food, raw materials, and luxuries are imported from abroad.

Southern Europe. The third great physical region, Southern Europe, consists of three major peninsulas, the Iberian (Spain and Portugal), Italian, and Balkan, together with young folded mountains north of the Mediterranean Sea forming a nearly continuous series of ridges from Cape Finisterre to the Dardanelles. Associated with the higher lands are basins, valleys, and small plains. The peninsulas differ in their geographical features. Iberia is predominantly a plateau. Italy is made up of the Apennine Mountains with associated hills and lowlands. The Balkans are principally rugged mountain country which in Greece has been partly submerged by the sea, leaving a coast of islands and hilly peninsulas.

The shores of the Mediterranean, with few exceptions, enjoy the mild Mediterranean climate. Inland, climatic conditions change to the continental type, with summer rains in place of Mediterranean winter rainfall; winters of the interior tend to be much colder than those of the southern shores.

Mountains and hills, along with several important basins and valleys, occupy the country between the Mediterranean Sea and the central plain. Eastward from the Alps are two major mountainous arcs. The northern extends through Austria and then continues in the giant curves of the Carpathian Mountains and Transylvanian Alps to the Danube River at the Iron Gate and into Bulgaria. Ridges of the other arc border the Adriatic Sea on the north in the Julian Alps and on the east in the Dinaric Alps, continuing southeastward into Greece as the Pindus Mountains. In Yugoslavia these ridges parallel the Adriatic and hinder penetration of the interior because few passes lead to the coast.

Mountains bordering the central European plain on the south are older than the rugged ridges near the Mediterranean Sea. As a result, mountains in southern Germany and central and northern France have rounded slopes and typically support extensive forests. Among these mountains most of the people live in basins and valleys. The largest basins include those of Bavaria, in which is situated the important city of Munich; the basin of Bohemia, in which Prague is located; and that of Hungary, in which Budapest is the metropolis. The Danube River gives access to these three basins and other fertile areas. The Danube affords a navigable waterway to seven nations and is a principal transportation corridor between Central and southeastern Europe.

As a consequence of enclosure of the Mediterranean Sea by highlands along its northern border, principal breaks through the mountain barriers determine the routes penetrating Central Europe. Some of these cross the Continent to the North and Baltic Seas. One follows valleys of the Rhone and Saône Rivers through the pass at Belfort to the Rhine Valley and thence to the North Sea. Another route leads from the head of the Adriatic Sea, north across the Danube River, through the pass called the Moravian Gate, to the Oder River and the Baltic Sea.

In the mountainous Balkan Peninsula the most accessible and historic route extends from Salonika on the Aegean Sea, up the Vardar River valley, over a divide to the Morava, and down this stream to the Danube near Belgrade. From Niš in Yugoslavia a branch extends eastward by way of Sofia, Bulgaria, to Istanbul on the straits between the Aegean and Black Seas. Armies, immigrants, pilgrims, and traders have marched and countermarched along these historic routes. Today railroads and improved highways utilize them.

To reach the Po Valley in northern Italy the longest tunnels in the world, the Simplon ($12\frac{1}{3}$ miles) and the St. Gotthard ($9\frac{1}{4}$ miles), were constructed through the Swiss Alps, whose height precluded railroad building over them. Although the Alps are a great barrier to transportation, they serve man by keeping from Italy the worst cold blasts of winter from the Russian steppes and by providing sources of the abundant water power he has developed.

Plains of Southern Europe are generally small, that of the Po Valley being largest. They are densely settled, and living standards for many farmers tend to be lower than those of northwestern Europe. In those parts having a Mediterranean climate, vineyards and orchards are important in the landscape, and fruit, olive oil, and wine are shipped to colder regions of Western and Northern Europe. Grazing of sheep, goats, and cattle is common, but there is little timber except in the Balkan Mountains. Coal, oil, and metals are scarce, and manufacturing is less important here than in more favored plains of Central Europe. Many of the cities, however, have numerous factories, particularly in Milan, Turin, Marseille, and Barcelona. Madrid is located on a semiarid plateau, but typically the larger Southern European cities are commercial ports or built near the sea; this is the case at Lisbon, Valencia, Barcelona, Genoa, Rome, Naples, Athens, and Istanbul.

Geographic Importance of Europe.   For several centuries Europe has carried on more foreign trade than any other continent. This is accounted for by the following factors:

1. The large population, which has a relatively high standard of living compared with that of most people who live on other continents.

2. Importance of manufactures, which can be exported and for which quantities of raw materials must be imported.

3. Lack of certain minerals, especially petroleum in most of Western and Southern Europe.

4. Necessity in many nations for importing foodstuffs for man and feed for animals.

5. Imports from regions of different climate.

6. The fact that much traffic, including specialized manufacturing, is foreign in Europe because of the small size of many nations, whereas in a large country with varied industries such trade would be domestic.

Europe has expanded its trade by different methods. The Continent has led not only in most lines of manufacturing but in building and operation of ocean shipping. Banking and foreign investments served Europe in its development of trade. Western civilization, which stems from Europe, has spread around the world, and its impacts can be perceived even in remote parts of the earth. European languages, religion, and culture have overrun the Americas, Australia and New Zealand, South Africa, and many islands and parts of Asia, and they have had profound effects in every nation of the world.

European powers have political control over much of Africa, a few spots in southern Asia, some parts of the Americas, and many of the world's islands. Recently there has been a strong tendency toward decline in the political domination of colonies by European countries. Some colonies, such as India, Pakistan, and Ceylon have become independent although they are members of the British Commonwealth of Nations. Others that have attained independence include Korea, Indonesia, Burma and South Vietnam.

Asia.   Asia is the largest continent and supports over half of the world's people. This continent has wide variations in climate, relief features, and ability to maintain life. Some parts of Asia enjoy very favorable soil and climate conditions, leading to intensive agriculture; others, with fewer advantages, are thinly populated.

Geographical handicaps that tend to retard Asiatic peoples include (1) pronounced shortage of first-class harbors, (2) difficulty of penetrating the interior of the continent because of great distances, high plateaus, mountains, and deserts, and absence of many favorable routes leading to the interior, (3) desert climate experienced by a large part of Asia and the climate that makes much of the far north too cold for human use. In consequence of these geographical conditions, many parts of interior Asia are so isolated from the rest of the world that people who live there have tended to stagnate.

Climate.   The different climatic regions in Asia, result from several factors, among which these rank first:

1. Continental location in stormy westerly winds of midlatitudes in northern Asia. Southward from the Arctic Ocean in the interior this factor causes broad belts of tundra, taiga, steppes and cold desert, with a humid continental type of climate in southeastern Siberia, northern China, Korea, and Japan.

2. Monsoon Asia, divided into subtropical and tropical types, includes the southern half of the east coast, the Malay Peninsula, and India.

3. Southwestern Asia from the Indus Valley to the Red Sea is desert.

4. A fringe along the Mediterranean Sea has Mediterranean climate.

5. The elevated interior has cold climates resulting largely from altitude.

The land utilization and natural vegetation of Asia are closely related to these climatic regions.

Highlands.   Asia is built around a mountain core, with high plateaus centering in Tibet and the Pamirs. All the way from Turkey to China is a double series of mountain ranges. From the Pamir knot of high plateaus and mountains, the Altai, Altyn Tagh, and Kunlun rise to the north and east, the Karakorum and Himalayas to the south, and the Hindu Kush and Sulaiman lie southwest of the "roof of the world."

Southeast from the Himalaya Mountains several ranges trend into China, Vietnam, the Malay Peninsula, and Indonesia. Westward the Hindu Kush and Elburz Mountains guard the plateau of Afghanistan and Iran (Persia) on the north, and mountain ranges continue westward into Turkey to the south of the Black Sea. In south and southwestern Asia are three peninsular plateaus, Anatolia (Asia Minor), Arabia, and the Deccan of India. Besides the mountains and Tibetan plateau in central Asia, there are lowland basins of which the Tarim and Dzungarian in China and the depression of the Caspian and Aral Seas are most important.

Plains.   Asia's fertile plains support most of the population in the east and south portions of the continent, but some extensive plains are unsuited climatically for cultivation because of low temperatures in the north and drought in the interior. The latter type of plain may be made useful if supplies of water for irrigation can be obtained. River and coastal plains are the most densely populated. Rivers of Asia drain to the north, east, and south from the Tibetan highlands. Most people and activities of southern and eastern Asia are concentrated in river valleys, the larger of which include the Tigris-Euphrates, Indus, Ganges, Brahmaputra, Irrawaddy, Menam, Mekong, Si-kiang

(West), Yangtze, Hwang (Yellow), and Amur. Deltas and coastal plains in India and China support millions of people, as do the Manchurian lowland and the interior basin of Szechwan in China. Offshore islands like Japan, Java, Sumatra, and the Philippines also are well developed and extensively used by man. Rice is the preferred food crop in the monsoon tropical and subtropical climates; cotton, jute, tea, and vegetable oils are also important products. Silk is manufactured, especially in Japan and China.

In cooler and drier regions, wheat, millet, and grain sorghum are favorite food crops. Soybeans are important in Manchuria. Much of Siberia is a vast lowland sloping toward the Arctic and drained by the Ob, Yenisei, and Lena Rivers; but because of cold climate, the population in these river basins is relatively sparse. Along the Arctic are little-used tundra lands, then to the south the broad taiga belt of spruce, fir, and pine. Next toward European Russia is a zone of fertile grasslands in which most of the Siberian production of wheat is cultivated; this area in turn grades into steppes and deserts of central Asia. Summers are hot in Russian Turkestan, east of the Caspian Sea, and there is little agriculture except in oases, where cotton, alfalfa, and some food crops for local use are raised by irrigation.

Natural resources. The natural resources of Asia have been very unevenly developed. Soil is used intensively in monsoon lands and is the principal support of man in this continent. Vast forests in Siberia are still little exploited. Potential water power is very great, but only Japan has developed important amounts of hydroelectric power for her own use. Mineral resources have been only partially tapped. Petroleum and coal production in particular seem to offer wide possibilities for the future. Tin, iron, gold, and other metals are being mined, but since much of Asia has not been prospected extensively, it is probable that many occurrences of metals remain undiscovered.

Transportation. In transportation, Asia has made progress but still remains behind both Europe and North America because natural features are less favorable than on those two continents and human management has been less effective. In all of Asia only one railroad, the Trans-Siberian, crosses the length of the continent, and over vast areas there are not even adequate highways. Only Japan and India have railroads reasonably adequate to their needs.

The largest seaports in Asia generally are located where they have easy access to a major valley or productive plain. Good harbors are not common along much of the Asiatic coast, and some great ports, like Shanghai, have developed where the harbor is poor but where location is convenient to a highly productive hinterland. Sometimes, where an irregular coast has many harbors, as in southeastern Asia, port cities are relatively small because mountain ranges near the coast hinder access to the interior.

Asiatic Nations and Their Trade. Before World War II, Japan carried on most of the foreign trade in Asia. Japan is a small nation in relation to its large population; most of the people live in cities and on scattered little areas of fertile farmland. Both light and heavy industry are well developed, considering the slender resources available in the home islands. Tokyo is the capital and largest city. With its port, Yokohama, it is a great manufacturing center. Extending in a zone west from Tokyo are other industrial centers which are also seaports, including Nagoya, Osaka, Kobe, and Nagasaki. Kyoto, the old capital, is inland. Iron goods, machinery, cotton textiles, rayon, silk, tea, and a host of small articles are among the exports. Raw cotton, petroleum, metals, and some foodstuffs must be imported.

The Indian peninsula is so large and so isolated from the rest of Asia that it is sometimes called a subcontinent. The Himalaya Mountains enclose the peninsula on the north; their southern slopes descend to fertile alluvial plains of the Indus and Ganges Rivers, and these in turn give way to the Deccan plateau further south. India is now an independent member of the British Commonwealth of Nations, as is also Moslem-peopled Pakistan, which includes West Pakistan, northwest part of the peninsula of India, and East Pakistan in the Ganges Delta area. Nearby Burma is independent, and Ceylon is essentially so, although a member of the British Commonwealth. Most parts of India are reached by railroads radiating from the important ports. Leading exports are cotton from Bombay, jute from Calcutta, and ores from Madras. Karachi, capital of Pakistan, and Colombo in Ceylon are two other leading seaports of this area. The Ganges Valley is particularly well developed for agriculture and commerce; numerous railroads and the river itself serve Delhi, Cawnpore, Benares, Lucknow, and other cities.

In Burma, in Thailand, in the former Indochina (now divided into northern and southern Vietnam, Laos, and Cambodia), and in the Malay Peninsula, transportation is by rivers, coastal steamer, short railroad lines, and increasingly by highway and airway. Seaports like Singapore and Georgetown on Penang Island, and the interior center of Kuala Lumpur handle much of the rubber, tin, and other exports of Malaya. Bangkok in Thailand, Saigon in South Vietnam, and Hanoi in North Vietnam are important ports and trade centers for shipping rice, rubber, and other tropical products. In the Indonesian Republic, Jakarta on Java is the capital and largest city. Java is famed for exports of coconut oil, sugar, rubber, tea, spices, and other tropical products. Makassar on Celebes, Palembang (sugar and rubber) on Sumatra, and Bandjermasin (petroleum) on Borneo are locally important seaports.

China is the most populous country in the world, but most of its people are subsistence farmers. There is relatively little manufacturing and large-scale or external trade though Chinese have been skilled artisans for many centuries.

One of the great needs of the nation is improved transportation. Rivers, especially the Yangtze, carry much freight and are supplemented by thousands of miles of canals in the deltas and floodplains of the Yangtze, Hwang (Yellow), and Si-kiang (West) Rivers. Short rail lines run inland from several coastal cities, but through lines are rare. The most important line connects Canton, Hankow (inland on the Yangtze), and Peking. The last also has rail connections with its port, Tientsin, and Manchuria.

Shanghai on the delta of the Yangtze is the greatest port in China, but normal trade was not operating in the 1950s. Dairen is the principal port of the Manchurian region, with Mukden and Harbin leading inland cities.

Siberia is the largest part of the U.S.S.R. in area, but it is only partly developed. The Trans-Siberian Railroad, which terminates at Vladivostok, ties the country together and traverses the most fertile and populated strip of land. Chita, Irkutsk, Tomsk, Omsk, and Novo-Sibirsk are among important cities in interior Siberia. Great areas of land are suitable for wheat and mixed farming. Although resources of forests, fish, furs, and minerals are great, they are only partly developed. Deposits of coal and iron ore have led to the construction of heavy industries in western and central Siberia.

Southwestern Asia is a land of plateaus, mountains, and plains, much of which has a desert or near-desert climate. Historically it is the site of ancient empires and civilizations, but it lacks many resources needed to prosper in today's world. Its population is scant except where climate favors human occupation and water can be obtained for irrigation.

The largest inland cities are Ankara, Turkey; Tehran, Iran; Baghdad, Iraq; and Damascus, Syria. These serve as capitals for their respective countries.

Control of the city of Jerusalem, center of concern for many pilgrims and tourists, is divided between Israel and Jordan. To Moslems, Mecca in Arabia is the great center for pilgrimages.

Petroleum is the most valuable mineral. Production is large and comes from Kuwait, Saudi Arabia, Iran, Iraq, Qatar, and Bahrein, all of which border the Persian Gulf.

Railroads are inadequate in number throughout this part of Asia; usually they are used as feeder lines to serve local seaports.

Africa. From a historic and cultural standpoint, the continent of Africa is divided into a northern fringe, always closely related to Asia and Europe in its races, politics, and culture, and the central and southern sections, populated largely by Negroes or negroid peoples. This section has long been isolated from contacts and trade with the rest of the world. The Sahara covers an area about the size of the United States and forms a barrier between these two African culture areas. In the past, only a few caravans crossed the desert yearly; today it is spanned with comparative ease by air.

North Africa. Northwestern Africa is backed by the Atlas Mountains; along its coast lies a zone of Mediterranean climate. From here many products, including grain, wine, olive oil, hides, iron ore, and phosphate rock, are shipped from Algiers, Casablanca, Tunis, and other ports to France and other countries, chiefly in Europe.

In Egypt, for the past six thousand years, irrigation has transformed the Nile Valley into a densely populated strip of productive land. Cotton from the Nile Delta shipped through the port of Alexandria is Egypt's principal export. The Suez Canal is situated entirely in Egypt. Upstream from Cairo river boats, supplemented by railroads which parallel much of the Nile and portage freight around the rapids and unnavigable stretches of the river, provide service to Khartoum in the Sudan. A railroad also runs from Khartoum to Port Sudan on the Red Sea, from which cotton and other products are exported.

Central and East Africa. Two-thirds of Africa south of the Sahara consists of a plateau of hard ancient rock material rising abruptly from the ocean in most localities. Conditions in tropical Africa so discouraged exploration, settlement, and opening of the interior to trade that it remained unexplored and undeveloped until late in the last century. It is difficult to land through the surf and hard to penetrate the forests from the shore. The edge of the plateau is marked by rapids and waterfalls in the rivers which prevent their use for navigation to reach the interior; the edge of this plateau resembles a mountain barrier in geographical effect.

If a coastal lowland is found at all around the continent, it is usually narrow and is either desert or covered with pestilential mangrove swamps and jungles. There are very few good harbors.

Central Africa is so difficult of access that it was first entered by Europeans from South Africa, a long but more open route. On the north was the wide barrier of the Sahara and difficult swamps, called the *sudd,* along the upper Nile. Near the equator the Congo River drains an interior basin of the same name and is an outlet for palm oil and other tropical products, though many rapids in its course are a distinct handicap to transportation.

The East African Plateau and that of Ethiopia and interior Eritrea have such high altitudes that they are reasonably healthy and invigorating, thereby encouraging some settlement by Europeans. The southern Belgian Congo and parts of Rhodesia are also favorable for white settlers because of altitude. Mountain ranges are rare in Africa, and much of the interior plateau surface is open and easy to cross. East Africa lacks long chains of mountains, but isolated mountain peaks do rise to such altitudes that they are snowcapped although on the equator. Examples include Kilimanjaro, Kenya, and Ruwenzori. A striking feature of this part of Africa is the presence of two *rift valleys*—narrow, elongated, and deep sunken trenches—crossing the plateau. The Great Rift Valley has several large lakes in its depths, including Tanganyika, Nyassa, Albert, and Rudolf. The largest lake, Victoria, is outside the Great Rift Valley. The highest peak in west central Africa is Mt. Cameroon, which rises near the angle of the Gulf of Guinea.

South Africa. This section of the continent is favored in climate and natural resources. The Mediterranean zone lies near Capetown;

inland the high veld has sufficient elevation to make the climate relatively cool. Near Durban on the east coast, the warmth and freedom from frost permit the growing of sugar cane and other subtropical crops. Principal exports from South Africa are wool, meats, and hides. The region is a great producer of gold at Johannesburg, diamonds at Kimberley, near Pretoria, among other places, and copper in Northern Rhodesia.

Transportation Conditions. Pushing into Africa long baffled explorers, and Africa's transportation problem is still difficult. Most railroads in tropical Africa are unconnected single lines running inland from little port cities to tap palm oil, peanuts, mahogany, and other export commodities. The southern part of the Belgian Congo has large copper mines in the Katanga district. To facilitate exports and to furnish the mines with machinery and other supplies railroads have been built to this area from Lobito on the Atlantic coast of Angola, from Beira in Mozambique on the Indian Ocean, and from Capetown on the south. In addition a slow route uses the Congo River with its portage railroads around rapids. Besides copper ore, the Belgian Congo produces uranium, radium, gold, and industrial diamonds.

Exports from East Africa include cotton, hides, coffee, and sisal fiber. Ethiopia (Abyssinia) is located on such a high rugged plateau that it is difficult to enter this part of Africa to carry on trade. Only a single narrow-gauge railroad runs to the capital, Addis Abeba, from a port in French Somaliland.

Air routes are of great importance in Africa. In a few hours, passengers, mail, and package freight now are flown distances that once took as many weeks or even months of weary travel by boat, animal transport, or on foot.

World Relations. Africa is important, geographically speaking, for its strategic location. Numerous European colonies serve as rich sources of needed raw materials to feed the factories of Europe.

The most strategic location in Africa is the Suez Canal, and the political and military control of this vital link for ocean shipping between Europe and southeastern Asia is of major concern. It is especially important for the transport of petroleum. Other highly strategic points are the constrictions in the Mediterranean Sea at the Strait of Gibraltar and near the island of Malta. Only about 1,600 miles of sea separate Africa from South America; planes can fly from Natal, Brazil, to Dakar and Freetown in Africa in a few hours. Ascension Island in the South Atlantic Ocean has become an emergency landing field on this route.

Africa was not defended strongly by native peoples when its riches attracted Europeans. The Great Powers found it so easy to establish colonies here that most of the continent came under their rule. European nations sought African colonies (1) to control sources of raw materials for manufacture, (2) to secure markets for goods and places for investment of funds, (3) to find outlets for emigration and settlement, (4) to acquire strategic sites and increase or maintain national power and prestige. Many colonies have not been economically successful and have represented a financial drain upon the governing power. Only Tunis, Algeria, and South Africa have large numbers of settlers of European descent. Many parts of Africa provide severe climatic handicaps to European settlement, as well as competition of cheap native labor.

Since the end of the Second World War, several former colonies have become independent or completely self-governing. These include Egypt, Sudan, Libya, Morocco, and Ghana (Gold Coast). Others (Uganda, Nigeria, Somaliland) are scheduled for independence. The Union of South Africa is a member of the British Commonwealth of Nations. The inhabitants of French-controlled overseas territories in Africa are represented in the French Parliament; those controlled by Portugal are considered citizens of that country.

As a source of raw materials, foodstuffs, and minerals, Africa is of great importance to Europe, which also supplies most of Africa's imports. Cotton, vegetable oils, wool, hides, cacao, grain, and some timber are among African products shipped to European cities. Mineral exports include iron ore, phosphate, fertilizers, copper, and cobalt. In general, Africa supplements European economy, and European nations desire to continue managing African trade and development of its resources.

THE NEW WORLD

The land area of the New World covers a scant half of that of the Old World, and its continents are more nearly separated from each other. Both North America and South America are roughly triangular, and they possess young mountain chains close to the Pacific and older worn-down mountains near the Atlantic Coast. A central lowland extends north and south between the two mountainous areas. Climatically, however, the similarities cease. North America is wholly north of the equator, the narrowest part of the continent lies within the tropics, and the land mass broadens in the midlatitudes where stimulating cyclonic storms occur. Furthermore, much of the land in the tropical zone consists of highlands, where altitude tends to counteract the handicaps of low-latitude location. In contrast, the greatest width of South America almost coincides with the equator, and much of that continent within the tropics consists of lowland, although extensive tropical highlands are beneficial for human use and health.

Only the narrow triangular southern portion of South America lies in the cyclonic belt of the midlatitudes. Trade-wind and "rain-shadow" deserts occur on both continents but are smaller than those of Asia, Africa, or Australia. Northern Canada, Greenland, and much of Alaska are far too cold for crops or tree growth. There population is sparse and little trade may be expected to develop. Only the southern tip of South America and the higher mountains and plateaus have a similar climate.

North America. Although the widest part of the continent is the least habitable because it is near the Arctic, North America does have several advantages in regard to use of land. The continent was favored for settlement by Europeans for many reasons: the presence of large plains with adequate rainfall and fertile soil, climates similar to those of Europe, favoring the transfer of familiar systems of farming and crops and livestock to the New World, great resources of timber, coal, iron, and other minerals; water power; a plentiful supply of fish and game, an irregular coast, and inland waterways and broad plains leading to the interior. The portion within the United States includes a major part of the continent most favored for farming, mining, and other occupations.

Since climatic conditions have been described in Chapters 6, 7, 8, 9, and 10, that material will not be repeated here. The relations of forest types to climatic conditions are included in Chapters 5 and 11; agriculture is described in Chapter 18.

Relief of the Land. The Canadian, or Laurentian, Shield is the principal area of ancient rock material in North America; it includes most of eastern Canada, Newfoundland, Labrador, and the Lake Superior region. The Adirondacks in New York State are an outlying area of the Shield.

Beyond this large, roughly triangular area most other major relief features are aligned approximately in a north-south direction. From east to west in the United States these include the Atlantic Coastal Plain, Piedmont Plateau, Appalachian Mountains, Appalachian Plateaus, Interior Lowland, the Great Plains, Rocky Mountains, Intermontane Plateaus and Basins, Sierra-Cascade Mountains, the great valleys of California, Oregon, and Washington, and the Pacific Coast ranges.

Beginning with the Interior Lowland, these features continue northward into Canada. The Interior Lowland on the south grades into the Gulf Coastal Plain, which is also a continuation of the Atlantic Coastal Plain. South of the Mexican boundary the principal features include a central upland or plateau with associated mountain ranges and numerous volcanoes; the coasts are fringed with narrow coastal plains along much of their distance.

Canadian Shield and the eastern highlands. The easternmost portion of North America is made up of resistant ancient rocks extending inland from the "stern and rockbound coast" of New England, Nova Scotia, Newfoundland, and Labrador. It must be noted, that other rocks in New England although hard and resistant, are younger than those of the Shield. The general surface appearance is different, too, in New England from that north of the border. A large part of Canada from the St. Lawrence and Great Lakes to Keewatin, west of Hudson Bay, is a peneplain consisting of eroded bases of ancient mountains. This area is named after its shape, the Canadian Shield, with the higher portion near the river being called the Laurentian Upland.

The New England upland, Canadian Shield, Adirondacks, and Lake Superior region experience a severe climate and the forests are principally coniferous. Some parts are well endowed with minerals, including deposits of gold, silver, copper, iron, nickel, uranium, and asbestos. Because of glaciation and the general resistance of the rock, these areas contain numerous lakes and enjoy a wealth of water power.

The Adirondack Mountains represent an outlying area of resistant rock. Another area of old crystalline rock extends southwest from a point near the Hudson River into Georgia, and forms the Piedmont Plateau.

The Appalachian Mountains and Plateaus are composed of sedimentary rocks and are much younger geologically than the Piedmont of the Laurentian Upland. Ridges and valleys of the Appalachian Mountains are west of the Piedmont and trend in a southwest-northeast direction, continuing all the way from northern Alabama to Newfoundland. Still farther inland is the deeply eroded Appalachian Plateau, divided into the Allegheny Plateau in the north

and the Cumberland in the south. Folded rocks related to those of the Appalachians occur in northern Arkansas. The Ozarks make up an outlying area of older rocks rising above the interior lowlands.

The plains. Beginning at Cape Cod and Long Island is the Atlantic Coastal Plain, which merges with the Gulf Coastal Plain in the South. The Atlantic and Gulf Coastal Plains are widest toward the south and include the whole of Florida and up the Mississippi Valley as far north as Cairo, Illinois. The Gulf Plain continues down the coast of Mexico and Middle America and includes all of the Yucatan Peninsula.

Interior lowlands occupy the upper Mississippi Valley and extend northward as far as the Arctic Ocean. They constitute the heart of both the United States and Canada. The lowlands rise to the westward; the elevated semiarid grasslands between the 100th meridian and the Rockies are called the Great Plains, and these extend well north into Canada. The whole Canadian area and the northern lowlands and a little of the northern Great Plains in the United States have been glaciated. This resulted in the formation of lakes, creation of water-power sites, and changes in the use of land for farming.

The vast plains between the Appalachians or the Canadian Shield and the Rockies are the "bread basket" of both the United States and Canada. In this country the Cotton Belt is included in the southern part. Occurrences of petroleum, coal, and building materials, along with iron, copper, lead, and zinc, are available near at hand and have contributed to the importance of manufacturing.

Western uplands and lowlands. The Rocky Mountains extend from a point near Santa Fe northward and northwest through Canada and into Alaska. The Rockies are important sources of minerals, timber, and water power, as well as water for irrigation. Since they are a considerable barrier to transportation, railroads and highways tend to be concentrated in the principal valleys and through the lower and most convenient mountain passes.

Between the Rockies and the Sierras and Cascades are plateaus and intermontane basins. The Columbia Intermontane province of plateaus, hills, mountains, and basins drained by the Columbia River is the northern one of these in the United States; the Fraser Plateau in British Columbia occupies a corresponding position on the other side of the boundary. The arid central portion between the Rockies and the Sierras has the Great Basin, or Basin and Range province; in southern Utah and adjacent parts of Colorado, Arizona, and New Mexico is the high Colorado Plateau, which is deeply trenched by canyons.

West of the intermontane regions are the Cascade and Sierra Nevada Ranges, then two broad lowlands, the Puget-Willamette trough and the Great Valley of California, separated by the Klamath Mountains. These valleys are followed by the Coast Ranges along the Pacific. Northward, Vancouver Island is an extension of the Coast Ranges, the lowland has been submerged, and the Pacific coast range of Canada becomes practically the continuation of the Cascades. Southward a coast range forms the Peninsula of Lower California, and most of the lowland east of this is submerged to form the Gulf of California.

The Alaska Range, the crest of North America, rises from the Gulf of Alaska without lowlands and is a pronounced barrier to transportation into interior Alaska. Further, it prevents the encroachment of marine air from the Pacific Ocean into the northern part of the continent. This towering range extends as an east-west trending arc and continues through the Alaska Peninsula and the volcanic Aleutian Islands toward Asia. Interior Alaska is a broad and rolling plateau or plain drained by the Yukon and Kuskokwim Rivers (Figure 10-7). It is bounded on the north by the Brooks Range, or arctic highland, beyond which is the arctic plain, tundras sloping toward the Arctic Sea.

Trade Centers of the United States and Canada. The United States carries on more foreign trade than any North American country; in proportion to its population, Canada is of similar importance. Both countries have vast resources, extensive plains, and generally favorable climate in the populated portions, and their people are able to develop and use these. The United States and southern Canada have natural routes, like the Great Lakes and St. Lawrence, which favor transportation of commodities, but man has supplemented natural advantages by building railroads. Many trade centers are primarily the result of railroad development.

Geography of the principal trade routes, land uses, and cities of the United States has been described in Chapters 22 and 24.

Mexico and Central America. Mexico is essentially a plateau bounded by mountains and narrow coastal plains on both sides. The surface of the interior plateau is interrupted by mountains, between which are basins often arid enough to lack drainage to the outside. East of the low Isthmus of Tehuantepec and south of the equally flat Peninsula of Yucatan are highlands that include several volcanoes; these mountains extend southward through Panama to South America. Popocatepetl (17,883 feet) and Orizaba (18,700 feet), both snow-capped, are among the volcanic peaks occurring in Mexico.

The concentration of population in Mexico occurs on the central plateau, and the people of Central America also live by preference in the highlands, which are healthier and cooler than lowlands in these latitudes. Mexico City and most other capitals and larger tropical cities of North America are likewise located in the highlands. In Mexico, livestock and subsistence farming are principal occupations, though plantations and *ejidos* (cooperative farms) supply most of the sisal of Yucatan and the cotton in several parts of Mexico. The country is a leader in mineral production, especially for copper, lead, zinc, and silver; it has some useful petroleum deposits. Coffee grown in the highlands and bananas in the lowlands are typical agricultural products of Central America.

More transportation facilities would be of great help in Mexico and in Central America. Mexico is moderately well supplied with rail lines and highways, both of which connect with the United States, but there is great need for extending both systems. Even more remains to be done in Central America, where railroads are short lines carrying bananas and coffee to various small ports on the route to world markets, and where large sections of the Pan-American Highway are still unfinished.

The Panama Canal is of the greatest international and strategic importance. Before the canal was finished, the Tehuantepec railroad across the isthmus of that name had much significance, but it is now of little consequence. The United States has arranged for rights to build a canal across Nicaragua and may in time exercise that privilege.

Excellent steamship and airplane service is available from the United States, especially between the Gulf ports, connecting with Central America, Mexico, and the Caribbean islands. Several air lines also provide fast service in this part of the world.

South America. Triangular-shaped South America is situated southeast of North America and is smaller and less favored for settlement than the northern continent. The principal physical features are comparatively simple:

1. Closely parallel to the Pacific shore is the mountain system of the Andes, one of the greatest in the world. Folds from the northern Andes extend eastward to enclose the Caribbean Sea along its southern shore.

2. The Central Lowland extends the length of the continent and is drained by three main river systems, the Orinoco, Amazon, and Paraná, the last-named flowing into an estuary called the Río de la Plata.

3. The highlands of Brazil with their crest near the Atlantic seaboard.

4. The Guiana highlands in the northern part of the continent.

The Brazilian and Guiana highlands have in general much more ancient rocks than the Andes or the lowlands. That part of the lowlands in the rainy tropics is covered with dense forests, and it repels rather than attracts settlers. Some highlands that would favor human use as far as temperature is concerned are too dry, rough, or rocky for successful farming.

Mineral resources of South America are great. Many important metals are mined, including copper, tin, gold, silver, and tungsten. Petroleum is abundant and there is much potential water power, but coal resources are of minor significance.

Although manufacturing is expanding, it is still of only local importance. The people of the continent must generally import most of the manufactured goods they use.

The Andes and West Coast. The Andes cordillera so closely adjoins the Pacific Ocean that drainage is divided most unevenly, with the large river systems all tributary to the Atlantic. The Andes traverse the full length of the continent and are its most outstanding single feature; they particularly affect the distribution of rainfall and the difficulty of travel. Associated high plateaus and mountain valleys in low latitudes are preferred by most Europeans and many natives as places of residence; they are usually more comfortable than hot rainy lowlands. Most republics in low latitudes have their capitals and principal cities at high elevations, sometimes more than 2 miles above sea level. Examples include Sucre, La Paz, Quito, Bogotá, and Caracas.

The coast of Peru and northern Chile, known as the Atacama Desert, has numerous oases, particularly in Perù. Here irrigated sugar cane and cotton are raised for export. In contrast, rainy tropical lowlands of western Ecuador produce cacao, tagua nuts, and fiber for manufacturing Panama hats. The Andes of Bolivia, Peru, and Chile have rich metal mines, and nitrates are still exported in some quantity from the Chilean desert.

In Chile, a coast range resembling that of western North America, borders the Pacific. A longitudinal valley lies inland, above which rise the Andes. A general picture of Chile's climatic types includes desert in the north, Mediterranean in the central part, and rainy west-coast marine climate in the south. The central valley is most important and has the capital city of Santiago with its principal outlet at the port of Valparaiso. Wheat, wine, and livestock come from this central region.

The northern desert region produces nitrates, iron ore, and copper; its ports exist mainly on mineral exports. Rail lines from Antofagasta and Arica extend into Bolivia and deliver tin ore and other minerals of that nation to ships that transport them to the United Kingdom and other countries. A longitudinal railway extends northward from Santiago into the desert, but it was built primarily for strategic reasons and carries little freight, since coastwise ships have lower charges. Another line runs from Santiago to Buenos Aires, when it is not blocked by snow and landslides.

The principal Peruvian port is Callao near Lima, the capital, and these cities are connected by rail. A second railroad also connects the inferior port of Mollendo with Lake Titicaca, which is crossed by ship to another rail line leading to La Paz in Bolivia. Cotton, sugar, wool, copper, and vanadium are sent out from Peru. Guayaquil, with its railroad to Quito, the capital, is the leading port of Ecuador.

The few railroads in Colombia and Venezuela, like those of Peru and Ecuador, are principally of local value. No rail connections link the capitals of nations in northern and Andean South America; highways are often poor and sometimes entirely lacking. Mountains rise within sight of the ocean and present difficult construction problems for railway and highway engineers. As a result, air travel is encouraged and is widely used throughout western parts of South America. Interior rain forests and grassy plains are thinly populated and as yet remain unreached by railways from the Pacific or the Caribbean.

In Colombia the Magdalena River is a principal route, although its use by river boats is handicapped by rapids and great variation in flow. Barranquilla on the lower Magdalena

River has its ocean outlet at Puerto Colombia nearby.

Venezuela is second to the United States in petroleum production; the fields being located at Maracaibo. In the 1950s large shipments of iron ore began from the Orinoco region in Venezuela to the eastern seaboard of the United States. Petroleum and coffee are the main exports of both Venezuela and Colombia.

South American Lowlands. Climates of the central lowlands of South America are governed by latitude; natural vegetation and land use vary accordingly. Tropical rain forest covers the coast of the Guianas, most lowlands near the Amazon River, and the very narrow coastal plain northward from Rio de Janeiro. North of the Amazon River Basin lie the Llanos of the upper Orinoco region; southward are the open woods (Campos) of the savanna region of southwestern Brazil and neighboring parts of Bolivia, Paraguay, and northern Argentina. To some extent, tropical grasslands are used for raising cattle, but the tropical rain forest has been developed little, though some sugar and rice are produced in Surinam and British Guiana.

Well-watered plains, or Pampa, of Argentina inland from Buenos Aires are devoted to raising wheat, corn, flax, alfalfa, and livestock. Westward and southward from the fertile Pampa the rainfall decreases in amount, and the countryside is used for grazing, except where irrigation has reclaimed some of the drier parts. The oasis at Mendoza is famous for its wine; others nearby produce sugar, rice, and cotton. Southern Argentina (Patagonia) is semiarid but colder than the northern part of the country; its precipitation is just enough to provide forage, and it is used almost wholly for extensive grazing of sheep.

The Pampa of Argentina is well served by rail lines (Figure 22-13), with tracks diverging inland from the principal ports of Buenos Aires, Rosario, and Bahía Blanca. One line, from Buenos Aires, connects in the north with Bolivian lines and thence with Pacific ports in

Chile, but most of Argentina's railroads are of local importance and were built to carry wheat, corn, flax, quebracho extract, wool, and livestock to seaports for shipment to Europe and the United States.

Buenos Aires, largest city in the Southern Hemisphere, is built upon a harbor that was originally shallow, but is now improved. This city is the capital, leading port, principal manufacturing center, and greatest business city of a very fertile and productive nation.

Across the La Plata estuary, Montevideo, capital of Uruguay, is located on an excellent harbor to which several railroads converge; these are used to transport cattle, sheep, and wool to the port; animal products are its chief export. Montevideo is the business center of this productive small country, but its population is only about one-fifth that of Buenos Aires because of its limited hinterland.

The Eastern Highlands. The eastern highlands of Brazil are the most productive parts of that country and support the largest part of the population. Soil and climatic conditions are favorable for crops like coffee, cotton, and corn; the altitude is high enough to make the region healthful and pleasant.

The Brazilian highlands consist of old resistant rock, representing eroded remnants of a former mountain massif. Their rounded hills offer sharp contrasts to the more youthful Andes chain, where narrow canyons and steep slopes dominate the mountain landscapes. Together with the Guiana highlands, they partly enclose the interior plains of South America. The eastern highlands rise steeply from the Atlantic and lie parallel to the coast; as a result, steep mountain grades that are necessary to cross the heights make railroad construction to inland centers difficult and costly. The Brazilian highlands contain valuable minerals, of which gold, manganese, and industrial diamonds are noteworthy. There are large resources of iron ore, which Brazil has begun to manufacture into steel.

Santos is the port for the city of São Paulo, the largest interior city of Brazil, and it is the leading port for coffee exports. The railroad connecting the two cities was exceedingly expensive to build. São Paulo is a wealthy city, important not only for coffee production but also, in increasing measure, for such industries as the manufacture of cotton textiles.

The largest city of Brazil is the capital, Rio de Janeiro, with nearly 2 million population. This is the leading seaport and business center of the country; it enjoys the advantage of a particularly fine harbor, although access to the hinterland is somewhat hampered by heights behind the city. Some rail connections lead to the interior, and one line traverses all of Brazil to the border of Bolivia.

Southern Brazil resembles part of the southern United States in climatic conditions and agricultural crops. Here pine lumber, cattle, swine, corn, and wheat are produced in quantity and are shipped from the leading ports of Porto Alegre and Rio Grande do Sul.

North of Rio de Janeiro, Bahía (São Salvador) and Pernambuco (Recife) are the principal urban centers and ports. They export large amounts of cane sugar, cotton, and cacao.

The Guiana highlands along the northern Brazilian boundary and in Dutch and British Guiana are seldom visited. They have some forest resources and some mineral deposits but are mostly undeveloped. Bauxite is mined in large quantities near the coast of British Guiana and Surinam (Dutch Guiana) and is exported to the United States and Canada for manufacture of aluminum.

SUMMARY

South American Potentialities. South America has many resources, some of which have been only slightly developed. There is opportunity for larger population density in most parts of the continent (Figure 23-4). Indeed the Amazon Valley is almost empty of people compared with the numbers it could support if practical problems of life in the rainy tropics could be overcome. The Pampa of Argentina, Llanos of Colombia and Venezuela, interior territory of Mato Grosso in Brazil, and a few other parts of the continent are capable of providing for many more people than those who now live there.

South America is significant for exports of raw materials, particularly minerals and farm products. The United States imports wool and flaxseed from Argentina, coffee from Brazil and Colombia, oil from Venezuela and Colombia, cacao from Ecuador and Brazil, tin from Bolivia, nitrates, copper, and iron ore from Chile, bauxite from the Guianas, and many other raw materials. Most of Argentina's meat and wheat are sent to Europe, and that continent also buys mineral products and coffee. South America imports most of its manufactured goods, but future industry can be expected to increase. Only Chile has important coal deposits, but there is much petroleum and water power available, and in time South America will supply most of its requirements for ordinary manufactured products. To both Europeans and North Americans, South America presents an attractive field for investment and expansion of trade.

Australia.   Australia lies south of the equator, athwart the southeast trades. This results in desert conditions over the whole of the central and most of the western sections. A rim of adequate rainfall follows the northern, eastern, and southern coasts, except for an arid strip along the Nullarbor coast of the Great Australian Bight. Another favored section appears in the southwest of the continent. Unfortunately, northern Australia has a wet-and-dry tropical climate with an average of six months of drought; its soils are generally poor, known resources are scant, and population is almost negligible. Most of Australia's population, over 9 million people, is concentrated in the southeast. There two large cities, Sydney and Melbourne; each has more than 1.5 million inhabitants. A well-peopled zone extends north into southeast Queensland, where Brisbane is the principal city. South Australia around Adelaide and part of southwest Australia are favored by a Mediterranean climate; these constitute other developed regions. A number of people live in

Tasmania, but scarcity of tillable land encourages only slow increase of population on that rugged island.

Australia rests on a firm foundation of ancient crystalline rocks which outcrop over most of the western and much of the central parts. Once this region was mountainous, but through millions of centuries the rugged highlands have been worn down to a nearly featureless peneplain only 1,000 to 2,000 feet in elevation; above this, a few ridges of resistant rock rise to greater heights. Most of this peneplain is a desert. Gold mines in western Australia have induced some settlement at Kalgoorlie, Coolgardie, Boulder, and other mineralized locations, but most of the enormous area is unpopulated and is unlikely ever to support any considerable numbers of inhabitants.

Australian railways and terminals. The location and gauge of Australian railways are accounted for by the conditions of its settlement as well as the facts of its geography. The continent has a rather regular coast line, and first-class harbors are uncommon although that of Sydney is one of the best in the world. At first Australia was divided into five separate colonies (six with Tasmania).

Provincial capitals were customarily founded on one of the few good harbors. The capital became the chief seaport and dominant trade center of each colony. When railways were built, they radiated from that capital city. This helped to concentrate commercial, manufacturing, and governmental activities in the six state capitals and caused so much urban growth that more than half the population is living in cities. Unfortunately, the different colonies, now states of the Commonwealth, did not adopt the same railway gauge. Thus New South Wales has standard gauge, Victoria a broad gauge, and Queensland a narrow gauge. Consequently, all freight, passengers, and mail must be transferred from one train to another at most state boundaries, an expensive nuisance, especially for transport between large cities like Melbourne and Sydney.

Much of Australia's freight is carried by coast ships, since the largest cities are seaports. Improved highways, including paved roads, have been built to connect cities in settled parts of Australia, especially in the southeast; but bus service is not generally available because the railroads are owned by the government, and authorities fear the railway income would suffer from competition with interstate busses. In the back country the roads are little improved, but extensive open plains make travel by car and truck possible in most sections.

Trade and commerce. Australia is most famous for its exports of animal products. The climate is mild, and stock require no shelter. Neither is feeding generally resorted to except during prolonged droughts; these are the greatest handicap to the grazing industry. Native grasses are excellent and recover quickly when rains follow a drought. Enemies of livestock are few, the principal one being a wild dog, the dingo, which kills some sheep, and the nonnative rabbit, which consumes the grass needed by sheep and cattle. With an area about equal to the United States, Australia has nearly three times as many sheep even though half the country is too hot or dry for keeping the animals. It leads the world in exports of wool. Ranches or sheep stations of the interior maintain excellent breeds for producing wool—merinos and crossbred merinos—with English mutton breeds. Fleeces are carefully clipped, handled, and graded for export. Exports of lamb and mutton are important but are exceeded by those from New Zealand.

Although cattle raising is a leading industry, it falls far behind that of sheep production. Most cattle are grown in the eastern section, but they are also raised in northern regions where the weather is too warm for sheep. An increasing dairying industry is of great importance, although in exports of butter and cheese, New Zealand is far ahead of Australia. Ships equipped with refrigeration facilities make it possible to export mutton, beef, and dairy products to distant markets.

Millions of rabbit skins are exported from Australia and used for making cheap furs and felt hats in the United States and Europe.

Wheat is the principal grain raised in Australia, and shiploads are exported, especially from ports of South Australia. Citrus fruit and grapes are grown principally in dry frost-free regions like the Murray River valley. Most of these are sold in the domestic market, but exports are increasing. Apples and berries are locally of importance in Tasmania.

Australia's future. Australia has some supplies of coal, mined chiefly in New South Wales and Victoria; the nation lacks petroleum, however, and must import gasoline and fuel oil. Iron ore occurs principally in South Australia and Western Australia and is smelted at Newcastle. Lead and zinc come from Broken Hill and other mining centers.

During and since the Second World War, manufacturing has greatly increased. Wool, metals, hides, wheat, and hardwood are among raw materials that are processed. Nevertheless Australians import a large part of the manufactured articles they use from the United Kingdom, the United States, and other nations.

The continent can probably support several times its present population with no decrease in living standards, but the large extent of desert and tropical land would seem to preclude a population density equal to that of the United States or Western Europe except in favored valleys and the southern corners of the Commonwealth.

Antarctica. Antarctica is the least known of any continent; it supports no permanent inhabitants. A vast glacier covers the land and rises to an ice plateau with an elevation of over 2 miles above the sea. There are a few exposures of bedrock, some of which contain coal beds, proof that once the climate here was mild enough for luxuriant plant growth. Only part of Antarctica has been explored and mapped, and the area of the continent is uncertain. Extensive ice floes and shelf ice prevent landings during most of the year. The nearby sea is the home of many whales, and whaling is the only commercial enterprise in the area at present. During the Geophysical

Year (1957–1958) explorations and scientific investigations were made in Antarctica by representatives of many nations.

SUMMARY

This final chapter indicates the next step for the student of geography—greater knowledge of the different parts of the earth and a more intensive study of the continents in particular. It is intended only as an introduction to the detailed regional studies that should follow in order to obtain a comprehensive view of the world.

In view of the current political and economic crises affecting Asia, Africa, and Europe, particular attention in the Old World should be devoted to three problem areas: Central Europe, the Soviet Union, and southeastern Asia. Africa and Australasia, only beginning to take their places in the modern world, should be regarded as land masses of great potentiality for human use. In the Western Hemisphere, concentrated geographical study of the eastern United States and Canada, and of the Brazilian highlands and the lands of the Ríb de la Plata is essential to understanding the future role of North and

South America in world affairs. Arctic and Antarctic realms become more important each year, particularly in this air age, and in themselves offer a topic of fascinating interest.

Outline
World Island or Old World
Europe: features, resources, and development
Asia: features, resources, and development
Africa: divisions, resources, world relations
New World
North America: features, resources, development
South America: features, resources, potentialities
Australia: characteristics, resources, possible future
Antarctica

QUESTIONS

1. What is the leading urban center for each of the following plains: Ulster Basin, Ukraine, Pampa, Red Basin, Po Valley, Bohemian Plain?

2. Compare and contrast from every possible geographical viewpoint the plains of the Rhine, the Rhone, the Po, and the Elbe.

3. From the human standpoint, which of the above river plains is the most useful? Defend your answer with necessary arguments.

4. How do you account for Japan's remarkable economic and social transformation in the last fifty years, whereas China has remained relatively unchanged?

5. Describe the geography of Northern Rhodesia as though you were convincing a friend that it

would be a favorable place to develop as a permanent residence.

6. What are the leading handicaps to:
The cattle industry in Africa
Agriculture along the Yangtze
Agriculture in Finland
Agriculture in South Africa
Forestry in Chile
The cattle industry in India
Industrial development of Siberia

7. If the Andes did not exist, would Patagonia be more or less habitable than it now is? Give reasons for your answer.

8. Compare the location and geographical characteristics of Japan and of the British Isles.

SELECTED REFERENCES

Carlson, Fred A.: *Geography of Latin America,* Prentice-Hall, Inc., Englewood Cliffs, N.J., 1952.

Cressey, George B.: *Asia's Lands and Peoples,* McGraw-Hill Book Company, Inc., New York, 1951.

Freeman, O. W. (ed.): *Geography of the Pacific,* John Wiley & Sons, Inc., New York, 1951.

⸻, and John W. Morris (eds.): *World Geography,* McGraw-Hill Book Company, Inc., New York, 1958.

Ginsburg, Norton S. (ed.): *The Pattern of Asia,* Prentice-Hall, Inc., Englewood Cliffs, N.J., 1958.

Hoffman, George W.: *A Geography of Europe,* The Ronald Press Company, New York, 1953.

Hubbard, George D.: *The Geography of Europe,* Appleton-Century-Crofts, Inc., New York, 1952.

James, Preston: *Latin America,* The Odyssey Press, Inc., New York, 1942.

Kish, George (ed.): *An Introduction to World Geography,* Prentice-Hall, Inc., Englewood Cliffs, N.J., 1956.

Lackey, E. E., and Esther S. Anderson: *Regions and Nations of the World,* D. Van Nostrand Company, Inc., Princeton, N.J., 1946.

Miller, George J., Almon E. Parkins, and Bert Hudgins: *Geography of North America,* John Wiley & Sons, Inc., New York, 1954.

Pounds, Norman J. G.: *Europe and the Mediterranean,* McGraw-Hill Book Company, Inc., New York, 1953.

Putnam, Donald F. (ed.): *Canadian Regions: A Geography of Canada,* Thomas Y. Crowell Company, New York, 1952.

Spencer, J. E.: *Asia, East by South,* John Wiley & Sons, Inc., New York, 1954.

Stamp, L. Dudley: *Africa: A Study in Tropical Environment,* John Wiley & Sons, Inc., New York, 1953.

Taylor, Griffith: *Australia: A Study of Warm Environments and Their Effects on British Settlement,* Methuen & Co., Ltd., London, 1949.

Van Valkenburg, Samuel, and Colbert C. Held: *Europe,* John Wiley & Sons, Inc., New York, 1952.

White, C. Langdon, and Edwin J. Foscue: *Regional Geography of Anglo-America,* Prentice-Hall, Inc., Englewood Cliffs, N.J., 1954.

Wright, Alfred J.: *United States and Canada: An Economic Geography,* Appleton-Century-Crofts, Inc., New York, 1956.

NOTE: The Geographical Press, C. S. Hammond & Co., Inc., publishes physiographic diagrams of Asia, Europe, South America, Africa, and the United States.

Appendix

TYPES OF CLIMATIC CLASSIFICATION

CLIMATOLOGISTS, meteorologists, and geographers recognize about a dozen different climatic types or realms, but the terms they have used to describe or identify the realms vary widely. For purposes of comparison, a few of the climatic classifications devised by other writers are appended.

JONES AND WHITTLESEY*

Low Latitude Types
1. Rainy low latitude
2. Low latitude wet and dry
3. Low latitude semi-arid
4. Low latitude desert

Middle Latitude Types
5. West margins continents
    (*lower middle latitude*)
6. East margins continents
    (*lower middle latitude*)
7. West margins continents
    (*higher middle latitude*)
8. Humid continental with long summers
9. Humid continental with short summers
10. East margins continents
    (*higher middle latitude*)
11. Middle latitude desert
12. Semi-arid middle latitude
13. Lower high latitude
14. Subpolar
15. Polar

BENGTSON AND VAN ROYEN†

I. Humid Tropical Climates
   A. Rainy

   B. Savanna
   C. Highland

II. Dry Tropical Climates
   D. Steppe
   E. Warm Desert

III. Subtropical Climates
   F. Humid
   G. Dry

IV. Humid Intermediate Climates
   H. Humid Continental
   I. East Coast Continental
   J. West Coast Marine
   K. Subpolar

V. Dry Intermediate Climates
   L. Middle Latitude Steppes
   M. Middle Latitude Deserts

VI. Polar Climates
   N. Tundra
   O. Icecap

VII. High Altitude Climates
   P. Mountains

WHITE AND RENNER‡

Tropical Zone
   1. Rainy Tropical
   2. Monsoon Tropical
   3. Semiarid Tropical
   4. Arid Tropical

Subtropical Zone
   5. Mediterranean Subtropical
   6. Humid Subtropical
   7. Dry Subtropical

* From *An Introduction to Economic Geography,* by Wellington Jones and Derwent Whittlesey. Used by permission of the authors and the publisher, University of Chicago Press, Chicago, 1925.

† From *Fundamentals of Economic Geography,* revised, by Nels A. Bengtson and William Van Royen. Used by permission of the publisher. Copyright, 1950, by Prentice-Hall, Inc., Englewood Cliffs, N.J.

‡ From *Introduction to College Geography* by C. Langdon White and George T. Renner. Used by permission of the authors and of the publisher, Appleton-Century-Crofts, Inc., New York, 1957.

Cyclonic Zone
  8*a*. Humid Continental, long summer
  8*b*. Humid Continental, medium summer
  8*c*. Humid Continental, short summer
  9. Dry Continental
  10. Temperate Marine
Polar Zone
  11. Subpolar
  12. Polar Icecap
Unclassified
  Highlands whose climates vary with altitude

TREWARTHA§

A. Tropical Rainy
  1. Wet (Rainforest)
  2. Wet and Dry (Savanna)
B. Dry Climates
  3. Semiarid or Steppe
    a. Tropical and Subtropical
    b. Middle Latitude
  4. Arid Desert
    a. Tropical and Subtropical
    b. Middle Latitude
C. Humid Mesothermal
  5. Dry-summer Subtropical (Mediterranean)
  6. Humid Subtropical (Warm Summer)
  7. Marine (Cool Summer)
D. Humid Microthermal
  8. Humid Continental, Warm Summer
  9. Humid Continental, Cool Summer
  10. Subarctic
E. Polar
  11. Tundra
  12. Ice Cap
F. Undifferentiated Highlands

KÖPPEN*

A. Tropical Rainy Climates
  1. Tropical Rainforest (Af, Am)
  2. Tropical Savanna (Aw)
B. Dry Climates
  3. Steppe (BS)
  4. Desert (BW)
C. Humid Mesothermal Climates
  5. Warm Climate with Dry Winter (Monsoon and Upland Savanna) (Cw)
  6. Warm Climate with Dry Summer (Mediterranean) (Cs)

  * From *An Introduction to Weather and Climate,* by G. T. Trewartha. Used by permission of the author and of the publisher, McGraw-Hill Book Company, Inc., New York, 1954.

  7. Humid Temperate Climate (Cf)
D. Humid Microthermal Climates
  8. Cold Climate with Moist Winter (Df)
  9. Cold Climate with Dry Winter (Monsoon Type) (Dw)
E. Polar Climates
  10. Tundra (ET)
  11. Climate of Perpetual Frost (EF)

W. Köppen's system of climatic classification is based upon specific values of temperature and precipitation indicated by the different symbols. The letter *A* signifies tropical rainy climates, for example. Then the letters *f, w,* or *s* may be added, denoting rain at all seasons, or drought in winter or summer; *m* stands for monsoon conditions. The symbols *Af* thus stand for wet Equatorial lands, and the symbols *Aw* represent wet-and-dry tropical savanna. *W* means desert; *S* stands for steppe lands, *T* for tundra, and *F* for ice.

THORNTHWAITE*

Precipitation Effectiveness
  A. Wet
  B. Humid
  C. Subhumid
  D. Semiarid
  E. Arid
Temperature Efficiency
  A′ Tropical
  B′ Mesothermal
  C′ Microthermal
  D′ Taiga
  E′ Tundra
  F′ Perpetual frost

The climatic classification devised by C. W. Thornthwaite is based on different values of precipitation effectiveness and temperature efficiency. Combinations of the values indicate the characteristics of the climatic realms; the symbols *AA′* for example signify the wet equatorial lands, and *BB′* indicates the humid subtropical realm. The symbols *r* and *d* are added to denote adequate rainfall at all seasons or deficient rainfall at all times. If winters are dry, *w* is added; *s* is added for regions of summer rain deficiency. Thus the symbols *BC′r* represent the west-coast marine climate.

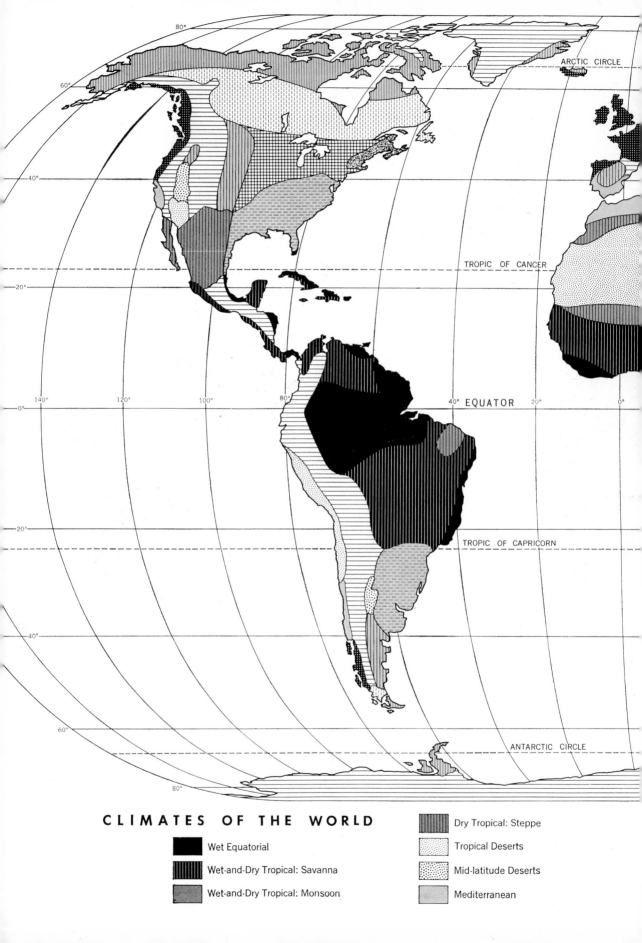

CLIMATES OF THE WORLD

- ■ Wet Equatorial
- ▮ Wet-and-Dry Tropical: Savanna
- ▨ Wet-and-Dry Tropical: Monsoon
- ▥ Dry Tropical: Steppe
- ⬚ Tropical Deserts
- ⣿ Mid-latitude Deserts
- ▦ Mediterranean

ARCTIC CIRCLE

TROPIC OF CANCER

EQUATOR

TROPIC OF CAPRICORN

ANTARCTIC CIRCLE

80°

60°

40°

20°

0°

20°

40°

60°

80°

140°   120°   100°   80°   40°   20°   0°

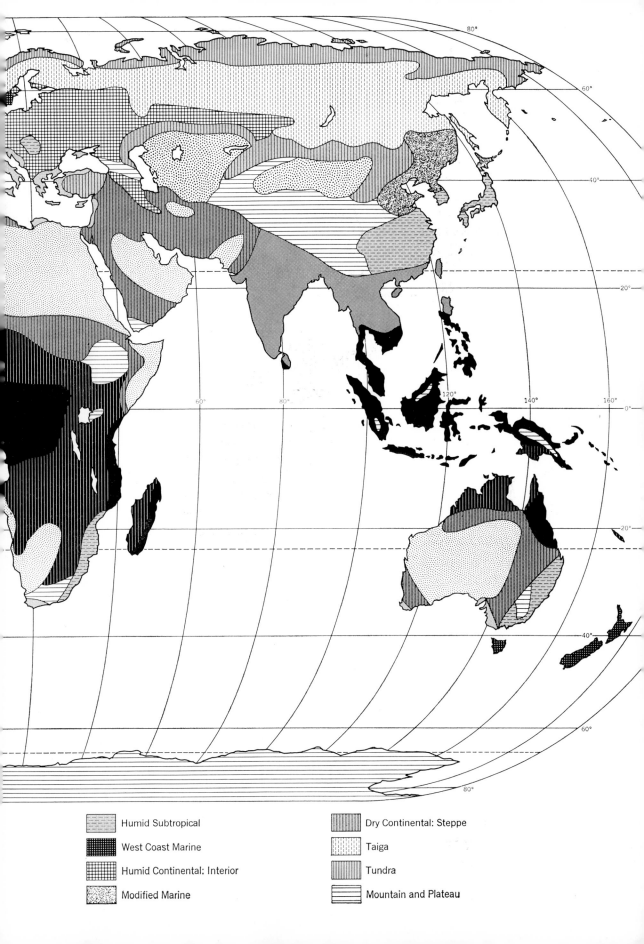

	Humid Subtropical		Dry Continental: Steppe
	West Coast Marine		Taiga
	Humid Continental: Interior		Tundra
	Modified Marine		Mountain and Plateau

Credits for Chapter Opening Illustrations

CHAPTER 1. *Aerial photograph showing the earth's curvature. Official United States Navy photograph.*

CHAPTER 2. *Taking a sun sight. U.S. Coast and Geodetic Survey.*

CHAPTER 3. *Clouds. Florida State News Bureau.*

CHAPTER 4. *Radiosonde. Friez Instrument Division.*

CHAPTER 5. *Lake McDermott. American Museum of Natural History.*

CHAPTER 6. *Latex trees in Sumatra. U.S. Rubber.*

CHAPTER 7. *Desert in Saudi Arabia. Arabian American Oil Company.*

CHAPTER 8. *Yucca plants in Florida Everglades. Florida State News Bureau.*

CHAPTER 9. *Connecticut River valley. Massachusetts Department of Commerce.*

CHAPTER 10. *Penguins in Antarctica. Official United States Navy photograph.*

CHAPTER 11. *Allegheny National Forest. U.S. Forest Service.*

CHAPTER 12. *Luray Caverns. Luray Caverns.*

CHAPTER 13. *Plateaus. Utah Tourist and Publicity Council.*

CHAPTER 14. *Climbing Annapurna. French Embassy Information Division.*

CHAPTER 15. *Sea gulls on Cape Cod. Massachusetts Department of Commerce.*

CHAPTER 16. *Rocks off the coast. Oregon State Highway Commission.*

CHAPTER 17. *Irrigating an orange grove. U.S. Bureau of Reclamation.*

CHAPTER 18. *Primitive plowing. Standard Oil Co. (New Jersey).*

CHAPTER 19. *Mining copper. The Anaconda Company.*

CHAPTER 20. *Fishing in British West Indies. British Information Services.*

CHAPTER 21. *Steel mill. U.S. Steel Corp.*

CHAPTER 22. *Freight yard. Standard Oil Co. (New Jersey).*

CHAPTER 23. *Fisherman repairing net. Albert Siegel.*

CHAPTER 24. *Boston and environs. Massachusetts Department of Commerce.*

CHAPTER 25. *United Nations headquarters. United Nations.*

CHAPTER 26. *Aerial photograph. Pan American World Airways.*

Index

28   233TF BR7 **6777** GBC ICI

06/92 24-950-00   LIBRARY BINDING

                                     CORPORATION INC.